# SOLID STATE MAGNETIC
## AND
# DIELECTRIC DEVICES

**edited by: H. W. Katz**

## authors:

**W. R. Chynoweth**
*Electronics Laboratory*
*General Electric Company*

**J. F. Elliott**
*Semiconductor Products Department*
*General Electric Company*

**H. W. Katz**
*Electronics Laboratory*
*General Electric Company*

**E. B. Mullen**
*Defense Systems Department*
*General Electric Company*

**C. A. Rosen**
*Stanford Research Institute*

**N. Schwartz**
*Electronics Laboratory*
*General Electric Company*

**B. Silverman**
*Electrical Engineering Department*
*Syracuse University*

**C. F. Spitzer**
*Lockheed Missiles Systems Division*

**S. W. Tehon**
*Electronics Laboratory*
*General Electric Company*

**H. J. Venema**
*Stewart Warner Electronics*
*Chicago, Illinois*

## contributions by:

**J. A. Baer**
*Lenkurt Electric Company*

**L. Budell**
*Electronics Laboratory*
*General Electric Company*

**H. D. Crawford**
*Medical-Technicological Research Dept.*
*St. Barnabas Hospital*

**J. F. Vize**
*International Business Machines Corporation*

# SOLID STATE MAGNETIC

## AND

# DIELECTRIC DEVICES

NEW YORK · JOHN WILEY & SONS, INC.

London · Chapman & Hall, Limited

# Preface

The introduction of new semiconductor and metallic materials in the 1950's has stimulated many additional areas of interest and investigation for the electrical engineer. Undoubtedly, single crystal germanium and silicon have been the most dramatically successful of these new materials. In fact, the terminology "solid state device" refers almost exclusively to the various germanium and silicon configurations which have been introduced to perform the necessary functions in electronic equipment. The over-all characterization of these devices can be reduced to the statement that their electrical performance is effected by the control of charge flow, analogous to the vacuum tube. However, there are numerous, functionally useful semiconductor materials which have led to a significant number of important new devices but whose technology is still in the initial stages of development. The utilization of these materials cannot be characterized in terms of controlled charge flow; here we are referring to those materials which exhibit magnetic and/or dielectric parameters suitable for performing certain electrical functions. The resulting magnetic and dielectric devices and their applications comprise the subject matter of this book.

We must recognize that magnetic and dielectric devices are less versatile in application than the transistor, since a transistor is capable of producing power gain from a d-c supply. Peculiarly, this feature to some extent complicates the logical presentation and study of magnetic and dielectric devices. With the advent of the transistor, there existed a well-developed discipline in the myriad applications of the vacuum tube which served as a model. However, in the magnetic and dielectric area the applications of a given device are normally restricted in scope. Furthermore, a great variety of physical effects which these materials can be made to exhibit, to greater or lesser degree, has been utilized in the ever broadening search for new components. This requires the student and practicing engineer to have a more intimate knowledge and understanding of the results of modern solid state physics than is ordinarily the case.

Therefore, the compilation of a textbook in this embryo field, encompassing many diverse areas in both theory and application, is difficult. No established discipline exists to serve as a model for the logical development and presentation of the subject matter. Every new field enjoys a rapid growth in its initial stages; whether new or old, every field experiences continually shifting emphasis and interest as dictated by the requirements of the then current engineering developments. This book attempts to treat an area of endeavor in which these perturbations to the orderly nature of things are pronounced to an extreme degree. It is necessary to understand the implications of this situation in order to appreciate the underlying philosophy of the volume and to derive maximum benefit from the study of the material presented.

The authors have tried to unify the diverse aspects of the broad field of magnetic and dielectric devices, and, in addition, they have attempted to present a comprehensive coverage. They have striven for a selection of material which will prove useful in later applications as well as be representative of developments of current interest with respect to the publication date of the volume.

Hence the particular topics chosen for extended discussion represent a compromise. The desire for comprehensive coverage is balanced by the appreciation for space limitations; the desire to present material which will remain applicable with the passage of time is balanced by not succumbing to the inclination to include those things which, though of great immediate interest, are too restricted in scope to remain in the forefront of pioneering developments.

The various chapters of the book fall into two broad categories. The first four chapters present the majority of the theoretical background utilized in the subsequent discussion. The succeeding eight chapters present specific applications of magnetic and dielectric devices. So that the reader may obtain an over-all appreciation of the material contained in the volume, a brief discussion of each of the chapters and of the appendix is given below.

## Chapter 1  Electrostatic and Magnetostatic Field Theory

If one adopts the philosophy that solid state devices can be described in a general manner as the theory and application of how electric and magnetic fields interact with matter, then a logical starting point is the analytic description of the macroscopic parameters defined as the magnetic and dielectric constants. As familiar as these constants $\mu$ and $\epsilon$ may be, they do not permit of the most general description of magnetic and dielectric behavior. A more basic model can be constructed in terms of the concepts of polarization and magnetization. Though these concepts are beginning to appear more widely in recent texts on field theory, their introduction is usually very late in the over-all development. Deeper insight into the problem can be obtained by the utilization of these concepts as a direct extension of free-space fields and isolated charges.

Thus the chapter begins with Coulomb's law and the definition of the electric field in free space. Since a prior course in field theory and vector analysis is assumed, the vector relationships which hold for **E** are given in summary form without detailed proof. The electric dipole and polarization are then introduced. This serves as a basis for defining the displacement **D** as well as the boundary conditions satisfied by **E** and **D**.

An analogous treatment is then given of **H** and **B** by using the magnetic dipole as the point of departure. This is then related to the magnetic fields produced by currents, and the new boundary conditions developed. In both the electric and the magnetic cases the dielectric and the magnetic constants are defined in terms of volume polarization and magnetization respectively.

## Chapter 2  Origin of Magnetic and Dielectric Properties

Chapter 1 is primarily concerned with the phenomenological description of matter, whereas Chapter 2 presents a review of the fundamental results of solid state physics. The objective is to show how the atomic structure of matter gives rise to the observed magnetic and dielectric effects. No attempt is made to delve into the quantitative calculations required by quantum mechanics as this is outside the scope of the present volume.

After a brief introduction dealing with matter in the solid state, classical descriptions of paramagnetism, diamagnetism, and ferromagnetism are given from the point of view of disordered and ordered arrays of atomic spins. The important phenomenon of ferrimagnetism [ferrites] is introduced as a special case of ordered magnetism.

The dielectric behavior of matter is described with primary emphasis on the various mechanisms which contribute to the observed polarization. The phenomenon of ferroelectricity is treated in considerable detail, the experimental data on barium titanate being used as the prototype example.

## Chapter 3    Electrostrictive and Magnetostrictive Systems *

The phenomena of electrostriction and magnetostriction have played an important role in many new devices, such as electromechanical delay lines and filters. These devices are best described in terms of linear equations which represent the relationship between the applied fields and mechanical stresses and the resultant polarization or magnetization. From this functional relationship the basic equations are utilized to develop the small signal equivalent circuits for various operating modes. Different sets of electromechanical coefficients are carefully defined for the conditions in which different quantities are taken as the independent variables. It is shown that specific geometries are more amenable to solution in terms of the proper set of coefficients. In addition, the matrix relationships among the coefficients are defined. The electromechanical coupling coefficient in particular is derived both in terms of energy and circuit concepts.

This chapter thus serves as the basic introduction to Chapter 5 on electromechanical filters.

## Chapter 4    Nonlinear Magnetic and Dielectric Materials †

Those materials which exhibit a square hysteresis loop have probably received the most attention and broadest application of the new magnetic and dielectric semiconductors. This has been particularly true in computer technology. Thus Chapter 4 is concerned with a detailed examination of the nonlinear switching characteristics of these materials,

---

* Although IRE Standards were used throughout the chapter it was necessary to introduce a change in the notation for the electric field. This was required in those equations where voltage [$E$] appeared in the same equation with the electric field [**E**]. In these few cases the symbol [$\varepsilon$] has been used for the electric field.

† Many of the ideas discussed in the first portion of this chapter are those of Dr. J. R. Horsch, of the General Electric Electronics Laboratory.

since the computer device is so intimately connected with the material characteristics. These materials are normally described by means of a hysteresis loop, and considerable attention is devoted to the various interpretations of the hysteresis loop under different driving conditions. The discussion includes metallic magnetic tape as well as ferrites, magnetic thin films, and barium titanate single crystals.

The final portion of the chapter deals with those materials whose characteristics can be approximated by a single-valued function. A typical solution is given for this type of problem. An approximation method is developed which leads to a graphic description of the phenomenon of nonlinear instability known as ferroresonance.

## Chapter 5    Electromechanical Applications

An extensive development is given of the application of the theory of Chapter 3 to the rapidly growing field of electromechanical filters which utilize electrostrictive materials. The equivalent circuits developed in Chapter 3 are suitably modified in order to simplify the calculations of the filtering characteristics of a four-terminal electromechanical transformer. The calculations are also carried out for several different geometrical configurations.

Though the techniques are illustrated for a four-terminal filter, they are also useful for other applications, such as sonic delay lines. The theoretical background developed in Chapter 3 is sufficiently general to include other small signal electromechanical devices.

## Chapter 6    Small Signal Applications

Those ferrites which have a relatively linear hysteresis loop have been used in a variety of conventional applications in which high permeability, low-loss magnetic materials are required. This chapter includes a discussion of these applications which extend in frequency up to several megacycles. The microwave applications are presented separately in Chapter 7. The present chapter includes a discussion of ferrite inductors in the form of toroids and cup cores, the effect of air gaps, TV deflection yokes and antenna rods. In addition, a novel application of ferrites in distributed constant delay lines is analyzed in considerable detail. A brief description is also presented of commercially available inductors and capacitors which are electrically controllable.

## Chapter 7    Ferrites at Microwave Frequencies

This chapter is intended to serve as a basic introduction to the properties exhibited by ferrites in the microwave region.  A derivation is given of the basic permeability tensor and the nonreciprocal properties, and several typical applications, such as isolators, switches, and circulators, are used as illustrative examples.  This chapter provides the basic background material for more recent microwave devices, although a detailed discussion is not included.

## Chapter 8    Magnetic and Dielectric Amplifiers

This chapter serves primarily as a basic survey of the many different magnetic and dielectric amplifier configurations which have been studied in the past.  The theoretical background for each of these configurations can be found in the extensive bibliography given at the end of the chapter.  The second half of the chapter deals with the specific problems and applications of the principle of ferroresonance, the theory of which is developed in Chapter 4.  Several different circuit configurations are given which utilize either the nonlinear inductor or capacitor.  The applications discussed are primarily in the computer field.

## Chapter 9    Digital Techniques Employing Square Loop Materials

This chapter contains further applications of square loop material.  However, these are differentiated from those of Chapter 8 by the fact that the present chapter is primarily concerned with those devices which utilize the storage capabilities of square loop materials.  The specific applications which were chosen are used primarily to illustrate the basic operating principles of various computer components rather than the extensive interconnections which are required to perform specific logic functions.  Magnetic counters and shift registers are typical component applications of simple toroidal structures.  In addition, a discussion of nonuniform geometries found in multiaperture ferrites is also given.  The utilization of these materials as basic memory elements is illustrated with the magnetic core memory, the thin film memory, a superconducting array, and the dielectric memory.  Several less conventional applications, such as pulse position modulation and the TV burst gate, are also included.

## Chapter 10   Magnetic Recording

This subject, which at first appears rather unusual for a text devoted to devices, actually represents a rather complex problem in the determination of dynamic hysteresis loop characteristics. In this chapter attention is focused primarily on the magnetic recording process itself rather than on the recording system. Detailed consideration is given to the various theories which are utilized to explain the process whereby nonlinear magnetic characteristics can produce a linear relationship between input and output. The concluding portion of the chapter is a brief summary of several dielectric recording techniques, although these have not reached the state of development of the magnetic counterpart.

## Chapter 11   Magnetic and Dielectric Measurements

A fundamental problem in all device work is to obtain satisfactory measurement data of the basic materials in order to produce more efficient device designs. In many instances the measurement techniques of such parameters as small signal permeability and dielectric constant are very well established in the literature. Hence this chapter deals primarily with three particular techniques which require a more extensive treatment. These are the design of a hysteresigraph for the measurement of square loop materials, the measurement of electrostrictive and magnetostrictive constants of ceramic materials, and the microwave permeability tensor. These measurements are supplemented by an extensive bibliography at the end of the chapter.

The final portion of the chapter contains a discussion of the mechanical mounting and bonding problems associated with the measurement and application of electromechanical devices. At the time that this section was written the primary electrostrictive material which was under investigation included many variations of the barium titanate group. These materials were quite temperature sensitive and underwent considerable aging. Very recently, however, a new material [PZT] was introduced by the Clevite Corporation. Many of the original difficulties with the barium titanate do not appear in this class of electrostrictive ceramic.

## Appendix

Several topics which are of broad interest but could not be included in the main text are treated as separate subjects in the appendix.

### 1  Reciprocity in Linear Systems

Both Chapter 3 on electromechanical systems and Chapter 7 on microwave ferrites introduce illustrations of linear systems which exhibit nonreciprocal characteristics. A general formulation of this phenomenon is derived in order to indicate which linear systems should be expected to give rise to nonreciprocal behavior.

### 2  Tensor Dielectric Constant of a Plasma

This is another illustration of the concept of polarization as applied to a gas and the nonreciprocal dielectric constant which arises in the presence of a magnetic field.

### 3  Magnetoresistance

It is difficult to classify in an exclusive manner the Hall effect device as a magnetic or a semiconductor device. However, a brief discussion is included of the relation between the Hall voltage, magnetoresistance, and the Corbino disc.

### 4  Parametric Devices

The application of parametric diodes, voltage dependent capacitors, and variable inductors has been so rapid that it was not possible to include a complete chapter on this exceedingly important area. Hence the material included in this appendix was concentrated primarily about the new Japanese parametron and its basic operating mode. A summary is also given of the various problems which can be treated under the general category of differential equations with periodic coefficients.

### 5  Tables

The tabulation of material characteristics should be interpreted as representative of magnetic and dielectric parameters which were available approximately two years ago. The particular manufacturer should be consulted for more recent data.

H. W. KATZ
EDITOR

*Syracuse, New York*
*January 14, 1959*

# Acknowledgments

During the several years in which this volume was being written we had the encouragement and support of many members of the General Electric Company. To the following individuals in particular we wish to express our sincere appreciation: Dr. G. H. Haller, Vice-President of the General Electric Company and General Manager of the Defense Electronics Division; Dr. W. R. G. Baker, formerly Vice-President of the General Electric Company; Mr. J. J. Farrell, General Manager of the Heavy Military Electronics Department; Dr. J. B. Russell, Manager of the General Electric Electronics Laboratory; Mr. A. P. Stern, Manager of the Electronic Components and Applications Laboratory; Dr. P. N. Russell, Manager of Solid State Materials in the Electronics Laboratory; Dr. L. T. DeVore of Hoffman Electronics Corporation (formerly Manager of the Electronics Laboratory); Dr. H. M. Sullivan, Manager of the General Electric Advanced Semiconductor Laboratory; and Mr. B. G. Walker, Defense Systems Department (formerly Manager of Magnetic Devices in the Electronics Laboratory.)

H. W. KATZ
EDITOR

# Contents

# Chapter one

# Electrostatic and Magnetostatic Field Theory

## 1.0 Introduction

The advent of new materials forms the basis upon which solid state devices have developed and matured. For the engineers who plan to study, apply, or develop these devices, it is essential that their background include a basic understanding of the phenomenological description of the dielectric and magnetic properties of matter as well as a more detailed exposition of the physical origin of these same properties. Although the latter area constantly undergoes modifications, the classical description of the electrical properties of matter still remains valid. However, the usual introduction to the concepts of dielectric constant and permeability is often so restrictive that it prevents a broad understanding of the many new devices which have appeared.

A much more flexible basis, and the oldest historically, begins with a study of the electric and magnetic field in free space and then introduces the concepts of polarization and magnetization as natural extensions when matter is introduced into the field.

The purpose of this chapter, therefore, is to provide a consistent treatment of the development of the subject so that the regions of applicability as well as the limitations are clearly defined. In order to present a complete picture, a very brief review of elementary electro-statics in free space is included. It is assumed that the student has already obtained a general background in field theory; hence the details in the first several sections have been omitted. The primary emphasis is placed on the electrical description of matter.

# / ELECTROSTATICS

## 1.1 Coulomb's Law in Free Space

The physical experiment that is used as the starting point for the discussion of the forces between static charges is Coulomb's law. The extrapolation of the experimental data to the force between two point charges $q_1$ and $q_2$ in vacuum is stated as

$$\mathbf{F} = \frac{q_1 q_2 \mathbf{i}_r}{4\pi\epsilon_0 r^2} \tag{1.1}$$

where $\mathbf{i}_r$ is a unit vector in the direction of the line joining the two charges which are separated by a distance $r$. The factor $1/4\pi\epsilon_0$ is an arbitrary constant determined by the choice of the unit system. More important, however, is the fact that this quantity does not represent a physical property of free space. However, $\epsilon_0$ is called the "permittivity of free space" and is equal to $8.85 \times 10^{-12}$ farad/m in the MKS system. This point is discussed further in subsequent sections.

With the establishment of Coulomb's law we can define the electric field $\mathbf{E}$ everywhere in space by

$$\mathbf{E} = \lim_{q \to 0} \frac{\mathbf{F}}{q}$$

In other words, $\mathbf{E}$ is the force exerted on a positive test charge by all the fixed charges of the system as the magnitude of the test charge approaches zero. The further properties of the vector $\mathbf{E}$ can be estab-lished by performing line and surface integrations of $\mathbf{E}$, which arises from a single point charge $q$. The results are the same for an array of charges.

The line integral of $\mathbf{E}$ around a closed curve is $\oint \mathbf{E} \cdot d\mathbf{l}$. If we employ spherical coordinates with the origin at the charge (Figure 1.1), then the only components remaining in the integration are the radial components of $\mathbf{E}$ and $d\mathbf{l}$. Hence

$$\oint \mathbf{E} \cdot d\mathbf{l} = \int_{r_a}^{r_a} \frac{q\,dr}{4\pi r^2 \epsilon_0} = 0 \tag{1.2}$$

The result that the closed line integral is zero is due to the fact that the electric field intensity produced by static charges is always in the radial direction and has a magnitude dependent only on the distance $r$.

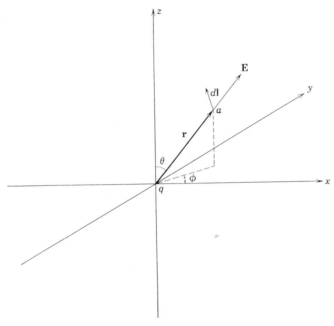

Figure 1.1.   Coordinate system for the calculation of the line integral of $\mathbf{E}$.

From equation 1.2 we can derive the equivalent point relationship for the $\mathbf{E}$-vector.   From Stokes' theorem we have

$$\oint \mathbf{E} \cdot d\mathbf{l} = \int \nabla \times \mathbf{E} \cdot d\mathbf{s} \tag{1.3}$$

Hence from equation 1.2 we obtain

$$\nabla \times \mathbf{E} = 0 \tag{1.4}$$

Additional information concerning the $\mathbf{E}$ vector in free space is obtained by evaluating the surface integral of $\mathbf{E}$, i.e., the total flux of $\mathbf{E}$

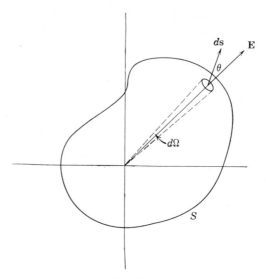

Figure 1.2.

through a closed surface. From Figure 1.2 the surface integral can be expressed as

$$\oint \mathbf{E} \cdot ds = \oint \frac{q \, ds \cos \theta}{4\pi\epsilon_0 r^2} \tag{1.5}$$

We note that the terms $ds \cos \theta$ is the area $dS$ projected onto a plane normal to the radial direction. Hence

$$\frac{ds \cos \theta}{r^2} = d\Omega \tag{1.6}$$

where $d\Omega$ is the solid angle subtended by the area $ds$ from the origin. Therefore, equation 1.5 becomes

$$\oint \mathbf{E} \cdot ds = \frac{q \int d\Omega}{4\pi\epsilon_0} = q/\epsilon_0 \tag{1.7}$$

when the integration is carried out over the entire surface.

With the aid of the divergence theorem, $\oint \mathbf{E} \cdot ds = \int \nabla \cdot \mathbf{E} \, dv$, equation 1.7 can also be converted to a point relationship. If we consider a volume charge distribution $\rho \, dv$ instead of the point charge, then

$$\oint \mathbf{E} \cdot d\mathbf{s} = \frac{1}{\epsilon_0} \int \rho \, dV = \int \nabla \cdot \mathbf{E} \, dv \tag{1.8}$$

Therefore,

$$\nabla \cdot \mathbf{E} = \rho / \epsilon_0 \tag{1.9}$$

## 1.2  Boundary Conditions

To discuss boundary conditions on $\mathbf{E}$ at this point may be somewhat artificial, since we have not yet introduced material media. However, for our later discussions there is some advantage in considering the change in $\mathbf{E}$ as one proceeds across a thin layer of surface charge density $\sigma$. By means of the "pillbox" technique (1) applied to the surface layer of Figure 1.3 we obtain from equation 1.8 that

$$E_{1n} - E_{2n} = \sigma / \epsilon_0 \tag{1.10}$$

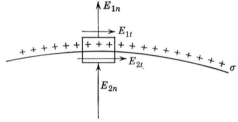

Figure 1.3.  Boundary relations for $\mathbf{E}$.

In other words, there is a discontinuity in the normal component of $E$ across a surface layer which is proportional to the surface charge density.*

Furthermore, if we apply equation 1.2 to the same configuration shown in Figure 1.3, we obtain the boundary conditions on the tangential components of $E$, namely

$$E_{1t} = E_{2t} \tag{1.11}$$

## 1.3  Poisson's Equation

We conclude our brief survey of the free-space problem with Poisson's equation. In particular, our interest at the moment is not in the equa-

* E.g., for an infinite plane sheet of charge $E_{1n} = E_{2n} = \sigma / 2\epsilon_0$.

tion itself as much as in the form of the scalar potential. From a comparison of the vector identity $\nabla \times \nabla\phi = 0$ (in which $\phi$ is a scalar function) with equation 1.4, we can define a scalar potential such that

$$\mathbf{E} = -\nabla\phi \qquad (1.12)$$

This equation combined with equation 1.8 yields

$$\nabla^2\phi = -\rho/\epsilon_0 \qquad (1.13)$$

which is the fundamental differential equation for electrostatic problems in a charged region of space. The solution can be expressed in an elementary integral form as the sum of the potentials due to each volume charge, i.e.,

$$\phi_P = \int \frac{\rho\, dV}{4\pi\epsilon_0 r} \qquad (1.14)$$

$r$ is the distance from the volume charge $\rho\, dv$ to the point $P$ where the potential is calculated.

## 1.4  Dielectric Media

There is no lack of experimental data to show that when matter is placed in an existing electric field there is a resultant change in the field distribution. The essential question at this point is what simple model may we construct for these dielectrics to enable us to measure certain significant parameters and to calculate how these materials alter the fields. The model which we finally choose should follow rather directly from the considerations of free-space fields. In addition, the model, for phenomenological calculations, should be quite independent of the detailed mechanisms which may give rise to dielectric behavior. An adequate system was established by Poisson and Maxwell long before the atomistic picture of matter became an experimental fact.

We consider that materials (unless treated in some specific manner *) exhibit no external electric field when placed in an originally field-free space. From this we conclude that each elementary volume of the material is electrically neutral. One way to obtain the latter condition is to consider that from an electrical viewpoint the charged particles occur in pairs (i.e., a positive and negative charge separated by a very small distance). This elementary pair we term a dipole. At the moment we are not concerned with the origin of the dipoles. They may already exist in a piece of material when it is formed, or they may be

---

* E.g., electrets.

produced by the application of an electric field. The significant point, however, is that if we know how the dipoles are distributed throughout the material the calculation of the field (if one exists) due to the presence of the dielectric reduces the problem to one already encountered in the free-space considerations. In other words, the distribution of dipoles is simply a specific charge distribution whose field can be calculated in principle.

## 1.5   Field of a Dipole

It is instructive to carry out the calculations of the field due to a single dipole, since they will prove illuminating for our further discussion. Figure 1.4 shows the positive and negative charge separated by a dis-

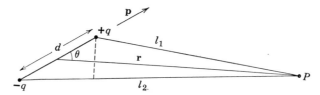

Figure 1.4.   The elementary dipole.

tance $d$. The field due to these two charges is most easily calculated from the potential. The potential at point $P$ due to both charges is

$$\phi_P = \left(\frac{-q}{l_2} + \frac{q}{l_1}\right)\frac{1}{4\pi\epsilon_0} \tag{1.15}$$

$$\phi_P = \frac{q}{4\pi\epsilon_0}\left(\frac{l_2 - l_1}{l_2 l_1}\right) \tag{1.16}$$

However,

$$l_1 = \left(r^2 + \frac{d^2}{4} - rd\cos\theta\right)^{\frac{1}{2}} \tag{1.17}$$

$$l_2 = \left(r^2 + \frac{d^2}{4} + rd\cos\theta\right)^{\frac{1}{2}} \tag{1.18}$$

If we assume that point $P$ is so located that $r \gg d$, then

$$l_1 \cong r - \frac{d}{2}\cos\theta + \left(\text{terms in }\frac{1}{r^n}\right) \tag{1.19}$$

$$l_2 \cong r + \frac{d}{2}\cos\theta + \left(\text{terms in }\frac{1}{r^n}\right) \tag{1.20}$$

Hence

$$l_2 - l_1 \cong d \cos \theta \tag{1.21}$$

$$l_1 l_2 \cong r^2 \tag{1.22}$$

Substitute the foregoing equations into equation 1.16:

$$\phi_P = \frac{qd \cos \theta}{4\pi \epsilon_0 r^2} \tag{1.23}$$

The approximation made in deriving equation 1.18 amounts to the fact that our point of observation $P$ cannot get close enough to the dipole so that we may examine the field pattern between or close to the charges. These are the limits to which our further equations apply.

Equation 1.23 can be rewritten in vector form by considering $qd$ as a dipole moment equal to $\mathbf{P}$ directed from the negative to positive charge.

Therefore

$$\phi_P = \frac{\mathbf{P} \cdot \nabla(1/r)}{4\pi \epsilon_0} \tag{1.24}$$

It should be noted that in equation 1.24 the gradient operator is evaluated with the mid-point of the dipole as the origin of the coordinate system.

The microscopic fineness with which we describe the electrical state of elementary volumes of material in terms of dipoles is now somewhat smeared out. We will describe each volume as consisting of a large number of similar dipoles aligned in the same direction (Figure 1.5).

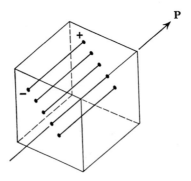

Figure 1.5.

The vector $\mathbf{P}$ which is known as the polarization will describe the dipole moment per unit volume such that $\mathbf{P} = \mathbf{p}n$ where $n$ is the number of dipoles per unit volume. Hence the potential at some point $P$ outside the dielectric is calculated from equation 1.24 as

$$\phi_P = \frac{1}{4\pi\epsilon_0} \int \mathbf{P} \cdot \nabla(1/r)\, dv \qquad (1.25)$$

A more instructive form of the equation can be obtained by the use of the following identity:

$$\nabla \cdot (\mathbf{P}/r) = \frac{1}{r} \nabla \cdot \mathbf{P} + \mathbf{P} \cdot \nabla(1/r) \qquad (1.26)$$

Hence

$$\phi_P = \frac{1}{4\pi\epsilon_0} \left[ \int \nabla \cdot \left(\frac{\mathbf{P}}{r}\right) dv - \int \frac{\nabla \cdot \mathbf{P}}{r} dv \right] \qquad (1.27)$$

By the use of the divergence theorem the first integral can be converted to a surface integral.

Therefore,

$$\phi_P = \frac{1}{4\pi\epsilon_0} \left( \int \frac{\mathbf{P} \cdot d\mathbf{s}}{r} - \int \frac{\nabla \cdot \mathbf{P}}{r} dv \right) \qquad (1.28)$$

By comparison of equation 1.28 with equation 1.14 we can interpret the total field $\mathbf{E}_p$ due to a distribution of dipoles as the sum of two components:

1. A volume charge density equal to $(-\nabla \cdot \mathbf{P})$.
2. A surface charge density equal to the normal component of $\mathbf{P}$ at the surface of the dielectric $(P_n)$.

The charge of type 1 is related to the field produced by the polarization in a manner similar to that of a field produced by a free charge (equation 1.9), i.e.,

$$\nabla \cdot \mathbf{E}_P = -\frac{\nabla \cdot \mathbf{P}}{\epsilon_0} \qquad (1.29)$$

If we now combine the field due to all the free charges which are in the material, plus that due to the polarization charge, we obtain

$$\nabla \cdot \mathbf{E} = (\rho - \nabla \cdot \mathbf{P})1/\epsilon_0 \qquad (1.30)$$

It should be noted that the complete description of the field, including the dielectric material, is in terms of the single vector $\mathbf{E}$. In order to obtain a vector whose divergence is a function only of the free charge, we define a vector $\mathbf{D}$ (displacement vector) as *

$$\mathbf{D} = \epsilon_0 \mathbf{E} + \mathbf{P} \qquad (1.31)$$

* In cgs units $D$ is defined as $D = E + 4\pi P$.

Hence

$$\nabla \cdot \mathbf{D} = \epsilon_0 \nabla \cdot \mathbf{E} + \nabla \cdot \mathbf{P} \qquad (1.32)$$

Using equation 1.30, we obtain

$$\nabla \cdot \mathbf{D} = \rho \qquad (1.33)$$

Poisson's equation inside the dielectric becomes

$$\nabla^2 \phi = \frac{1}{\epsilon_0}(\rho - \nabla \cdot \mathbf{P}) \qquad (1.34)$$

It is also significant to note that $\mathbf{D}$ and $\mathbf{E}$ in free space differ only by $\epsilon_0$. The MKS unit system arbitrarily gives $\mathbf{D}$ and $\mathbf{E}$ different dimensions. As we have seen, the dielectric properties of media are related primarily to the polarization $\mathbf{P}$.

## 1.6   Polarization Vector P

The essence of the electrostatic problem in the presence of dielectric material is the determination of the polarization $\mathbf{P}$. In fact, all dielectric applications depend upon the ability to vary $\mathbf{P}$ in some manner. Among the many variables we may use are electric field, mechanical strain, and temperature. However, in most problems we desire to know how $\mathbf{P}$ varies as a function of $\mathbf{E}$. In a crystal the relationship may be very complex in that the resultant polarization in a given direction is a function of the fields in all three directions. The simplest case is that in which $\mathbf{P}$ is directly proportional to $\mathbf{E}$, i.e.,

$$\mathbf{P} = \epsilon_0 k \mathbf{E} \qquad (1.35)$$

where $k$ is a dimensionless scalar quantity defined as the dielectric susceptibility. Under these conditions equation 1.31 becomes

$$\mathbf{D} = \epsilon_0 \mathbf{E} + \epsilon_0 k \mathbf{E} = \epsilon_0 \epsilon_r \mathbf{E} \qquad (1.36)$$

where $\epsilon_r$ is the relative dielectric constant equal to $1 + k$.* Materials in which $k$ does not vary throughout the volume can contribute to the electric field only by virtue of the effective surface charges which are produced (when the body does not contain any free volume charges). This can be seen by noting that equation 1.30 yields $\nabla \cdot \mathbf{E} = 0$ for $\rho = 0$ and $\mathbf{P} = k\mathbf{E}$. Hence $\nabla \cdot \mathbf{P} = 0$, and there is no contribution due to the volume polarization charge.

* E.g., $\epsilon_r = 80$ for water.

Another variation of **P** occurs with ferroelectric material (e.g., $BaTiO_3$) in which the relation between **P** and **E** exhibits hysteresis. In this case care must be taken when ascribing a dielectric constant for such a material. Figure 1.6 indicates the various dielectric constants which are defined for a nonlinear material. The initial permittivity $\epsilon_i$ is defined as the slope of the normal polarization curve at $E = 0$. The incremental dielectric constant $\epsilon_\Delta$ is defined as $\Delta D/\Delta E$ about a given

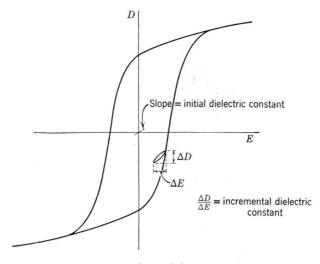

**Figure 1.6.**

point on the hysteresis loop. The reversible dielectric constant $\epsilon_r$ is defined as the limit of $\Delta D/\Delta E$ as $\Delta E$ approaches zero.

## 1.7  Coulomb's Law for Dielectrics

An interesting illustration of the use of the polarization concept is the calculation of the field inside a dielectric for the geometry of Figure 1.7.

A charged conducting sphere of radius $R$ and total charge $q$ is immersed in an infinite homogeneous medium of dielectric constant $\epsilon_r$. The electric field **E** at point $a$ is due to the following sources:

1. The free charge on the surface of the sphere which produces a field

$$E_1 = q/4\pi\epsilon_0 r^2 \tag{1.37}$$

2. The surface polarization charge density $(-P_m)$ which occurs at

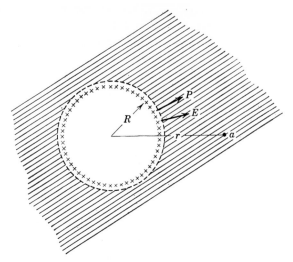

**Figure 1.7.**

the interface between the medium and the sphere. The field due to this charge is

$$E_2 = -\frac{P_n R^2}{\epsilon_0 r^2} \tag{1.38}$$

3. The surface polarization charge density which occurs at infinity. This term introduces zero field.

4. The volume distribution $(-\nabla \cdot \mathbf{P})$. Since $\nabla \cdot \mathbf{D} = 0$, then $\nabla \cdot \mathbf{E} = 0$, and therefore $\nabla \cdot \mathbf{P} = 0$. Hence there is no contribution to the field from the volume polarization. The total field at $r$ is then

$$\mathbf{E} = \mathbf{E}_1 + \mathbf{E}_2 \tag{1.39}$$

There only remains the calculation of $P_n$. Since

$$P_n = \epsilon_0 k E|_{r=R} \tag{1.40}$$

equation 1.39 yields

$$\mathbf{E}|_{r=R} = \left(\frac{q}{4\pi R^2 \epsilon_0} - \frac{P_n}{\epsilon_0}\right)\mathbf{i}_r \tag{1.41}$$

$$= \left(\frac{q}{4\pi R^2 \epsilon_0} - k E|_{r=R}\right)\mathbf{i}_r \tag{1.42}$$

Therefore,

$$P_n = \frac{kq}{4\pi R^2(1 + k)} \tag{1.43}$$

Substitution of equation 1.43 into equation 1.39 yields

$$E = \left( \frac{q}{4\pi r^2 \epsilon_0} - \frac{kq}{4\pi\epsilon_0(1+k)r^2} \right) i_r \tag{1.44}$$

$$E = \frac{qi_r}{(1+k)4\pi r^2 \epsilon_0} = \frac{qi_r}{4\pi r^2 \epsilon_r \epsilon_0} \tag{1.45}$$

Hence by a detailed consideration of all the "charges" in the system we arrive at the usual form for Coulomb's law inside the medium. It should be noted that the $E$ defined in equation 1.45 is not the field acting on a single dipole of the medium but rather the field averaged over a large number of elementary dipoles at the point in question. In order to determine the field acting on an isolated charge at the point $a$, it is necessary to examine the medium locally in finer detail.*

## 1.8   Cavity Definitions for $E$ and $D$

The local field discussed in Section 1.6 is determined by the geometric shape of the cavity in which the charge is assumed to reside.   Figure

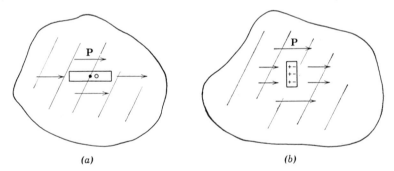

*(a)*                                        *(b)*

**Figure 1.8.**   (a) "Pillbox" cavity in a polarized medium; pillbox axis parallel to polarization.   (b) "Pillbox" cavity in a polarized medium; pillbox axis perpendicular to polarization.

1.8a shows a small cavity which is constructed so that its long dimension is parallel to the local polarization of the medium.   The total field $E$ at point 0 inside the cavity is due to

1. All the free charges and surface and volume polarization charges outside the cavity.   Denote this field by $E_1$.

* See Chapter 2.

2. All the surface polarization charges produced by the introduction of the cavity. These charges occur only at the end walls. However, the field produced at 0 by these charges can be neglected if the cavity is long and thin.

Hence $E = E_1$, i.e., the field at 0 is due to all the charges in the system. However, the cavity dimensions are not too small, so that the atomic structure of the body need not be considered.

If the cavity of Figure 1.8a is rotated so that it is perpendicular to the polarization, the total field will then include a contribution from the cavity surface (Figure 1.8b). The field inside the cavity due to the surface polarization charge is $P/\epsilon_0$; the total field is

$$\mathbf{E} = \mathbf{E}_1 + \mathbf{P}/\epsilon_0 \tag{1.46}$$

Therefore,

$$\epsilon_0 \mathbf{E} = \epsilon_0 \mathbf{E}_1 + \mathbf{P} = \mathbf{D} \tag{1.47}$$

since the inner region of the cavity is free space.

Another common choice of cavity geometry is that of a sphere. In this case the surface polarization has a distribution $P \cos \theta$ on the surface of the sphere. The field $\mathbf{E}$ at any point inside the spherical cavity can be shown to be $\mathbf{P}/3\epsilon_0$.

## 1.9   Depolarizing Factors

In many problems it is of interest to know the change in field produced by a dielectric body introduced into a uniform electric field. For certain simple geometries, such as spheres, cylinders, and ellipsoids of revolution, the dielectric becomes uniformly polarized. Hence the only contribution to the field inside the dielectric is due to the surface polarization charge. Moreover, for these specific shapes the depolarizing field inside the dielectric is uniform. The total internal field $E_i$ is usually given in the following form for each component:

$$E_{i_x} = E_{a_x} - N_x P_x \tag{1.48}$$

where $E_a$ is the uniform applied field and $\mathbf{N}$ is the depolarizing factor whose components for the general ellipsoid satisfy the relationship $N_x + N_y + N_z = 1/\epsilon_0.$[*]

[*] In the cgs system this sum is $4\pi$. Calculated values of $\mathbf{N}$ for various ratios of ellipsoidal semiaxes can be found in the references (9).

Table 1.1 contains the value of $N$ for commonly encountered geo-metries. The same factors are also true for the analogous magnetostatic case. In addition, these factors, except for a minus sign, hold for the case in which there are holes of the same geometry inside a large uni-formly polarized body.

## Table 1.1

### Depolarizing Factors

| | | |
|---|---|---|
| Thin plate $l \gg d$ | | $N_z = 1/\epsilon_0$ |
| Sphere | | $N_z = 1/3\epsilon_0$ |
| Cylinder | | $N_z = 1/2\epsilon_0$ |

## 1.10   Boundary Conditions on D and E

We are now in a position to summarize the complete boundary condi-tions on the two vectors **D** and **E**. The tangential components of **E** are determined by the use of equation 1.2 and the familiar "pillbox" calculation.

Hence $E_{1t} = E_{2t}$ across any boundary; the tangential components of **D** are determined in a similar manner, i.e.,

$$\oint \mathbf{D} \cdot d\mathbf{l} = \epsilon_0 \oint \mathbf{E} \cdot d\mathbf{l} + \oint \mathbf{P} \cdot d\mathbf{l} \tag{1.49}$$

$$\oint \mathbf{D} \cdot d\mathbf{l} = \oint \mathbf{P} \cdot d\mathbf{l} \tag{1.50}$$

Hence $D_{1t} - D_{2t} = P_{1t} - P_{2t}$ when $P_{1t}$ and $P_{2t}$ are the tangential components of **P** on either side of the boundary.

The normal components of $\mathbf{E}$ across a boundary are computed from equation 1.30 (Figure 1.9):

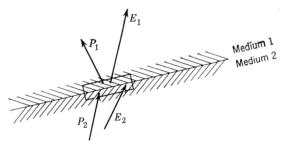

**Figure 1.9.**

$$\oint \mathbf{E} \cdot d\mathbf{s} = \frac{\text{total surface charge on the boundary}}{\epsilon_0} \tag{1.51}$$

$$E_{1n} - E_{2n} = \frac{\sigma}{\epsilon_0} - \frac{P_{2n} - P_{1n}}{\epsilon_0} \tag{1.52}$$

where $\sigma$ is the free charge density on the surface, and $(P_{2n} - P_{1n})$ the net surface polarization charge.

## / MAGNETOSTATICS

### 1.11  Introduction

There are a number of varied approaches to the subject of magneto-statics. The problem is somewhat more complex than the electrostatic because of the existence of magnetic fields due to magnets and to current-carrying conductors. Hence the question soon turns to the representation of magnetism by currents or magnetic dipoles. We have adopted the latter approach for two general reasons:

1. From the device standpoint it provides the simplest analogous treatment between magnetic and dielectric devices.
2. From the materials standpoint the greater portion of the present literature in the field discusses magnetism from this point of view.

## 1.12   Permanent Magnets

Let us first consider the magnetic fields in free space produced by permanent magnets. From well-known experiments performed on long thin magnets we can arrive at a "Coulomb's law" for magnetostatics. It is possible to describe the field produced by such magnets in terms of magnetic "poles" which are postulated to "exist" at the ends of the long magnet. In addition, we could also conclude from the same experiment that isolated magnetic poles do not occur but are rather in pairs of opposite polarity. Hence our description of magnetostatic phenomena is in terms of distributions of magnetic dipoles, although the basic definitions are in terms of magnetic poles. This yields a formulation which is analogous to that for electrostatics.

Coulomb's law for "magnetic charges" $q_1$, $q_2$, separated by a distance $r$ in free space, is given by

$$\mathbf{F} = \frac{q_1 q_2 \mathbf{i}_r}{4\pi\mu_0 r^2} \tag{1.53}$$

Again it must be emphasized that the factor $1/4\pi\mu_0$ similar to $1/4\pi\epsilon_0$ in electrostatics is merely an attribute of the unit system that is employed. In the MKS system $\mu_0$ is $4\pi \times 10^{-7}$.

Hence, given a distribution of magnetic charges, we can define a magnetic field vector at a point as $\mathbf{H}$, where $\mathbf{H}$ is the force on a unit positive (north) charge. Since the functional form of the force law is the same as that for electrostatics, we can carry over the vector properties of $\mathbf{E}$ to those of $\mathbf{H}$. The results, which are so far restricted to permanent magnets, can be summarized as follows:

**Line Integral of H**

$$\oint \mathbf{H} \cdot d\mathbf{l} = 0 \tag{1.54}$$

From this we can derive a magnetic scalar potential $\phi_m$ such that

$$\mathbf{H} = -\nabla\phi_m \tag{1.55}$$

Furthermore, we can conclude that

$$\nabla \times \mathbf{H} = 0 \tag{1.56}$$

**Surface Integral of H**

The source of the field $H$ is up to this point due to permanent magnets. It might be well to clarify our definition of an ideal permanent magnet. At each point in the volume we can define a magnetic dipole moment per volume equal to $\mathbf{M}$ (commonly termed the magnetization vector). The ideal property of $\mathbf{M}$ for a permanent magnet is such that its magnitude and direction inside the body cannot be changed by any external field. Hence to calculate the field due to a given distribution of $\mathbf{M}$ we can employ the results of our previous discussion of electrostatic dipoles. In other words, the magnetic scalar potential $\phi_m$ both inside and outside the magnetized volume is given by

$$\phi_m = \frac{1}{4\pi\mu_0}\left(\int \frac{\mathbf{m}\cdot d\mathbf{s}}{r} - \int \frac{\nabla\cdot\mathbf{M}}{r}\,dv\right) \tag{1.57}$$

Therefore the field due to a permanent magnet can be considered to arise from a volume distribution of magnetic "charge" $(-\nabla\cdot\mathbf{M})$ and a surface distribution due to $M_m$.

Therefore, if we integrate $\mathbf{H}$ over a closed surface, we should obtain

$$\oint \mathbf{H}\cdot d\mathbf{s} = \frac{\mathbf{Q}_m}{\mu_0} \tag{1.58}$$

where $\mathbf{Q}_m$ is the total magnetic charge enclosed inside the surface. If the surface is taken so as to completely enclose the magnet, then the value of the integral is zero, since there are no isolated magnetic poles.

However, if the surface is taken completely inside the magnet volume, there will be a contribution due to an apparent distribution of magnetic charge equal to $(-\nabla\cdot\mathbf{M})$. Hence we conclude that, in general,

$$\nabla\cdot\mathbf{H} = -\frac{\nabla\cdot\mathbf{M}}{\mu_0} \tag{1.59}$$

## 1.13 Permeable Material

A second class of magnetic material is defined by the property that the magnetization is a function of $\mathbf{H}$.

If "soft" magnetic material of this type is introduced into the vicinity of the permanent magnet, there is a change in $\mathbf{H}$ everywhere. This change, of course, arises from the fact that the new material has become magnetized; i.e., each elementary volume in the material assumes a value of $\mathbf{M}$, dependent on the total field $\mathbf{H}$ that exists at that point. As we have already seen, the total $H$ is due to

1. The field produced by the permanent magnet.
2. The field produced by the effective volume magnetic charge $(-\nabla\cdot\mathbf{M})$.
3. The field produced by the surface magnetization.

The third field is often called the demagnetizing field. The determination of the exact distribution of **M** inside the permeable material is in general a very complex problem due primarily to the fact that the basic relationship between the magnetization and the field producing it is usually very complicated and dependent on the previous history of the specimen. Hence only the simplest geometries are amenable to solution.

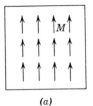

(a)

## 1.14  B Vector

The introduction of the **B** vector (magnetic induction) is carried out in a manner similar to the electrostatic problem. **B** is defined as*

$$\mathbf{B} = \mu_0\mathbf{H} + \mathbf{M} \quad (1.60)$$

The important property of the **B** vector is found by taking the divergence of both sides of equation 1.58.

$$\nabla\cdot\mathbf{B} = \mu_0\nabla\cdot\mathbf{H} + \nabla\cdot\mathbf{M} \quad (1.61)$$

Therefore, $\nabla\cdot\mathbf{B} = 0$ from equation 1.59. This result is due to the fact that we have no "free" magnetic charge.

A permanent magnet affords an interesting vehicle for indicating the differences between **B** and **H**. Figure 1.10a is an idealized, long, cylindrical, permanent magnet in which the magnetization **M** is uni-

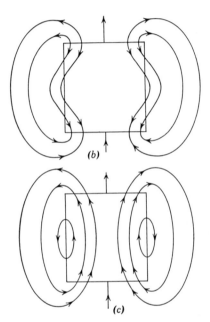

Figure 1.10. (a) Permanent magnetization; (b) lines of **H**; (c) lines of **B**.

form. Hence the field **H** is due solely to the surface magnetization **M**, with no contribution due to the volume magnetization, since $\nabla\cdot\mathbf{M} = 0$. A plot of the field **H** is shown in Figure 1.10b. At the top surface, for example, a positive pole would be repelled from the surface, whereas just inside the magnet the positive pole would be repelled in roughly the opposite direction. In other words, there is a discontinuity in **H**

* In the cgs system $B = H + 4\pi M$.

as the surface is crossed. However, if at each point inside the magnet **M** is added to **H** vectorially, a plot of the field of **B** (Figure 1.10c) is obtained. In this case the **B** field is continuous across the boundary. **B** and **H** outside the magnet have the same configuration, whereas inside the magnet they are markedly different (5).

## 1.15 Boundary Conditions for B and H

The boundary conditions in magnetostatics for **B** and **H** are similar to those of **D** and **E** in electrostatics when no free electric charge is prescribed. These conditions are summarized here. At the boundary between two different magnetic media

1. The normal component of **B** is continuous.

$$B_{1n} = B_{2n} \tag{1.62}$$

2. The normal component of **H** is discontinuous.

$$H_{1n} - H_{2n} = M_n/\mu_0 \tag{1.63}$$

where $M_n$ is the net surface magnetization between the two boundaries.

3. The tangential component of **H** is continuous.

$$H_{1t} = H_{2t} \tag{1.64}$$

4. The tangential component of **B** is discontinuous.

$$B_{1t} - B_{2t} = M_{1t} \tag{1.65}$$

where $M_{1t}$ is the net tangential component of the magnetization between the two surfaces.

## 1.16 Material Characteristics

Essentially the description of magnetic materials and devices hinges on the relationship that exists between **H** and **M** for a particular material. The various parameters which may affect this relationship serve as the source of the various magnetic applications which are encountered. Among these factors we might mention the following as in the electrostatic case:

1. **M** as a function of temperature.
2. **M** as a function of strain.
3. **M** as a function of magnetic field, etc.

However, the commonest uses of magnetic materials involve the relationship of $\mathbf{M}$ as a function of $\mathbf{H}$. The simplest form of this relationship occurs when the magnetization is directly proportional to the magnetic field, i.e., $\mathbf{M} = \mu_0 k \mathbf{H}$ where $k$ is called the magnetic susceptibility. For this case

$$\mathbf{B} = \mu_0 H(1 + k) \tag{1.66}$$

The factor $1 + k$ is defined as the relative permeability of the material ($\mu_r$). Hence for this class of materials we are led to the familiar re-

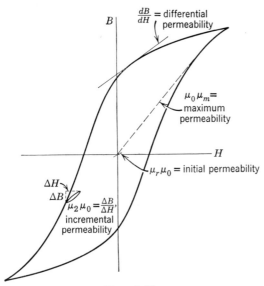

**Figure 1.11.**

lationship $\mathbf{B} = \mu_r \mu_0 \mathbf{H}$. Magnetic materials for which this linear relationship exists are divided into two classes, dependent upon the sign of $k$. Diamagnetic materials have a negative $k$ of the order of $10^{-4}$ to $10^{-6}$, and paramagnetic materials have a positive value of $k$ with about the same orders of magnitude. It is unreasonable to identify these systems in terms of permeability which would have a value of $\mu_r = 1 + 10^{-6}$.

The third large group of materials is that in which the resultant magnetization is one to several orders of magnitude greater than the applied field $\mu_0 \mathbf{H}$. This group is known as the ferromagnetic materials. Unfortunately, the relationship between $\mathbf{M}$ and $\mathbf{H}$ is nonlinear and exhibits the familiar hysteresis effect. Hence we must be careful when defining a permeability for the ferromagnetic systems. In fact, several permeabilities are used in various modes of operation. From the hysteresis loop shown in Figure 1.11 we can note the different permeabilites. For extremely small signals about the origin the permeability is denoted by $\mu_r\mu_0$, the initial permeability. The maximum slope of the secant to the major loop is called $\mu_0\mu_m$, the maximum permeability, and the ratio of $\Delta B/\Delta H$ centered about a bias field is termed the incremental permeability. Sometimes the term differential permeability is used; it is defined as $dB/dH$, the slope of the magnetization curve at the point of interest.

## 1.17 Magnetic Fields Produced by Steady Currents

There are many ways to approach the magnetic field due to a distribution of d-c currents. The method chosen here is in keeping with our original starting point in terms of magnetic dipoles. The relationship between a magnetic dipole and a current element must be determined from experiment. If we use a small magnet as equivalent to an elementary dipole, we find that in free space, at a point sufficiently well removed from the magnet, the field produced by the magnet is the same as that produced by a small current loop oriented at right angles to the magnet. Figure 1.12 shows the schematic relationship.

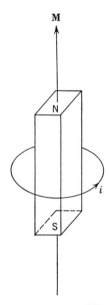

If the magnet and current loop are sufficiently small, then the following quantitative relationship is found:

$$\mathbf{M} = \mu_0 i\, d\mathbf{s} \qquad (1.67)$$

In other words, the equivalent magnetic moment $\mathbf{M}$ is equal to the magnitude of the current times the cross-sectional area of the loop. The factor $\mu_0$ is again inserted for dimensional purposes only. The direction of $\mathbf{M}$ is related to the current direction.

**Figure 1.12.** The equivalence of a bar magnet and current loop in producing a magnetization **M**.

In order to determine the field due to an arbitrarily large current loop, we can perform the following construction (Figure 1.13$a$). On the curve $ABCD$ formed by the current loop erect a surface $S$ which has the curve $(ABCD)$ as one of its boundaries. Subdivide the entire surface into many small loops, as shown. If we associate a mesh current $i$ with each loop, it can be seen that adjacent meshes cancel their common currents. This canceling procedure occurs over the entire surface except for those meshes which have the original contour as one side of the mesh. Thus the array of current loops produces the same magnetic field as the original current contour.

Now it is possible to replace the small current loop with its equivalent magnetic dipole oriented normal to the surface $S$. The problem then reduces to one of finding the field due to this distribution of dipoles of

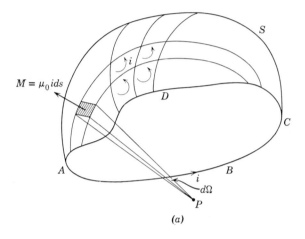

(a)

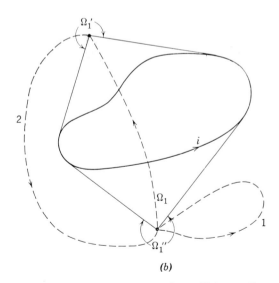

(b)

**Figure 1.13.** (a) Equivalent current sheet; (b) integration paths.

equal magnitude. Figure 1.13$a$ shows one element of the surface and a point $P$ at which it is desired to find the magnetic field $H$. It is simpler to find the potential $\phi_P$. From equation 1.22 the potential due to an elementary dipole is

$$d\phi_P = \frac{m \cos \theta}{4\pi\mu_0 r^2} \tag{1.68}$$

For the dipole equivalent to the current element $m = \mu_0 I \, ds$

$$\phi_P = \frac{I}{4\pi} \int \frac{ds \cos \theta}{r^2} \tag{1.69}$$

where the integration is carried out over the entire surface. From a previous derivation, equation 1.6, it is recalled that the integrand in equation 1.69 is the solid angle $(d\Omega)$ subtended by the elementary area at point $P$. Hence the integrated value is the total solid angle $\Omega_1$ subtended by the original current loop at point $P$.

$$\phi_P = \frac{I\Omega_1}{4\pi} \tag{1.70}$$

In order to evaluate the line integral of $\mathbf{H}$, it is now necessary to specify the path of integration. If we start at $P$ and return to $P$ via a path (curve 1 of Figure 1.13$b$) that does not encircle the current loop, then

$$\oint \mathbf{H} \cdot d\mathbf{l} = 0$$

since the solid angle at the start and finish of the path is the same. However, if we use a path which goes through the loop, it can be seen that the solid angle changes from $\Omega_1$ to $\Omega_1'$ to $\Omega_1''$ as we progress back to $P$. Since the total change in $\Omega_1$ is $4\pi$, the change in potential around this path is $I$. Therefore we arrive at Ampere's law

$$\oint \mathbf{H} \cdot d\mathbf{l} = I \tag{1.71}$$

where the path 1 encircles the total current $I$.* For a point relationship we obtain from equation 1.71

$$\nabla \times \mathbf{H} = \mathbf{J} \tag{1.72}$$

where $\mathbf{J}$ is the current density.

---

* Hence in general the magnetic field $H$ due to currents is not derivable from the gradient of a scalar potential.

We are now in a position to combine both magnetic materials and current sources. The total magnetic field $\mathbf{H}$ is the sum of two components:

$$\mathbf{H} = \mathbf{H}_I + \mathbf{H}_M \qquad (1.73)$$

$\mathbf{H}_I$ is due to all the real conduction currents.

$\mathbf{H}_M$ is due to the magnetic material in the form of volume and surface polarization.

If we calculate $\oint \mathbf{H} \cdot d\mathbf{l}$ for this case, we obtain

$$\oint \mathbf{H} \cdot d\mathbf{l} = \oint \mathbf{H}_m \cdot d\mathbf{l} + \oint \mathbf{H}_I \cdot d\mathbf{l} = I \qquad (1.74)$$

since $\mathbf{H}_m$ is derivable from a scalar potential, and therefore its line integral is zero. We may thus conclude that $\mathbf{H}$ is a function of the currents and the magnetic materials present, but that the integrated value of $\mathbf{H}$ is a function of the currents only, i.e., equation 1.71 is now generally true.

We may now examine the $\mathbf{B}$ vector for the general case. $\mathbf{B}$ is still defined as

$$\mathbf{B} = \mu_0 \mathbf{H} + \mathbf{M} \qquad (1.75)$$

where $\mathbf{H}$ is the total field. Take the curl of both sides of equation 1.75:

$$\nabla \times \mathbf{B} = \mu_0 \nabla \times \mathbf{H} + \nabla \times \mathbf{M} \qquad (1.76)$$

$$\nabla \times \mathbf{B} = \mu_0 \mathbf{J} + \nabla \times \mathbf{M} \qquad (1.77)$$

The term $\nabla \times \mathbf{M}$ may be viewed as the current density equivalent to the volume magnetization. This equivalent current is known as the "Amperian" current of a magnetic material. This point is further studied in Section 1.18.

## 1.18   Boundary Conditions for Magnetostatics Including Currents

### H Vector

The tangential components of $\mathbf{H}$ are continuous across a boundary ($H_{1t} = H_{2t}$), unless one passes across a thin current sheet. In the latter case

$$H_{1t} - H_{2t} = I \qquad (1.78)$$

where $I$ in this case is the linear current density.

The normal components of **H** are discontinuous across a boundary, i.e.,

$$H_{1n} - H_{2n} = \frac{M_n}{\mu_0} \tag{1.79}$$

where $M_n$ is the net normal component of magnetization at the boundary. In other words, if two magnetized media share a common surface, $M_n$ is equal to $M_{n1} - M_{n2}$.

### B Vector

Since the div **B** is identically zero, the normal components of **B** are continuous across a boundary.

The relationship that exists between the tangential components of **B** can be found by integrating equation 1.75 around the familiar pillbox erected at the boundary between the two media.

$$\oint \mathbf{B} \cdot d\mathbf{l} = \mu_0 \oint \mathbf{H} \cdot d\mathbf{l} + \oint \mathbf{M} \cdot d\mathbf{l} \tag{1.80}$$

If we consider the case in which no current sheets exist at the boundary, then

$$B_{1t} - B_{2t} = M_{1t} - M_{2t} \tag{1.81}$$

For example, if we consider the cylindrical magnet of Figure 1.10, the difference in tangential components of **B** across either the top or bottom surface is zero, since there the magnetization is normal to the interface. However, the difference in tangential components of **B** across the cylindrical surface is equal to the magnetization **M**, i.e.,

$$B_{1t} - B_{2t} = M \tag{1.81b}$$

If this equation is compared in form to equation 1.78, then the value of **M** in equation 1.81b can be considered as a surface "current" which produces the same field as the distributed magnetization produced outside the magnet. These "currents" are commonly referred to as Amperian.

Since the $\nabla \cdot \mathbf{B} = 0$, then **B** is in general derivable from a vector potential **A**, i.e.,

$$\nabla \times \mathbf{A} = \mathbf{B} \tag{1.82}$$

The integral form for **A** is (1)

$$\mathbf{A} = \frac{\mu_0}{4\pi} \left( \int \frac{\mathbf{J} \, dv}{r} + \int \frac{\nabla \times \mathbf{M}}{r} \, dv + \int \frac{\mathbf{M} \times d\mathbf{s}}{r} \right) \tag{1.83}$$

The last two integrals represent the contribution of the equivalent volume current $\nabla \times \mathbf{M}$, and the equivalent surface current $\mathbf{M} \times \mathbf{n}$ due to the variable magnetization $\mathbf{M}$. This form for the vector potential is analogous to the scalar potential due to real electric charges and volume and surface polarization charges in equation 1.28.

## 1.19   Illustrations of Concepts

In order to make these ideas more concrete, it is instructive to examine several examples, albeit simple ones.  The main emphasis is on pointing out the technique of viewing the total magnetic field ($\mathbf{H}$) as the sum of the contributions due to the currents plus the magnetizable media that may be present. It is felt that in this manner we can appreciate more readily the detailed role played by the magnetic material in the production of the field.  However, the technique for solving a particular problem need not involve such detailed considerations.  The exact method chosen will depend greatly on the novelty of the configuration under analysis.

### Toroid

The simplest configuration for magnetic purposes is the toroid of uniform cross section.  If a very uniform winding is placed on the toroid, then the field $\mathbf{H}_I$ produced by the current is constant and everywhere circumferential (Figure 1.14$a$).  The magnetic material does not add to the field $\mathbf{H}$ because there are no surfaces across which there is a discontinuity in the normal component of $\mathbf{M}$ (i.e., no surface charges are produced).  However, if an air gap is introduced in the material, the field configuration is altered.  As can be

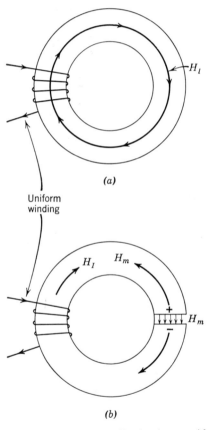

(a)

Uniform
winding

(b)

Figure 1.14.   Field distribution in a toroid with and without an air gap.

seen in Figure 1.14b, the field $\mathbf{H}_I$ produced by the current is still the same as before. The normal discontinuity of magnetization which occurs at the air gap produces a new field $\mathbf{H}_m$. Inside the gap the field adds to that produced by the current and is actually the largest contribution to the total field, whereas inside the magnetic medium it subtracts from the field of the current. Because of the uniformity of the winding the total $\mathbf{H}$ field inside the medium is essentially constant around the circumference.

A more interesting example is provided in the case in which a high permeability toroid is wound with all of its turns concentrated on one side of the toroid, as shown in Figure 1.15a (2). From experience it is

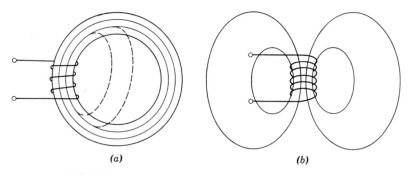

(a)                                    (b)

**Figure 1.15.** (a) Field due to concentrated coil on magnetic toroid; (b) field due to coil alone.

known that the distribution of $\mathbf{B}$ is very nearly constant around the circumference of the toroid. How does this come about when the field produced by the windings alone is far from uniform (Figure 1.15b)? The effect is produced by the additional field due to the surface charge produced on the inner and outer edges of the toroid (Figure 1.15a). In other words, what we choose to call the "leakage" field is in essence the reason for the almost uniform total field inside the core material. The magnetization must have a small normal component at the surface in order to provide the necessary surface charge. A more detailed calculation for this type of configuration appears in the applications section on television deflection yokes.

A somewhat more academic illustration is obtained when we consider the field of a permanent magnet of spherical shape which is magnetized uniformly (Figure 1.16). It is comparatively straightforward to calculate the $\mathbf{H}$ field everywhere outside the sphere. If the sphere is now placed in an infinite medium of permeability $\mu_r$, the field inside the medium is increased, but not by the factor $\mu_r$. Rather, the proportionality factor is $3\mu_r/2\mu_r + 1$. Here again the nonuniform surface polarization at the interface between the medium and the permanent magnet is the source of the additional field.

This situation may be contrasted to the case of an infinitely long straight wire carrying current placed inside a permeable medium of infinite extent. In this case there are no new sources of field, since **H** is tangential to the interface between the medium and the conductor. Hence the field **H** at a point P is the same with or without the magnetic medium.

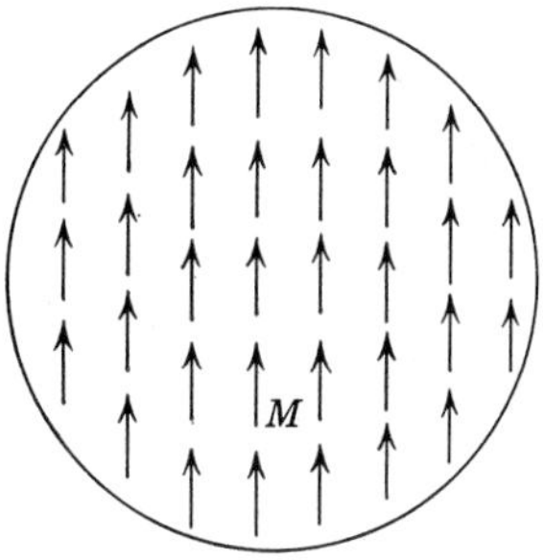

Let us pursue the last illustration a bit further by examining the equation for the force exerted on a current in a magnetic field, i.e.,

$$F = BIL \qquad (1.84)$$

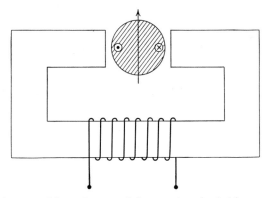

Figure 1.16.

If we apply this equation to a current carrying conductor ($\mu_r = 1$) placed in a magnetic field **H** in free space, then

$$F = \mu_0 HIL \qquad (1.85)$$

If the conductor is now immersed in a medium of permeability $\mu_r$, the field at the conductor is actually decreased rather than increased. Figure 1.17 shows a somewhat idealized motor in which the current-carrying conductors are completely embedded in the magnetic armature.

Figure 1.17. A rotor with conductors of the armature buried in magnetic material.

In this case the actual field at the conductor is extremely small, yet the torque on the armature has increased by virtue of the magnetic core. Essentially, the increased torque is due to the fact that the armature current has magnetized the core so that it appears as a dipole of very large moment. The torque exerted on the "dipole" is large by virtue of the high permeability of the armature.

Equation 1.84 becomes more meaningful for the case of a charged particle actually moving through the magnetic medium rather than a conductor. A summary of the experimental data taken on the deflection of charged particles through magnetic material is best summarized in a recent book (3), from which we quote:

If the motion of the charged particle is truly random relative to the magnetized material—that is if it is not affected by the presence of the magnetized medium, to a first approximation—then the force that is exerted on it corresponds to the use of **B** as the magnetic field in the force equation. If, on the other hand, the particle is moving slowly, and its motion is substantially affected by the magnetized medium, then it is effectively prevented from passing through the equivalent atomic current loops, and in this case, since the individual current loops act like impenetrable dipoles, the averaging process forms a deflection that corresponds to the use of **H** in the force equation.

In addition to the above, we can also add some experimental results of Hall effect measurements in ferromagnetic materials (4). In these experiments we are essentially interested in the magnetic field that acts on a conduction electron in the material:

Considerable thought has been given to the possibility that an effective magnetic field deflects the conduction electrons. That is,

$$H_{\text{eff}} = \mu_0 H + \alpha M_S$$

where $H$ = magnetizing force, $M_S$ = saturation magnetization in a domain, and $\alpha$ is a parameter which would usually be much greater than unity.

## 1.20 Energy of Magnetization

Of the many formulas that are used to calculate the energy of a magnetic material placed in a magnetic field, perhaps the most important is the energy required to bring the material to a given state of magnetization. This expression can be derived by considering the force on an elementary volume of material and then calculating the total work necessary to magnetize the material.

Consider an elementary dipole of moment $m \, \Delta l$ placed in an inhomo-

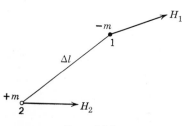

Figure 1.18.

geneous field $\mathbf{H}$ (Figure 1.18). If the negative end of the dipole is at point 1 and the positive end at point 2, then the total force is

$$\mathbf{F} = -m\mathbf{H}_1 + m\mathbf{H}_2 = m(\mathbf{H}_2 - \mathbf{H}_1) \tag{1.86}$$

If we consider the $x$-component of the force, then

$$F_x = m(H_{2x} - H_{1x}) \tag{1.87}$$

However, since $H$ is a function of $(x, y, z)$,

$$H_{2x} = H_{1x} + \frac{\partial H_{1x}}{\partial x} \Delta x + \frac{\partial H_{1x}}{\partial y} \Delta y + \frac{\partial H_{1x}}{\partial z} \Delta z \cdots \tag{1.88}$$

Hence equation 1.87 becomes

$$F_x = m \, \Delta x \frac{\partial H_{1x}}{\partial x} + m \, \Delta y \frac{\partial H_{1x}}{\partial y} + m \, \Delta z \frac{\partial H_{1x}}{\partial z} \tag{1.89}$$

Define

$$m \, \Delta x = M_x$$
$$m \, \Delta y = M_y \tag{1.90}$$
$$m \, \Delta z = M_z$$

With similar expressions for the remaining two components of the force, we obtain for the force per unit volume

$$\mathbf{F} = (\mathbf{M} \cdot \nabla)\mathbf{H} \tag{1.91}$$

where $\mathbf{M}$ is now the magnetization per unit volume. Note that a net force exists on the magnetization only in a nonuniform field.

The energy per unit volume is thus

$$dW_1 = -[(\mathbf{M} \cdot \nabla)\mathbf{H}] \cdot dl \tag{1.92}$$

By expanding the right-hand side of equation 1.92 and noting that $\nabla \times \mathbf{H} = 0$, it can be shown that

$$[(\mathbf{M} \cdot \nabla)\mathbf{H}] \cdot dl = \mathbf{M} \cdot d\mathbf{H} \tag{1.93}$$

Therefore

$$W_1 = -\int_0^H \mathbf{M} \cdot d\mathbf{H} \tag{1.94}$$

This is the total work done in moving the volume from infinity to the point at which the field has the value $\mathbf{H}$. In this process not only does $\mathbf{H}$ vary from point to point but so does $\mathbf{M}$. The more useful expression would be the amount of work necessary to magnetize the specimen when the volume is held fixed and the field increased from zero to its final value.

Consider the identity

$$\int d(\mathbf{M} \cdot \mathbf{H}) = \int \mathbf{H} \cdot d\mathbf{M} + \int \mathbf{M} \cdot d\mathbf{H} \qquad (1.95)$$

The integral on the left-hand side represents the amount of work necessary to move a dipole of fixed magnetization $\mathbf{M}$ through the field $\mathbf{H}$. This can be shown as follows. Let $\phi_1$ represent the magnetic potential at the negative end of the dipole and $\phi_2$, the potential at the positive end. Then

$$\Delta W_2 = M(\phi_2 - \phi_1) \qquad (1.96)$$

is the amount of work necessary to bring a dipole of fixed magnitude into the field. If we expand $\phi_2$ in a series similar to that of equation 1.88, we obtain

$$\Delta W_2 = \mathbf{M} \cdot \nabla \phi \qquad (1.97)$$

Therefore,

$$\Delta W_2 = -\mathbf{M} \cdot \mathbf{H} \qquad (1.98)$$

and from equation 1.95 we obtain

$$\int \mathbf{H} \cdot d\mathbf{M} = \Delta W_1 - \Delta W_2 = \Delta W_3 \qquad (1.99)$$

This represents the difference between the amount of work necessary to bring the unmagnetized and the magnetized material into the field. Equation 1.99 is the work necessary to magnetize the specimen when the material is fixed in position and the field is varied.*

The field energy per unit volume is

$$W_f = \frac{\mu_0 H^2}{2} \qquad (1.100)$$

or

$$dW_f = \mu_0 \mathbf{H} \cdot d\mathbf{H} \qquad (1.101)$$

Therefore the total energy per unit volume required to create the field and magnetize the material is

$$dW_{fm} = dW_f + dW_3 \qquad (1.102)$$

and

$$dW_m = \mathbf{H} \cdot (\mu_0 \, d\mathbf{H} + d\mathbf{M})$$

$$dW_m = \mathbf{H} \cdot d\mathbf{B}$$

$$\Delta W_m = \int \mathbf{H} \cdot d\mathbf{B} \qquad (1.103)$$

* This expression does not include energy terms due to mechanical strains which may be introduced.

Each of the terms in equation 1.95 is illustrated on the magnetization curve $(M, H)$ of Figure 1.19.

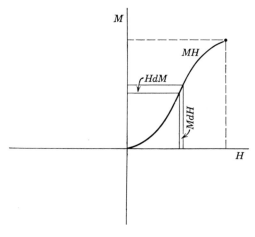

**Figure 1.19.**

The formula for the electrostatic case in which there are no free electric charges on the body is completely analogous to equation 1.103, i.e.,

$$\Delta W_E = \int \mathbf{E} \cdot d\mathbf{D} \tag{1.104}$$

## 1.21  Torque on Dipole

Another useful formula particularly for magnetic problems is the torque that a uniform magnetic field exerts on a magnetized volume. Since in this case the force on each end of the dipole is the same, the torque is simply

$$\mathbf{T} = \mathbf{M} \times \mathbf{H} \tag{1.105}$$

## 1.22  References

1. Smythe, W. R., *Static and Dynamic Electricity*, McGraw-Hill Book Company, New York, 1939.
2. Hammond, P., "Leakage Flux and Surface Polarity in Iron Ring Stampings," *Proc. I.E.E.*, Part C, **102**, No. 1, March 1955, p. 138.
3. Panofsky, A., and M. Phillips, *Classical Electricity and Magnetism*, Addison-Wesley Publishing Company, Cambridge, Mass., 1956.
4. Pugh, E. M., and N. Rostoker, "Hall Effect in Ferromagnetic Materials," *Revs. Modern Phys.*, **125**, No. 1, January 1953, p. 152.

5. Abraham, M., and R. Becker, *Classical Theory of Electricity and Magnetism*, Vol. 1, Hafner Publishing Company, New York, 1932.
6. O'Rahilly, A., "Electro-Magnetics" Great Britain, 1938.
7. Cullwick, F. G., *Fundamentals of Electro-Magnetism*, Cambridge University Press, 1949.
8. Swann, W. F. G., "Theoretical Discussion of the Deviation of High Energy Charged Particles in Passing Through Magnetized Iron," *Phys. Rev.*, **49**, 1936, p. 574.
9. Osborn, J. A., "Demagnetization Factors of the General Ellipsoid," *Phys. Rev.*, **67**, 1945, p. 357.
10. "Coulomb's Law Committee," *Am. J. Phys.*, **18**, January 1950, pp. 1–25; February 1950, pp. 69–88.

# Chapter two

# Origin of Magnetic and Dielectric Properties

## 2.0 Introduction

The magnetization, **M**, and the polarization, **P**, have been defined as the magnetic and electric dipole moment per unit volume of matter, respectively. By the use of these quantities materials are characterized and the macroscopic aspects of the phenomena in question are accounted for. However, in order to gain insight into the fundamental atomic processes which give rise to magnetization and polarization, the dielectric and magnetic properties of substances must be examined from a microscopic point of view.

A complete treatment of the physical laws which govern atomic interactions is beyond the scope of this book. Use can be made, however, of some of the results of modern physics to gain a basic qualitative understanding of the origin of the dielectric and magnetic behavior of matter. In this connection, a brief discussion is given on the binding forces in solids and the characterization of these forces in terms of a generalized potential energy function. This is followed by a detailed account of the basic magnetization and polarization mechanisms which contribute to the observed microscopic behavior.

## / THE SOLID STATE

### 2.1   Binding Forces in Solids

Matter in the solid state is composed of atoms held together in a condensed phase.   As the atoms are brought into the proximity of one another, they experience, at far and intermediate distances, attractive forces.  At close distances the forces experienced are repulsive.  The potential energy associated with these forces can be represented schematically as shown in Figure 2.1.

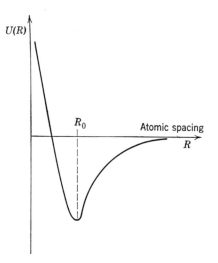

Clearly, an equilibrium condition exists when the atomic spacing $R_0$ corresponds to a minimum in the potential energy curve.

In a given solid the minimum in the potential energy curve determines the lattice spacing, and the elastic constants of the material are related to the steepness of the sides.   The asymmetry of the potential energy curve determines the thermal expansion coefficient.

**Figure 2.1.**   Schematic representation of interatomic potential energy function.

The specific shape of the generalized potential energy curve shown in Figure 2.1 depends upon the details of the atomic interactions.   The various interactions experienced are conveniently classified into five principal types, although the distinction among them is not always sharp.   These types of binding are

1. Ionic
2. Covalent or homopolar
3. Metallic
4. Molecular or Van Der Waals
5. Hydrogen-bonded

In Table 2.1 we give a summary of identifying properties and examples of crystals which exhibit the various types of binding.

## Table 2.1

| Material | Examples | Melting Point | Solid State | | Type of Binding |
|---|---|---|---|---|---|
| Rare gases | He, Ne, A, Kr, Xe | Very low | Insulators | Atomic lattice | Molecular |
| Polyatomic gases | $H_2$, $N_2$, $O_2$, $Cl_2$, CO, $CO_2$, HCl | Low | Insulators | Molecular lattice | Molecular |
| Salts | NaCl, AgCl (alkali and silver halides in general), BaO, MgO | High | Insulators ionic con- ductors | Ionic lattice | Ionic |
| Metals | Na, Mg, Cu | High | Electronic conductors | Atomic lattice | Metallic |
| Diamondlike | Diamond, SiC, Ge, Si | Very high (mostly) | Insulators | Atomic lattice | Covalent |
| | $H_2O$ (ice), HF | | | | Hydrogen-bonded |

### 2.1.1  Ionic Crystals

Ionic crystals are made up of positive and negative ions. The ions arrange themselves so that the electrostatic repulsion between like ions is less than the electrostatic attraction between unlike ions. The equilibrium configuration is effected by virtue of a repulsion which is practically zero until the separation of the constituent ions falls below a certain value, at which time the repulsion increases very rapidly. The repulsive force is due to the overlap of the electronic charge configurations of the atoms.

### 2.1.2  Covalent Crystals

In ionic crystals the electronic charge density between adjacent ions is low. This allows the approximation that the valence electrons are attached to definite atoms. On the other hand, the covalent or homopolar bond is characterized by a rather high electronic charge density between atoms. The covalent bond is formed by two electrons, one from each atom participating in the bond, with the spins of the two electrons antiparallel.

### 2.1.3  Metal Crystals

The binding in metal crystals is conceptually more complicated than that in ionic or covalent crystals. In the light metals, such as sodium, the binding is due primarily to the conduction electrons. In the heavier metals, such as iron or tungsten, considerable binding is due to the interaction of unfilled inner electron shells of adjacent atoms.

### 2.1.4 Molecular Crystals

Molecular crystals are bound together by weak electrostatic forces known as Van Der Waals' forces. The electric field outside a neutral atom is essentially zero. However, this zero field must be construed as an average field in time. The instantaneous field will fluctuate as the electrons execute their individual motions and will induce an instantaneous dipole moment in neighboring atoms. The average interaction between the original instantaneous moment and the induced moment gives rise to an attractive force between atoms.

### 2.1.5 Hydrogen-Bonded Crystals

Under certain conditions an atom of hydrogen forms a bond between two different atoms. The hydrogen atom loses its electron to another atom in the molecule and the proton forms the bond. Because of the small size of the proton only two nearest neighbor atoms are permitted. The hydrogen bond is to a large extent responsible for the physical properties of water and ice. It is also important in certain ferroelectric crystals.

## 2.2 Potential Energy Function

If the potential energy curve shown in Figure 2.1 is a reasonable approximation for a given solid, considerable insight can be gained concerning certain material properties. Examples of properties which are affected by the detailed shape of the potential energy curve are the bulk modulus, or compressibility, and the thermal expansion coefficient. Actually, all the elastic constants which play an important role in the operation of electromechanical devices, are involved, and to some extent the ionic contribution to the electric polarizability.

As an illustration, we consider the dependence of the compressibility on the shape of the potential energy curve.

### 2.2.1   The Compressibility (1)

The compressibility of a substance is defined as

$$K = - \frac{1}{V} \frac{dV}{dp} \qquad (2.1)$$

where $V$ is the volume of the sample and $p$ the hydrostatic pressure. From the first law of thermodynamics we have for the differential of internal energy

$$dU = dQ - dW \qquad (2.2)$$

in which $dQ$ and $dW$ are the heat flow into and the work done by the system, respectively. If we consider experiments carried out only at very low temperatures, $dQ$ may be neglected, since the specific heat vanishes at $0°$ K, and we write

$$\frac{d^2 U}{dV^2} = - \frac{dp}{dV} \qquad (2.3)$$

since $dW = p \, dV$. From equations 2.1 and 2.3 *

$$\frac{1}{K} = V \frac{d^2 U}{dV^2} \qquad (2.4)$$

For simplicity we choose a simple cubic array so that

$$V = NR^3 \qquad (2.5)$$

where $N$ is the total number of atoms and $R$ the nearest neighbor distance. Since

$$\left. \frac{dU}{dR} \right|_{R_0} = 0 \qquad (2.6)$$

it then follows from equations 2.4 and 2.5 that

$$\frac{1}{K} = \frac{1}{9NR_0} \left. \frac{d^2 U}{dR^2} \right|_{R_0} \qquad (2.7)$$

Specific assumptions must be made regarding the form of the potential energy function $U(R)$. For the sake of definiteness, we consider an ionic

---

* Equations 2.1 and 2.4 for $K$ are rigorous only for $T = 0°$ K. The proper expression for the isothermal value for $T > 0°$ K is $K = - \frac{1}{V} \left. \frac{\partial V}{\partial p} \right|_T$. The adiabatic value is $K = - \frac{1}{V} \left. \frac{\partial V}{\partial p} \right|_s$, where $s$ is the entropy. At $T = 0$, $dQ = T \, ds = 0$.

crystal. One contribution to $U(R)$ is the coulomb attraction of the ions, which can be written

$$U_{\text{coulomb}} = -\frac{N\alpha e^2}{8\pi\epsilon_0 R} \tag{2.8}$$

where $\alpha$, known as the Madelung constant, is a constant dependent upon the structure of the crystal and the charge on individual ions. We use for the repulsive term

$$U_{\text{repulsive}} = \frac{N\beta}{2} R^{-q} \tag{2.9}$$

where $\beta$ and $q$ are parameters which characterize the repulsive force. $U(R)$ is then the sum of the terms given in equations 2.8 and 2.9:

$$U(R) = \frac{N\beta}{2} R^{-q} - \frac{N\alpha e^2}{8\pi\epsilon_0 R} \tag{2.10}$$

The use of equation 2.6 gives one relation among the various parameters

$$R_0^{q-1} = 4\pi\epsilon_0 \; q\beta/\alpha e^2 \tag{2.11}$$

and, using equation 2.7, we have

$$\frac{1}{K} = \frac{1}{4\pi\epsilon_0} \frac{(q-1)e^2\alpha}{18R_0^4} \tag{2.12}$$

The experimental value of the compressibility, or bulk modulus, and the value of $R_0$ obtained from X-ray measurements yield the parameter $q$, since $e$ and $\alpha$ are known. Then, using equation 2.11, $\beta$ may be evaluated, thus completing the characterization of the potential energy curve $U(R)$. For NaCl, $\alpha = 1.75$, $K = 3.3 \times 10^{-12}$ cm$^2$/dyne at absolute zero temperature, $R_0 = 2.82$ A, so that $q = 9.3$. We see then that the repulsive force increases very rapidly at small ionic separation.

The foregoing calculations given for the compressibility illustrate one method used to relate the microscopic behavior of solids to ordinary macroscopic parameters.

### 2.2.2 The Atomic Separation

We have already pointed out that the position of the minimum in $U(R)$ determines the lattice spacing in a solid and that the mechanical properties depend upon the shape of $U(R)$ near $R_0$. Some electrical and magnetic properties are also strongly dependent upon the parameters which characterize $U(R)$. In ionic crystals the ionic polarizability arises from the displacement of the ions from their zero field equilibrium positions by the application of an electric field. The ease with which these ions move under the application of a field is determined by the curvature of $U(R)$ near $R_0$.


## / MAGNETIC PROPERTIES


### 2.3  The Atomic Magnetic Moment

The electrons in an atom (or ion) execute orbital motion about the nucleus. Since the electron carries a charge, this motion constitutes an electric current. Therefore, one contribution to the atomic magnetic moment arises from the vector sum of moments contributed by the individual electrons due to their orbital motions.*

Another, and for our purposes more important, contribution to the atomic magnetic moment arises from the spin of the electron. The spinning electron acts like a tiny magnet, as would, for instance, a small spherical charge rotating on its axis. The total contribution to the atomic moment due to spin is the vector sum of the individual spins of the electrons. It should be pointed out that the results of quantum mechanics require that the spin direction of a single electron be parallel or antiparallel to a specified direction in space. Intermediate directions between these two extremes do not occur.

The net magnetic moment is thus the vector sum of the electronic orbital moments and spin moments.


### 2.4  The Exchange Energy

Since the electron has mass, the spin contributes to the atomic angular momentum as well as to the magnetic moment. In quantum mechanics it is shown that the atomic spin angular momentum can take on only half-integral and integral multiples of $h/2\pi$, where $h$ is Planck's constant. The net spin vector is denoted by **S**. The magnitude of **S** in units

---

* It is shown (Section 2.7) that the magnetic moment is directly proportional to the angular momentum. The proportionality constant is known as the gyromagnetic ratio.

$h/2\pi$ represents the maximum component of the spin angular momentum in a specified direction in space.

If two atoms $i$ and $j$ carry spins $\mathbf{S}_i$ and $\mathbf{S}_j$, then it can be shown that the interaction energy of the atoms $i, j$ contains a term

$$W_{\mathrm{ex}} = -2J\mathbf{S}_i \cdot \mathbf{S}_j \qquad (2.13)$$

$W_{\mathrm{ex}}$ is called the *exchange energy* and $J$, the *exchange integral*. The exchange energy has no classical analogue; it is of purely quantum mechanical origin. It is electrostatic in nature in that $W_{\mathrm{ex}}$ expresses the difference in Coulomb interaction energy of the atoms $i, j$ when the spins are parallel or antiparallel. The Pauli exclusion principle requires that in quantum mechanics the relative direction of two spins cannot be changed without making changes in the spatial charge distribution. The exchange integral $J$ plays a dominant role in the magnetic behavior of solid state materials.

The phenomena of ferromagnetism and paramagnetism are discussed at length in subsequent sections. However, at this time it is worthwhile to point out a certain feature of magnetic behavior which concerns itself with the equilibrium position $R_0$ shown in Figure 2.1.

If we consider the interaction between two atoms for which $J$ is positive, the spin moments align parallel to one another. When $J$ is negative the spin moments align themselves antiparallel. It has been shown that the sign of $J$ generally depends upon the separation of the atoms. At medium and far distances $J$ is positive. As the atoms are brought closer together, the parallel alignment is first strengthened, but at a certain near separation $J$ becomes negative and the spins set themselves antiparallel.

This effect is illustrated in Figure 2.2. The energy of interaction $J$ is plotted as a function of the ratio of the atomic separation to the diameter of the unfilled atomic shell. (The theory described applies to the transition metals; thus the critical dependence upon the size of the unfilled shells (2).)

The magnitude of $J$ also determines the Curie temperature of the common ferromagnets. It can be shown that

$$J \cong kT_c/Z$$

where $Z$ is the number of nearest neighbors with which interaction occurs, $k$, Boltzmann's constant, and $T_c$, the Curie temperature (see Section 2.8.2).

It should be pointed out that the curve in Figure 2.2 is based on an approximate and probably inadequate theory. But, for our purposes, it does indicate the dependence of certain magnetic phenomena on the

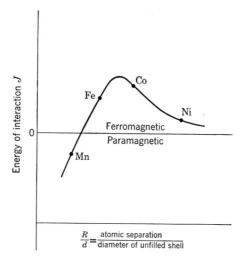

**Figure 2.2.** (Bozorth, *Ferromagnetism*, p. 444.)

atomic separation. The curve of Figure 2.2 has found use in predicting the ferromagnetic behavior of alloys.

## 2.5  Paramagnetism

Paramagnetic materials have associated with them a small positive magnetic susceptibility. A substance generally exhibits paramagnetism if in the absence of an applied field the individual magnetic moments of the atoms comprising the substance are oriented at random.

The origin of the paramagnetic susceptibility can be understood from the following. Consider a substance with $N$ atoms per $m^3$, each carrying a magnetic moment $\mu_m$. Then in an applied field $H$ the energy density associated with the magnetization (from Chapter 1) is

$$W = -H \sum_i N_i \mu_m \cos \theta_i \qquad (2.14)$$

where $N = \sum_i N_i$ and $\theta_i$ is the angle between $H$ and $\mu_m$ for the $i$th atom. $N_i$ is the number of atoms with $\mu_m$ making an angle $\theta_i$ with $H$.

The quantity $N_i$ depends upon the strength of the applied field and the temperature. As the applied field is increased, at a given temperature the number of atomic moments with components parallel to the field increases. For a given field the increased thermal agitation due to an increase in temperature tends to decrease the net alignment in the direction of $H$. In order to represent the effects of field and temperature in a quantitative way, it is necessary to make some assumption concerning the distribution of moments $N_i$. We do this by using a result from statistical mechanics which states

$$N_i = AN\epsilon^{(\mu_m H/kT)\,\cos\,\theta_i} \qquad (2.15)$$

where $T$ is the absolute temperature and $k$, Boltzmann's constant. The quantity $A$ is chosen to make $\sum_i N_i = N$.

Substituting into equation 2.14, we have

$$W = -AH \sum_i N\mu_m \cos\theta_i \epsilon^{a\,\cos\,\theta_i} \qquad (2.16)$$

where $a = (\mu_m H)/kT$.

If we write equation 2.16, using the magnetization $M$ measured in the direction of $H$, then

$$W = -H \cdot M \qquad (2.17)$$

The magnetization, or magnetic moment per unit volume, is then

$$M = AN\mu_m \sum_i \cos\theta_i \epsilon^{a\,\cos\,\theta_i} \qquad (2.18)$$

We further assume $a \ll 1$ and write

$$\epsilon^{a\,\cos\,\theta_i} \cong 1 + a\cos\theta_i \qquad (2.19)$$

and equation 2.18 becomes

$$M = AN\mu_m \sum_i (\cos\theta_i)(1 + a\cos\theta_i) \qquad (2.20)$$

In real atomic systems the angular momentum, and thus the magnetic moment, can take on only discrete orientations relative to a given direction in space. For our purposes, however, we may assume that the allowed values of $\theta_i$ are continuous and cover the entire interval 0 to $\pi$. Under this assumption the summation in equation 2.20 may be replaced by an integration over $\theta$, so that

$$M = AN\mu_m \int_0^\pi \cos\theta(1 + a\cos\theta)2\pi \sin\theta \, d\theta \qquad (2.21)$$

or

$$M = \frac{\mu_m{}^2 NH}{3kT} (4\pi A) \qquad (2.22)$$

When writing equation 2.21 for the summation in equation 2.20 note that the integration takes place over the solid angle $d\Omega = 2\pi \sin\theta \, d\theta$

rather than the angular interval $d\theta$. To the approximation used here the factor $A$ is obtained from

$$A \int_0^\pi \epsilon^{a \cos \theta} 2\pi \sin \theta \, d\theta = 1 \qquad (2.23)$$

$$2\pi A \int_0^\pi \sin \theta \, d\theta \cong 1 \qquad (2.24)$$

or

$$A \cong 1/4\pi \qquad (2.25)$$

From equations 2.22 and 2.25 we may write the paramagnetic susceptibility $(k_{m_p})$ for $\mu_m H \ll kT$ as

$$k_{m_p} = \frac{M}{\mu_0 H} = \frac{\mu_m^2 N}{3kT\mu_0} \qquad (2.26)$$

The important result contained in equation 2.26 is that for high temperature the susceptibility $k_{m_p}$ varies as $1/T$ and is independent of $H$. The same result is obtained when the situation is represented more realistically by using quantum mechanics.

The magnetic susceptibilities for some common paramagnetic substances (3) are given in Table 2.2, in which the molar susceptibility is

## Table 2.2

### Magnetic Susceptibilities (Molar)

| Substance | $k_{m_p}$(mole) $\times 10^6$ |
|---|---|
| Oxygen | 3,380 |
| Copper oxide | 1,340 |
| Uranium oxide | 2,240 |
| Ferrous chloride | 13,200 |
| Ferric chloride | 13,900 |

defined as the cgs magnetic moment per mole of substance per oersted. To obtain the susceptibility in units of magnetic moment per unit volume per oersted, multiply the listed values by $(\rho/A)$ where $\rho$ is the density and $A$ the molecular weight.

### 2.5.1. The Molecular Field

The analysis of the paramagnetic susceptibility given above assumes that the individual atomic moments do not interact with one another. This assumption is valid for gases and for dilute solutions of the magnetic "atom." As a result, many solid paramagnetics do not obey equation 2.26, since in the solid phase there are strong atomic interactions.

Equation 2.26 is of the form

$$k_{m_p} = c/T$$

This is known as Curie's law. It is found that many substances obey a modification of this law which may be represented as

$$k_{mp} = \frac{c}{T - T_c} \qquad (2.27)$$

This is known as the Curie-Weiss law. The quantity $T_c$, known as the Curie temperature, is a measure of the interatomic interaction and may be negative or positive. For positive $T_c$ equation 2.27 holds only for temperatures such that $T > T_c$.

Weiss extended the theory leading to equation 2.26 by assuming that the effective field $H_e$, acting on a given magnetic atom, is the resultant of the external field $H$ and an internal field $H_i$ proportional to the magnetization, i.e.,

$$H_i = \eta M \qquad (2.28)$$

where $\eta$ is some constant. $H_i$ represents the internal field acting on a given atom due to all other atoms. Then

$$H_e = H + M\eta$$

and, using equation 2.25, equation 2.22 is modified to become

$$M = \frac{\mu_m{}^2 N}{3kT} (H + M\eta) \qquad (2.29)$$

Solving this equation for $M$ and using $k_{m_p} = M/\mu_0 H$, we have

$$k_{mp} = \frac{\mu_m{}^2 N}{3k(T - T_c)} \qquad (2.30)$$

where

$$T_c = \frac{\eta \mu_m{}^2 N}{3k} \qquad (2.31)$$

The concept of the molecular, or internal, field plays a major role in the theory of ferromagnetism. It should be pointed out that the origin of $H_i$ is essentially electrostatic in nature and for two neighboring atoms arises from the exchange energy, i.e., the difference in Coulomb energy when the atomic spins are parallel or antiparallel. Quantitative comparison of observed and calculated values of $\eta$ indicates that ordinary magnetic forces are much too weak to account for the origin of the internal field.

## 2.6 Diamagnetism

The case of paramagnetism was treated in Section 2.5, and the results obtained indicated that $k_{m_p}$, the paramagnetic susceptibility, is positive and independent of field at low fields. In a diamagnet the magnetization is also generally proportional to the field, but $k_{m_d}$, the diamagnetic susceptibility, is negative.

All materials exhibit a diamagnetic effect. However, this effect becomes observable only when the net paramagnetic atomic moment is zero in zero field. That is, when the paramagnetic susceptibility is not zero it is generally much larger than $k_{m_d}$ in magnitude.

The origin of the diamagnetic susceptibility can be understood by considering an electron in an atom executing a circular orbit of radius $r_i$ about a nucleus of charge $Ze$. With no field applied, the balance of forces requires

$$m\omega_0^2 r_i = \frac{Ze^2}{4\pi\epsilon_0 r_i^2} \tag{2.32}$$

where $m$ is the electron mass and $\omega_0$, the angular frequency of revolution in zero field. In a field $H$ perpendicular to the plane of the orbit the Lorentz force

$$\mathbf{F} = \mu_0 e \mathbf{v} \times \mathbf{H} \tag{2.33}$$

must be considered and the new balance of forces becomes

$$m\omega_H^2 r_i = \frac{Ze^2}{4\pi\epsilon_0 r_i^2} - \mu_0 e r_i \omega_H H \tag{2.34}$$

where $\omega_H$ is the angular frequency in a magnetic field $H$, or

$$m\omega_H^2 r_i = m\omega_0^2 r_i - \mu_0 e r_i \omega_H H \tag{2.35}$$

From which

$$\omega_H = \omega_0 - \frac{eH\mu_0}{2m} \tag{2.36}$$

neglecting terms in $H^2$.

The magnetic moment associated with a charge $e$ moving in a circular orbit with angular velocity $\omega$ and radius $r_i$ can be obtained from

$$\mu_m = \mu_0 A I$$

where $A$ is the area of the current loop and $I$ the current.* Thus

$$\mu_m = (\pi r_i{}^2) \left(\frac{\omega}{2\pi}\right) e\mu_0 \tag{2.37}$$

Therefore, in zero field the magnetic moment is †

$$\mu_m{}^0 = \frac{\mu_0 e \omega_0 r_i{}^2}{2} \tag{2.38}$$

and in field $H$

$$\mu_m{}^H = \frac{\mu_0 e \omega_H r_i{}^2}{2} \tag{2.39}$$

We now have, using

$$\Delta\mu_m = \mu_m{}^H - \mu_m{}^0 \tag{2.40}$$

$$\Delta\mu_m = \frac{\mu_0 e r_i{}^2}{2}\left[\left(\omega_0 - \frac{\mu_0 eH}{2m}\right) - \omega_0\right] \tag{2.41}$$

$$\Delta\mu_m = -\frac{\mu_0{}^2 e^2 H}{4m} r_i{}^2 \tag{2.42}$$

This equation gives the change in magnetic moment per electron. If there are $Z$ electrons per atom, then the change in atomic moment is

$$\Delta\mu_{mA} = -\frac{\mu_0{}^2 e^2 H}{4m} \sum_{i=1}^{Z} r_i{}^2 \tag{2.43}$$

If there are $N$ atoms per $m^3$, then the change in magnetization is $N \Delta\mu_{mA}$ and the diamagnetic susceptibility becomes

$$k_{md} = -\frac{N \Delta\mu_{mA}}{\mu_0 H} \tag{2.44}$$

$$k_{md} = -\frac{\mu_0 N e^2}{4m} \sum_{i=1}^{Z} r_i{}^2 \tag{2.45}$$

In equation 2.45 $r_i$ refers to a circular orbit the plane of which is perpendicular to the applied field $H$. If $\rho_i$ is defined by

$$\rho_i{}^2 = x_i{}^2 + y_i{}^2 + z_i{}^2 \tag{2.46}$$

where $(x_i, y_i, z_i)$ are the rectangular coordinates of the $i$th electron

---

* See Chapter 1, Section 1.17.

† Equation 2.38 can be written as $\mu_m{}^0 = (e/2mc)(m\omega_0 r_i{}^2)$ in cgs units. The quantity $e/2mc$, usually denoted by $\gamma$, is called the magneto-mechanical ratio and measures the ratio of orbital magnetic moment to angular momentum for electrons.

referred to the nucleus, then $\sum_i r_i^2$ may be replaced by $\frac{2}{3} \sum_{i=1}^{Z} \rho_i^2$. $\rho_i^2$ is the mean square distance of the $i$th electron from the nucleus. Then equation 2.45 becomes

$$k_{m_d} = -\frac{\mu_0 N e^2}{6mc^2} \sum_{i=1}^{Z} \rho_i^2 \qquad (2.47)$$

We may summarize by pointing out that the paramagnetic suscepti-bility arises because of a favorable orientation of atomic moments in the direction of the applied field and is positive. The diamagnetic susceptibility, on the other hand, arises by virtue of a change in magni-tude of electronic orbital moments and is negative. Since the diamag-netic effect deals with the individual electrons in an atom, $k_{m_d}$ does not vanish even though the atom has zero initial moment.

## 2.7 Ordered Magnetism

Our discussions on the paramagnetic and diamagnetic effects have assumed for the most part systems in which the individual atoms did not interact with one another. Thus the direction of the atomic mag-netic moment associated with a given atom was not dependent upon the direction of the moments on neighboring atoms. Indeed, a fundamental assumption required that the individual magnetic moments be oriented at random. In some solids interatomic interactions play an important role in determining the ultimate magnetic character and behavior of these substances. These materials exhibit what we call ordered mag-netism.

To describe what we mean by ordered magnetism we first assume that the atoms comprising the solid are distributed over a periodic space lattice. That is, our material is crystalline. Now we assign to each atom an atomic moment and by ordered magnetism mean that there exists an ordered array of atomic moments over the space lattice. Three important cases are illustrated in Figure 2.3.

In Figure 2.3a similar atoms are shown with their atomic moments aligned parallel. In Figure 2.3b the atoms are similar, but neighboring moments are aligned antiparallel. Figure 2.3c represents the important case in which dissimilar neighboring atoms have atomic moments of unequal magnitude and are aligned antiparallel.

A material which exhibits an array implied by Figure 2.3a is said to be ferromagnetic, and magnetic phenomena related to the consequences of such an array are classed as ferromagnetism. The common magnetism associated with iron, cobalt, and nickel and their alloys falls in this class. Magnetic phenomena associated with the alignment indicated in Figure 2.3b are classed as antiferromagnetism. Antiferromagnetic materials are not so well known as the common ferromagnets, but many substances exhibit this magnetic array. Examples are ferrous and nickel oxides, FeO and NiO. In these oxides the metal atoms exist as divalent ions with net magnetic moments.

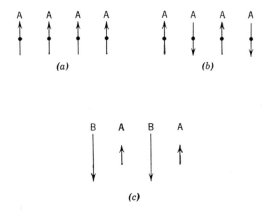

**Figure 2.3.** Schematic representation of ordered magnetic arrays.

If the four atoms shown in Figure 2.3a are considered to comprise one molecule, then the molecule has a net magnetic moment four times as large as the individual atomic moment. The molecule of Figure 2.3b, however, has a zero net magnetic moment by virtue of the antiferromagnetic alignment. Clearly, the molecule depicted in Figure 2.3c has a hybrid magnetic character when compared with the other two cases. The net moment for the molecule of Figure 2.3c is $2(\mu_B - \mu_A)$. This type of magnetic ordering is known as ferrimagnetism. The ferrite materials, which are nonmetallic and as a result are rather good electrical insulators and magnetic in the commonly accepted sense, are examples of the important class of magnetic materials known as ferrimagnets.

In materials which exhibit ordered magnetism strong internal fields exist which tend to align the individual atomic moments in some particular array. Considerable success has been enjoyed by extending the molecular field theory of Weiss, introduced to account for the paramagnetic susceptibility variation with temperature, to the cases of ordered magnetism. These internal, or molecular, fields have their origin in the exchange forces between atoms even though the exchange energy is electrostatic in nature.

## 2.8    Ferromagnetism.    Easy Directions of Magnetization

In Section 2.7 we pointed out that strong internal fields exist in a ferromagnet that align the individual atomic moments parallel to one another. The theory of the internal field does not include a mechanism that couples the direction of magnetization with the crystallographic axes of the associated crystal. Experimentally, however, it is found that in an unstrained crystal with no applied field the magnetization vector tends to lie along certain preferred directions. In iron, for instance, the preferred directions are the cube axes. For cobalt, which has an hexagonal structure, the preferred direction is perpendicular to the basal plane. These preferred directions are known as easy directions of magnetization.

In order to move the magnetization vector from an easy direction to an arbitrary direction, a certain amount of energy is required. Thus, if in Figure 2.4 $PP'$ is an easy direction, energy must be supplied to rotate $\mathbf{M}$ through the angle $\theta$.

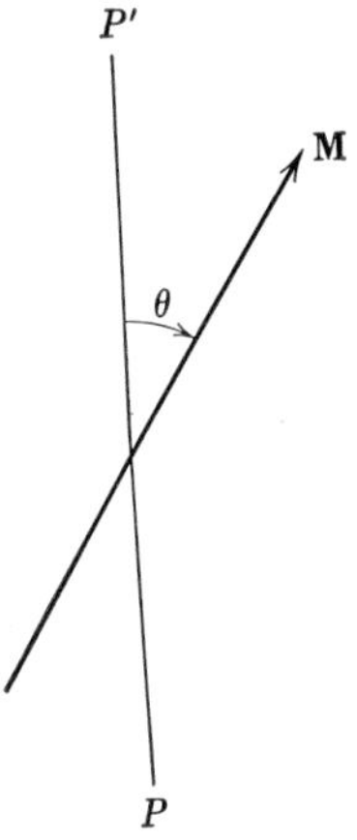

We arrive at an expression for this energy, per unit volume, by using empirical methods. In a cubic system a satisfactory expression for many applications is

$$W_c = K_1(\alpha_1{}^2\alpha_2{}^2 + \alpha_2{}^2\alpha_3{}^2 + \alpha_1{}^2\alpha_3{}^2) \quad (2.48)$$

Figure 2.4. Rotation of magnetization vector from easy to hard direction.

where $\boldsymbol{\alpha} = (\alpha_1, \alpha_2, \alpha_3)$ is a vector whose components are the direction cosines of the magnetization vector referred to the cubic axes. If $K_1$ is negative, $W_c$ is a minimum when $\mathbf{M}$ lies along the cube diagonal; if $K_1$ is positive $\mathbf{M}$ lies along a cube edge. The constant $K_1$ is called the magnetocrystalline anisotropy constant. The existence of easy directions of magnetization exercises a profound effect on many magnetization processes.

### 2.8.1    Domains

In an unmagnetized sample of ferromagnetic material there exist small regions in which the atomic moments are all aligned parallel to one another at temperatures far below the Curie point. These regions are called domains. Each region is magnetically saturated and has a net magnetic moment. However, the domains are randomly oriented so that the net bulk magnetic moment is zero. These domains exist in single crystals as well as in polycrystalline samples.

In this section we wish to indicate the origin of the domains and to consider the contributions to the energy which govern domain formation.

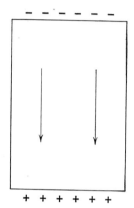

Figure 2.5 shows a sample of a ferromagnet saturated in the direction indicated. The discontinuity of the magnetization at the surface of the sample gives rise to a magnetic-pole-density distribution as shown. The existence of the poles at the surface gives rise to a contribution to the total energy of the magnetic system. This energy can be expressed as

$$W_p = -\frac{1}{2} \int \mathbf{H}_p \cdot \mathbf{M} \, dV \qquad (2.49)$$

Figure 2.5. Saturated ferromagnetic sample.

where $\mathbf{H}_p$ is the field due to surface poles and the integration is to be carried out over the volume of the sample. Since $\mathbf{H}_p$ and $\mathbf{M}$ are essentially antiparallel within the sample, this energy term is positive and usually rather large. Physical systems tend to attain states of minimum energy. The magnitude of the term $W_p$ can be reduced if a mechanism is introduced which changes the dipolar distribution shown to a higher order pole configuration. This can be accomplished by introducing a transition region between the two halves of the sample $A$ and $B$ (Figure 2.6). The surface pole distribution is now such that the associated magnetic energy is reduced. The poles on the $A$-side of the sample give rise to a field parallel to $\mathbf{M}$ in the $B$-region, and the poles on the $B$-side, a field parallel to $\mathbf{M}$ in the $A$-region. This mutual interaction contributes positive terms to the integrand of equation 2.49, and $W_p$ is reduced. The regions $A$ and $B$ are domains, and the transition layer is called a domain wall.

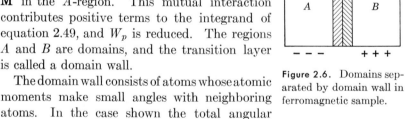

Figure 2.6. Domains separated by domain wall in ferromagnetic sample.

The domain wall consists of atoms whose atomic moments make small angles with neighboring atoms. In the case shown the total angular variation is 180°, and the transition layer is known as a 180° wall. If we assume that in the regions $A$ and $B$ the magnetization lies along an easy direction, then the atomic moments in the transition layer do not lie in an easy direction of magnetization. Energy must, therefore, be expended in the creation of the domain wall. Additional domains will form only if the decrease in surface pole energy is greater than the energy required to create the wall.

Clearly, the surface pole energy can be further reduced by the introduction of more domain walls. Some possible configurations are shown in Figure 2.7.

In Figure 2.7b and 2.7c the surface pole energy has been reduced to zero. The triangular regions are called "domains of closure," since they

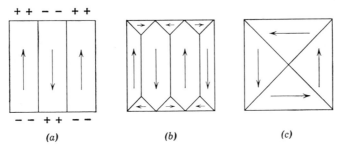

Figure 2.7. Some possible domain configurations.

act to complete the flux path within the sample. Of the great many possible domain configurations, the equilibrium configuration in a real sample is governed by the requirement that the sum of the total wall energy and the surface pole energy be a minimum.

The demagnetized state of a ferromagnetic material below the Curie temperature corresponds to a domain configuration which gives rise to zero net magnetization in any given direction. This condition can be written as

$$\mathbf{M} = \frac{\sum\limits_{i=1}^{N} M_i \cos \theta_i \, \delta V_i}{\sum\limits_{i=1}^{N} \delta V_i} = 0 \qquad (2.50)$$

where $M_i$ is the magnetization of the $i$th domain, $\theta_i$, the angle between $M_i$ and a given direction, $\delta V_i$, the volume of the $i$th domain, and $N$, the total number of domains in the volume. The magnetized state occurs when the foregoing summation does not vanish. This can arise by the application of an external field: the $\cos \theta_i$ change by virtue of rotation of the $M_i$, and the $\delta V_i$ change because of the growth of favorably oriented domains. The shape of the common magnetization curve is determined by the relative importance of these effects. The magnetization process is considered in more detail in a real sample in a later section.

### 2.8.2 Saturation Magnetization and the Curie Point

In describing ferromagnetism from the point of view of ordered magnetism, it was assumed that all atomic moments in a given domain are aligned parallel. Such a state, however, can be possible only at the absolute zero of temperature. At temperatures above the absolute zero some disorder to the parallel alignment exists because of thermal agitation. Thus, for increasing temperature, the saturation magnetization decreases in magnitude. At a critical temperature, called the Curie point, the magnetization in a domain under zero external field vanishes. Above the Curie point the substance becomes paramagnetic.

A reasonably satisfactory theory can be given of the variation of the saturation magnetization with temperature and the behavior above the Curie point by utilizing the molecular field concept introduced earlier (Section 2.5). In this theory the effective field is taken as

$$H_e = H + M\eta \tag{2.51}$$

where $\eta$ is the molecular field constant. We have already seen (equation 2.30) that this assumption leads to an expression for the susceptibility of the form

$$k_m = \frac{(T_c/\eta)}{T - T_c}$$

when $\mu_m H_e/kT \ll 1$. Thus, if $1/k_m$ is plotted versus $T$, the intercept on the temperature axis yields $T_c$ and the slope of the line can be made to give $\eta$.

When the molecular field constant $\eta$ is positive it is possible to show that for temperatures less than $T_c$ a spontaneous magnetization can exist in zero applied field. In order to do this, it is necessary to re-examine the situation described by equation 2.18 and consider the general case rather than the special one of $\mu_m H_e \ll kT$. We again assume all orientations of the individual moments are allowed and write

$$M = M_0 \frac{\int_0^\pi \cos\theta \epsilon^{a\cos\theta} 2\pi \sin\theta \, d\theta}{\int_0^\pi \epsilon^{a\cos\theta} 2\pi \sin\theta \, d\theta} \tag{2.52}$$

where $M_0 = N\mu_m$ is the saturation magnetization at $T = 0° K$. Since

$$a = \frac{\mu_m H_e}{kT} = \frac{\mu_m(H + M\eta)}{kT} \tag{2.53}$$

the parameter $a$ becomes

$$a_0 = \frac{\mu_m M\eta}{kT} \tag{2.54}$$

for the applied field $H = 0$.

If we place $M_s$ equal to the spontaneous magnetization, that is $M_s = M(H = 0)$, then equation 2.52 becomes

$$\frac{M_s}{M_0} = \frac{\displaystyle\int_{-1}^{1} y\epsilon^{a_0 y}\, dy}{\displaystyle\int_{-1}^{1} \epsilon^{a_0 y}\, dy} \tag{2.55}$$

The above integrals are easily evaluated by using

$$\frac{\partial}{\partial\beta} \int_{y_1}^{y_2} \epsilon^{\beta y}\, dy = \int_{y_1}^{y_2} y\epsilon^{\beta y}\, dy \tag{2.56}$$

and we find

$$M/M_0 = \coth a_0 - \frac{1}{a_0} \tag{2.57}$$

or

$$M/M_0 = L(a_0) \tag{2.58}$$

The function $L(a_0)$ is known as the Langevin function. In Figure 2.8a curve 1 shows $M_s/M_0$ as a function of the parameter $a_0$.

There exists a second relation between $a_0$ and $M_s$, namely equation 2.54. Thus

$$\frac{M_s}{M_0} = \left(\frac{NkT}{M_0^2\eta}\right) a_0 \tag{2.59}$$

This equation is plotted in Figure 2.8a as curve 2 (4). Curve 2 will intercept curve 1 if the molecular field constant $\eta$ is positive and if the slope is less than the initial slope of $L(a_0)$. It is easy to show that $\dfrac{dL}{da_0}\Big)_{a_0=0}$ is equal to $\frac{1}{3}$, so that for positive $\eta$ we obtain $M_s/M_0 > 0$ when

$$\frac{NkT}{M_0^2\eta} < \frac{1}{3} \tag{2.60}$$

or

$$T < \frac{1}{3}\frac{M_0^2\eta}{Nk} \tag{2.61}$$

But, recalling that $M_0 = \mu_m N$ and using equation 2.31, equation 2.61 becomes $T < T_c$. Thus a stable state of spontaneous magnetization exists at temperatures below the Curie point. Equation 2.59 may be written

$$\frac{M_s}{M_0} = \left(\frac{T}{T_c}\right)\left(\frac{a_0}{3}\right) \tag{2.62}$$

and $a_0$ eliminated between equations 2.62 and 2.57, giving

$$\frac{M_s}{M_0} = f\left(\frac{T}{T_c}\right) \tag{2.63}$$

where $f(T/T_c)$ approaches 1 as $T$ goes to zero and equals zero for $T = T_c$.

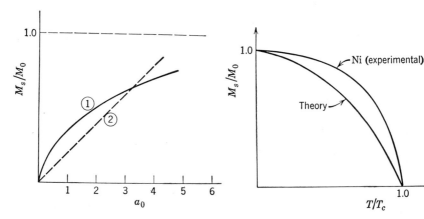

**Figure 2.8a.** Normalized saturation magnetization $M_s/M_0$ versus $a_0(a_0 = \mu_m M_s \eta)$.

**Figure 2.8b.** Normalized saturation magnetization $M_s/M_0$ versus relative temperature $T/T_c$.

In Figure 2.8b $f(T/T_c)$ is plotted as a function of $T/T_c$, and the experimentally observed values of $M_s/M_0$ for nickel are shown for comparison.

It should be pointed out that theory and experiment are in much better agreement when only the allowed discrete orientations of the atomic moments are used to determine the dependence of $M_s/M_0$ on $T/T_c$.

## 2.9 Magnetostriction

We have seen that a ferromagnetic substance exhibits a spontaneous magnetization below the Curie point. In this state the relative separation of the individual atoms depends upon the direction of magnetization.

As the direction of the magnetization is made to change, for example, by an external field, the atoms experience a slight rearrangement such that the magnetocrystalline anisotropy energy is kept at a minimum. This rearrangement gives rise to dimensional changes of the crystalline cell.

This is a qualitative microscopic explanation of the phenomenon of magnetostriction. The macroscopic aspects are described in detail in Chapter 3. It should be clear that large static fields give rise to a static magnetostriction and introduce a set of static strains. We are primarily concerned with the dynamic magnetostrictive response which results from alternating fields of small amplitude. The alternating field gives rise to time-dependent strains which may result in one of many possible modes of mechanically resonant vibration determined by the geometry of the sample.

The dynamical magnetostrictive parameters are dependent upon the state of magnetization of a given sample. The microscopic phenomenological theory from which the parameters can be calculated is beyond the scope of the present volume.

## 2.10   The Magnetization Process

The relation between the applied magnetic field and the magnetic induction in a real ferromagnetic specimen is represented by the familiar hysteresis loop. The hysteresis loop, shown in Figure 2.9, is characterized by the saturation induction $B_s$, the remanent induction $B_r$, and the coercive field $H_c$.

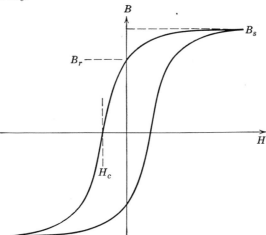

**Figure 2.9.**   Hysteresis loop of ferromagnet.

The remanent induction and the coercive field are structure-sensitive quantities and depend strongly on the presence of voids, inclusions, internal strains, and other imperfections in the sample. The saturation induction, however, is structure insensitive and depends upon the chemical constitution and the temperature.

We wish to consider the magnetization process in terms of the magnetization changes in the individual domains which comprise the ferromagnetic sample. As we have seen, equation 2.64, the component of net magnetization in a given direction, can be written

$$M = \frac{\sum_i M_i \cos \theta_i \, \delta V_i}{\sum_i \delta V_i} \tag{2.64}$$

The application of equation 2.64 can be illustrated by considering the simple situation presented in Figure 2.10. The specimen as shown con-

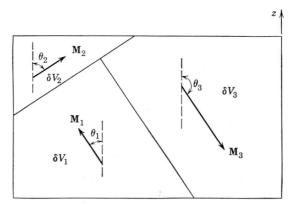

Figure 2.10. Illustrative magnetic state of ferromagnetic specimen.

sists of three domains. We wish to calculate the component of magnetization in the $z$-direction.

From Figure 2.10

$$M_z = \frac{M_1 \cos \theta_1 \, \delta V_1 + M_2 \cos \theta_2 \, \delta V_2 + M_3 \cos \theta_3 \, \delta V_3}{\delta V_1 + \delta V_2 + \delta V_3} \tag{2.65}$$

If we assume that the specimen is chemically homogeneous, all the $M_i$ are equal in magnitude, and, for a given temperature $T$, equation 2.64 becomes

$$M = M_s \frac{\sum_i \cos \theta_i \, \delta V_i}{\sum_i \delta V_i} \tag{2.66}$$

When a field $H$ is applied to the system the domain walls will move, changing the magnitudes of the $\delta V_i$, and the $M_i$ will rotate, changing the angles $\theta_i$. The motion of the domain walls is impeded by the presence of imperfections in the material, and the rotation of the $M_i$ is hindered because of the existence of magnetocrystalline anisotropy forces discussed in Section 2.8. Thus the effective permeability is finite.

If a ferromagnetic sample is magnetized to saturation and the magnetizing field reduced to zero, a remanent state obtains, as domains are nucleated and the resulting $M_i$ relax to the nearest easy directions of magnetization.

The coercive field $H_c$ is the field required to reduce the induction at remanence to zero. The origin of the coercive field lies in the existence of imperfections, such as voids and inclusions. Energy is required to move a domain wall over an imperfection. The details of the demagnetization which occurs between zero field and $H_c$ are extremely complicated and are not discussed at length here. A quantitative discussion can be given in only a few simplified cases.

We may point out that the coercive force is perhaps the most structure-sensitive property in magnetic materials. The primary problem is to determine the threshold field that will give rise to irreversible magnetization. Several possible contributions to the coercive force can be listed as (5)

1. $H_c$ resulting from magnetocrystalline anisotropy.
2. $H_c$ resulting from shape anisotropy.
3. Dependence of $H_c$ on particle size.
4. Dependence of $H_c$ on density of packing.
5. Effect of inclusions without associated closure domains.
6. Effect of inclusions with closure domains.
7. Contribution due to nucleation of reversal domains at grain boundaries and lamellar precipitates.
8. Surface tension of expanding walls.

Contributions 1 to 4 are of primary interest when particles of the material are essentially single-domain regions. Contributions 5 to 8 are important when primary magnetization processes are due to wall motion.

### 2.10.1 Permanent Magnets

The ability to control the coercive force of magnetic materials is important in the development of permanent magnets. In applications the magnetic circuit associated with a permanent magnet invariably contains an air gap. The existence of the gap gives rise to a demagnetizing field, the effect of which is to reduce the operating remanent induction to a value below that which would exist in a closed magnetic path. For example, a bar or horseshoe magnet is subject to the demagnetizing field of the poles at its ends. Thus, although it is obvious that a large remanence is desirable for a material to be a strong permanent magnet, this condition is not sufficient. It is necessary that the remanent induction remain high under the influence of the demagnetizing field mentioned. Clearly, the larger the coercive force the more nearly the apparent remanence will approach the true remanence. A rough measure of the effectiveness of a permanent magnet material is given by the product of the coercive force $H_c$ and the remanent induction $B_r$.

A very common type of permanent magnet material is Alnico 5, the composition of which is 24 per cent cobalt, 14 per cent nickel, 8 per cent aluminum, 3 per cent copper, and 51 per cent iron. Alnico 5 has a coercive force of 600 oersteds and a remanent induction of 12,500 gauss. Oxide permanent magnets are also available at the present time. These materials are related to the ferrites and are commercially available under the names Ferroxdur, Indox, and Magadur. Chemically their compositions can be described as $BaO \cdot 6Fe_2O_3$. They exhibit coercive forces between 1600 and 2000 oersteds and a remanent flux density between 2000 and 3700 gauss. The high value of the coercive force in the oxidic permanent magnets arises because of an extremely large magnetocrystalline anisotropy.

## 2.11   The Initial Permeability

If a magnetic sample in a demagnetized state is subjected to a small field $H$, the initial permeability $\mu_i$ is the ratio of the resulting flux density to the applied field.

High initial permeability is obtained, generally, when the material has high saturation magnetization, low coercive force, low magnetocrystalline anisotropy, and small magnetostriction. $\mu_i$ is a structure-sensitive property and can be radically affected by heat treatment, magnetic anneal, and stress (either external or internal).

When the initial permeability is caused by wall displacement its value is determined by the strength of the force exerted by the trapping centers intercepted by the wall. This aspect makes $\mu_i$ structure-sensitive, particularly when many different types of trapping center are present. It can be said that for each contribution to the coercive force there will be an attendant contribution to the initial permeability. $\mu_i$

is a measure of the stiffness or restoring force, and $H_c$, a measure of the maximum restoring force before irreversible magnetization occurs.

For rotational processes the essential dependence is

$$\mu_i - 1 \sim \frac{M_s^2}{K_1} \tag{2.67}$$

and for wall motion

$$\mu_i - 1 \sim \frac{M_s^2}{\sigma_w} \tag{2.68}$$

where $M_s$ is the saturation magnetization, $K_1$, the magnetocrystalline anisotropy, and $\sigma_w$, the wall energy per unit area for a 180° wall.

This discussion applies at low frequencies of operation. Since the initial permeability is associated with the "stiffness" of the magnetization, we may expect dispersion in the permeability characteristic as the frequency of operation approaches the natural frequency of the "spring" system. In rotational processes the restoring force is due to the magnetocrystalline anisotropy. For this case the initial permeability characteristic is shown in Figure 2.11. The specific shape of the dispersion

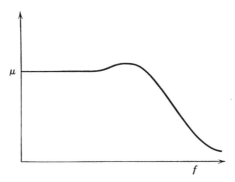

Figure 2.11. Typical initial permeability characteristic for nonconducting magnetic material whose initial magnetization proceeds by rotation.

curve arises from the fact that all incremental elements of the magnetization are not subject to equivalent restoring forces. Thus the changes in permeability observed take place over a broad frequency interval. Generally, this characteristic is observed only in the nonconducting magnetic materials, since the internal resonance effects are masked by the skin effect in metallic ferromagnets.

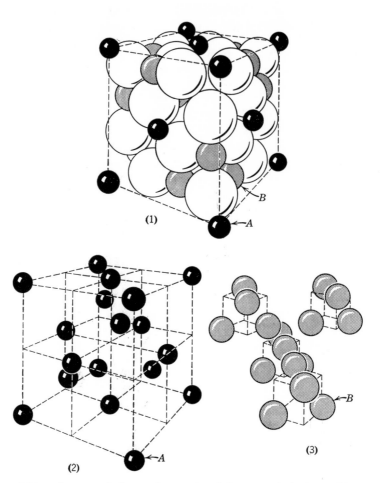

**Figure 2.12a.** Inverse spinel crystal structure of the magnetic ferrites. (1) Volume inside the cube corresponds to eight molecules. The largest spheres are negative oxygen ions ($O^{2-}$) on a face-centered cubic lattice. (2) Interstitial positive trivalent iron ions ($Fe^{3+}$) abstracted from the structure shown at (1). These are on A-sites. (3) Interstitial positive metal ions, also abstracted from (1), on B-sites. Half of these are positive trivalent iron ions ($Fe^{3+}$): the other half are positive divalent ions which may be, for example, $Mn^{2+}$, $Fe^{2+}$, $Co^{2+}$, or $Ni^{2+}$. (Brailsford, F., *Proc. IEE* (London), 104 Pt. B, supplement, p. 137, 1957.)

## 2.12  Ferrites

The class of substances known as the magnetic ferrites correspond to the general chemical formula $MO \cdot Fe_2O_3$, where $M$ is a metallic cation of valence two. Common examples of these materials are

$NiO \cdot Fe_2O_3$—nickel ferrite
$FeO \cdot Fe_2O_3$—ferrous ferrite (magnetite)
$MgO \cdot Fe_2O_3$—magnesium ferrite

The examples listed exhibit magnetic behavior similar to the behavior of iron and nickel. The magnetic susceptibility is large, and the B-H characteristic shows the hysteresis effect common to the metallic ferromagnets.

The ferrites crystallize in what is known as the spinel lattice. The structure is isomorphous to the mineral spinel $MgAlO_4$. This structure is characterized by a face-centered oxygen lattice and two interpenetrating sublattices of metallic ions. The metallic ions occupy $A$-sites, the orientation of which are tetrahedral relative to the oxygen ions, and $B$-sites which are octahedral relative to the oxygen ions. Visualization of this situation is rather difficult, but some insight can be gained by referring to Figure 2.12$a$.

The spontaneous magnetization of a given ferrite depends upon the distribution of the metallic ions over the available tetrahedral and octahedral sites. Zinc ferrite and cadmium ferrite are nonmagnetic. In these materials the zinc or cadmium ions are all on $A$-sites and the iron ions on $B$-sites. On the other hand, nickel ferrite has half the available $Fe^{3+}$ ions on $A$-sites and half on $B$-sites; $Ni^{2+}$ ions occupy $B$-sites. This material is magnetic and has a high saturation magnetization.

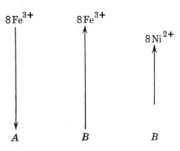

Figure 2.12$b$. Schematic representation of $A$ and $B$ sublattice magnetization in nickel ferrite.

Generally, the magnetic moment associated with ferrites arises from a ferrimagnetic ordering. This type of ordered magnetism is discussed in Section 2.7. The ionic magnetic moments associated with the $A$-sites are aligned antiparallel to the moments on the $B$-sites. A net magnetization exists, however, because of the difference in magnitude of the individual magnetic moments. As an example, consider the case of nickel ferrite. This substance, as stated above, has $Fe^{3+}$ ions on $A$-sites and equal numbers of $Ni^{2+}$ and $Fe^{3+}$ distributed at random on $B$-sites. The magnetic moments of the $Fe^{3+}$ $A$-site ions cancel the contribution due to moments of $B$-site $Fe^{3+}$ ions, leaving a net moment due to the $Ni^{2+}$ ions. The situation is represented in Figure 2.12$b$.

Néel has proposed a molecular field theory to account for the behavior of the saturation magnetization in ferrites (6). This theory is an extension of the Weiss molecular-field theory introduced in the discussions of paramagnetism and ferromagnetism. The molecular field acting on an ion at an $A$-site is due to the magnetization associated with the $A$-sublattice and that of the $B$-sublattice, and we write

$$H_A = -\gamma M_A - \beta M_B \tag{2.69}$$

Similarly, the molecular field acting on a $B$-site ion is

$$H_B = -\lambda M_B - \beta M_A \tag{2.70}$$

In these equations the constants $\gamma$, $\beta$, and $\lambda$ are positive, so that an essential feature of Néel's theory requires that the molecular field be directed opposite to the magnetization of a given sublattice. It will be recalled that the molecular field in the ferromagnetic case was assumed to be in the same direction as the magnetization. This is a principal difference between the origins of ferromagnetism and ferrimagnetism.

The interaction between the molecular fields and the sublattice magnetizations gives rise to an energy density

$$W = -\tfrac{1}{2}(H_A \cdot M_A + H_B \cdot M_B) \tag{2.71}$$

Substituting equations 2.69 and 2.70 into equation 2.71, we have

$$W = \tfrac{1}{2}\gamma M_A{}^2 + \beta \mathbf{M}_A \cdot \mathbf{M}_B + \tfrac{1}{2}\lambda M_B{}^2 \tag{2.72}$$

Equation 2.72 represents a lower energy when $M_A$ is antiparallel to $M_B$ than when $M_A$ is parallel to $M_B$ because of the nature of the middle term. This energy must be compared with the case $M_A = M_B = 0$ to determine whether or not the state of lowest energy is paramagnetic or ferrimagnetic. The appropriate criterion can be written

$$\beta | M_A \cdot M_B | > \tfrac{1}{2}(\gamma M_A{}^2 + \lambda M_B{}^2) \tag{2.73}$$

When equation 2.73 is satisfied the lowest energy state corresponds to a ferrimagnetic ordering with net magnetization of magnitude $M = M_A - M_B$.

### 2.12.1 Commercial Aspects of Ferrite Materials

In commercial fabrication great use is made of mixed ferrites in order to enhance certain desirable properties and suppress undesirable ones. The mixed systems of Ni-Zn, Mn-Zn, and Mg-Mn have been extensively studied, and considerable information is available on these systems. It must be stressed, however, that many of the observed effects are not completely understood, even though great technological advances have been made in recent years.

Commercial ferrite materials are ceramic semiconductors. As a result, the electrical conductivity in these materials is of very small magnitude, 7 to 15 orders of magnitude lower than the conductivity of metallic ferromagnets. The usefulness of ferrites in applications arises mainly from this fact. They can be formed for use in inductor cores without the need for laminations. Disadvantages arise mainly from the low saturation magnetization and permeability associated with the ferrites.


## / DIELECTRIC PROPERTIES


## 2.13   Introduction

The dielectric properties of matter are described in terms of the electric polarization $\mathbf{P}$. Although in most dielectric materials the polarization is induced by an applied electric field, in ferroelectric materials the polarization is spontaneous (i.e., the applied electric field is zero). In other materials, called electrets (27), the polarization is induced initially by an electric field and is retained quasi-permanently after the external field is removed. The following discussion is concerned with an examination of the manner in which this polarization arises in atoms, molecules, and crystals. Particular attention is given to the phenomena of ferroelectricity and piezoelectricity.

In Chapter 1 the relationship between $\mathbf{P}$ and $\mathbf{E}$ at a point in simple materials was given as

$$\mathbf{P} = \epsilon_0 k_e \mathbf{E} \tag{2.74}$$

where $k_e$ is the electric susceptibility. However, it will be recalled that the value of $\mathbf{E}$ in this expression is the value averaged over a large number of particles. We shall define $E_{\text{loc}}$ as the local field acting on

an atom or molecule which produces the charge separation or polarization. The relationship between the resulting electric dipole moment
$\mu_e$ and $E_{\text{loc}}$ is

$$\mu_e = \alpha \left| E_{\text{loc}} \right| \tag{2.75}$$

where $\alpha$ is defined as the polarizability. This factor describes the ease
with which the elementary dipole can be polarized. If there are $N$
dipoles per unit volume, then

$$\mathbf{P} = N\mu_e = N\alpha\mathbf{E}_{\text{loc}} \tag{2.76}$$

This enables us to derive a relationship between the measured dielectric constant $\epsilon_r$ in terms of the polarizability. Since

$$\mathbf{D} = \epsilon_0\mathbf{E} + \mathbf{P} \tag{2.77}$$

then

$$\mathbf{D} = \epsilon_0\mathbf{E} + N\alpha\mathbf{E}_{\text{loc}} \tag{2.78}$$

The observed dielectric constant is defined by $\mathbf{D} = \epsilon_0\epsilon_r\mathbf{E}$. Therefore,

$$\epsilon_r = 1 + N\alpha\frac{\left| E_{\text{loc}} \right|}{\left| E \right|} \tag{2.79}$$

In order to calculate $\epsilon_r$ from observed experimental data, it is first necessary to calculate the local electric field. This problem is discussed in
Section 2.14.

## 2.14   Local Field

One of the most important problems in the theory of dielectrics is
that of calculating the electric field acting on an atom or molecule in
the interior of a body when the body itself is subjected to an applied
external field. In order to calculate the local field, we shall separate
the problem into three parts. These three contributions are shown in
Figure 2.13. First, we shall imagine that we are removing from the
dielectric a sphere of matter surrounding the point at which the field is
to be calculated. The radius of this sphere shall be large in comparison
with an atomic radius. By this mathematical device, first proposed by
Lorentz, it is possible to treat the remaining parts of the dielectric on a
macroscopic basis. The second step is to calculate the effect at point
$A$ of the individual dipoles contained in the matter which was removed.
This contribution $(\mathbf{E}_2)$ must be treated microscopically. Finally, the
effect of the surface charges which give rise to a "depolarizing field"
$(\mathbf{E}_3)$ is investigated.

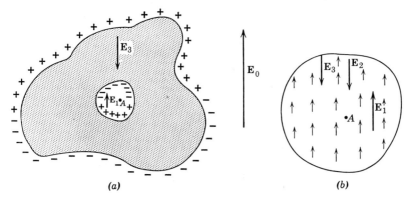

**Figure 2.13.** The various contributions to the local field acting at a point inside a dielectric: (a) the depolarizing field $E_3$ due to the charge accumulation on the surface and $E_1$ due to the surface charge of the *cavity;* and (b) the ordered dipole array in the portion of the material removed to form the cavity. This ordered structure gives rise to the microscopic field $E_2$.

### 2.14.1 Lorentz Field

The field $E_1$ is due to the polarization charges on the surface of the imaginary cavity. This surface charge density is $-P \cos \theta$ where $\theta$ is the polar angle with reference to the direction of polarization. The field at the center of the sphere or, for that matter, at any point within a sphere of radius $a$ is * $E_1 = P/3\epsilon_0$.

### 2.14.2 Field of Adjacent Dipoles

The field $E_2$ produced by the dipoles inside the cavity must be treated microscopically; consequently $E_2$ will depend upon the symmetry of the dipoles around the point $A$. For certain special crystal structures the value of $E_2$ has been computed. These crystal structures include the cubic, tetragonal, and simple hexagonal (9, 10) as well as the isotropic case. It has been shown that $E_2 = 0$ for the cubic and the isotropic structures.

### 2.14.3 Depolarization Field

The shape of the sample is of great importance in any experimental investigation involving dielectric materials. A depolarizing field $E_3$ is produced by the surface charge distribution. It is possible to calculate this field for certain simple geometries.†

* Section 1.7.                    † Section 1.8.

For the special case of an isotropic substance or for one having cubic symmetry with attached metal electrodes we have

$$E_{loc} = E + \frac{P}{3\epsilon_0} \tag{2.80}$$

If equation 2.80 is substituted into equation 2.76, then

$$E_{loc} = \frac{E}{1 - (N\alpha/3\epsilon_0)} \tag{2.81}$$

In this illustration the dielectric constant from equation 2.79 results in the following relationship:

$$\epsilon_r = 1 + \frac{N\alpha}{1 - (N\alpha/3\epsilon_0)} \tag{2.82}$$

## 2.15 Polarization Mechanisms

If the polarizability of a substance is determined as a function of frequency (by measuring the dielectric constant or index of refraction), in general a variation, as shown in Figure 2.14, will be found.

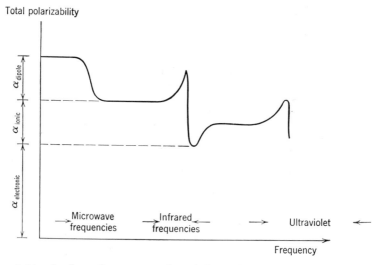

Figure 2.14. A schematic representation of the various contributions to the total polarization of a material. The frequency regions at which the various types of polarization are no longer effective are also noted. (Kittel, 1956.)

It is observed that there are three frequency ranges over which $\alpha$, although having a different value in each range, is essentially constant. Thus the experimental results indicate that there are three contributions to the total polarizability. It has been shown that these individual contributions arise (1) from the deformation of the electron shells about the nucleus, electronic polarization; (2) the displacement of ions or groups of ions, ionic polarization; and (3) orientation of molecules possessing a permanent dipole moment, orientation polarization. Although these three types of polarization are the only ones of fundamental interest, there also exists in heterogeneous materials an interfacial or space-charge polarization.

### 2.15.1 Electronic Polarization

It is possible to show by a simple calculation that the polarization observed in the range of optical frequencies ($10^{15}$ cps) is a consequence of the deformation of the electron shell around the nucleus. Consider the hydrogen atom. The binding energy of the electron is 13.7 ev, or $21.9 \times 10^{-19}$ joule. The frequency at which dispersion in the polarizability is expected to occur is of the same order of magnitude as the frequency associated with the quantum of energy required to ionize the hydrogen atom. That is,

$$f_0 \cong \frac{21.9 \times 10^{-19}}{h} \cong 3 \times 10^{15} \text{ cps}$$

where $h$ is Planck's constant,* $6.67 \times 10^{-34}$ joule-sec.

The magnitude of the electronic polarizability can be obtained from the properties of the hydrogen atom, and proper calculation shows that

$$\alpha_{\text{electronic}} \cong a_0{}^3$$

where $a_0$ is the radius of the first Bohr orbit, $0.53 \times 10^{-10}$ m. Thus, $\alpha_{\text{electronic}} = 1.5 \times 10^{-31}$ m$^3$.

### 2.15.2 Ionic Polarization

The relative permittivity for ionic crystals such as NaCl, KCl, RbCl, etc., for static or low-frequency fields is found to be of the order of 5. If the relative permittivity of these same substances is calculated from optical data, it is found to be about 2. Under low-frequency excitation

---

* An even better approximation results when the energy difference between the ground and first excited state 12.8 ev is used for $hf_0$.

there are two mechanisms contributing to the polarization in this type of material. The first is, of course, the electronic polarization which has already been discussed. The other is the displacement in opposite directions of the positive and negative ions themselves. As the frequency of excitation is increased above the natural mechanical vibration frequency of the ions, the ions cannot follow the field. Hence the ionic polarization becomes negligible, and at optical frequencies only the electronic polarization contributes to the polarization. This dispersion takes place at frequencies of the order of $10^{12}$–$10^{13}$ cps or for wavelengths of 10–100 microns as seen in Figure 2.14.

Many attempts have been made to calculate the ionic polarization with varying degrees of success. Generally, the problem reduces to the determination of the polarization of an ionic crystal arising from the application of a static field. Upon application of the field the electronic shells will deform and the ions will be displaced to new equilibrium positions. The magnitude of the ionic displacement per unit field determines the extent of the ionic polarization. The forces which are balanced at equilibrium are the electronic force and the gradient of a potential energy function similar to $U(R)$ in equation 2.10. Using this approach, reasonably good agreement is found with the experimentally determined values for the ionic polarizability.

### 2.15.3 Orientational Polarizability

In liquids and gases and, to a lesser extent, in some solids polarizability arising from the orientation of molecules having a permanent electric dipole moment is quite important. A permanent dipole moment results when one of the atoms of a molecule has a greater attraction for electrons than the others. Debye has explained the high static dielectric constant of certain liquids, such as water and alcohol, by assuming the existence of permanent dipole moments. The calculations also provide an expression for the temperature dependence of the static dielectric constant.

The model for the calculation consists of a collection of similar molecules, each having a permanent dipole moment which can assume any direction with respect to the field and whose magnitude $\mu_e$ is unaffected by the applied field. Furthermore, the interaction energy between dipoles must be small (i.e., the gas has a low density).

When molecules with a permanent moment are placed in an electric field they tend to line up in the direction of the field. However, thermal agitation tends to keep the distribution random. The result of these two opposing influences is a statistical equilibrium which permits the sample as a whole to have a dipole moment.

The potential energy of a molecule of permanent moment $\mu_e$ in an electric field $\mathbf{E}$ is

$$U = -\boldsymbol{\mu}_e \cdot \mathbf{E} = -\mu_e E \cos\theta \tag{2.83}$$

where $\theta$ is the angle between the moment and the direction of the field. The polarization will be

$$P = N\mu_e \overline{\cos\theta} \tag{2.84}$$

where $N$ is the number of molecules per unit volume and $\overline{\cos\theta}$ the average over the distribution of $\cos\theta$.

The quantity $\overline{\cos\theta}$ has been calculated in Section 2.5 in connection with the paramagnetism of an assembly of noninteracting magnetic dipoles in thermal equilibrium. Thus, for $\mu_e\mathbf{E} \ll kT$, which is the usual experimental condition, the orientational susceptibility is

$$k_e = \frac{N\mu_e^2}{3kT\epsilon_0} \tag{2.85}$$

in direct analogy with equation 2.26.

The foregoing polarization description applies to gases and liquids when the molecules are free to rotate. In solids the shape of the molecules and the strength of the interaction between dipoles determine the ease of rotation. Unsymmetrical molecules, such as $H_2O$ and $HCl$, can be rotated only to certain stable orientations, whereas other molecules, such as methane ($CH_4$), rotate quite freely.

The total polarizability can be written

$$\alpha_{\text{static}} = \alpha_0 + \frac{\mu_e^2}{3kT} \tag{2.86}$$

where $\alpha_0 = \alpha_{\text{electronic}} + \alpha_{\text{ionic}}$, the contributions of electronic and ionic polarization.

At high frequencies the orientational polarization is damped and

$$\alpha_{\text{high}} = \alpha_0 \tag{2.87}$$

The difference between equations 2.86 and 2.87 gives the contribution of the permanent dipoles. The magnitude of $\mu_e$ is found from the temperature dependence of the orientational susceptibility.

### 2.15.4 "Polarization Catastrophe"

If the value of orientational susceptibility in equation 2.85 is substituted into equation 2.82, there will be a temperature $T_0 = N\mu_e^2/q\epsilon_0 k$ at which the dielectric constant tends toward infinity. Under this condition the substance would be spontaneously polarized. Actually, this phenomenon is not found in polar liquids. In materials which do become spontaneously polarized the mechanism is quite different from that discussed in the preceding sections.

The "catastrophe" arose because we had assumed that all of the neighboring dipoles were aligned parallel to each other. In general, the permanent dipoles of a polar liquid are not parallel, so that equation 2.80 is not valid for these materials.

## 2.16 Ferroelectricity and Piezoelectricity

In recent years two further dielectric phenomena have attained great practical importance. These are ferroelectricity and piezoelectricity. Ferroelectricity, particularly of the type that exists in such materials as barium titanate, is of special interest to the device engineer for two reasons. First, it provides a material of high dielectric constant which is nonlinear in the sense that the polarization is not a linear function of the applied electric field. Second, the microscopic conditions that are required for ferroelectricity are also the sufficient conditions for piezoelectricity.

The phenomenon of piezoelectricity is of interest to the engineer, as it provides him with a means of converting electrical energy to mechanical energy and vice versa.

### 2.16.1 Ferroelectricity

If the "center of gravity" of the positive and negative charges in a body do not coincide in the absence of an applied electric field, the substance has an electric dipole moment and is said to be spontaneously polarized. Such a substance is called *ferroelectric*.* Ferroelectric substances exhibit hysteresis loops (i.e., the polarization is a double-valued function of the applied field), and saturation takes place in high fields. They have Curie temperatures, above which a Curie-Weiss law is followed, and domain structures are often easily seen. The choice of the name ferroelectricity is somewhat unfortunate, however, as the molecular mechanism is considerably different from that of ferromagnetism.

* After a ferroelectric crystal has been polarized in a given direction, the external evidence that the substance possesses a dipole moment gradually disappears because of the collection of free charges from the atmosphere on the surface and by conduction through the crystal.

### 2.16.2   Additional Effects

As already stated, the phenomena associated with charge separation in crystals which are subjected to mechanical stresses are termed piezo-electric effects.   In some cases charge separation can also be brought about through heating, and materials which exhibit charge separation on heating are called *pyroelectric*.   A relatively common pyroelectric substance is tourmaline.

In an analogous manner to the magnetic phenomena of antiferro-magnetism there exist the dielectric phenomena of *antiferroelectricity*, in which neighboring lines of spontaneously polarized ions are aligned in antiparallel directions.

When solidified in the presence of an electric field certain organic materials appear to have a net electric moment frozen in.   The moments produced in this manner may persist for years, yet it is generally believed that this polarized state is a metastable state and the stable state is unpolarized.   Materials of this type are called *electrets* (28).   Anti-ferroelectricity, pyroelectricity, and electrets are not considered further. The literature should be consulted for more information.

### 2.16.3   Ferroelectric Materials

The first substance that was recognized as being ferroelectric is Rochelle salt, $NaK(C_4H_4O_6) \cdot 4H_2O$.   Rochelle salt has a very narrow temperature range of about $40°$ C in which it is ferroelectric.   Because of this, and the associated complex crystal structure, the understanding of its behavior has been exceedingly difficult.   The water of hydration appears to be of great importance, however, as evidenced by the fact that when $D_2O$ (heavy water) is substituted for $H_2O$ the range in which Rochelle salt is ferroelectric is increased some $17°$ C.

A second group of ferroelectric substances includes potassium di-hydrogen phosphate $(KH_2PO_4)$ and its isomorphous salts.   These materials are of little practical value, since they all have low Curie temperatures.   When the hydrogen is replaced with deuterium the Curie temperatures increase many tens of degrees, and in some cases the satu-ration polarization nearly doubles.   These observations strongly suggest that in these materials the ferroelectricity is closely connected with the protons and the hydrogen bonds.

Other ferroelectric materials are barium titanate $(BaTiO_3)$ and similar substances which crystallize in the perovskite or ilmenite structure.*   A

* E.g., lead zirconate titanate (PZT) and lead metaniobate.

great deal of experimental and theoretical work has been devoted to the titanates during the past ten years, as these are the simplest of all ferroelectrics. In general, it may be said that at least qualitatively the ferroelectric phenomena are understood in these materials.

Recently a fourth class of ferroelectrics, which is apparently unrelated to the other groups, has been found. It is represented by guanidine aluminum sulfate hexahydrate (GASH). This material may find important applications because of its square hysteresis loop.

### 2.16.4   Properties of Barium Titanate

The dielectric constant of ceramic barium titanate as a function of temperature is shown in Figure 2.15. The data show that this substance

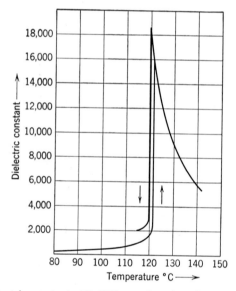

Figure 2.15. Dielectric constant of $BaTiO_3$ as a function of temperature. (Drougard and Young, 1954.)

follows a Curie-Weiss law and has a Curie point in the neighborhood of 120° C. As the temperature is lowered, the dielectric constant has a sharp maximum, and hysteresis loops typical of ferroelectric materials appear. If the temperature is lowered still further, additional anomalies appear in the dielectric-constant versus temperature curve at approximately 0 and −100° C, shown in Figure 2.16 for a single crystal of barium titanate. The spontaneous polarization of a single crystal of barium titanate as a function of temperature is shown in Figure 2.17.

If various amounts of $Ba^{2+}$ ion are replaced by $Pb^{2+}$ ions, there is a systematic increase in the Curie point (Figure 2.18) until it reaches 490° C for pure lead titanate ($PbTiO_3$). If, on the other hand, the

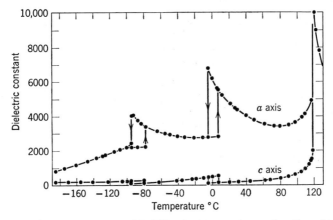

**Figure 2.16.** Dielectric constant of $BaTiO_3$ single crystals as a function of temperature. (Merz, 1949.)

$Ba^{2+}$ is replaced by $Sr^{2+}$, the Curie point is lowered. Pure strontium titanate is nonferroelectric.

Finally, Figure 2.19 shows the dielectric constant as a function of frequency at a constant temperature. Of interest is the dispersion that takes place in the kilo-megacycle range.

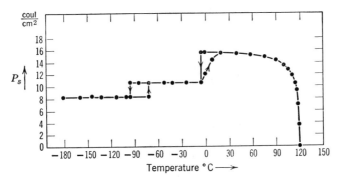

**Figure 2.17.** Spontaneous polarization of $BaTiO_3$ single crystals as a function of temperature. (Merz, 1949.)

The crystal structure of barium titanate is perovskite, as shown in Figure 2.20. The structure is cubic with $Ba^{2+}$ ions at the corners of the cube, $O^{2-}$ ions at the face centers, and a $Ti^{4+}$ ion at the body center.

Of particular importance is the fact that the titanium ion is surrounded by six oxygen ions in an octahedral configuration. Above the Curie

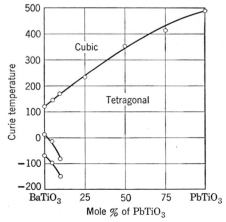

**Figure 2.18.** Phase diagram of the $BaTiO_3$—$PbTiO_3$ system. (Shirane and Suzuki, 1951.)

temperature the $TiO_6$ octahedron has a center of symmetry so that the dipole moment is zero. A net permanent moment will result from the octahedron only if the positive titanium ion is displaced toward one of

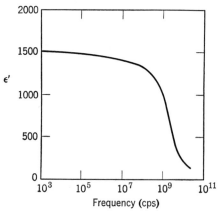

**Figure 2.19.** The dielectric constant as a function of frequency for $BaTiO_3$; from smoothed data of von Hippel and Powles and Jackson. (Kittel, 1951.)

the negative oxygen ions. It is of interest to calculate what the order of magnitude of this displacement must be to account for the observed saturation polarization below the Curie point.

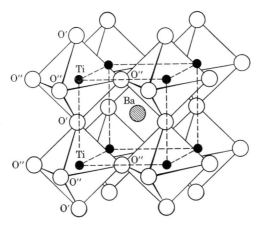

**Figure 2.20.** The $BaTiO_3$ structure, showing the octahedra of oxygen atoms about the titanium atoms. (Kittel, 1956.)

### 2.16.5 Origin of Permanent Moment in Barium Titanate

At room temperature the saturation polarization $P_s$ of barium titanate is approxmately 0.16 coulomb/$m^2$. The lattice constant is $4 \times 10^{-10}$ m, so that the number of unit cubes per $m^3$, $N$, is $1.6 \times 10^{28}$. Therefore, the dipole moment per unit cube $\mu_e$ is $10^{-29}$ coulomb-m. If it is assumed that $\mu_e$ is due to the displacement of the titanium ion $Ti^{4+}$, then the displacement $d$ is

$$d = \frac{\mu_e}{4e} \approx 1.6 \times 10^{-11}\text{m} \qquad (2.88)$$

Expressed in Angstrom units, $d = 0.16$ A, a reasonable magnitude.

Having seen, therefore, that the displacement required for the $Ti^{4+}$ ion is reasonable, we now inquire why this displacement takes place. It is believed that the occurrence of ferroelectricity in $BaTiO_3$ is a result of a polarization "catastrophe" in which the electric field arising from the polarization increases at a faster rate than the elastic-restoring forces between the ions.

From Section 2.14.3, the local field, given by $E_0 + P/3\epsilon_0$, is valid only if all the atoms have cubic or isotropic surroundings. In the case of barium titanate (Figure 2.20) the barium and titanium atoms have cubic surroundings but the oxygen atoms have not. Thus it is necessary to carry out a separate calculation to see if the magnitudes of the internal fields are conducive to a polarization "catastrophe" in the case of barium titanate.

The method used by Slater (17) is to set up expressions for the local field at each lattice point in terms of the applied field and the polarizations of the various types of atom. There are four types of atom to be considered: Ba, Ti, O', and O'', where the O' atoms are on lines parallel to the $z$-direction (direction of the applied field) and passing through the titanium atoms; the remaining oxygen atoms are the O'' atoms (Figure 2.20).

Using these expressions and the experimental data for the electronic polarization of the various types of atom, the dielectric constant of $BaTiO_3$ is obtainable in terms of the ionic polarization of the titanium atom. The local field equations indicate that the spontaneous polarization is due largely to the strong interaction between the Ti and O' ions.

The question of why the perovskite structure is conducive to ferroelectricity has thus been partially answered. The polarization of the Ti ions increases the local field at the O' ion sites. This increases the polarization of the O' ions which in turn further polarize the Ti ions, etc. The process continues until such time that anharmonic elastic restoring forces dominate. The net effect is that linear chains of dipoles, all pointing in the same direction, are built up.

Above the Curie point barium titanate obeys a Curie-Weiss law, as shown in Figure 2.15. Below the Curie point a polarization "catastrophe" takes place, with the resulting shift of some or all of the ions. The fact that a physical shift of the ions occurs is confirmed by X-ray evidence which shows that below the Curie temperature the crystal structure of barium titanate is slightly tetragonal.

A number of attempts have been made to check the magnitude and direction of the shift of the ions in $BaTiO_3$ using X-rays. Because of the uncertainties arising from thermal oscillation a unique structure determination has not been accomplished. The X-ray evidence shows that two models are possible. In the first model the O'' type ions remain in place and the Ti ions and O' type ions move in opposite directions. In the second model the two types of oxygen ion move in the same direction, whereas the titanium ion moves in the opposite direction. In this second model one can consider the cubic oxygen network to be only slightly distorted, and thus nearly fixed with respect to the nonferroelectric structure, and regard the Ti and Ba ions as shifting in the same direction but with the Ti moving farther.

Recently the problem of determining the structure of barium titanate has been attacked with neutron diffraction techniques (18, 19). The results of this work are conclusive and show that the second model is the correct one. The actual displacement of the Ti ion in the $z$-direction is 0.06 A.

### 2.16.6 Piezoelectricity

When an electric field is applied to a substance it becomes polarized. As we have seen, this means that the electrons and nuclei have assumed new geometrical positions. Such a rearrangement of the elementary particles causes the mechanical dimensions of the substance to be altered. The situation can be demonstrated by the two-dimensional unit cell shown in Figure 2.21. Here we have shown an array of positive and

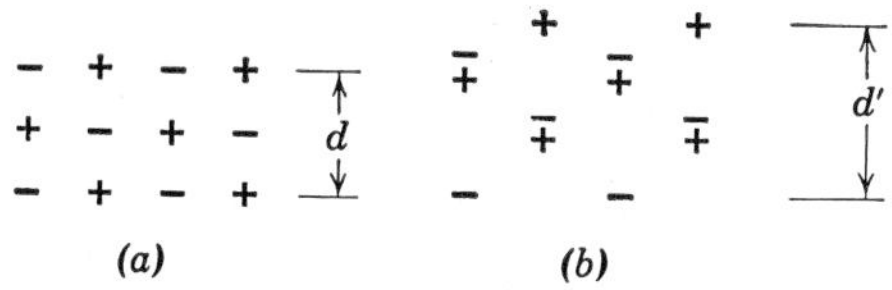

**Figure 2.21.** The phenomenon of electrostriction for an array of charges: (*a*) before the field is applied; (*b*) after the field is applied, causing a change in the physical dimensions of the array.

negative charge. When the field is applied, as in (*b*), the charges assume new positions and the linear dimension of the sample changes. If the electric field is reversed, a similar change in dimension occurs. Furthermore, if the change is an expansion in the first case, it will also be an expansion when the field is reversed. This phenomenon is called *electrostriction*. It is now of interest to inquire into the reverse effect, i.e., do mechanical stresses produce a polarization?

Consider the same two-dimensional lattice as before, subjected to a mechanical compressional force (Figure 2.22). Since the force acts only on mass points, it cannot distinguish between points of different charge.

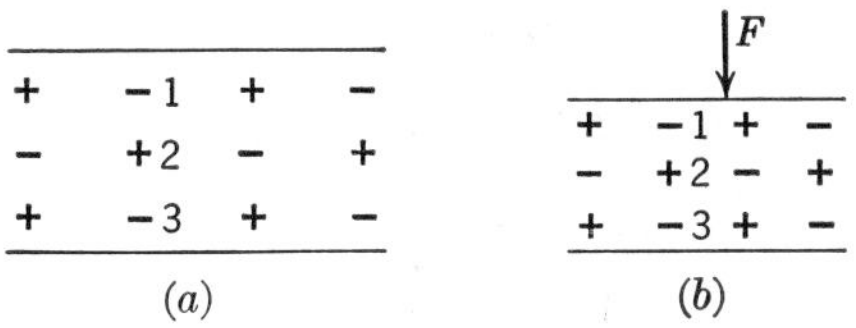

**Figure 2.22.** An array of point charges having mass: (*a*) before a mechanical force is applied; (*b*) after the application of a force *F*. In (*b*) the distance between row (1) and (2) is equal to the distance between (2) and (3); hence there is no change in the electric moment of the charge array. Note that row (2) is a line of symmetry for the array.

Thus mass point 1 moves closer to point 2, decreasing the dipole moment between 1 and 2. At the same time, however, point 3 has also moved closer to point 2, decreasing the moment between 2 and 3 but in the opposite direction. In other words, the effect of the compression has been to induce two new dipole moments of equal magnitude but opposite in direction. Thus the net effect is negligible, since the two antiparallel dipoles cancel each other. We may say, therefore, that in general the inverse phenomenon to electrostriction does not exist.

The crystal lattice chosen in Figures 2.21 and 2.22 is a special one in that it contains a center of symmetry for the constituent point charges. The situation is different if a lattice is chosen for which there is no center of symmetry. Suppose the system consisted of two lines of charge, one positive and one negative, as in Figure 2.23$a$. When the field is applied (Figure 2.23$b$), the two lines of charge separate $(d_1 > d)$. If the field is reversed (Figure 2.23$c$), the two lines of charge move closer together $(d_2 < d)$. In addition, if a compressional force is applied to the system, the dipole moment is decreased, and, if a tension is applied,

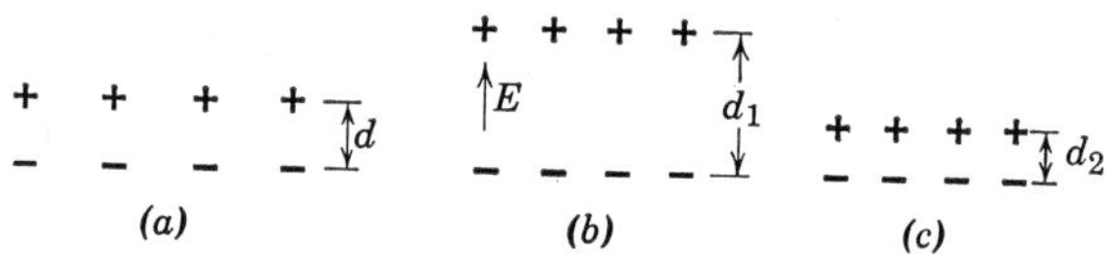

Figure 2.23. A charge array having no center of symmetry: ($a$) zero field; ($b$) field applied; ($c$) field reversed.

the moment of the system is increased. This is an indication that for geometries in which the permanent dipoles have no center of symmetry the state of polarization can be changed by the application of external stresses. Substances which exhibit this phenomenon are called *piezoelectric*. It should be noted that an artificial asymmetry can be introduced into a ceramic material merely by polarizing the specimen. In this case the electrostrictive material will have the properties of piezoelectric materials if small variations in strain are made about the bias value.

All crystals may be grouped into seven crystal *systems* (cubic, tetragonal, triclinic, etc.) according to the symmetries of their external forms. Each one of the crystal systems is further divided into a number of crystal *classes*, each class having various other symmetry elements. In all, there are thirty-two different crystal classes of which only twenty lack a center of symmetry; hence they are possible piezoelectric crystals.

Von Hippel, by using dipole configurations corresponding to the symmetries of the twenty piezoelectric crystal classes, has shown in a graphical manner which of the piezoelectric coefficients are independent and nonvanishing (26). Such models are very helpful in understanding why certain piezoelectric coefficients exist in some crystals but in others are zero. Unfortunately, the models do not give any information regarding the magnitude of these coefficients.

## 2.17 Domain Structure in Barium Titanate

In Section 2.8.1 it is pointed out that the net magnetization is zero in an unmagnetized ferromagnetic body below the Curie temperature because of the existence of randomly oriented domains. The domain concept is also used in explaining ferroelectric phenomena, even though the analogy cannot be considered complete. Domain structures in ferroelectric crystals can be studied with a microscope and polarized light (20, 21, 22). This is possible because the index of refraction varies with direction relative to the crystallographic axes.

Shirane, Jona, and Pepinsky (23) have shown very clearly how domain studies are performed and interpreted. The possible domain configurations of a BaTiO$_3$ plate may be visualized schematically with the help of Figure 2.24, which shows a cube of BaTiO$_3$ consisting of

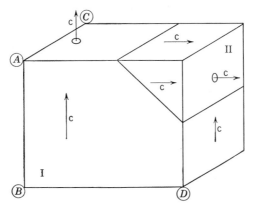

**Figure 2.24.** Schematic domain structure of a tetragonal BaTiO$_3$ crystal with 90° domain walls. (Shirane, et al., 1955.)

two domains, I and II. The direction of the $c$-crystallographic axis (i.e., the direction of the spontaneous polarization) is indicated on each of the faces.

A thin plate is cut from the cube perpendicular to the direction $AB$ and close to the top edge of the cube. This plate is observed in a polarizing microscope with the light traveling in the direction of the plate's thickness. Since the optic axis (i.e., the $c$-axis) of Domain I is parallel to the light, it will appear dark regardless of the orientation of the plate about this axis. Such a domain is called a *c-domain*. Domain II has its optic axis in the plane of the plate. Therefore, there are two positions separated by 90° at which this region will appear dark. This type of domain is called an *a-domain*. The boundary between the two domains is called a 90° wall.

In addition to 90° walls, 180° walls are also found in $BaTiO_3$. These walls separate domains which are polarized in opposite directions. It is necessary to apply a d-c field perpendicular to the direction of polarization to see these types of domains. The field slightly rotates the polar axes of the domains in opposite directions. Thus the positions for extinction of the two domains will deviate from one another. Merz has shown, using this technique, that supposedly single domains are in

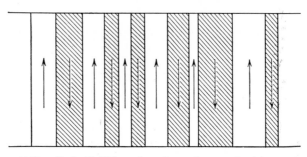

**Figure 2.25.** 180° walls in $BaTiO_3$: edge of a *c*-plate strained by an applied field. (Shirane, et al., 1955.)

reality a number of domains with antiparallel polarization. The edge of a $BaTiO_3$ plate which has been strained by a field is shown in Figure 2.25.

Hooton and Merz (24) developed the one other technique necessary for the complete identification of the domain orientation. By etching the crystal of $BaTiO_3$ with hydrochloric acid they were able to distinguish the polarity of the domain. When the etched crystal is viewed by reflected light it is found that the rate at which the domain etches depends upon whether the positive or negative end of the dipole is exposed to the acid. The positive end etches rapidly while the tails are only slightly affected.

One difference between the domain structure in ferroelectric materials and that in ferromagnetic materials lies in the nature of the walls that separate the domains. In the ferromagnetic case the wall consists of a transition region in which the spin vector gradually changes from one direction of magnetization to the opposite. This relatively large wall thickness is a result of a compromise between the exchange energy, which tends to make the transition region between oppositely aligned domains as large as possible, and the anisotropy energy, which tends to make the region as thin as possible.

In the ferroelectric case, however, the situation is considerably different. The dipole interaction, which corresponds to the exchange energy in the magnetic case, is such that an abrupt change from polarization in one direction to the other is favored. The anisotropy term is also large. In addition, the elastic energy, which favors a thin region, is of the same order of magnitude as the dipole interaction energy. Thus the wall thickness in the ferroelectric case is many times smaller than in the analogous ferromagnetic situation.

The domain wall thickness in ferroelectrics was first calculated by Mitsui and Furuichi (25) for Rochelle salt. The results of this calculation indicated a wall thickness of the order of a few lattice constants. Calculations on potassium dihydrogen phosphate and barium titanate (20) have yielded similar results. In comparison, the wall thickness in the magnetic case is of the order of 250–300 lattice constants.

### 2.17.1 Nucleation and Wall Motion

The nucleation and wall motion of 90° domains in barium titanate have been investigated by Little (21) with pulsed electric fields and optical techniques. Type $a$-domain plates were used with electrodes placed on opposite edges of the crystal. As the field, which is initially at 90° to the direction of the polarization, is slowly increased, 90° wedges are nucleated at the crystal boundaries (Figure 2.26) at some critical field $E_c$ and extend across the crystal at a velocity greater than 5 cm/sec.

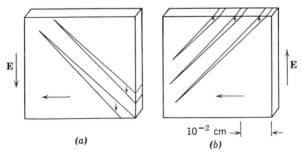

Figure 2.26. 90° wedge nucleation in a [100] crystal: ($a$) positive field; ($b$) negative field. (Little, 1955.)

In general, it is noted that the wedges are usually nucleated on the cathode side of the crystal. The critical field necessary to nucleate the domains was measured as a function of temperature and was found to be about 2.4 kv/cm at room temperature and to approach zero as the temperature approached the Curie temperature.

The initial growth of the 90° wedges was investigated as a function of time and field strength by applying a square pulse and counting the number of wedges formed at the completion of the pulse. These data are shown in Figure 2.27. No wedges were observed for $\frac{1}{4}$ μsec pulses

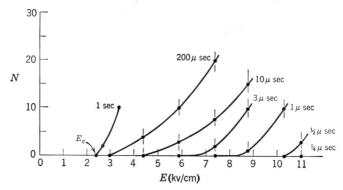

**Figure 2.27.** Number $N$ of 90° wedges nucleated by a square pulse as a function of pulse length and pulse height. (Little, 1955.)

with $E \approx 11$ kv/cm. For pulses greater than 1 μsec all the wedges observed extended across the crystal. For pulses longer than 10 μsec the wedges would widen slightly after they had traversed the crystal. The correlation of these data indicates that the limiting velocity in the forward direction for the wedges at high fields is of the order of the velocity of sound, i.e., about $10^6$ cm/sec.

After the wedges have been introduced into the plate the domain growth can be described in terms of the wall motion. The particularly interesting point of the wall motion is that walls move sideways with a decreasing velocity and with some irregularity. It also appears that the 90° walls are considerably thicker than 180° walls.

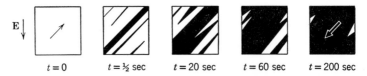

**Figure 2.28.** Schematic diagram of 180° domain switching process in a [101] crystal. (Little, 1955.)

Similar studies have been carried out by Merz (20) and Little (21) on the nucleation and growth of 180° domains in barium titanate. Of particular importance is the fact that there is little sideways motion of 180° walls. The reversal of polarization is accomplished by the nucleation of many new domains of opposite polarization. As a reversing field is applied, thin spikes starting from both edges of the plate extend across the crystal. These spikes appear to nucleate at identical places at the crystal edges when the experiment is repeated. The number of spikes initiated depends upon the magnitude of applied field. At high field strengths the trend seems to be toward the nucleation of new domains at the walls of existing domains. Figure 2.28 is a schematic representation of this process.

## 2.18 References

1. Kittel, C., *Introduction to Solid State Physics*, 1st ed., John Wiley and Sons, New York, 1956, p. 78.
2. Bozorth, R. M., *Ferromagnetism*, D. Van Nostrand Company, Inc., Princeton, N. J., 1951, p. 444.
3. *American Institute of Physics Handbook*, McGraw-Hill Book Company, New York, 1957.
4. Stoner, E. C., *Magnetism*, Methuen & Company, Ltd., London, 1948, p. 72.
5. Goodenough, J. B., and N. Menyuk, *A Theory of Domain Creation, Coercive Force, and Flux Reversal in Polycrystalline Ferromagnetics*, Digital Computer Laboratory, MIT, Cambridge, Mass., 1955.
6. Néel, L., *Ann. Phys.*, **3,** p. 137, 1948.
7. Kittel, C., *Revs. Modern Phys.*, **21,** 1950, p. 541.
8. Bates, L. F., *Modern Magnetism*, Cambridge University Press, 1951.
9. Mueller, H., "Theory of Photoelastic Effect of Cubic Crystals," *Phys. Rev.*, **47,** 1935, p. 947, and "The Optical Properties of Nonpolar Liquids," *Phys. Rev.*, **50,** 1936, p. 547.
10. McKeehan, L. W., "Magnetic Dipole Energy in Hexagonal Crystals," *Phys. Rev.*, **43,** 1933, pp. 1022, 1025.
11. Drougard, M. E., and D. R. Young, "Dielectric Behavior of Single Domain Crystals of Barium Titanate in the Vicinity of the Curie Point," *Phys. Rev.*, **95,** 1954, p. 1152.
12. Merz, W. J., "The Electrical and Optical Behavior of $BaTiO_3$ Single Domain Crystals," *Phys. Rev.*, **76,** 1949, p. 1221.
13. Shirane, G., and K. Susuki, "On the Phase Transition in Barium Lead Titanate," *J. Phys. Soc. Japan*, **6,** 1951, p. 274.
14. von Hippel, A., "Ferroelectricity, Domain Structure, and Phase Transitions of Barium Titanate," *Revs. Modern Phys.*, **22,** 1950, p. 221.
15. Powles, J. G., "Dielectric Properties of Titanates at Ultra-High Frequencies," *Nature*, **162,** 1948, p. 614; *Proc. Inst. Elec. Engrs. (London)* Part III, **96,** 1949, p. 383.
16. Kittel, C., "Domain Boundary Motion of Ferroelectric Crystals and the Dielectric Constant at High Frequency," *Phys. Rev.*, **83,** 1951, p. 458.
17. Slater, J. C., "The Lorentz Correction in Barium Titanate," *Phys. Rev.*, **78,** 1950, p. 748.
18. Frazer, B. C., H. Danner, and R. Pepinsky, "Single Crystal Neutron Analysis of Tetragonal $BaTiO_3$," *Phys. Rev.*, **100,** 1955, p. 745.
19. Frazer, B. C., and R. Pepinsky, "Single Crystal Neutron Diffraction Refinement

of Tetragonal BaTiO$_3$ Structure," *Bull. Am. Phys. Soc.*, Series II, **2**, January 1957, p. 23.

20. Merz, W. J., "Domain Formation and Domain Wall Motion in Ferroelectric BaTiO$_3$ Single Crystals," *Phys. Rev.*, **95**, 1954, p. 690.

21. Little, E. H., "Dynamic Behavior of Domain Walls in Barium Titanate," *Phys. Rev.*, **98**, 1955, p. 978.

22. Forsbergh, P. W., "Domain Structure and Phase Transitions in Barium Titanate," *Phys. Rev.*, **76**, 1949, p. 1187.

23. Shirane, G., F. Jona, and R. Pepinsky, "Some Aspects of Ferroelectricity," *Proc. I.R.E.*, **43**, 1955, p. 1738.

24. Hooton, J. A., and W. J. Merz, "Etch Patterns and Ferroelectric Domains in BaTiO$_3$ Single Crystals," *Phys. Rev.*, **98**, 1955, p. 409.

25. Mitsui, T., and J. Furuichi, "Domain Structure of Rochelle Salt and KH$_2$PO$_4$," *Phys. Rev.*, **90**, 1953, p. 193.

26. von Hippel, A., *Dielectrics and Waves*, John Wiley and Sons, New York, 1954, and *Dielectric Materials and Applications*, John Wiley and Sons, New York, 1954.

27. Gutmann, F., "The Electret," *Revs. Modern Phys.* **20**, 1948, p. 457.

28. Wieder, H. H., and S. Kaufman, "Plastic Electrets and Their Applications," *Elec. Eng., AIEE*, June 1953, p. 511.

# Chapter three

# Electrostrictive
# and Magnetostrictive
# Systems

## 3.0 Introduction

Single crystal quartz has been used as a resonant electromechanical element for many years in various phases of radio circuitry. Although extreme temperature stability and low mechanical loss are among its unique properties, it is a relatively difficult material to fabricate. The recent introduction of dielectric and magnetic ceramics which have similar electromechanical properties has brought renewed interest in electromechanical transducers for many applications (4, 19, 21, 24). Not only are these ceramics simpler to fabricate, they are also not so subject to surface effects as quartz and possess much higher coupling coefficients. At present, however, their temperature and aging stability is usually not so favorable as that of the best quartz crystals.*

The purpose of the present chapter is to review the analytic techniques for relating the mechanical parameters to the applied voltages and currents. The end result is to arrive at a method for the determination of equivalent circuits from which to calculate and visualize the behavior

---

* Recent advances have resulted in marked improvements in the temperature and aging stability.

of the vibrating system. The procedure is very similar to that employed in the linear approximation of vacuum tube or transistor circuitry. In a triode vacuum tube, for example, the plate current $i_b$ is a function of the grid to cathode voltage $e_c$ and the plate voltage $e_b$, i.e.,

$$i_b = f(e_c, e_b) \tag{3.1}$$

Small changes in these voltages about some fixed bias produce a change in current which can be calculated from the differential

$$di_b = \frac{\partial i_b}{\partial e_c}\bigg|_{e_b} de_c + \frac{\partial i_b}{\partial e_b}\bigg|_{e_c} de_b \tag{3.2}$$

The partial derivatives, evaluated at the bias values $e_b = E_{b0}$ and $e_c = E_{c0}$, are then the linear parameters of a mutual conductance $g_m$ and a plate conductance $g_p$. These parameters are functions of the bias voltages but are constants for a given operating point for small signal analysis. The differentials in equation 3.2 are then replaced by their small signal values, i.e.,

$$
\begin{aligned}
i_p &= di_b \\
e_g &= de_c \\
e_p &= de_b
\end{aligned}
\tag{3.3}
$$

The basic triode equation 3.2 then becomes

$$i_p = g_m e_g + g_p e_p \tag{3.4}$$

from which we can then derive an equivalent circuit.

Linear electromechanical theory may be developed in exactly the same manner. In order to consider electrostriction and magnetostriction as a unified subject, both sets of equations are given in parallel.

## 3.1 Linear Electromechanical Equation

The mechanical deformation of these ceramics as a function of the polarization or magnetization usually follows a square law curve (1) of the form shown in Figure 3.1. The operating point is determined by the polarization or magnetization bias which is applied.* Point $a$ corresponds to operation at residual bias.

Consider an elementary volume of polarized or magnetized material as a "free body" which is subjected simultaneously to an applied stress

* For quartz crystal the operating point $a$ is at the origin, since the crystal may be viewed as having a built-in asymmetry (see Section 2.16.3).

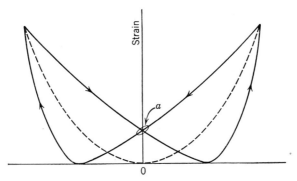

**Figure 3.1.** Dotted curve is strain as a function of polarization or magnetization. Solid curve is strain as a function of field intensity **E** or **H**, illustrating the effects of hysteresis.

**T** and an external field **E** or **H** (Figure 3.2).* The choice of independent variables for this system is arbitrary. If we choose the resultant strain

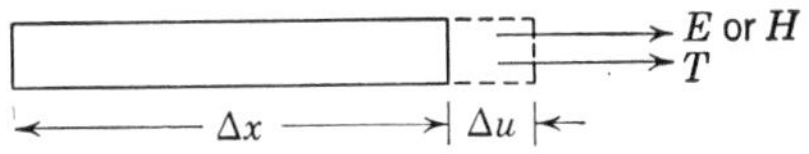

**Figure 3.2.** Elementary volume with applied field and stress.

$S$ and the flux density as the the independent variables, the following functional dependence is obtained:

$$T = T(S, D) \qquad T = T(S, B) \qquad (3.5)$$

$$E = E(S, D) \qquad H = H(S, B) \qquad (3.6)$$

The total differentials of these functions are

$$dT = \frac{\partial T}{\partial S}\bigg|_D dS + \frac{\partial T}{\partial D}\bigg|_S dD \qquad dT = \frac{\partial T}{\partial S}\bigg|_B dS + \frac{\partial T}{\partial B}\bigg|_S dB \qquad (3.7)$$

$$dE = \frac{\partial E}{\partial S}\bigg|_D dS + \frac{\partial E}{\partial D}\bigg|_S dD \qquad dH = \frac{\partial H}{\partial S}\bigg|_B dS + \frac{\partial H}{\partial B}\bigg|_S dB \qquad (3.8)$$

The various partial derivatives can be defined as follows: †

$$\frac{\partial T}{\partial S}\bigg|_D = c^D, \text{ the elastic modulus (one dimensional) measured at constant } D \qquad (3.9a)$$

* For the purposes of the following discussion all strains are assumed to occur in only one dimension. The extension of this analysis to three dimensions is carried out in a later section.

† I.R.E. standards (14.S1). See preface.

$$\left.\frac{\partial E}{\partial D}\right|_S = \frac{1}{\epsilon^S}, \text{ the reciprocal of the dielectric constant measured}$$
$$\text{at constant strain} \qquad (3.9b)$$

$$\left.\frac{\partial T}{\partial S}\right|_B = c^B, \text{ the elastic modulus measured at constant } B * \qquad (3.9c)$$

$$\left.\frac{\partial H}{\partial B}\right|_S = \frac{1}{\mu^S}, \text{ the reciprocal of the permeability measured at}$$
$$\text{constant strain} \qquad (3.9d)$$

$$\left.\frac{\partial T}{\partial D}\right|_S \text{ and } \left.\frac{\partial E}{\partial S}\right|_D \text{ are the electrostrictive coefficients representing}$$
$$\text{inverse operations} \qquad (3.9e)$$

$$\left.\frac{\partial T}{\partial B}\right|_S \text{ and } \left.\frac{\partial H}{\partial S}\right|_B \text{ are the magnetostrictive coefficients} \qquad (3.9f)$$

The relationship between the two coefficients in equation 3.9e can be obtained by a consideration of the changes in the internal energy of the elementary volume when it is subjected to a simultaneous strain $dS$ and the electric displacement $dD$,† i.e.,

$$dw = T\,dS + E\,dD \qquad (3.10)$$

If the system is conservative, then $dw$ must be an exact differential (18). Under this condition

$$\left.\frac{\partial T}{\partial D}\right|_S = \left.\frac{\partial E}{\partial S}\right|_D = -h \qquad (3.11)$$

The operations expressed by the partial derivatives of equation 3.9e are equal and defined as $-h$.

The energy equation for the magnetic case is similar, i.e.

$$dw = T\,dS + H\,dB \qquad (3.12)$$

and therefore

$$\left.\frac{\partial T}{\partial B}\right|_S = \left.\frac{\partial H}{\partial S}\right|_B = -h_m \qquad (3.13)$$

If the coefficients defined above are substituted into equations 3.7 and 3.8, we obtain this fundamental set of electromechanical equations which describes the behavior of the elementary volume of Figure 3.2.

$$T = c^D S - hD \qquad T = c^B S - h_m B \qquad (3.14)$$

$$E = -hS + D/\epsilon^S \qquad H = -h_m S + B/\mu^S \qquad (3.15)$$

* For a thin bar stressed along its length the elastic modulus is usually called Young's modulus ($Y^D$ or $Y^B$) (see Section 3.4.3).

† Adiabatic conditions are assumed.

The differentials have been replaced by their small a-c signal equivalents in a manner similar to the vacuum tube problem.

### 3.1.1 Electromechanical Coupling Coefficient

Another parameter can be derived from the coefficients of equations 3.14 and 3.15. The parameter which is defined as the electromechanical coupling coefficient serves as one of the figures of merit of the ceramic material. Consider the case in which the elementary volume of Figure 3.2 is an electrostrictive material with conducting electrodes on either face which are shorted together. The strain under an applied stress can be calculated from equations 3.14 and 3.15 when $E$ is zero.

$$T = S \left( 1 - \frac{h^2 \epsilon^S}{c^D} \right) c^D \qquad (3.16)$$

The factor $h^2 \epsilon^S / c^D$ is equal to $k_E{}^2$ where $k_E$ is the electrostrictive mechanical coupling coefficient.* Hence the effective elastic modulus $(T/S)$ measured under short circuit conditions is $(1 - k^2)$ times the elastic modulus measured under constant $D$ or open circuit conditions.

This coupling coefficient is similar to that provided in a four-terminal electric network described by the nodal equations

$$I_1 = y_{11}E_1 + y_{12}E_2$$
$$I_2 = y_{12}E_1 + y_{22}E_2 \qquad (3.17)$$

Under short circuit conditions $E_2$ is zero; hence the new input admittance is

$$\left. \frac{I_1}{E_1} \right|_{sc} = y_{11} \left( 1 - \frac{y_{12}{}^2}{y_{11}y_{22}} \right) \qquad (3.18)$$

### 3.1.2 Coupling Coefficient in Terms of Energy

Another useful interpretation of the electromechanical coupling coefficient can be obtained by considering the conversion of electrical to mechanical energy and vice versa. Assume that no stress is applied to the elementary volume of Figure 3.2. The total change in energy due to an applied electric field is

$$dw = E \, dD \qquad (3.19)$$

Substitute equations 3.14 and 3.15 with $T = 0$ into equation 3.19.

_____

* For the magnetic case $k_m{}^2 = h_m{}^2 \mu^S / c^B$.

Hence

$$dw = E\,dD = c^D(1/k^2 - 1)S\,dS \qquad (3.20)$$

or by integration

$$\Delta W = c^D\left(\frac{1 - k^2}{k^2}\right)\frac{S^2}{2} \qquad (3.21)$$

If the material were not electrostrictive, the amount of work necessary to produce a strain $S$ would be $c^D S^2/2$. However, for the electrostrictive case we must use the elastic modulus determined under short circuited conditions, i.e., $c^D(1 - k^2)$. Thus in equation 3.21 $k^2\,\Delta W$ represents the mechanical energy stored in the volume. Hence only $k^2$ of the total input electrical energy is converted to stored mechanical energy. Furthermore, from equation 3.20 it can be seen that $k \leq 1$, since $\Delta W$ must be positive.

A similar calculation carried out for the case in which an external stress is applied with the conducting plates short circuited would yield

$$\Delta W = \frac{D^2}{2\epsilon^S}\frac{1 - k^2}{k^2} \qquad (3.22)$$

In other words, only $k^2$ of total input mechanical energy appears as electrical energy stored in the material.

## 3.2 Mechanical Vibrations

The second portion of the problem is the determination of the nature of the mechanical vibrations which result from the applied stresses and fields of equations 3.14 and 3.15. This requires a calculation of the net force acting on the elementary volume and then applying Newton's equations of motion. In general, there are two types of force which may enter the problem. The first group consists of the surface stresses depicted in Figure 3.2. The second group consists of the body or volume forces. In the latter classification we could include the gravitational force, an electrostatic force, if the material contained free charges, and a magnetic force, if current were flowing in the material. Under normal conditions these forces either do not exist or can be entirely neglected. Hence our considerations are directed only toward normal surface stresses.*

* Shearing stresses are included in a later section.

For the one-dimensional problem under discussion, Figure 3.3 shows an elementary volume in the unstrained and in the strained condition. The left-hand surface has been displaced a distance $u$, and the right-hand surface, a distance $u + (\partial u/\partial x)\, \Delta x$. The resultant strain (change in length per unit length) is $S = \partial u/\partial x$. In a similar manner, if $T$ is

**Figure 3.3.** Variation of stress and displacement under strain.

the applied stress on the left-hand surface, then $T + (\partial T/\partial x)\, \Delta x$ is the stress on the right-hand surface. The net force is

$$F = \frac{\partial T}{\partial x}\, \Delta x A \qquad (3.23)$$

where $A$ is the cross-sectional area in Figure 3.3.

Therefore,

$$\frac{\partial T}{\partial x}\, \Delta x A = \rho\, \Delta x A\, \frac{\partial^2 u}{\partial t^2} \qquad (3.24)$$

from Newton's equation where $\rho$ is the density of the material.

Hence

$$\frac{\partial T}{\partial x} = \rho\, \frac{\partial^2 u}{\partial t^2} \qquad (3.25)$$

The problem now involves a solution of equation 3.25 in conjunction with equations 3.14 and 3.15. In general, this would be a very formidable task, since for an arbitrary geometry it is necessary to solve for the electric or magnetic field distributions which in turn affect the stress distributions. Before indicating the nature of the assumptions which permit us to overcome this limitation to some extent, let us assume that the distribution of fields and stresses has been determined. The final step in the problem is that of relating these solutions to the applied voltages and currents and thus determining the equivalent electrical circuit.

For problems in electrostriction the voltage between conducting electrodes is

$$E = -\int \mathbf{E} \cdot \mathbf{dl} \qquad (3.26)$$

The current $i$ at the electrode surface can be calculated from the displacement vector $D$, since

$$\oint D \cdot ds = Q \tag{3.27}$$

and

$$i = \frac{dq}{dt} \tag{3.28}$$

For magnetostrictive problems in which a coil is wound about the material the relation between the fields and the applied voltage and current is given by

$$\oint H \cdot dl = NI \tag{3.29}$$

$$E = -\frac{d}{dt} \int B \cdot ds \tag{3.30}$$

## 3.3  Electrostrictive Plate

The simplest geometry to illustrate the principles discussed in the preceding sections is a broad plate which has been polarized in thickness. The configuration is shown in Figure 3.4 with conducting electrodes on surfaces 1 and 2. In general, external stresses may be applied at the

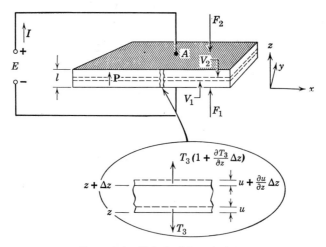

Figure 3.4.  Polarized broad plate.

faces simultaneously with the voltage. It is then desired to know the manner in which the forces and velocities at the faces are related to the voltage and current at the electrical terminals.

The longitudinal vibrations are obtained from a solution of equation 3.25 in which equation 3.14 has been substituted for $T$. The elementary volume in this case is a thin slice with faces parallel to the electrodes. It is assumed that the plate is so broad that no appreciable motion takes place except in thickness. Under this assumption

$$c^D \frac{\partial^2 u}{\partial z^2} - h \frac{\partial D}{\partial z} = \rho \frac{\partial^2 u}{\partial t^2} \tag{3.31}$$

If the bar possesses a relatively high dielectric constant, it may be assumed that very little leakage flux can occur. To the extent that this is true then $\partial D/\partial z = 0$ since $\nabla \cdot D = 0$ everywhere inside the plate. Equation 3.31 reduces to

$$c^D \frac{\partial^2 u}{\partial z^2} = \rho \frac{\partial^2 u}{\partial t^2} \tag{3.32}$$

which is the equation of vibrational motion as though the bar possessed no electrostrictive activity except for the use of an elastic modulus measured under constant $D$. This implies that the vast body of purely mechanical vibration problems which has already been solved in the literature can be carried over directly into the magnetostrictive or electrostrictive problem. The feature in which all the flux ($D$ or $B$) is confined to the material appears in certain favored geometries. Other problems can be solved only through less exact approximation.

The solutions to the wave equation 3.32 are well known for the case in which the time variation is sinusoidal. The result is

$$u = (B_1 \sin \beta z + B_2 \cos \beta z)e^{j\omega t} \tag{3.33}$$

where $\beta = \omega \sqrt{\rho/c^D}$

$\sqrt{c^D/\rho} = c =$ velocity of propagation for longitudinal vibrations. The force $F_1$ can be obtained from equations 3.33 and 3.14 at $z = 0$.

$$-F_1 = AT\big|_{z=0} = A(c^D S - hD)\big|_{z=0} \tag{3.34}$$

$$= Ac^D \beta B_1 - AhD \tag{3.35}$$

The velocity at $z = 0$ is

$$V_1 = \frac{\partial u}{\partial t} = j\omega u\big|_{z=0}$$

$$= j\omega B_2 \tag{3.36}$$

The velocity at $z = l$ is

$$V_2 = -j\omega(B_1 \sin \beta l + B_2 \cos \beta l) \tag{3.37}$$

Using equation 3.36,

$$V_2 = -j\omega B_1 \sin \beta l - V_1 \cos \beta l \tag{3.38}$$

Hence

$$B_1 = -\left(\frac{V_2 + V_1 \cos \beta l}{j\omega \sin \beta l}\right) \tag{3.39}$$

Substitution of equations 3.39 and 3.36 into equation 3.34 yields

$$F_1 = A c^D \left[ gD - j\frac{\beta}{\omega}\left(\frac{V_2 + V_1 \cos \beta l}{\sin \beta l}\right) \right] \tag{3.40}$$

A similar equation can be obtained for the force at $x = l$.

$$F_2 = A c^D \left[ gD - j\frac{\beta}{\omega}\left(\frac{V_1 + V_2 \cos \beta l}{\sin \beta l}\right) \right] \tag{3.41}$$

where $c^D g = h$.

The relationship between the current and the flux density $D$ can be obtained from equations 3.27 and 3.28.

$$I = j\omega A D \tag{3.42}$$

In addition, we define a mechanical characteristic impedance similar to that of electrical transmission lines, i.e.,

$$Z_0 = \lim_{l \to \infty} \left(\frac{F_1}{V_1}\bigg|_{D=0}\right) = A\sqrt{\rho c^D} = A\rho c \tag{3.43}$$

Equations 3.40 and 3.41 then become

$$F_1 = \frac{-jZ_0}{\tan \beta l} V_1 - \frac{jZ_0 V_2}{\sin \beta l} + \frac{c^D g}{j\omega} I \tag{3.44}$$

$$F_2 = \frac{-jZ_0 V_1}{\sin \beta l} - \frac{jZ_0 V_2}{\tan \beta l} + \frac{c^D g}{j\omega} I \tag{3.45}$$

From equation 3.15 we can obtain the final relationship between the applied voltage $(E)$ and the resultant velocities and current

$$E = \int_0^l \mathbf{E} \cdot d\mathbf{z} = \int_0^l \left( -hS + \frac{D}{\epsilon^S} \right) dz \qquad (3.46)$$

$$= \frac{Dl}{\epsilon^S} = -h \int_0^l \frac{\partial u}{\partial z} dz$$

$$= \frac{Dl}{\epsilon^S} + \frac{V_1 + V_2}{j\omega} c^D g \qquad (3.47)$$

where the substitution $h = c^D g$ has been made.

From equation 3.42

$$E = \frac{Il}{j\omega A \epsilon^S} + \frac{c^D g}{j\omega} (V_1 + V_2) \qquad (3.48)$$

In order to simplify this equation, longitudinal clamped electrical impedance is defined as

$$Z_E{}^{LC} = \frac{E}{I} \bigg|_{V_1 = V_2 = 0} = \frac{l}{j\omega A \epsilon^S} \qquad (3.49)$$

The complete set of equations relating the mechanical and electrical terminals are thus

$$F_1 = \frac{-jZ_0 V_1}{\tan \beta l} - \frac{jZ_0 V_2}{\sin \beta l} + \frac{c^D g I}{j\omega}$$

$$F_2 = \frac{-jZ_0 V_1}{\sin \beta l} - \frac{jZ_0 V_2}{\tan \beta l} + \frac{c^D g I}{j\omega} \qquad (3.50)$$

$$E = \frac{c^D g V_1}{j\omega} + \frac{c^D g V_2}{j\omega} + Z_E{}^{LC} I$$

If current is taken as a quantity analogous to velocity, it is possible to draw an equivalent electric network which would have the form shown in Figure 3.5a. However, each of the elements would be a complicated mixture of electrical and mechanical parameters. Through the introduction of an ideal transformer, it is possible to obtain the comparatively simple six-terminal equivalent shown in Figure 3.5b. The mechanical and electrical elements are now easily visualized.

If there is no electrostrictive effect, then $\phi$ becomes zero, and the network reduces to the equivalent lossless transmission line network. The existence of an electrostrictive effect introduces a distributed force along the bar which appears as an additional force in the equivalent network common to both mechanical meshes. Illustrations of the use of this network are given in Chapter 5.

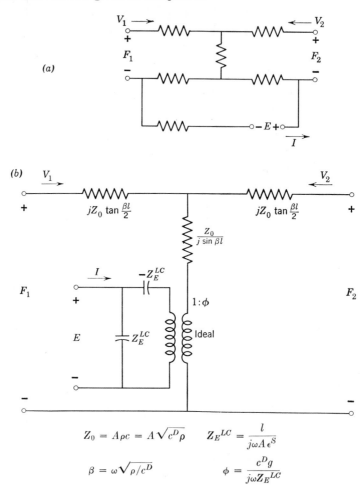

$$Z_0 = A\rho c = A\sqrt{c^D \rho} \qquad Z_E{}^{LC} = \frac{l}{j\omega A\,\epsilon^S}$$

$$\beta = \omega\sqrt{\rho/c^D} \qquad \phi = \frac{c^D g}{j\omega Z_E{}^{LC}}$$

Figure 3.5. Equivalent circuits for broad-plate resonators.

## 3.4 Generalized Electromechanical Equations (1, 3, 7, 12, 13, 15, 25)

The preceding equations, in particular 3.14 and 3.15, cannot be applied to a more general problem, since the coupling between displacements in orthogonal directions has been completely neglected. In other words, for the general case the coefficients in equations 3.14 and 3.15 are matrix quantities rather than scalar quantities. This does not increase the difficulty of the problem but rather requires a systematic notation to prevent confusion of the various coupling terms.

In matrix form equations 3.14 and 3.15 can be rewritten as

$$[T] = [c^D][S] - [h]_t[D] \tag{3.51}$$

$$[E] = -[h][S] + [\beta^s][D] \tag{3.52}$$

The elements of each of the matrices are again determined by expanding the stress components and the field components in terms of all the strain and flux density components. It is simplest to write out the terms in rectangular coordinates and then to perform the required substitutions for other coordinate systems.

### 3.4.1 Stress Matrix

Figure 3.6 shows an elementary cubic volume with the nine possible stress components. Three of the components are stresses which are

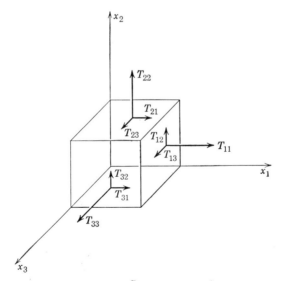

Figure 3.6. Stress components.

normal to the cube surfaces. The remaining six are shear stresses parallel to the cube faces. Since elastic theory presupposes rotational equilibrium for the elementary volume, it follows that

$$T_{23} = T_{32}$$
$$T_{12} = T_{21} \qquad (3.53)$$
$$T_{31} = T_{13} \text{ *}$$

Hence there are only six independent components of stress. These are arranged to form the stress matrix which is a single column (25). Therefore,

$$[T] = \begin{bmatrix} T_1 \\ T_2 \\ T_3 \\ T_4 \\ T_5 \\ T_6 \end{bmatrix} \qquad (3.54)$$

in which $T_4 = T_{23}$, $T_5 = T_{13}$, and $T_6 = T_{12}$.

### 3.4.2 Strain Matrix

The strains represent the deformations, both elongation and shear, of the various faces of the elementary cube. Figure 3.7 shows one of

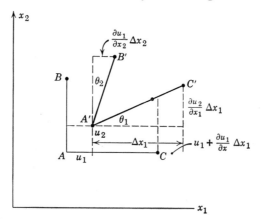

**Figure 3.7.** Strain in the $x_1$-$x_2$ plane.

the faces in the $x_1$, $x_2$ plane in the undeformed $(BAC)$ and deformed $(B'A'C')$ configuration. Point $A$ has been displaced to point $A'$, and

* The standard terminology is to use the numbers 1, 2, 3 to represent the rectangular coordinates $x_1$, $x_2$, $x_3$.

the lines $AB$ and $AC$ inclined by the angles $\theta_2$ and $\theta_1$, respectively. If $u_1$ represents the displacement of point $A$ in the $x_1$ direction, then $u_1 + (\partial u_1/\partial x_1)\,\Delta x$ represents the displacement of point $C$. Hence the total change in length per unit length is

$$S_1 = \frac{\partial u_1}{\partial x_1} \tag{3.55}$$

In a similar manner the two remaining displacement strains are

$$S_2 = \frac{\partial u_2}{\partial x_2}$$

$$S_3 = \frac{\partial u_3}{\partial x_3} \tag{3.56}$$

The shearing strain $S_{12}$ is defined as $(\theta_1 + \theta_2)/2$
However,

$$\theta_1 \cong \tan \theta_1 = \frac{\partial u_2}{\partial x_1} \tag{3.57}$$

and

$$\theta_2 \cong \tan \theta_2 = \frac{\partial u_1}{\partial x_2} \tag{3.58}$$

Therefore,

$$S_{12} = \frac{1}{2}\left(\frac{\partial u_1}{\partial x_2} + \frac{\partial u_2}{\partial x_1}\right) \tag{3.59}$$

Similarly,

$$S_{23} = \frac{1}{2}\left(\frac{\partial u_2}{\partial x_3} + \frac{\partial u_3}{\partial x_2}\right) \tag{3.60}$$

$$S_{13} = \frac{1}{2}\left(\frac{\partial u_1}{\partial x_3} + \frac{\partial u_3}{\partial x_1}\right) \tag{3.61}$$

The strain matrix is represented as a column matrix.

$$[S] = \begin{bmatrix} S_1 \\ S_2 \\ S_3 \\ S_4 \\ S_5 \\ S_6 \end{bmatrix} \tag{3.62}$$

where $S_4 = 2S_{23}$, $S_5 = 2S_{13}$, and $S_6 = 2S_{12}$.

### 3.4.3  E, D Matrices

Since there are only three components of the field vectors, they are written as column matrices:

$$[E] = \begin{bmatrix} E_1 \\ E_2 \\ E_3 \end{bmatrix} \qquad [D] = \begin{bmatrix} D_1 \\ D_2 \\ D_3 \end{bmatrix} \qquad (3.63)$$

### 3.4.4  $c^D$ Matrix

If we assume for a moment that the electrostrictive material under consideration is maintained under constant $D$ during elastic deformation, then each of the stress components $T_i$ is a linear function of all the strains, e.g.,

$$T_1 = c_{11}{}^D S_1 + c_{12}{}^D S_2 + c_{13}{}^D S_3 + c_{14}{}^D S_4 + c_{15}{}^D S_5 + c_{16}{}^D S_6$$

$$(3.64)$$

The coefficients $c_{ij}{}^D$ are the various elastic moduli which the material in general may possess, e.g., $c_{33}{}^D$ is the elastic modulus for the one-dimensional case discussed in Section 3.1. If all the components were written out, the $c^D$ matrix would be a $6 \times 6$ matrix in which $c_{ij}{}^D = c_{ji}{}^D$ because of reciprocity. The superscript $D$ is used to indicate that these elastic moduli are measured at constant electric displacement.*

### 3.4.5  h Matrix

To the strain terms in equation 3.64 we must add a linear combination of the $D$ components, i.e.,

$$T_1 = \sum_{i=1}^{6} c_{1i}{}^D S_i - h_{11}D_1 - h_{21}D_2 - h_{31}D_3 \qquad (3.65)$$

The $h$ coefficients relate the electrical to the mechanical properties of the material. Note that the subscripts on $h$ are reversed from their normal order. The same coefficients are used to define the relationship between the electric field and the strain (equation 3.11). The $h$ matrix is customarily defined for this latter case and is therefore a $3 \times 6$ matrix of the following form:

$$[h] = \begin{bmatrix} h_{11} & h_{12} & h_{13} & h_{14} & h_{15} & h_{16} \\ \cdot & & & & & \\ \cdot & & & & & \\ \cdot & & & & & \\ h_{31} & \cdots\cdots\cdots\cdots\cdots\cdots\cdots\cdots \end{bmatrix} \qquad (3.66)$$

* See Chapter 11 on measurement techniques.

Hence the matrix in equation 3.65 is the transpose of $h(=h_t)$; i.e., the rows and columns are interchanged.

### 3.4.6 $\beta^s$ Matrix

In general, each component of the electric field is a linear combination of $D$ components as well as the strain components, i.e.,

$$E_1 = \beta_{11}{}^S D_1 + \beta_{12}{}^S D_2 + \beta_{13}{}^S D_3 - \sum_{i=1}^{6} h_{1i} S_i \qquad (3.67)$$

The superscripts indicate that these coefficients are measured at constant strain. Note that $\beta_{33}{}^S$ is the reciprocal of the dielectric constant discussed in the one-dimensional illustration. The $\beta^S$ matrix is thus a $3 \times 3$ array in which $\beta_{ij}{}^S = \beta_{ji}{}^S$.*

## 3.5 Coefficients for Polarized Ceramic

The materials that are of prime importance in this text are the polycrystalline ceramics which have been polarized in a particular direction. Under these conditions the various matrices discussed above are somewhat simplified (3.7), since the polarized direction is the only anisotropic axis, i.e., the properties measured in any two directions at right angles to this axis must be the same. If the polarized axis is chosen as the 3-axis, then the following relations hold:

$$[c^D] = \begin{bmatrix} c_{11}{}^D & c_{12}{}^D & c_{13}{}^D & 0 & 0 & 0 \\ c_{12}{}^D & c_{11}{}^D & c_{13}{}^D & 0 & 0 & 0 \\ c_{13}{}^D & c_{13}{}^D & c_{33}{}^D & 0 & 0 & 0 \\ 0 & 0 & 0 & c_{44}{}^D & 0 & 0 \\ 0 & 0 & 0 & 0 & c_{44}{}^D & 0 \\ 0 & 0 & 0 & 0 & 0 & c_{66}{}^D \end{bmatrix} \qquad (3.68)$$

where $c_{66}{}^D = 2(c_{11}{}^D - c_{12}{}^D)$.

$$[h] = \begin{bmatrix} 0 & 0 & 0 & 0 & h_{15} & 0 \\ 0 & 0 & 0 & h_{15} & 0 & 0 \\ h_{31} & h_{31} & h_{33} & 0 & 0 & 0 \end{bmatrix} \qquad (3.69)$$

$$[\beta^S] = \begin{bmatrix} \beta_{11}{}^S & 0 & 0 \\ 0 & \beta_{11}{}^S & 0 \\ 0 & 0 & \beta_{33}{}^S \end{bmatrix} \qquad (3.70)$$

* This reciprocity relationship of dielectric constants $\epsilon_{ij} = \epsilon_{ji}$ is not generally true (see Appendix 2).

## Table 3.1

### D-Theory Piezoelectric Equations

$$\begin{cases} T = c^D S - h_t D \\ E = -hS + \beta^S D \end{cases}$$

$$\begin{cases} S = s^E T + d_t E \\ D = dT + \epsilon^T E \end{cases}$$

$$\begin{cases} S = s^D T + g_t D \\ E = -gT + \beta^T D \end{cases}$$

$$\begin{cases} T = c^E S - e_t E \\ D = eS + \epsilon^S E \end{cases}$$

$$s^E - s^D = g_t d = d_t g$$
$$c^D - c^E = h_t e = e_t h$$
$$\epsilon^T - \epsilon^S = ed_t = de_t$$
$$\beta^S - \beta^T = gh_t = hg_t$$

$$s^D = (c^D)^{-1}$$
$$\epsilon^T = (\beta^T)^{-1}$$

$$s^E = (c^E)^{-1}$$
$$\epsilon^S = (\beta^S)^{-1}$$

$$d = \epsilon^T g = es^E$$
$$e = dc^E = \epsilon^S h$$
$$g = hs^D = \beta^T d$$
$$h = \beta^S e = gc^D$$

Note: 1. Superscript represents the variable which is maintained constant. 2. $(-1)$ power represents an inverse matrix. 3. Subscript $t$ represents a transposed matrix.

## Table 3.2

### B-Theory Magnetostriction Equations

$$\begin{cases} T = c^B S - h_t B \\ H = -hS + \nu^S B \end{cases}$$

$$\begin{cases} S = s^H T + d_t H \\ B = dT + \mu^T H \end{cases}$$

$$\begin{cases} S = s^B T + g_t B \\ H = -gT + \nu^T B \end{cases}$$

$$\begin{cases} T = c^H S - e_t H \\ B = eS + \mu^S H \end{cases}$$

$$s^H - s^B = g_t d = d_t g$$
$$c^B - c^H = h_t e = e_t h$$
$$\mu^T - \mu^S = e_t d_t = de_t$$
$$\nu^S - \nu^T = gh_t = hg_t$$

$$s^B = (c^B)^{-1}$$
$$\mu^T = (\nu^T)^{-1}$$

$$s^H = (c^H)^{-1}$$
$$\mu^S = (\nu^S)^{-1}$$

$$d = \mu^T g = es^H$$
$$e = dc^H = \mu^S h$$
$$g = hs^B = \nu^T d$$
$$h = \nu^S e = gc^B$$

## 3.6   Other Matrix Formulations

The choice of $S$ and $D$ as the independent variables was completely arbitrary. For many problems it may be more feasible to choose some other combination. Table 3.1 lists the more common possible choices (25). The relationships between the new coefficients and those already discussed are also shown. Table 3.2 is an almost identical formulation for magnetostriction (15) in which $D$, $E$ have been replaced by $B$ and $H$, respectively.

## 3.7   Electrostrictive Side-Plated Bar.   Longitudinal Vibration

As an illustration of the foregoing principles we consider the derivation of the equivalent circuit of the ceramic bar polarized in the thin direction shown in Figure 3.8.

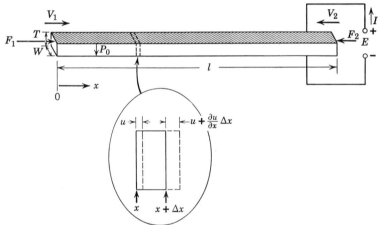

**Figure 3.8.**   Side-plated thin bar.

The simplest mode for this configuration consists of lengthwise vibrations, piezoelectrically coupled to electric field in the thickness direction. It is assumed that all values of stress except $T_{11}$ are zero and that the electric field is directed in thickness and assumes the same value simultaneously everywhere in the bar.

For this transverse coupling it is most convenient to choose from Table 3.1 the matrix equations (see footnote † p. 89)

$$[S] = [s^E][T] + [d_t][\mathcal{E}] \tag{3.71}$$

$$[D] = [d][T] + [\epsilon^T][\mathcal{E}] \tag{3.72}$$

By applying the initial assumptions with the matrix forms for ceramics we can obtain the full set of equations:

$$
\begin{bmatrix} S_1 \\ S_2 \\ S_3 \\ S_4 \\ S_5 \\ S_6 \end{bmatrix} = \begin{bmatrix} s_{11}{}^E & s_{12}{}^E & s_{13}{}^E & 0 & 0 & 0 \\ s_{12}{}^E & s_{11}{}^E & s_{13}{}^E & 0 & 0 & 0 \\ s_{13}{}^E & s_{13}{}^E & s_{33}{}^E & 0 & 0 & 0 \\ 0 & 0 & 0 & s_{44}{}^E & 0 & 0 \\ 0 & 0 & 0 & 0 & s_{44}{}^E & 0 \\ 0 & 0 & 0 & 0 & 0 & s_{66}{}^E \end{bmatrix} \begin{bmatrix} T_1 \\ 0 \\ 0 \\ 0 \\ 0 \\ 0 \end{bmatrix} + \begin{bmatrix} 0 & 0 & d_{31} \\ 0 & 0 & d_{31} \\ 0 & 0 & d_{33} \\ 0 & d_{15} & 0 \\ d_{15} & 0 & 0 \\ 0 & 0 & 0 \end{bmatrix} \begin{bmatrix} 0 \\ 0 \\ \mathcal{E}_3 \end{bmatrix}
$$

(3.73)

$$
\begin{bmatrix} D_1 \\ D_2 \\ D_3 \end{bmatrix} = \begin{bmatrix} 0 & 0 & 0 & 0 & d_{15} & 0 \\ 0 & 0 & 0 & d_{15} & 0 & 0 \\ d_{31} & d_{31} & d_{33} & 0 & 0 & 0 \end{bmatrix} \begin{bmatrix} T_1 \\ 0 \\ 0 \\ 0 \\ 0 \\ 0 \end{bmatrix} + \begin{bmatrix} \epsilon_{11}{}^T & 0 & 0 \\ 0 & \epsilon_{11}{}^T & 0 \\ 0 & 0 & \epsilon_{33}{}^T \end{bmatrix} \begin{bmatrix} 0 \\ 0 \\ \mathcal{E}_3 \end{bmatrix}
$$

(3.74)

It can be seen that the shear strain components $S_4$, $S_5$, and $S_6$ are zero, as are the displacement components $D_2$ and $D_3$. The vibration problem involves only $S_1$ and $D_3$, which can be written in algebraic form as

$$S_1 = s_{11}{}^E T_1 + d_{31}\mathcal{E}_3 \tag{3.75}$$

$$D_3 = d_{31} T_1 + \epsilon_{33}{}^T \mathcal{E}_3 \tag{3.76}$$

The elastic constant $s_{11}{}^E$ is the effective value for the thin bar, since all stresses except $T_1$ are zero. It is customarily regarded as a fundamental constant for the material, and the value of its reciprocal, known as *Young's modulus*, $Y_1{}^E$, is in common use. The equation of motion for an elementary section of bar length is

$$\frac{\partial T_1}{\partial x} - \rho \frac{\partial^2 u}{\partial t^2} = 0 \tag{3.77}$$

However, from equation 3.76 and the initial assumptions

$$\frac{\partial T_1}{\partial x} = \frac{1}{s_{11}{}^E} \frac{\partial S_1}{\partial x} = \frac{1}{s_{11}{}^E} \frac{\partial^2 u}{\partial x^2} \tag{3.78}$$

The equation of motion can then be written in terms of Young's modulus as

$$Y_1{}^E/\rho \, \frac{\partial^2 \mu}{\partial x^2} = \frac{\partial^2 \mu}{\partial t^2} \tag{3.79}$$

This can be recognized by comparison with equation 3.32, as the wave equation, and would yield the velocity of propagation

$$c = \sqrt{Y_1{}^E/\rho} \tag{3.80}$$

Since the bar is thin, strains and stress may be considered uniform over the thin cross section, and the vibration propagates as a plane wave along the bar with sinusoidal excitation. The solutions for displacement, velocity, and strain are given by

$$u = (B_1 \sin \beta x + B_2 \cos \beta x)e^{j\omega t} \tag{3.81}$$

$$v = \frac{\partial u}{\partial t} = j\omega u \tag{3.82}$$

$$S_1 = \frac{\partial u}{\partial x} = \beta(B_1 \cos \beta x - B_2 \sin \beta x)e^{j\omega t} \tag{3.83}$$

where

$$\beta = \omega/c \tag{3.84}$$

The general solution and mechanical boundary values are formally identical to those considered for the wide plate in Section 3.3, and the arbitrary constants can be written from equations 3.36 and 3.39 as

$$B_1 = -\left(\frac{V_2 + V_1 \cos \beta l}{j\omega \sin \beta l}\right) \tag{3.85}$$

$$B_2 = V_1/j\omega \tag{3.86}$$

The end forces are

$$F_1 e^{j\omega t} = -TWT_1|_{x=0} = -TWY_1{}^E(S_1 - d_{31}\mathcal{E}_3)|_{x=0} \tag{3.87}$$

$$F_2 e^{j\omega t} = -TWY_1{}^E(S_1 - d_{31}\mathcal{E}_3)|_{x=l} \tag{3.88}$$

With substitutions from equations 3.83, 3.85, and 3.86, these can be written

$$F_1 = TWY_1{}^E\left[d_{31}\mathcal{E}_3 e^{-j\omega t} - j\frac{\beta}{\omega}\left(\frac{V_2 + V_1 \cos \beta l}{\sin \beta l}\right)\right] \tag{3.89}$$

$$F_2 = TWY_1{}^E\left[d_{31}\mathcal{E}_3 e^{-j\omega t} - j\frac{\beta}{\omega}\left(\frac{V_1 + V_2 \cos \beta l}{\sin \beta l}\right)\right] \tag{3.90}$$

where, from original assumptions,

$$\mathcal{E}_3 = Ee^{j\omega t}/T \tag{3.91}$$

The electrode current is

$$I e^{j\omega t} = \frac{d}{dt} \int_0^l W D_3 \, dx \tag{3.92}$$

This can be evaluated from equations 3.76, 3.75, 3.81, and 3.91 as

$$I e^{j\omega t} = j\omega W \int_0^l [d_{31}(Y_1^E S_1 - Y_1^E d_{31}\mathcal{E}_3) + \epsilon_{33}^T \mathcal{E}_3] \, dx$$

$$= j\omega W \left( d_{31} Y_1^E u \Big|_{x=0}^l + \epsilon_{33}^T \left( 1 - \frac{d_{31}^2 Y_1^E}{\epsilon_{33}^T} \right) \mathcal{E}_3 l \right)$$

$$I = -W d_{31} Y_1^E (V_2 + V_1) + j\omega \frac{Wl}{T} \epsilon_{33}^T \left( 1 - \frac{d_{31}^2 Y_1^E}{\epsilon_{33}^T} \right) E \tag{3.93}$$

The electromechanical coupling coefficient with transverse coupling is given by

$$k_{31}^2 = \frac{d_{31}^2 Y_1^E}{\epsilon_{33}^T}$$

so the longitudinally clamped electric impedance is the capacitive value

$$Z_E^{LC} = \frac{E}{I}\Big|_{V_1=V_2=0} = \frac{1}{j\omega(Wl/T)\epsilon_{33}^T(1 - k_{31}^2)} \tag{3.94}$$

The mechanical characteristic impedance of the bar is

$$Z_0 = TW\rho c = TW\sqrt{\rho Y_1^E} \tag{3.95}$$

With these symbols, equations 3.89, 3.90, and 3.93 can be rearranged to give

$$F_1 = \frac{Z_0}{j \tan \beta l} V_1 + \frac{Z_0}{j \sin \beta l} V_2 + W d_{31} Y_1^E E \tag{3.96}$$

$$F_2 = \frac{Z_0}{j \sin \beta l} V_1 + \frac{Z_0}{j \tan \beta l} V_2 + W d_{31} Y_1^E E \tag{3.97}$$

$$I = -W d_{31} Y_1^E (V_1 + V_2) + \frac{1}{Z_E^{LC}} E \tag{3.98}$$

In order to continue the analogy of force and voltage, equation 3.98 is substituted into equations 3.96 and 3.97.

$$F_1 = \left(\frac{Z_0}{j \tan \beta l} + \phi^2 Z_E{}^{LC}\right) V_1 + \left(\frac{Z_0}{j \sin \beta L} + \phi^2 Z_E{}^{LC}\right) V_2 + \phi Z_E{}^{LC} I$$

$$F_2 = \left(\frac{Z_0}{j \sin \beta l} + \phi^2 Z_E{}^{LC}\right) V_1 + \left(\frac{Z_0}{j \tan \beta l} + \phi^2 Z_E{}^{LC}\right) V_2 + \phi Z_E{}^{LC} I$$

$$E = \phi Z_E{}^{LC} V_1 + \phi Z_E{}^{LC} V_2 + Z_E{}^{LC} I \tag{3.99}$$

where $\phi = W Y_1{}^E d_{31}$.

The equivalent electrical network which represents the set of equations 3.99 is shown in Figure 3.9. Particular note should be taken of the slightly different form of equation 3.99 as compared to equation 3.50.

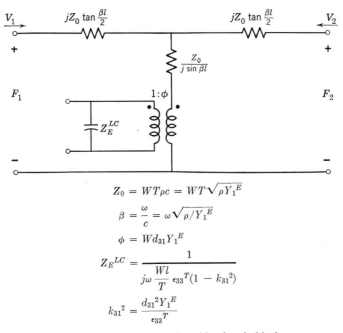

$$Z_0 = WT\rho c = WT\sqrt{\rho Y_1{}^E}$$

$$\beta = \frac{\omega}{c} = \omega\sqrt{\rho/Y_1{}^E}$$

$$\phi = W d_{31} Y_1{}^E$$

$$Z_E{}^{LC} = \frac{1}{j\omega \dfrac{Wl}{T} \epsilon_{33}{}^T (1 - k_{31}{}^2)}$$

$$k_{31}{}^2 = \frac{d_{31}{}^2 Y_1{}^E}{\epsilon_{33}{}^T}$$

**Figure 3.9** Equivalent circuit—side-plated thin bar.

The mechanical terms now contain a factor which depends on the electrical constants. This is due primarily to the fact that in the broad plate the flux density was assumed to be constant through the thickness, whereas the electric field was constant in the side-plated bar. This feature also appears in the equivalent circuit (Figure 3.9) in which the element $(-Z_E{}^{LC})$ is missing.

## 3.8 End-Plated Piezoelectric Bar

It is also possible to excite longitudinal vibrations in a bar polarized in length, as shown in Figure 3.10$a$. The electromechanical coupling is greater than for the transverse excitation discussed in Section 3.7, since applied field directly induces strains in the direction of wave propagation. The bar is polarized in length by means of end electrodes which are also used as the piezoelectric coupling electrodes.

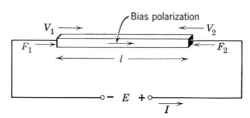

**Figure 3.10$a$.** End-plated thin bar.

We may analyze the end-plated bar with the procedure described in Section 3.7 under simple mechanical and electric field conditions. The bar is assumed thin, with no laterally applied stresses, so that only the stress $T_3$ is not zero. It is also assumed that the lateral components $D_1$ and $D_2$ are zero (i.e., there is no fringing), from which it follows that

$$\frac{\partial D_3}{\partial z} = 0 \tag{3.100}$$

The simplest set of piezoelectric equations for these assumptions (Table 3.1) is

$$[S] = [s^D][T] + [g]_t[D]$$

$$[E] = -[g][T] + [\beta^T]_t[D] \tag{3.101}$$

With the initial assumptions and the matrix forms for a ceramic, these give the values

$$S_1 = S_2 = s_{13}{}^D T_3 + g_{31}D_3 \tag{3.102}$$

$$S_3 = s_{33}{}^D T_3 + g_{33}D_3 \tag{3.103}$$

$$S_4 = S_5 = S_6 = 0 \tag{3.104}$$

$$\mathcal{E}_1 = \mathcal{E}_2 = 0 \tag{3.105}$$

$$\mathcal{E}_3 = -g_{33}T_3 + \beta_{33}{}^T D_3 \tag{3.106}$$

where $\beta_{33}{}^T = 1/\epsilon_{33}{}^T$ for a ceramic.

The equation of motion, written for a short length of the bar, is

$$\frac{\partial T_3}{\partial z} = \rho \frac{\partial^2 W}{\partial t^2} = 0 \qquad (3.107)$$

where $W$ is the mechanical displacement along the $Z$-axis.

From equation 3.103, using Young's modulus $Y_3^D = 1/S_{33}^D$, we can write

$$T_3 = Y_3^D S_3 - Y_3^D g_{33} D_3 \qquad (3.108)$$

The equation of motion can then be written in terms of mechanical displacement as

$$\rho \frac{\partial^2 W}{\partial t^2} = Y_3^D \left( \frac{\partial^2 W}{\partial z^2} - g_{33} \frac{\partial D_3}{\partial z} \right) = Y_3^D \frac{\partial^2 W}{\partial z^2} \qquad (3.109)$$

The detailed solution need not be carried out, since the electrical and mechanical boundary conditions, as well as the mathematical expressions 3.106 and 3.109, are equivalent to those in the wide plate of Section 3.3. By identifying the constants $-g_{33} Y_3^D$ and $Y_3^D$ with $h$ and $c^D$, respectively, in equation 3.31, we can write the complete solution from equation 3.50:

$$F_1 = \frac{Z_0}{j \tan \beta l} V_1 + \frac{Z_0}{j \sin \beta l} V_2 + \frac{Y_3^D g_{33}}{j \omega} I$$

$$F_2 = \frac{Z_0}{j \sin \beta l} V_1 + \frac{Z_0}{j \tan \beta l} V_2 + \frac{Y_3^D g_{33}}{j \omega} I \qquad (3.110)$$

$$E = \frac{Y_3^D g_{33}}{j \omega} V_1 + \frac{Y_3^D g_{33} V_2}{j \omega} + Z_E^{LC} I$$

where $Z_0 = A \rho c = A \rho \sqrt{Y_3^D / \rho}$

$$\beta = \omega/c = \omega \sqrt{\rho/Y_3^D}$$

$$1/Z_E^{LC} = j \omega \epsilon_{33}^T \left( 1 - \frac{Y_3^D g_{33}^2}{\epsilon_{33}^T} \right) \frac{A}{l} = j \omega \epsilon_{33}^T (1 - k_{33}^2) \frac{A}{l}$$

A corresponding equivalent circuit is shown in Figure 3.10b.

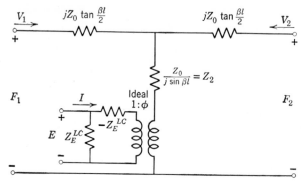

Cross-sectional area: A

$$Z_0 = A\sqrt{\rho Y_3{}^D}$$

$$\beta = \omega\sqrt{\rho/Y_3{}^D}$$

$$\phi = \frac{A Y_3{}^D g_{33}}{(\beta_{33}{}^T + Y_3{}^D g_{33}{}^2 l)} = \frac{A}{l} Y_3{}^E d_{33}$$

$$Z_E{}^{LC} = \frac{l}{j\omega A}(\beta_{33}{}^T + Y_3{}^D g_{33}{}^2) = \frac{l}{j\omega A \,\epsilon_{33}{}^T(1 - Y_3{}^E g_{33}{}^2 \epsilon_{33}{}^T)}$$

**Figure 3.10b.** Equivalent circuit–end plated thin bar.

## 3.9 Magnetostrictive Thin Bar

Figure 3.11 shows a magnetostrictive rod which is biased by means of an external magnet and driven by a coil loosely wound about the rod. For this geometry an exact solution is extremely difficult, since the magnetic path both for the bias and a-c driving signal is not well defined. However, it is worthwhile to consider an approximate solution in some detail, since some rather interesting aspects of the equivalent circuit arise in the course of the solution. The basic assumption is that the flux density is uniform throughout the rod, i.e., no leakage flux along the rod. One set of equations (Table 3.2) which might be used is

$$S_3 = s_{33}{}^B T_3 + g_{33} B_3 \qquad (3.111)$$

$$H_3 = -g_{33} T_3 + \frac{1}{\mu_{33}{}^T} B_3 \qquad (3.112)$$

The formal solution for the mechanical vibration follows the same pattern as in the electrostrictive thin bar. The coil voltage, however, is related to the flux density by

$$E = j\omega N B_3 A \qquad (3.113)$$

Hence $B_3$ can be substituted in equation 3.111, and we obtain the expressions for the force at each end in terms of the voltage and the velocities.

$$F_1 = \frac{Z_0}{j \tan \beta l} V_1 + \frac{Z_0}{j \sin \beta l} V_1 + \frac{Y_3{}^B g_{33}}{j\omega N} E \tag{3.114}$$

$$F_2 = \frac{Z_0}{j \sin \beta l} V_1 + \frac{Z_0}{j \tan \beta l} V_2 + \frac{Y_3{}^B g_{33}}{j\omega N} E \tag{3.115}$$

where $Z_0 = A\rho c$

$$\beta = \omega \sqrt{\rho/Y_3{}^B}$$

$$c = \sqrt{Y_3{}^B/\rho}$$

The equation for the current is obtained from equation 3.112 and

$$\oint H \cdot dl = NI \tag{3.116}$$

However, since the field distribution outside the rod is extremely difficult to determine, except experimentally, let us assign an effective external reluctance $R_{\text{ext}}$. Therefore,

$$NI = \int_0^L H_3 \cdot dl + A B_3 R_{\text{ext}} \tag{3.117}$$

where $H_3$ is obtained from equation 3.112. The expression for $I$ is then

$$I = \frac{g_{33} Y_3{}^B V_1}{j\omega N} + \frac{g_{33} Y_3{}^B V_2}{j\omega N} + Y_E{}^{LC} E \tag{3.118}$$

where

$$Y_E{}^{LC} = \frac{L}{j\omega N^2 A} \left( \frac{1}{\mu_{33}{}^T} + g_{33}{}^2 Y_3{}^B + \frac{A R_{\text{ext}}}{L} \right)$$

Equations 3.114, 3.115, and 3.118 can be rearranged by algebraic manipulation to form the system matrix:

$$\begin{bmatrix} F_1 \\ F_2 \\ I \end{bmatrix} = \begin{bmatrix} \dfrac{Z_0}{j \tan \beta l} & \dfrac{Z_0}{j \sin \beta l} & \dfrac{Y_3{}^B g_{33}}{j\omega N} \\[2ex] \dfrac{Z_0}{j \sin \beta l} & \dfrac{Z_0}{j \tan \beta l} & \dfrac{Y_3{}^B g_{33}}{j\omega N} \\[2ex] \dfrac{Y_3{}^B g_{33}}{j\omega N} & \dfrac{Y_3{}^B g_{33}}{j\omega N} & Y_E{}^{LC} \end{bmatrix} \begin{bmatrix} V_1 \\ V_2 \\ E \end{bmatrix} \tag{3.119}$$

The equivalent network is shown in Figure 3.11.

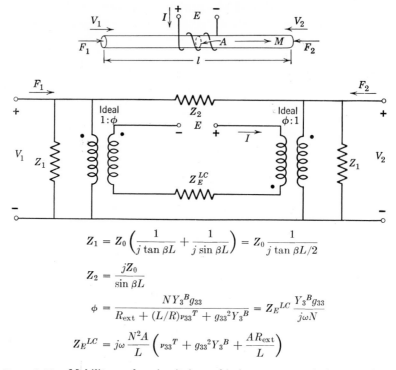

$$Z_1 = Z_0 \left( \frac{1}{j \tan \beta L} + \frac{1}{j \sin \beta L} \right) = Z_0 \frac{1}{j \tan \beta L/2}$$

$$Z_2 = \frac{jZ_0}{\sin \beta L}$$

$$\phi = \frac{NY_3{}^B g_{33}}{R_{\text{ext}} + (L/R)\nu_{33}{}^T + g_{33}{}^2 Y_3{}^B} = Z_E{}^{LC} \frac{Y_3{}^B g_{33}}{j\omega N}$$

$$Z_E{}^{LC} = j\omega \frac{N^2 A}{L} \left( \nu_{33}{}^T + g_{33}{}^2 Y_3{}^B + \frac{A R_{\text{ext}}}{L} \right)$$

Figure 3.11. Mobility analog circuit for a thin-bar magnetostrictive transducer.

In this case the analogy of current and force was used in order to obtain a matrix whose mutual coupling terms are of the same sign. However, in the electrostrictive side-plated bar the analogy of voltage and force was used. Had the current-force analogy been used in the latter case, the matrix would contain mutual coupling terms of opposite signs (see equation 3.86). Either set of equations may be used for purposes of calculation, but in order to obtain an electrical equivalent circuit with reciprocal elements it is necessary to have a matrix representation in which the mutual coupling terms have the same sign. A more complete discussion of this problem is given in Appendix 1.

## 3.10 Gyrator

If an electromechanical system operates with both magnetic and electric field coupling, neither analogy discussed in Sections 3.3 and 3.9 can be used throughout, hence no reciprocal circuit exists. The ideal gyrator (26, 27) is a theoretical device which provides equivalent circuits for all passive linear systems with any form of reciprocity.

The gyrator (Figure 3.12) is defined mathematically by its mesh equations:

$$E_1 = -I_2 R \tag{3.120}$$

$$E_2 = I_1 R \tag{3.121}$$

when $R$ is the "gyration" resistance. In matrix form the relationship is

$$\begin{bmatrix} E_1 \\ E_2 \end{bmatrix} = \begin{bmatrix} 0 & -R \\ R & 0 \end{bmatrix} \begin{bmatrix} I_1 \\ I_2 \end{bmatrix} \tag{3.122}$$

A gyrator preceding a network terminal pair effectively interchanges voltage and current with a scale factor of $R$ ohms.

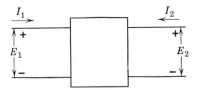

Figure 3.12. Four-pole representation of an ideal gyrator.

If $R$ is chosen as 1 ohm, the gyrator can be used in conjunction with the set of equations 3.119 to obtain a simple equivalent circuit for the magnetostrictive bar (Figure 3.13). In this representation the mechanical system has the same form as the electrostrictive case, with only a change in the input electrical network.

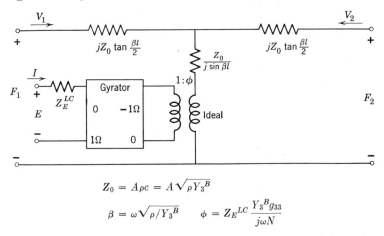

$$Z_0 = A\rho c = A\sqrt{\rho Y_3{}^B}$$

$$\beta = \omega\sqrt{\rho/Y_3{}^B} \qquad \phi = Z_E{}^{LC}\frac{Y_3{}^B g_{33}}{j\omega N}$$

Figure 3.13. Force-voltage equivalent circuit for a magnetostrictive rod.

Figure 3.14 indicates the transformations that a gyrator performs on a series impedance, a shunt impedance, and an ideal transformer.

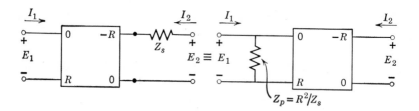

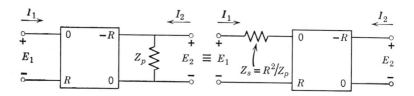

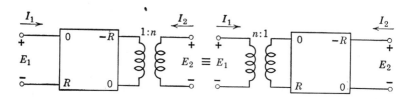

**Figure 3.14.** Gyrator circuit transformations.

## 3.11 Magnetostrictive Toroid (15, 19)

The thin-walled toroid is the simplest configuration for which the magnetic path is well defined. Hence accurate magnetostrictive measurements are always carried out with toroidal specimens. Furthermore, the biasing field can be obtained by magnetizing the toroid at a selected remanent point rather than by providing an external magnet or d-c bias. If the toroid is provided with a uniform circumferential bias and wound with a uniform excitation winding, then there is only one possible mode of vibration. The circumferential stress permits the inner and outer radii to move in phase.

Figure 3.15 shows an elementary volume of a thin-walled toroid whose average radius is $r$. The only stress acting on this volume is a uniform circumferential stress $T$. For the sake of completeness we will write out the general strain relationships (excluding shear) in polar coordinates

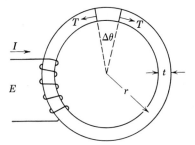

**Figure 3.15.** Magnetostrictive toroid.

(16). Let $u$ equal the elongation in the radial direction and $V$ equal the elongation in the circumferential direction. The strains are

$$S_r = \frac{\partial u}{\partial r} \tag{3.123}$$

$$S_\theta = \frac{u}{r} + \frac{1}{r}\frac{\partial V}{\partial \theta} \tag{3.124}$$

If $T_r$ and $T_\theta$ are the two surface stresses, then the resultant force in the $r$ and $\theta$ directions due to the variations of these stresses are

$$F_r = \left(\frac{\partial T_r}{\partial r} + \frac{T_r - T_\theta}{r}\right) b\,\Delta r \tag{3.125}$$

$$F_\theta = \left(\frac{1}{r}\frac{\partial T_\theta}{\partial \theta}\right) br\,\Delta\theta \tag{3.126}$$

where $b$ is the height of the toroid.

For the particular problem at hand the following conditions apply:

$$\frac{\partial}{\partial \theta} = 0; \qquad \frac{\partial u}{\partial r} = 0$$

Therefore, the remaining strain is

$$S_\theta = \frac{u}{r} \tag{3.127}$$

and the resultant force is in the radial direction

$$F_r = -\frac{T_\theta}{r} b\,\Delta r \tag{3.128}$$

The appropriate set of electromechanical equations in which the 3-3 direction corresponds to the theta direction is taken from Table 3.2

$$T_\theta = Y_{33}{}^B \frac{u}{r} - h_{33}B_\theta \tag{3.129}$$

$$H_\theta = -h_{33}\frac{u}{r} + \frac{B_\theta}{\mu_{33}{}^S} \tag{3.130}$$

The solution then proceeds just as in the bar example. From Newton's equation

$$F_r = m\frac{\partial^2 u}{\partial t^2} = -(\rho r b\omega^2 t\,\Delta\theta)u \tag{3.131}$$

The magnetic field is related to the current by

$$H_\theta = \frac{NI}{2\pi r} \tag{3.132}$$

The applied voltage is

$$E = N\frac{d\phi}{dt} \tag{3.133}$$

$$= j\omega NtbB_\theta \tag{3.134}$$

where $t$ is the wall thickness.

Equations 3.129 through 3.134 can be solved for the current as a function of the applied voltage

$$I = \frac{E}{\dfrac{j\omega N^2 tb\mu_{33}{}^S}{2\pi r}} + \frac{\dfrac{h_{33}{}^2\mu_{33}{}^S}{Y_{33}{}^B}V}{\left(\dfrac{r^2\rho\omega^2}{Y_{33}{}^B} - 1\right)\left(\dfrac{j\omega N^2 tb\mu_{33}{}^S}{2\pi r}\right)} \tag{3.135}$$

This equation can be rewritten in a more compact form as

$$I = \frac{E}{j\omega L_0} + \frac{k_{33}{}^2 E}{j\omega L_0\left(\dfrac{\omega^2}{\omega_0{}^2} - 1\right)} \tag{3.136}$$

where $L_0 = N^2 tb\mu_{33}{}^S/2\pi r$ is the inductance measured at constant strain, i.e., at frequencies higher than the mechanical resonant frequency $\omega_0$.

$$\omega_0 = Y_{33}{}^B/\rho r^2$$

$$k_{33}{}^2 = \frac{h_{33}{}^2\mu_{33}{}^S}{Y_{33}{}^B}$$

In the neighborhood of resonance $\omega \approx \omega_0$. Hence equation 3.136 can be approximated by

$$I = \frac{E}{j\omega_0 L_0} + \frac{E}{\dfrac{j\omega L_0}{k^2} - j/\omega C_0} \tag{3.137}$$

where $\omega_0{}^2 = 1/L_0 C_0$. The equivalent circuit represented by this equation is shown in Figure 3.16.

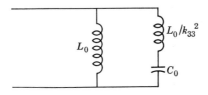

**Figure 3.16.** Equivalent circuit of magnetostrictive toroid.

## 3.12  Losses

The results which have been derived in the preceding sections have tacitly assumed that there are no losses in either the electrical or the mechanical branches. Corrections of the original equations can be made by assuming that all of the coefficients are complex. For example, the original elastic equation without loss was given as

$$T = c^D S \tag{3.138}$$

If a viscous damping term is included, then

$$T = c^D S + R\dot{S} \tag{3.139}$$

For sinusoidal time variation equation 3.116 becomes

$$T = c^D S + j\omega R S$$

$$= (c^D + j\omega R)S \tag{3.140}$$

The same procedure can then be carried through for the remaining coefficients, including a complex dielectric constant and permeability. Figure 3.17 is the equivalent circuit for the end plated-thin bar in which the losses have been included. The trigonometric functions have become hyperbolic functions, and the turns ratio of the ideal transformer, as well as all the other electromechanical coefficients, is also complex. However, the hyperbolic functions can be considerably simplified for the

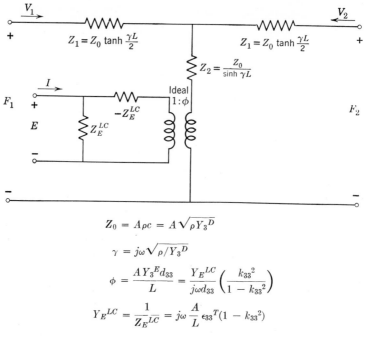

$$Z_0 = A\rho c = A\sqrt{\rho Y_3{}^D}$$

$$\gamma = j\omega\sqrt{\rho/Y_3{}^D}$$

$$\phi = \frac{A Y_3{}^E d_{33}}{L} = \frac{Y_E{}^{LC}}{j\omega d_{33}}\left(\frac{k_{33}{}^2}{1 - k_{33}{}^2}\right)$$

$$Y_E{}^{LC} = \frac{1}{Z_E{}^{LC}} = j\omega\frac{A}{L}\epsilon_{33}{}^T(1 - k_{33}{}^2)$$

**Figure 3.17.** Equivalent circuit: end-plated ceramic thin bar.

usual case in which the losses are small and the frequency of operation occurs at one of the resonant points

$$\beta l = \frac{n\pi}{2} \qquad n = 1, 2, 3, \cdots$$

When the coefficient $c^D$ is complex the propagation constant $\gamma$ is complex.

$$\gamma = \alpha + j\beta = j\omega\sqrt{\frac{\rho}{c_1{}^D + jc_2{}^D}}$$

where the ratio $c_1{}^D/c_2{}^D$ is the mechanical $Q$ of the material ($Q_m$). Therefore,

$$\gamma = j\omega\sqrt{\frac{\rho}{c_1{}^D}}\sqrt{\frac{1}{1 + j(1/Q_m)}} \tag{3.141}$$

$$\gamma \cong j\omega\sqrt{\frac{\rho}{c_1{}^D}}\left(1 - \frac{j}{2Q_m}\right) \tag{3.142}$$

The $\tanh(\alpha + j\beta)l$ can be expanded as

$$\tanh (\alpha + j\beta)l = \frac{\sinh \alpha l \cos \beta l + j \cosh \alpha l \sin \beta l}{\cosh \alpha l \cos \beta l + j \sinh \alpha l \sin \beta l}$$

$$= \frac{\sinh \alpha l \cosh \alpha l + j \sin \beta l \cos \beta l}{\sinh^2 \alpha l + \cos^2 \beta l} \qquad (3.143)$$

upon rationalization.

For small values of $\alpha l$, $\sinh \alpha l \cong \alpha l$ and $\cosh \alpha l \cong 1$. Hence

$$\tanh (\alpha + j\beta)l \cong \frac{\alpha l + j \sin \beta l \cos \beta l}{\alpha^2 l^2 + \cos^2 \beta l} \qquad (3.144)$$

$$\cong \frac{(\alpha l/\cos^2 \beta l) + j \tan \beta l}{(\alpha^2 l^2/\cos^2 \beta l) + 1} \qquad (3.145)$$

When, for example, $\beta l$ is approximately $\pi/2$, let $\beta l - (\pi/2) = \epsilon$, a small angle. Since the ratio $\alpha/\beta = 1/2Q_m$, from equation 3.142 $\alpha l \cong \pi/4Q_m$. Therefore,

$$\tanh (\alpha l + j\beta l) \cong \frac{\dfrac{\pi}{4Q_m \cos^2 \left(\dfrac{\pi}{2} + \epsilon\right)} + j \tan \left(\dfrac{\pi}{2} + \epsilon\right)}{\left(\dfrac{\pi}{4Q_m \cos \left(\dfrac{\pi}{2} + \epsilon\right)}\right)^2 + 1} \qquad (3.146)$$

$$\cong \frac{\dfrac{\pi}{4Q_m{}^2 \sin^2 \epsilon} - \dfrac{j}{\tan \epsilon}}{\dfrac{\pi^2}{16Q_m{}^2 \sin^2 \epsilon} + 1} \qquad (3.147)$$

$$\cong \frac{\dfrac{\pi}{4Q_m\epsilon^2} - j/\epsilon}{\dfrac{\pi^2}{16Q_m{}^2\epsilon^2} + 1} \qquad (3.148)$$

$$\cong \frac{4Q_m}{\pi} \left(\frac{1}{1 + j\,\dfrac{4Q_m\epsilon}{\pi}}\right) \qquad (3.149)$$

Another parameter which is useful in later applications is the factor $r$ defined by

$$r = \frac{\epsilon}{\pi/2} = \frac{\beta l - \beta_0 l}{\beta_0 l} = \frac{\beta}{\beta_0} - 1 \tag{3.150}$$

where $\beta_0$ is the phase constant at the resonant frequency $\omega_0$. Using the definition of $\beta$ in equation 3.33,

$$r = \frac{\omega}{\omega_0} - 1 = \frac{\omega - \omega_0}{\omega_0} \tag{3.151}$$

$$\tanh rl \cong \frac{4Q_m}{\pi} \frac{1}{1 + j2Q_m r} \tag{3.152}$$

for $\beta_0 l = \pi/2$.

## 3.13  Equivalent Lumped Constants

All of the equivalent circuits which have been derived in the previous sections are valid over the entire frequency range for which the original assumptions are true. In the equivalent circuits resonance behavior in the mechanical elements appears usually as hyperbolic tangent functions. Although accurate computations can be carried out from the expansions in Section 3.12, it is useful to extend the equivalent circuit representation in the form of lumped resistances, inductances, and capacitance. Since a transducer is a distributed system, it cannot be described exactly by a finite number of lumped elements. However, over any small frequency range it is accurate to represent the frequency response with simple equivalent lumped elements. At frequencies far from resonance it is often sufficient to have only a qualitative representation, so that the lumped elements are accurately chosen only in the neighborhood of resonance.

For example, in the equivalent circuit for a bar which is mechanically free at one end (see Section 3.14) both the hyperbolic tangent and its reciprocal appear. The series arm can be evaluated with the aid of equation 3.152.

$$\frac{2Z_0}{\tanh rl/2} \cong \frac{Z_0 \pi}{2Q_m} \left[ 1 + j2Q_m \left( \frac{\omega - \omega_0}{\omega_0} \right) \right] \tag{3.153}$$

for a half wavelength bar.

## Table 3.3

### Lumped Element Equivalents for Hyperbolic Functions

| Function | Impedance $R \tanh \gamma L$ $\cong R \dfrac{(\beta L)_0}{2Q_m}(1 + jx)$ | Impedance $R \tanh \gamma L$ $\cong R \dfrac{2Q_m}{(\beta L)_0(1 + jx)}$ | Admittance $G \tanh \gamma L$ $\cong G \dfrac{(\beta L)_0}{2Q_m}(1 + jx)$ | Admittance $G \tanh \gamma L$ $\cong G \dfrac{2Q_m}{(\beta L)_0(1 + jx)}$ |
|---|---|---|---|---|
| Resonance | $(\beta L)_0 = 0, \pi, 2\pi, 3\pi, \cdots$ | $(\beta L)_0 = \dfrac{\pi}{2}, \dfrac{3\pi}{2}, \dfrac{5\pi}{2}, \cdots$ | $(\beta L)_0 = 0, \pi, 2\pi, \cdots$ | $(\beta L)_0 = \dfrac{\pi}{2}, \dfrac{3\pi}{2}, \dfrac{5\pi}{2}, \cdots$ |
| Equivalent circuit | $R_m \quad L_m \quad C_m$ (series) $R_m = \dfrac{R(\beta L)_0}{2Q_m}$ $L_m = \dfrac{R_m Q_m}{\omega_0}$ $C_m = \dfrac{1}{\omega_0^2 L_m}$ | $L_m,\ C_m,\ G_m$ (parallel) $G_m = \dfrac{(\beta L)_0}{2Q_m R}$ $C_m = \dfrac{Q_m G_m}{\omega_0}$ $L_m = \dfrac{1}{\omega_0^2 C_m}$ | $L_m,\ C_m,\ G_m$ (parallel) $G_m = \dfrac{G(\beta L)_0}{2Q_m}$ $C_m = \dfrac{Q_m G_m}{\omega_0}$ $L_m = \dfrac{1}{\omega_0^2 C_m}$ | $R_m \quad L_m \quad C_m$ (series) $R_m = \dfrac{(\beta L)_0}{2Q_m G}$ $L_m = \dfrac{R_m Q_m}{\omega_0}$ $C_m = \dfrac{1}{\omega_0^2 L_m}$ |

The impedance of a series $RLC$ circuit is

$$Z_m = R_m + j\omega L_m + \frac{1}{j\omega C_m} \tag{3.154}$$

$$= R_m \left[ 1 + jQ_m \left( \frac{\omega^2 - \omega_0{}^2}{\omega_0 \omega} \right) \right] \tag{3.155}$$

where $\omega_0{}^2 = 1/L_m C_m$
$\qquad Q_m = \omega_0 L_m / R_m$

Over a narrow frequency range the term $\omega^2 - \omega_0{}^2$ may be approximated by $(\omega - \omega_0)(\omega + \omega_0) \cong 2\omega(\omega - \omega_0)$.

Hence

$$Z_m = R_m \left[ 1 + j2Q_m \left( \frac{\omega - \omega_0}{\omega_0} \right) \right] \tag{3.156}$$

which has the same form as equation 3.153 with

$$R_m = \frac{Z_0 \pi}{2Q_m}$$

Thus the series arm can be represented by a series $RLC$ circuit, although the shunt arm is a reciprocal form, hence is represented by an equivalent parallel $RLC$ network. Table 3.3 summarizes the equivalent elements for other resonant frequencies.

## 3.14 Equivalent Circuits for Special Cases

In many cases it is not necessary to utilize the complete six-terminal networks which have been derived for the general case. Frequently one

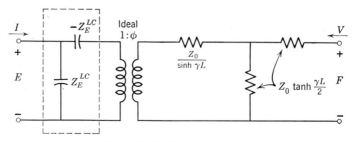

Figure 3.18. End-plated thin ceramic bar, one end free.

end of the device is either allowed to vibrate freely or is rigidly clamped. Under these conditions the equivalent network can be considerably

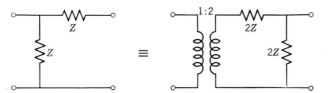

Figure 3.19. Norton equivalent network.

simplified. For example, the equivalent circuit for the end-plated ceramic thin bar (Figure 3.17) can be reduced to the four-terminal network
(Figure 3.18 *) for the case in which one end is free, i.e., $F_1 = 0$. A

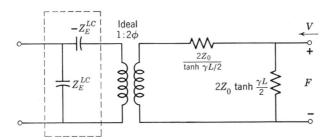

Figure 3.20. Simplified circuit for end-plated bar, one end free.

further simplification may be obtained by employing a special theorem
due to Norton (17). This theorem states that the four-terminal networks shown in Figure 3.19 are completely equivalent. If this is applied

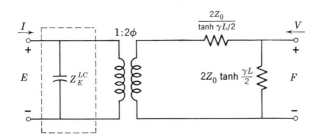

Figure 3.21. Equivalent circuit for side-plated bar, one end free.

to Figure 3.18, we obtain Figure 3.20, in which the following identity
has been used:

$$\frac{2}{\sinh A} + \tanh \frac{A}{2} = \frac{1}{\tanh A/2} \tag{3.157}$$

* Mechanical losses have been included in Figure 3.18.

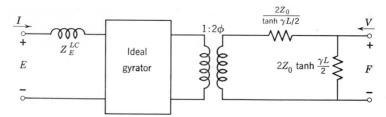

**Figure 3.22.** Magnetostrictive bar, one end free.

If the same technique is applied to the side-plated bar (Figure 3.9), we obtain the same mechanical network but a different electrical input (Figure 3.21). Figure 3.22 is the equivalent network for a magneto-strictive bar with one end free. Figure 3.23 is the mechanical portion

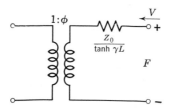

**Figure 3.23.** Mechanical portion of the equivalent circuit for a thin-bar clamped at one end.

of the equivalent network for the end-plated bar in which one end is rigidly clamped, i.e., $V_1 = 0$. The following identity has been used in deriving Figure 3.23:

$$\frac{1}{\sinh A} + \tanh \frac{A}{2} = \frac{1}{\tanh A} \tag{3.158}$$

## 3.15 Other Vibrational Modes (20, 22, 28)

The various electromechanical transducers which have been discussed in the preceding sections utilize the simplest vibrational mode, i.e., longitudinal. For many applications it is desirable to excite other modes. In particular, for very low frequency vibrations there are modes which require smaller dimensions than those necessary for longitudinal motion. At very high frequencies the proper mode leads to dimensions which are conveniently larger than those obtainable with longitudinal vibra-tions. Furthermore, the methods for mounting the vibrating element are greatly simplified in many cases when one of the complex modes is chosen. Another consideration in this choice is the susceptibility of certain modes to spurious excitation when subjected to mechanical shock.

The analysis of these modes in terms of their equivalent electric networks is in general very complex, though it follows the outline al-

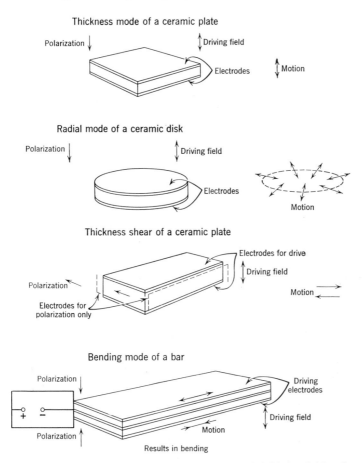

**Figure 3.24.** Various modes produced by a superposition of driving field and permanent polarization. (*Electrical Manufacturing*, December 1955, p. 103.)

ready presented. The basic details include rewriting the original equations, and the equations of motion, in terms of a new coordinate system. The latter portion of the problem is greatly simplified by the many solutions which already exist in the literature on mechanical vibrations without electromechanical coupling.

The method of excitation of the various modes for ceramics with the proper geometry is determined by the general principle that the motion takes place along the direction of the resultant field (a-c excitation plus bias). For example, a hollow magnetostrictive cylinder can be excited in torsion if the bias field is circumferential while the driving field is parallel to the axis of the cylinder (19).

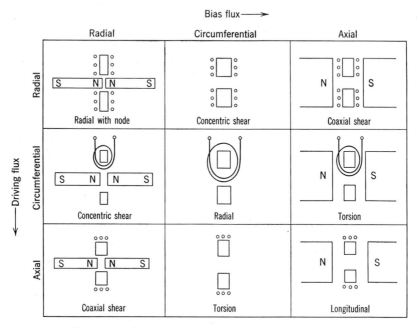

**Figure 3.25.** Various combinations of driving coil arrangements and bias fluxes for toroidal-ferrite resonators. (*R C A Review*, **14**, March 1953.)

Figure 3.24 shows some of the more common modes for electrostrictive materials. Figure 3.25 shows several possibilities with magnetostrictive materials. Included is a tabulation (Table 3.4) of the fundamental resonant frequency in terms of the specimen parameter. These formulas, however, do not include any effect of the electromechanical coupling and for materials with low electromechanical coupling coefficients ($k < 0.1$) are quite accurate.

## Table 3.4

### Resonant Frequency of Simple Geometries without Electromechanical Activity

Bar (longitudinal):

$$f_n = \frac{n}{2L}\sqrt{\frac{Y}{\rho}}$$

Thickness Resonance of Plate or Cylinder:

$$f_n = \frac{n}{2t}\sqrt{\frac{Y}{\rho}\frac{(1-\delta)}{(1+\delta)(1-2\delta)}}$$

Radial Resonance of Disk:

$$f_n = \frac{Z_n}{2\pi r}\sqrt{\frac{Y}{\rho(1-\delta^2)}}$$

where $r$ = radius

$$Z_n = (1-\delta)\frac{J_1(Z_n)}{J_0(Z_n)}$$

$J_1, J_0$ = Bessel function

Torsional Resonance of a Rod:

$$f_n = \frac{n}{2L}\sqrt{\frac{Y}{2\rho(1+\delta)}}$$

where $L$ = length
$Y$ = Young's modulus
$\rho$ = density
$\delta$ = Poisson ratio
$t$ = thickness

(Source: *Electrical Manufacturing*, December 1955, p. 103.)

### 3.16 References

1. Mason, Warren P., *Piezoelectric Crystals and Their Application to Ultrasonics*, D. Van Nostrand Company, Inc., Princeton, N. J., 1950.
2. Fry, William J., John M. Taylor, and Bertha W. Henvis, *Design of Crystal Vibrating Systems*, Dover Publications, Inc., New York, 1948.
3. Cady, W. G., *Piezoelectricity*, McGraw-Hill Book Company, New York, 1946.
4. Brush Development Company, *Piezotronics, Piezotronic Technical Data.*
5. Roth, Wilfred, *Piezoelectric Transducers*, Res. Lab. of Electronics, MIT, Technical Report No. 43, July 1947, and *Proc. I.R.E.* **37**, No. 7, July 1949, pp. 750–758.
6. von Hippel, A., *Ferroelectricity, Domain Structure, and Phase Transitions of Barium Titanate*, Revs. Modern Phys. **22**, July 1950, pp. 221–237.
7. Bond, W. L., *The Mathematics of the Physical Properties of Crystals*, Bell System Tech J., 22, 1943, pp. 1–72.

8. Devonshire, A. F., *Theory of Barium Titanate, Phil. Mag.*, **40**, 1949, pp. 1040–1063.

9. International Nickel Company, Inc., *Magnetostriction*.

10. Bozorth, R. M., *Ferromagnetism*, D. Van Nostrand, Company, Inc., Princeton, N. J., 1955.

11. Hunt, Frederick V., *Electroacoustics*, John Wiley and Sons, 1954.

12. Haskins, J. F., and J. S. Hickman, *A Derivation & Tabulation of the Piezo-electric Equations of State, J. Acoust. Soc. Am.*, September 22, 1950, pp. 584–588.

13. Brillouin, L., *Les Tenseurs en Méchanique et en Élasticité*, Dover Publications, Inc., New York, 1946.

14. Vigoureux, P., and C. F. Booth, *Quartz Vibrators*, H.M. Stationery Office, London, 1950.

15. Burgt, C. M., vander, *Magnetostrictive Excitations of Vibrations in Ferrites Philips Research Repts.*, **8**, April 1953, p. 91.

16. Timoshenko, S., *Vibration Problems in Engineering*, 2nd ed., D. Van Nostrand Company, Inc., Princeton, N. J., 1939.

17. Mason, W. P., *Electromechanical Transducers and Wave Filters*, 2nd ed., D. Van Nostrand Company, Inc., New York, 1948, Chapter 6.

18. Burrington, R. S., and C. C. Torrance, *Higher Mathematics*, McGraw Hill Book Company, New York, 1939.

19. Roberts, Van B., "Some Applications of Permanently Magnetized Ferrite Magnetostriction Resonators," *R C A Rev.* **14**, March 3–16, 1953.

20. Haskins, J. F., and J. L. Walsh, "Vibrations of Ferroelectric Cylindrical Shells with Transverse Isotropy: I. Radial Polarized Case," *J. Acoust. Soc. Am.*, **29**, No. 6, June 1957, p. 729.

21. George, R. W., "Conventric-Shear-Mode 455 kc Electromechanical Filter," *R C A Rev.*, **18**, No. 2, June 1957, p. 186.

22. Petermann, L. A., "Producing Motion with Magnetostrictive and Piezoelectric Transducers," *Elec. Mfg.*, December 1955, p. 103.

23. Sharme, R. L., "Equivalent Circuit of a Resonant Finite, Isotropic Elastic Circular Disk," *J. Acoust. Soc. Am.*, **28**, November 1956, pp. 1153–1158.

24. vander Burgt, C. M., "Performance of Ceramic Ferrite Resonators as Transducers and Filter Elements," *J. Acoust. Soc. Am.*, **28**, November 1956, pp. 1020–1032.

25. "Standards on Piezoelectric Crystals, 1949," *I.R.E. Standard*, 49, *I.R.E.* 14.S1. Also *Proc. I.R.E.* **37** (1949); *I.R.E. Standard*, 58, *I.R.E.* 14.S1.

26. Tellegen, B. D. H., "The Gyrator, A New Electric Network Element," *Philips Research Repts.*, **3**, April 6, 1948, pp. 81–101.

27. Tehon, S., "The Gyrator as a Circuit Element," *Proc. Symposium on Circuit Analysis*, University of Illionois, 1955.

# Chapter four

# Nonlinear Magnetic
# and Dielectric Materials

## 4.0 Introduction

The analytic solution of physical problems in which one or more of the elements exhibit some form of nonlinearity has always been formidable. The degree of success from a practical point of view is usually determined by the nature of the assumptions that are made in the attempt to obtain tractable answers. However, workable solutions can be obtained within certain classes of problem. For small nonlinearities we can convert the nonlinearity into an equivalent small-signal system. This technique is the familiar one that is applied in vacuum-tube or transistor-circuit analysis. Though the parameters in this case may be functions of biasing potentials, it is assumed that the signal is not large enough to affect the same parameters.

Further up the scale we encounter those problems in which the nonlinearity can be approximated by some simple algebraic expression that permits the solution of the differential equations in closed form. Many times it is necessary to assume unrealistic forms for these expressions in order to solve the necessary equations. Some value may still be gained from this method, since it allows us to obtain some knowledge of the nature of the solution.

Additional complexity also arises in the nature of the applied signal. If, for example, a sufficiently large driving signal is applied, the character of the steady-state solution usually becomes a strong function of the initial condition. Thus it becomes difficult to predict the resultant operation accurately. This is particularly true when the nonlinearity is also multivalued, e.g., the $B$-$H$ characteristic of magnetic material.

The first part of this chapter, Square Loop Switching, develops several points of view concerning the nature and behavior of square loop magnetic and dielectric materials. The second part, Analysis on the Nonlinear Circuits, is concerned with the approximate analysis of nonlinear systems.

# /SQUARE LOOP SWITCHING

## 4.1 Magnetic-Hysteresis Loops

The magnetic characteristic of a ferromagnetic material is usually defined by depicting a plot of $B$ versus $H$ for a complete cycle of operation. Unfortunately, this is not a unique description for all modes of

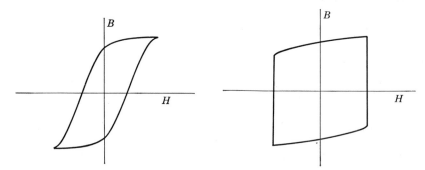

Figure 4.1. Magnetic hysteresis loop.    Figure 4.2. Hysteresis loop obtained under constant current drive.

operation. In linear systems it is sufficient to know the response to a sinusoidally applied signal in order to determine the behavior for some other arbitrary waveform. However, for magnetic material the losses are so dependent on the amplitude of the frequency components of the driving signal that in general many sets of curves of $B$ versus $H$ are needed in order to form a clear picture of the magnetic behavior. Figure 4.1 is a typical hysteresis loop for the case in which the flux density $B$ is maintained sinusoidal through the entire cycle.

Figure 4.2 is a plot for the condition in which the current is maintained as a square wave. The loop in the second case appears to have become more square. However, this is rather artificial, for the current is maintained constant, and thus the loop is forced to have vertical sides. What is not shown is the rate at which $B$ is changing throughout the cycle, since the parameter time has been eliminated.

## 4.2 Dynamic Hysteresis Loops in Metallic Tapes (1, 2, 3, 9)

In order to illustrate the changes which a hysteresis loop may undergo, let us consider the distortion introduced when metallic magnetic tapes are subjected to various drive conditions. The choice of metallic tapes is the simplest for this purpose because in the thicker tapes the effects can be attributed for the most part to eddy current phenomena. The case in which it is assumed that the magnetic core material could be described by a permeability $\mu$, which is constant throughout the medium, has been treated in great detail in the literature on eddy current phenomena. However, in the modern application of square loop material with thin tapes the condition of a true permeability $\mu$ cannot be successfully approximated but must actually be concerned with the motion of individual domain walls.

Consider a single layer of tape wound in a toroidal form. The magnetic properties of this tape are described by a square hysteresis loop. The idealized static loop is shown in Figure 4.3. These materials are highly grain oriented so that they possess a single axis of easy magnetization.

Suppose that a high-frequency constant-voltage sinusoidal signal is applied to the core. If a conductivity ($\sigma$) is assumed for the material,

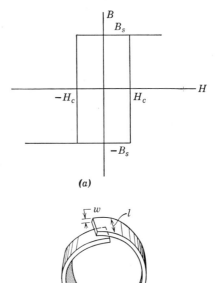

**Figure 4.3.** (a) Idealized square loop; (b) single wrap tape.

what changes will occur in the measured hysteresis loops at these higher frequencies? The following simplifying assumptions are made:

1. The curvature of the tape about the bobbin is neglected. This is tantamount to assuming that the tape is infinitely long directed into the paper and reduces the problem to a two-dimensional one (Figure 4.4).

2. The height of the tape $l$ is much greater than the thickness $w$.

3. The excitation coil is assumed to be a plane infinite current sheet tangential to the tape.

4. At time $t = 0$ the tape is magnetized to negative saturation $(-B_s)$ directed out of the paper. The voltage $(V_m \sin wt)$ is applied at time $t = 0$.

5. The thickness of the domain wall is neglected.

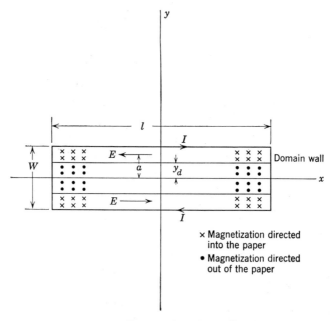

Figure 4.4. Cross section of metallic tape.

The magnetization proceeds by the formation of two domain walls at the outer edges, and the walls then move inward toward the center. For very low frequencies the walls could form at the outer edges parallel to the $y$-axis, and then move toward the center. However, the time for complete reversal of the magnetization is then of the order of seconds. We are interested in reversal times of the order of microseconds.

If it were not for the eddy currents, the magnetization would reverse everywhere throughout the volume almost instantaneously when the applied current reached a value corresponding to the coercive force ($H_c$). We are neglecting for the moment any other retarding force. As a result of the changing magnetization, an electric field $E$ is produced in the region in which the magnetization has already reversed. The resulting eddy currents produce a magnetic field opposed to that produced by the driving current.

The electric **E** is calculated from Faraday's law:

$$\oint \mathbf{E} \cdot d\mathbf{l} = -\oint \frac{\partial \mathbf{B}}{\partial t} \cdot d\mathbf{s} \tag{4.1}$$

Let us integrate **E** around a curve parallel to the $x$-axis at a distance $a$ from the $x$-axis and neglect the small contribution along the edges. The curve is completed by integration along the $x$-axis. Since the only flux change through the plane surface formed by this curve is due to the moving wall, the value of $E$ is the same from $y = 0$ to $y = W/2$. The right-hand side of equation 4.1 can be evaluated as follows:

The total flux enclosed by the surface is

$$\phi = B_s y_d l - B_s(a - y_d)l \tag{4.2}$$

$$\frac{d\phi}{dt} = 2B_s l \frac{dy_d}{dt} \tag{4.3}$$

Therefore

$$El = -2B_s l \frac{dy_d}{dt} \tag{4.4}$$

The eddy current density that results is

$$i = \sigma E = -2\sigma B_s \frac{dy_d}{dt} \tag{4.5}$$

The total current per unit depth in the region in which the magnetization has been reversed is

$$I_e = \left(\frac{W}{2} - y_d\right) i = -2\sigma B_s \left(\frac{W}{2} - y_d\right) \frac{dy_d}{dt} \tag{4.6}$$

Note that since $dy/dt$ will be negative, $I_e$ will be positive in the direction indicated. The total magnetic field $H$ which exists inside the tape is the resultant field due to the four parallel current sheets. Since the driving current is assumed to be in an infinitely thin sheet, the magnetic field it produces must be discontinuous across the boundary.

Figure 4.5 is a plot of the field due to the two driving current sheets as a function of $y$. Positive $H$ is directed along the negative $z$-axis, i.e., into the paper. The magnetic field due to the eddy currents is a continuous function, since the current flows through a region of nonzero thickness. Figure 4.5 also contains a plot of the field due to these currents. The fields due to the eddy currents thus add in the region between $+y_d$ and $-y_d$ and are opposed to the direction of the applied field.

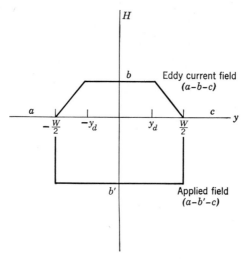

**Figure 4.5.** Field distribution inside tape.

The boundary conditions which determine the rate at which the wall moves is the value of $H$ between $+y_d$ and $-y_d$. This value must be $H_c$ (coercive force), since the magnetization has not reversed in this region. Hence

$$H_c = I_{\text{app}} - I_e \quad \text{at} \quad y = \pm y_d \qquad (4.7)$$

We are now in a position to calculate the externally measured $B$-$H$ loop for various driving conditions.

### 4.2.1  Sinusoidally Applied Voltage

Let $V = E_m \sin \omega t$ for $t \geqq 0$. Hence from equation 4.4

$$E_m \sin \omega t = -2B_s l \frac{dy_d}{dt} \qquad (4.8)$$

Therefore,

$$\frac{dy_d}{dt} = \frac{-E_m}{2B_s l} \sin \omega t \qquad (4.9)$$

Hence the wall velocity is forced to be sinusoidal in time. Integration of equation 4.9 yields

$$y_d = \frac{E_m}{2B_s l \omega} \cos \omega t + K \tag{4.10}$$

Since at $t = o$, $y_d = w/2$,

$$K = \frac{-E_m}{2B_s l \omega} + \frac{W}{2} \tag{4.11}$$

Substitute equations 4.9 and 4.10 into equations 4.7 and 4.6 and solve for $I_{\mathrm{app}}$.

$$I_{\mathrm{app}} = H_c + \frac{E_m{}^2 \sigma}{2B_s l^2 \omega} \sin \omega t (1 - \cos \omega t) \tag{4.12}$$

Figure 4.6 is a sketch of equation 4.12 superimposed on the original static loop. The voltage $E_m$ has been adjusted so that saturation is reached in almost one half cycle.

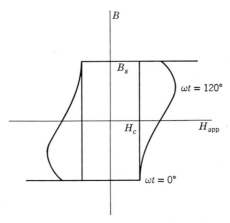

**Figure 4.6.** Loop distortion with sinusoidal applied voltage.

This is the type of distortion which is obtained in metallic tapes approximately 1 to 4 mils thick. It should be noted that although the applied voltage is changing at its maximum rate near $\omega t = \pi/2$, the maximum current does not appear until $\omega t = 2\pi/3$. The eddy current density is also a maximum at $\omega t = \pi/2$, but the cross-sectional area through which this current flows is small at that time. The product of current density and wall penetration does not reach its maximum until $\omega t = 120°$.

In order to minimize this effect, it is necessary to make the tape thinner. The complete reversal of the magnetization then takes place before the critical value of $\omega t = 120°$ has been reached.

### 4.2.2 Sinusoidal Current Drive

With a sinusoidal voltage drive the time to change from one direction of saturation to the other is determined completely by the magnitude of the applied voltage and its frequency. However, with a sinusoidal current drive, the switching time for the reversal of magnetization is determined by the eddy currents for the thick tapes. The calculation for this case proceeds in a very similar manner by substitution of $I_{\text{app}} = I_m \sin \omega t$ into equations 4.7 and 4.6.

$$H_c = I_m \sin \omega t + 2\sigma B_s \frac{dy_d}{dt} \left( \frac{w}{2} - y_d \right) \qquad (4.13)$$

Integration of this equation yields

$$K_1 + H_c t + \frac{I_m}{\omega} \cos \omega t = 2\sigma B_s \frac{w}{2} y_d - \sigma B_s y_d^2 \qquad (4.14)$$

Since the flux will not change until the current reaches the value $H_c$, the initial conditions are $y_d = w/2$ at $\omega t = \theta_0$ where $\sin \theta_0 = H_c/I_m$. Therefore,

$$K_1 = - \left( \frac{H_c \theta_0}{\omega} + \frac{I_m}{\omega} \cos \theta_0 - \sigma B_s \frac{w^2}{4} \right) \qquad (4.15)$$

The resulting voltage is $V = d\phi/dt = 2B_s l(dy_d/dt)$. Therefore,

$$V = \frac{l}{\sigma} \left( \frac{H_c - I_m \sin \omega t}{(w/2) - y_d} \right) \qquad (4.16)$$

Equation 4.16 is rather complex, since we must solve the quadratic equation 4.14 for $y_d$. However, we can plot the distorted loop easily (Figure 4.7) when the current is forced to be sinusoidal. It is a rather peculiar shape, since the parameter time does not appear.

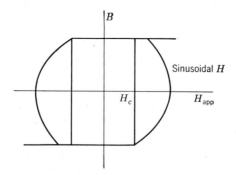

**Figure 4.7.** Loop distortion with sinusoidal applied current.

### 4.2.3 Constant Voltage Pulse

Perhaps a more practical driving signal to study would be a constant voltage pulse or current pulse, since these are the ones most frequently encountered in digital applications. The solutions in these cases are also much simpler to handle.

For the constant voltage pulse shown in Figure 4.8, applied to the same cross section shown in Figure 4.4,

$$\frac{dy_d}{dt} = \frac{-E_m}{2B_s l} \qquad (4.17)$$

$$y_d = \frac{-E_m t}{2B_s l} + K_1 \qquad (4.18)$$

where $K_1 = w/2$, since $y_d = w/2$ at $t = 0$.

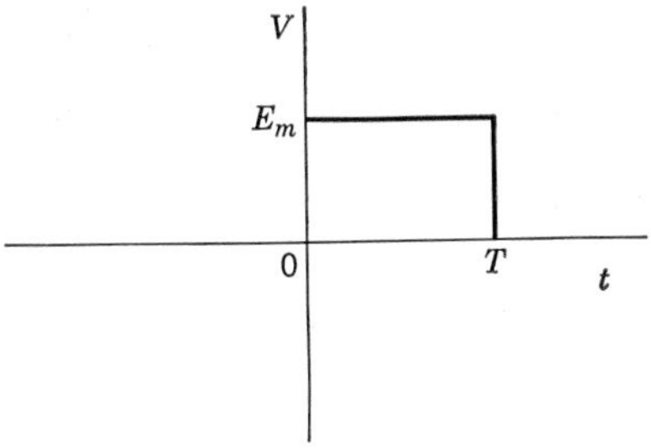

**Figure 4.8.** Constant voltage pulse.

Therefore, equation 4.7 for this case becomes

$$I_{\mathrm{app}} = H_c + \frac{\sigma E_m^2 t}{2B_s l^2} \qquad (4.19)$$

The resultant loop now distorts in the very simple way shown in Figure 4.9.

The switching time is again determined by the area of the voltage pulse, and the applied current increases linearly with time.

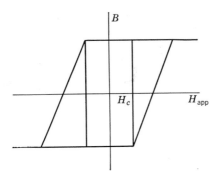

**Figure 4.9.** Loop distortion with applied constant voltage pulse.

### 4.2.4   Constant Current Pulse

This case is used for such applications as storage, switching, and gating techniques. In equation 4.7 let $I_{\text{app}} = I_m$. Therefore,

$$H_c = I_m + 2\sigma B_s \frac{dy_d}{dt}\left(\frac{w}{2} - y_d\right) \tag{4.20}$$

With the same boundary conditions as before the solution of the above equation is

$$y_d = \frac{w}{2} - \sqrt{\left(\frac{I_m - H_c}{\sigma B_s}\right)t} \tag{4.21}$$

The resultant voltage $V$ is

$$V = -2B_s l \frac{dy_d}{dt} = l \sqrt{\frac{(I_m - H_c)B_s}{\sigma}} \frac{1}{\sqrt{t}} \tag{4.22}$$

The loop still remains square as far as external measurements are concerned, since the current is maintained constant. However, the rate of change of $B$ or the resultant voltage $V$ now varies as shown in the plot of equation 4.22 (Figure 4.10). There is a rapid rise in voltage initially, and then the voltage decays with increasing time. Obviously, all the mechanisms contributing to the reversal process have not been included, since equation 4.22 shows an infinite voltage at time $t = 0$. Before discussing the additional factors that are involved let us calculate the time $T$ necessary to switch or reverse the magnetization under these conditions. This condition is determined from equation 4.21 when $y_d = 0$.

$$T = \frac{\sigma B_s w^2}{4(I_m - H_c)} \tag{4.23}$$

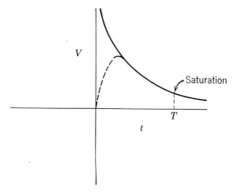

Figure 4.10.   Switching voltage with constant applied current.

This is a typical form for the switching time expression found for square-loop magnetic devices, i.e., the switching time is inversely proportional to the driving field in excess of the coercive force.

### 4.2.5 Nucleation of Domain Walls

The idealized equation 4.22 indicates that the switching voltage would be infinite at the beginning of the pulse. It was assumed at the outset that the initial reversal of magnetization occurred instantaneously and uniformly over the entire height ($l$) of the tape at the surface. Not only is this highly unlikely because of the nonuniform characteristic of the tape material (especially its surface), but in addition we have neglected the energy which is required to form the wall. Furthermore, it was assumed that the wall was of negligible thickness. A portion of the input energy must be consumed in order to form the wall. The exact distribution of energetically feasible points for the initiation of regions of reverse magnetization is highly speculative. Voids, inclusions, and other similar points of discontinuities are very likely places for the formation of the domain walls. Figure 4.11 indicates a possible geometry

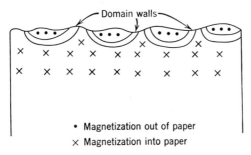

Figure 4.11. Formation of domain walls during initial stages of switching process.

of domain-wall formation during the early stages of reversal. With continued application of the impressed signal, additional walls are formed while the old ones grow. This process continues until the individual walls form into two parallel walls, and the motion proceeds as indicated in the previous discussion. This nucleation process is made evident in the sinusoidal voltage hysteresis loop taken on metallic tapes. Figure 4.12 shows a typical loop taken at several kilocycles per second. The distinctive feature is the requirement of a larger value of $H$ to initiate the reversal of domain walls than the $H$ required to maintain the motion of walls toward reverse saturation. When the tapes become ultrathin (less than 1 mil) it is not unlikely that the entire reversal mechanism is far from uniform and undoubtedly is concerned primarily with rotation of the magnetic moments rather than simple wall motion. For a more complete discussion of this problem the reader is referred to the available literature.

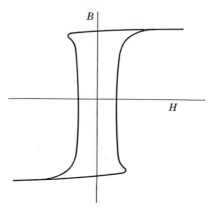

**Figure 4.12.** Hysteresis loop of a metallic tape. Corners indicate the nucleation of domain walls.

### 4.2.6  Thin Magnetic Films (18–20)

In the metallic tapes discussed in the preceding sections the switching mechanism involved the nucleation of domains of reverse magnetization and the propagation of domain walls through the tape. A more ideal reversal mechanism, especially for very fast switching speeds, would involve only a rotational process without the formation of domain walls. A geometry which is very favorable toward such a mechanism is a thin magnetic film several thousand Angstroms thick.

The usual method for preparing such films it to coevaporate in vacuum an alloy of approximately 80% Ni–20Fe. The film is usually laid down on a heated glass substrate in the presence of a strong magnetic field oriented in the plane of the film (Figure 4.13a). The completed film is thus magnetized to saturation in the direction of the applied field. Although the magnetic path is not closed, it is still possible to maintain the saturated state without an applied field. The extremely large length-to-thickness ratio produces a negligible demagnetizing field which permits a large remanent magnetization.

There are other methods for producing thin films which are still in the experimental stages. One is the electrodeposition of the film directly from solution (21). Another is a chemical reduction that takes place directly on the glass substrate. These methods have the advantage of not requiring a high vacuum during the processing operation and are thus subject to greater control.

The actual switching time that has been obtained with vacuum-deposited films depended to a large extent on the method of excitation, i.e., rise time of driving field and uniformity of the field in the plane of the film. Switching speeds under coincident current operation have been obtained as short as 20 m$\mu$sec. Theoretically, if a uniform field is applied 180° to the magnetization (Figure 4.13$a$), then the switching time would

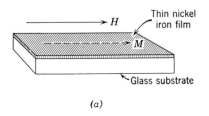

(a)

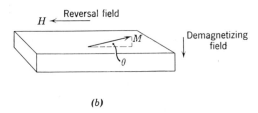

(b)

Figure 4.13.  ($a$) Thin magnetic film deposited in the presence of a magnetic field; ($b$) magnetization reversal in thin films.

be infinite, since the torque applied by the field (**M × H**) would be zero. However, if the field is applied perpendicular to the magnetization in the plane of the film, the torque would be a maximum. The magnetization under the latter condition would turn through 90° but would return to its original direction upon the removal of the field. Therefore, the shorter switching times would be obtained by some combination of a 180° field plus a small 90° field (18).

The actual motion of the magnetization during the rotation process is quite complex. The applied torque at first tends to rotate the magnetization about the applied field. Figure 4.13$b$ shows the small angle that the magnetization would make with the plane of the film. The magnetization then precesses about the demagnetizing field generated by the small angle of inclination. This precessional motion produces the over-all rotation of the magnetization in the plane of the film. A more detailed description of the preparation of the films and their magnetization reversal process is given in the references cited.

Considerable experimental work has been undertaken to improve the reproducibility characteristics of these films.

## 4.3   Square Loop Ferrites (4, 6)

The problem of switching in polycrystalline ferrites is somewhat more complicated than in thin metallic tapes.  Whereas in the latter material an easy direction of magnetization for the bulk material is induced by mechanical working (grain orientation), no similar process is carried out for the ferrite.  The ceramic nature and the method of preparation of the ferrite would almost seem to preclude the possibility of very square hysteresis loops.  In other words, no external means (i.e., applied magnetic field or applied stresses) are used in the usual processing of ferrites to obtain an easy direction of magnetization.  This has been shown rather graphically in a recent experiment.  From a ferrite toroid which exhibited a reasonably square loop at moderate driving fields (3–4 oe) two smaller toroids were cut.  One toroid was in the plane of the original toroid, and the second was in a plane at 90° to first direction.  Both toroids had hysteresis loops which were very similar to the original square loop.  It should be pointed out that in each case for very large driving fields (>40 oe) the hysteresis loop departed very markedly from the square loop obtained at smaller fields (i.e., the ratio of the remanent to the maximum flux density was approximately 0.7).

### 4.3.1   Flux Reversal in Ferrite

The detailed theory of the conditions necessary to obtain a square loop in a polycrystalline ceramic is beyond the scope of the book.  However, one of the salient features of the theory is worthy of closer examination.

The very nature of the ceramic implies the existence of many discontinuities, such as grain boundaries, voids, and inclusions.  Associated with each of these is a discontinuity in the magnetization which gives rise to various surface pole distributions.  For example, if a planar grain boundary separates two domains whose saturation magnetizations are at angles $\theta_1$ and $\theta_2$ with respect to the boundary, the surface pole density would equal $M_s(\cos \theta_1 - \cos \theta_2)$.  The magnetostatic energy would be proportional to $M_s^2(\cos \theta_1 - \cos \theta_2)^2$.  In order to obtain a square loop, this energy must be small compared to the energy necessary to form domains of reverse magnetization. In metallic tapes this energy term is reduced by grain orientation, i.e., $(\cos \theta_1 - \cos \theta_2)$ is made small. In ferrites the saturation magnetization $M_s$ is about ten times smaller than in the metals. Hence the magnetostatic energy is decreased because of the smaller factor $M_s^2$ rather than a grain-to-grain alignment.

The actual flux reversals are due to the formation and motion of many 180° walls when fields larger than $H_c$ are applied. Although the thicknesses of the ferrites used are much larger than the thin tapes, it is possible to obtain fast switching in the ferrite because the walls move only very small distances before encountering other 180° walls. Futhermore, the high resistivity of the ferrite prevents the formation of eddy currents which might otherwise delay the nucleation of reverse domains throughout the body of the ferrite.

### 4.3.2 Switching Time (2, 7, 8)

Figure 4.14 is a plot of the reciprocal of the switching time $(\tau_s)$ as a function of a constant applied field $H$, for the ferrites as well as the metallic tapes. These data were taken by measuring the switching

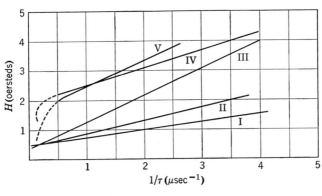

I — $\frac{1}{8}$ mil permalloy
II — $\frac{1}{4}$ mil permalloy
III — $\frac{1}{2}$ mil permalloy
IV — general ceramics ferrite $S$-1
V — general ceramics ferrite $S$-3

**Figure 4.14.** Typical switching data for several materials.

time after the core had been reset to saturation with a very large current pulse. The value of $\tau_s$ was taken as the time interval between the 10 per cent points of output voltage waveform (Figure 4.15a). Sometimes the switching time is taken as the interval between the 10-to-90 per cent points on the integrated output voltage waveform (Figure 4.15$b$). These two values are quite different, since in the latter case the time depends on the magnitude of the flux change, whereas the former is a measure of the rate of change of flux. In other applications the switching time is given for symmetrically applied pulses.

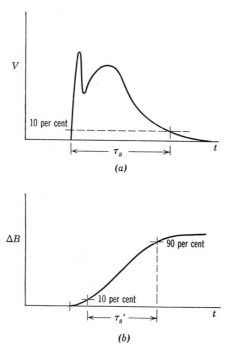

**Figure 4.15.** Measurement of switching time as observed from output voltage and integrated voltage or flux change.

The ferrites and tapes both have large regions in which the switching time obeys the relationship $\tau_s = S_w/(H - H_c')$ where $S_w$ is the slope of the curves in Figure 4.14 and $H_c'$ is the projected intercept and is not necessarily equal to the d-c coercive force. The dotted portion of the ferrite curves shows that for very small fields the apparent switching time decreases. This is due to an incomplete reversal of flux for small constant current pulses and implies that switching times of greater than $2\mu\text{sec}$ cannot be accomplished for the $S-1$ cores with constant current pulses. However, if the current is permitted to have a small positive slope after the initial fast rise, it is then possible to switch for arbitrarily long intervals.

## 4.4 Minor Loops

The preceding analysis is concerned primarily with the general nature of the hysteresis loop when it is subjected to various types of excitation sufficient to drive the core from one state of saturation to the other. For many applications it is necessary to consider the behavior of the core when the applied pulses are removed before the core has completely reversed its magnetization. Of particular interest in these problems is the question of whether or not the dynamic minor loops are also "square." Hysteresigrams for a tape core and a ferrite core show that the ferrites have better minor loop behavior than the tapes. For small changes in the flux density the tape cores probably produce the circular types of domain wall shown in Figure 4.11. When the applied pulse is removed these walls are no longer in a stable state. Because of the surface tension of the curved wall there is a tendency for the wall to decrease in size and fall back to a lower remanent point. For larger applied fields the "circular" domain walls become contiguous and form a stable configuration.

## 4.5 Deviations from Squareness

Though the vertical sides of the loop are extremely steep, the saturation slopes do not approach the theoretical value of one for practical field strengths. In the case of metal tapes this slope ranges from 10 to 30, whereas in the ferrite the slope is closer to the value of 10. For current pulses with extremely fast rise times this will introduce additional noise into the system. This slope also accounts for the large spikes in the output voltage waveform of Figure 4.15a.

A gradual rounding of the B-H curve while going into saturation is also encountered. Essentially, this region is concerned with rotation of entire domains rather than domain-wall motion which retards the switching process. The rounding is severer in the case of the ferrite than in that of metallic tapes. The previous simple analysis indicated that the output voltage should drop abruptly to zero when the domain walls are completely annihilated. However, the actual output voltage shows a rather long tail. In the case of the ferrites this long tail gives the appearance of a macroscopic eddy-current type damping.

The over-all effect that these various factors have on circuit operation depends largely on the nature of the circuit. The cores should be tested and evaluated with signal voltages and currents of the same amplitude and rise time that will be encountered under operating conditions. The internal nonlinearity of the core probably precludes a complete analytic expression of the response to arbitrary excitation conditions.

## 4.6 Circuit Aspects of Square Loop Material

The considerations which have been discussed in the preceding sections emphasized the relationship between driving signals and the physical processes which determine the shape of the *B-H* loop. However, from a circuit viewpoint it is exceedingly helpful to relate the square loop behavior in terms of factors such as input "impedance," stored versus dissipated energy, and circuit $Q$.

### 4.6.1 Energy Storage

Perhaps the most interesting feature to examine from this viewpoint is the "inductive" nature of a square loop core. We are accustomed to thinking of magnetic circuits in terms of the storage of kinetic energy during one portion of a cycle and the return of that energy during the succeeding half cycle. It is well to look at this in more detail. Suppose we had a two-terminal black box and we wished to determine by measurements made at its input terminals whether the internal system was capable of storing energy. Essentially, the following sequence of operations could be performed. At time $t = 0$ increase the voltage from zero to some value which produces the maximum input current in the positive direction shown. During this entire time energy is continuously supplied to the black box. As far as the input terminals are concerned, this energy may be entirely dissipated, entirely stored, or some combination of both. However, after calculating the total energy during this time we note the amount of energy returned to the generator during the interval of time when the current is reduced from its maximum value back to zero. If all the energy is returned, the black box, of course, stored energy during each portion of input period. If all the input energy is not returned, the difference will have been dissipated, but how much of the input energy is being stored and how much dissipated during any particular portion of the cycle cannot be determined.

Let us relate this to a square loop core. As shown in Chapter 1, the amount of energy required to change the induction $B$ per unit volume of matter is $\int H \, dB$. For the case of an ideal square loop in Figure 4.16 increase the current from point $a$ to point $b$ and allow the core to reach point $c$. During this time the input energy equals $\int H\,dB = 2H_cB_s$. As the input current now decreases to point $d$, the energy returned to the circuit equals $\int H\,dB = 0$. In other words, all of the input energy has been dissipated in the core, although the core is now saturated at point $d$. If we return to the starting point $a$ via $d$-$e$-$a$-, energy of the amount $2H_cB_s$ is again required from the generator. The conclusion is reached that the core behaves exactly like a nonlinear resistor rather than an inductance which stores energy and then returns the energy to the source. This may seem rather odd, considering the fact that the core is saturated at point $d$. It might be said that information, but no retrievable energy, is stored at point $d$.

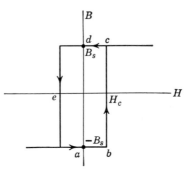

Figure 4.16.

In a strict sense it is not the relationship between $B$ and $H$ that is square, but rather the relationship of the magnetization $M$ and the field $H$. In this case

$$\int H\,dB = \int H\,d(\mu_0 H + M) \tag{4.24}$$

$$= \mu_0 \int H\,dH + \int H\,dM \tag{4.25}$$

The integral of $H\,dH$ around a closed loop is zero. This term represents the field energy independent of the core and is returned to the source each half cycle. $\int H\,dM$ is the energy lost during the magnetization process, and it is much larger than the field energy.

For the case of a hysteresis loop of the shape shown in Figure 4.17 area $A_1$ represents the total loss per cycle and $A_2$ could represent the stored energy. If a large signal $Q$ is defined for the core in the same manner as in a linear system,

$$Q = 2\pi \frac{A_2}{A_1} \tag{4.26}$$

It is interesting to calculate the $Q$ for a linear $R$, $L$ circuit with this definition and then compare that expression to the standard definition $Q = \omega L/R$. In order to obtain a "hysteresis" curve for a linear system, it is necessary to plot two variables which are related to each other so that the total area of the curve represents the energy lost in the linear $R$.

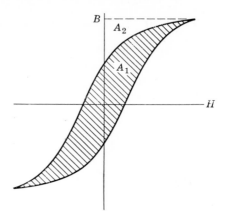

Figure 4.17.

For the circuit shown in Figure 4.18 the input energy is $\int ei\, dt$. This can be rewritten as $\int i\, d\left[\int e\, dt\right]$. Hence if $\int e\, dt$ is plotted as the $y$-coordinate and $i$ as the $x$-coordinate, the area between the curve and the vertical axis represents the input energy. For the case of a linear $R$ and $L$ the relationship between $e$ and $i$ is

$$e = E_m \sin \omega t \tag{4.27}$$

$$i = I_m \sin (\omega t - \theta) \tag{4.28}$$

where $\tan \theta = \omega L/R$.

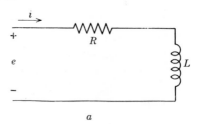

Figure 4.18.

The plot of $\int e\, dt$ versus $i$ is an ellipse (Figure 4.19) with the corresponding points in the voltage-current cycle shown in Figure 4.20.

The area $A_1$ is the energy lost per cycle. If the areas $A_2$ and $A_1$ are calculated, the expressions are as follows:

$$A_1 = \frac{I_m E_m \pi}{\omega} \cos \theta \qquad (4.29)$$

$$A_2 = \frac{I_m E_m}{2\omega} \left( \theta - \frac{\sin 2\theta}{2} \right) \cos \theta - \frac{I_m E_m}{2\omega} \sin^3 \theta \qquad (4.30)$$

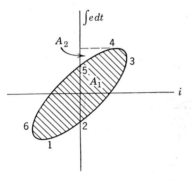

Figure 4.19. "Hysteresis" loop for linear $RL$ circuit.

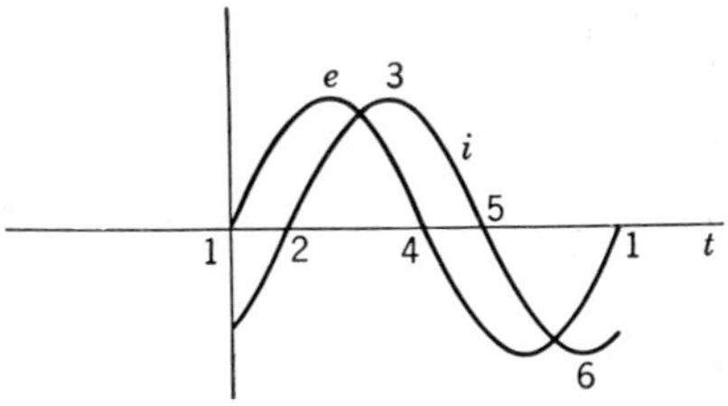

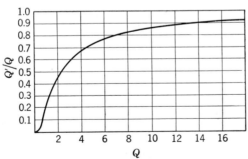

Figure 4.20. Current-voltage waveforms for linear $RL$ circuit.

Define $Q'$ as in equation 4.26. Therefore,

$$Q' = \sin^2 \theta \tan \theta + \sin \theta \cos \theta - \theta \qquad (4.31)$$

With the usual value of $Q$ defined as $\omega L/R$

$$Q = \tan \theta \qquad (4.32)$$

Therefore,

$$Q'/Q = 1 - \theta/\tan \theta \qquad (4.33)$$

A plot of $Q'/Q$ versus $Q$ is shown in Figure 4.21.

Figure 4.21.

It is noted that only for large values of $Q(>10)$ do the two definitions become similar. The difference is due to the fact that in the linear case the loss element $(R)$ can be separated from the inductive element $(L)$, whereas from the hysteresis loop dissipation is measured on the increasing and as well as on the decreasing portion of the cycle. Measurements made at the input terminals cannot make a separation of the two components.

### 4.6.2 Transformer Material

Another area is the use of square loop material as a transformer core material. The criteria for an ideal transformer material are perhaps best stated in a negative manner:

1. The core should not distort the waveform.
2. The core should not store any energy.
3. The core should not dissipate any energy.

The first and third criteria imply a straight-line relationship between **B** and **H** and no hysteresis. A square loop core meets the second criteria, since it *stores no energy*. If the coercive force were reduced to

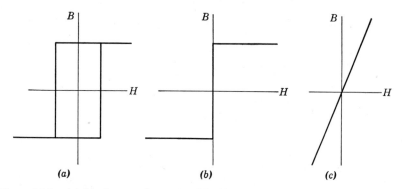

(a)　　　　　　　　(b)　　　　　　　　(c)

**Figure 4.22.** (*a*) Ideal square loop material; (*b*) ideal transformer material; (*c*) ideal linear magnetic material.

zero (Figure 4.22*b*), it would meet requirements 1 and 3. From another point of view, we could begin with a high permeability material which would meet 1 and 3 (Figure 4.22*c*), although it *stores* considerable energy. This could be rectified by making the slope approach infinity, and again 1 obtains (Figure 4.22*b*). In other words, we can start with materials at opposite ends of the scale with respect to stored energy and the two will merge into the same ideal transformer material.

### 4.6.3    Input Impedance

When we use a component containing a square loop core in a more complex system it is helpful to be able to calculate an input impedance for the component in order to determine its interaction with the remainder of the system. Though the concept of impedance for a nonlinear system is usually rather hazardous, we can make some inroads when the cores are used under pulsed conditions. In those cases in which the hysteresis loop is reasonably square for both constant-current and constant-voltage pulse excitation the following relationship holds:

$$e = AK(H_a - H_c')B_s \qquad (4.34)$$

where $H_a$ = the driving magnetic field;
$H_c'$ = coercive force taken from the switching time versus applied field curve;
$K$ = the slope of the same curve;
$A$ = the cross-sectional area.

In other words, the switching time versus driving field is an almost linear relationship over the useful range for thin metallic tapes and ferrite cores. When there is considerable departure from linearity then the value of $K$ will have to be suitably changed. Since the driving current $i$ is equal to

$$i = H_a l/N \qquad (4.35)$$

then the "input impedance"

$$z = \frac{AKNB_s}{l}(1 - H_c'/H_a) \qquad (4.36)$$

Since the voltage pulses due to a constant current are not actually square, this formula must be used with caution. At best, it gives an order of magnitude calculation at the time of the peak output voltage.

In conjunction with the input impedance we might ask whether devices utilizing the square loop cores are "voltage" or "current" devices. Normally, we plot the resultant flux for a given current, hence tend to think of the core as a current device. However, we shall see in the applications section that there are many times when it is desirable to use constant voltage pulses. At this time the flux becomes the independent variable rather than the current. Therefore, the square-loop magnetic core is not restricted to either concept. In digital techniques our viewpoint would be considerably narrowed by the arbitrary restriction to current as the independent parameter.

## 4.7 Square Loop Dielectrics (13, 14)

It is not unexpected to find dielectric materials which can perform functions similar to those of magnetic materials. The foregoing discussions of magnetic square loop characteristics can be carried over almost by analogy. However, there are enough significant differences so that it is worthwhile to discuss the variations. It should be noted that at the present time the general application of square loop dielectric material is very limited. The basic difficulty lies in the fact that the best square loop materials are at present available only in the form of small single crystals (in particular BaTiO₃). The attendant difficulties in mass producing uniform crystals has retarded what might otherwise be a rapid development in the utilization of such material. Consequently, our discussion is limited to some of the general aspects of dielectric material.* A more detailed examination of the problem is given in the list of references.

## 4.8 Basic Parameters

The square loop property is displayed as a hysteresis loop in which **D** is plotted as a function of **E**. The measurements are made on a parallel plate capacitor. For this geometry **D** is simply related to the capacitor charge $Q$ by $D = Q/A$ where $A$ is the surface area of the capacitor. Since $Q = \int i\,dt$, $D$ is obtained by integrating the current $i$ through the capacitor. A typical loop for a single crystal of BaTiO₃ is shown in Figure 4.23.

From a formal point of view the magnetic and dielectric cases appear very similar. However, in the magnetic case it is necessary to use the toroid as the basic configuration, since any air gap present tends to demagnetize the system. In the dielectric area thin wafers with very carefully applied conducting electrodes are used. It is interesting to follow the polarization process for various geometries.

Consider at first a hypothetical case shown in Figure 4.24. A thin disk of dielectric having no conducting coatings is placed in a strong uniform electric field $E$ which is sufficient to polarize the sample to saturation. If the field is reduced to zero, would the sample remain at the remanent polarization point? If this were the case, there would be a depolarizing field $E_d$ equal to $-P_r/\epsilon_0$. For the loop shown in Figure

* See Section (2.17).

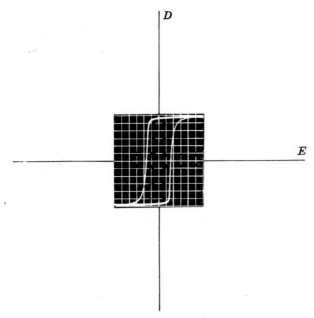

**Figure 4.23.** Typical hysteresis loop of single-crystal barium titanate.

4.23 this would be approximately $10^8$ volt/cm, which would almost depolarize the specimen. The same situation is encountered in magnetics, and the only solution is the construction of a closed magnetic path to avoid the formation of surface poles. In the dielectric case the existence of free charge is used to form a new field to oppose the field $E_d$.

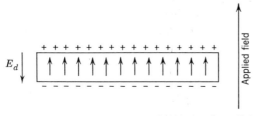

**Figure 4.24.** Charge distribution on unelectroded square-loop dielectric material.

Figure 4.25 is a more practical arrangement where conductors have been placed on the thin disk. The conductors are shown slightly displaced from the dielectric merely to show the charge distribution.*

* It should be noted that since the vertical slope of the dielectric hysteresis loop is so great ($10^5$ to $10^6$) any physical air gap between the conducting plates and the dielectric will produce degrading effects. Evaporated conducting films to form the electrodes appear to give the best results.

In this case, if a field $E_c$ is applied, there is a flow of charge so that at the interface between the conductor and dielectric there is a partial charge cancellation. At point $a$ on the hysteresis loop the total charge on each conductor plate is composed of two parts (assume no conduction through the dielectric). One portion is just sufficient to balance the surface polarization on the dielectric, and the remainder produces the field $E_c$. If the switch is in position 2, so that the applied field is reduced to zero (point $b$), there is a transfer of charge between the two plates.

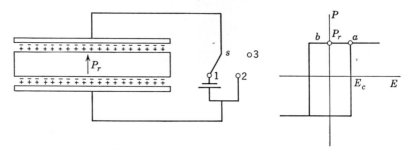

**Figure 4.25.** Charge distribution on electroded square-loop dielectric material.

In this condition the surface polarization charge is exactly balanced by the conduction charge on the plates. If the switch is now put into position 3 (open circuit), the dielectric will remain in the polarized state. This condition is feasible only if there are no other sources of charging. If, for example, the surrounding atmosphere contained charged particles, they could be deposited on the conducting plates and would neutralize the conduction charges. This would have the effect of increasing the depolarizing field and slowly depolarizing the specimen.*

## 4.9  Switching Time

Since the problem of domain wall motion in dielectric material has already been discussed in Section 2.16, the present section is concerned with representative data for a typical square loop material. The switching current waveform obtainable from a good single-crystal specimen of $BaTiO_3$ is similar to the switching voltage of a magnetic core (Figure 4.15$a$). The characteristic spike at the beginning of the pulse is a function of the rate of rise of the applied voltage pulse and the

---

* Recent experimental data on certain ferroelectrics indicates that applied fields less than the coercive field tend to depolarize the crystal over an extended period of time (16, 18).

relatively large slope of the flat portion of the hysteresis loop. This slope corresponds to a relative dielectric constant of the order of 200 to 300, whereas the slope for the square-loop magnetic case corresponds to a relative permeability of 10 to 30.

The remaining portion of the current waveform follows a shape very similar to that of the output-voltage pulse for the magnetic material. The similarity can be carried still further by noting that the switching time is linearly related to the applied voltage over a large range. Figure 4.26 is a plot of the switch-

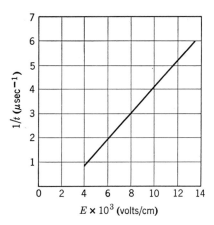

**Figure 4.26.** Switching characteristic of single-crystal barium titanate. (Merz, 1956.)

ing time obtained for a sample which was only $5 \times 10^{-3}$ cm thick. Hence very fast switching times are obtainable at rather low voltages.

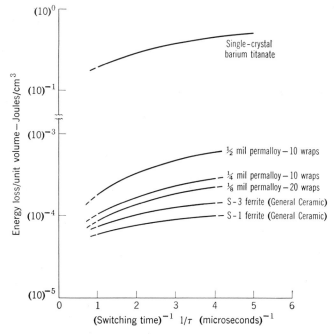

**Figure 4.27.** Switching losses of ferroelectric and ferromagnetic materials.

A comparison of presently available square-loop magnetic and dielectric materials can be obtained by calculating the energy required per unit volume of material for a given switching time. These data are shown in Figure 4.27 for switching times greater than 1 $\mu$sec. Thus very thin single crystals of $BaTiO_3$ are required in order to compete energywise with the magnetic materials.

## / ANALYSIS OF NONLINEAR CIRCUITS

### 4.10   Introduction (22, 24)

As pointed out in Section 4.0, an analytic study of a system containing one or more nonlinear elements appears discouraging from the outset. At the present stage of development of the theory of nonlinear differential equations only a very few methods which result in closed-form solutions are available. Even these are restricted in applicability to physical systems, since most methods require a single-valued parameter relation defining the nonlinearity. Occasionally, a graphical solution may be possible (18). Even so, analysis is often lengthy, if possible at all, and in most cases accuracy is doomed a priori.

This section does not presume to be a treatise on the theory of nonlinear systems. Rather, in order to make available at least some of the tools necessary for a quantitative attack on circuits and systems containing nonlinear elements, some of the more generally applicable methods have been selected for discussion. Also, a discussion of convergence criteria for the resultant solutions has not been included. For a more complete exposition the reader is referred to the references listed at the end of this section.

### 4.11   Single-Valued Approximations to Hysteresis Loop

The first difficulty is, of course, the mathematical formulation of the problem. The initial step is, in general, the single-valued approximation of the nonlinear relation. Thus, whenever the flux-current relation is given by a nest of hysteresis loops the temptation is strong to use the "normal magnetization curve," i.e., the locus of minor loop tips, as such an approximation (Figure 4.28). Experience suggests that better results are obtained sometimes by assuming an approximation to the hysteresis loop such that the tangents to the single-valued approximation curve match the tangents to the normal magnetization curve near the origin and in the saturated range (all lines $a$, $a'$, $b$, and $b'$: Figure 4.28). To this end the following power series is chosen to represent the approximation curve:

$$i = a_1\phi + a_3\phi^3 + a_5\phi^5 + \cdots \tag{4.37}$$

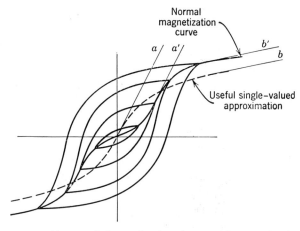

**Figure 4.28.** Nest of hysteresis loops showing the normal magnetization line as the locus of the major loop tips. A useful single-valued approximation has similar slopes for small values and for large values of currents.

Only the first two terms of this series are considered in most cases to avoid complications. It is usually found that this limitation prevents congruency of the approximation with the original curve. The attempt to match slopes is frequently more rewarding. Since the significant relation in magnetic circuits is the rate at which the flux varies with current rather than the actual value of the flux, a considerable deviation from congruency may be permitted with small sacrifice in the accuracy of the predicted result.

In systems containing nonlinear capacitors similar reasoning holds. Here the rate of change of charge with voltage rather than the absolute value of the charge for a given voltage is significant. The following power series may be useful:

$$e = b_1q + b_3q^3 + b_5q^5 \cdots \tag{4.38}$$

In many instances the assumption of a single-valued parameter relation as given by equations 4.37 and 4.38 cannot be tolerated. In such cases either stepwise linear solutions or graphical techniques appear more fruitful than the methods subsequently described.

## 4.12 Determination of the Nonlinear Parameters

A simple and rather direct method for the determination of, for example, the current-flux coefficients in the case of a nonlinear inductor is based on the availability of calibrated hysteresis loop equipment. (See Chapter 11 for a discussion of hysteresigraphs.) If a "nest" of hysteresis loops is taken, the loop tips can be connected by the "magnetization curve."

Once the approximated magnetization curve is determined the desired coefficients can be found. Thus, from equation 4.37

$$\frac{1}{a_1} = \frac{d\phi}{di}\bigg|_{\phi=0} \tag{4.39}$$

With $a_1$ determined, a point near the knee and another point near the extreme end of the magnetization line yield the necessary data to solve two simultaneous equations for the nonlinearity coefficients $a_1$ and $a_3$ (in matrix form):

$$\begin{bmatrix} \phi_a^3 & \phi_a^5 \\ \phi_b^3 & \phi_b^5 \end{bmatrix} \begin{bmatrix} a_3 \\ a_5 \end{bmatrix} = \begin{bmatrix} i_a - a_1\phi_a \\ i_b - a_1\phi_b \end{bmatrix} \tag{4.40}$$

Alternately, three points, resulting in three simultaneous equations, can be chosen on the magnetization line:

$$\begin{bmatrix} \phi_a & \phi_a^3 & \phi_a^5 \\ \phi_b & \phi_b^3 & \phi_b^5 \\ \phi_c & \phi_c^3 & \phi_c^5 \end{bmatrix} \begin{bmatrix} a_1 \\ a_3 \\ a_5 \end{bmatrix} = \begin{bmatrix} i_a \\ i_b \\ i_c \end{bmatrix} \tag{4.41}$$

The loops should be taken at the operating frequency of the circuit under examination and thus very nearly represent dynamic operating conditions.

## 4.13 Use of Incremental Inductance

A second method for the determination of the coefficients is measuring with a bridge the slope (incremental inductance) of the magnetization curve as a function of bias current. If a two-term approximation of the magnetization curve is assumed, i.e.,

$$i = a_1\phi + a_3\phi^3 \equiv \phi(a_1 + a_3\phi^2) \qquad (4.42)$$

then the incremental inductance is given by

$$L_i \overset{\Delta}{=} N\frac{d\phi}{di} \qquad (4.43)$$

It follows from equation 4.42 that

$$L_i = \frac{N}{a_1 + 3a_3\phi^2} \qquad (4.44)$$

Thus the initial inductance is given by

$$L_o = N\frac{d\phi}{di}\bigg|_{\phi=0} = \frac{N}{a_1} \qquad (4.45)$$

hence the linearity coefficient becomes

$$a_1 = \frac{N}{L_o} \qquad (4.46)$$

If equation 4.46 is substituted into equation 4.44, the following expression for flux can be obtained:

$$a_3\phi^2 = \frac{N}{3}\left(\frac{1}{L_i} - \frac{1}{L_o}\right) \quad \text{or} \quad \phi = \sqrt{\frac{N}{3a_3}\left(\frac{1}{L_i} - \frac{1}{L_o}\right)} \qquad (4.47)$$

The nonlinearity coefficient can be solved for by substitution of the equations 4.46 and 4.47 into equation 4.42.

$$a_3 = \frac{N^3}{27i^2}\left(\frac{1}{L_i} - \frac{1}{L_o}\right)\left(\frac{1}{L_i} + \frac{2}{L_o}\right)^2 \qquad (4.48)$$

Since the curve of $L_i$ versus $i$ is in general obtained by measurement, the closeness of the fit of the curve given by equation 4.42 and the coefficients of equations 4.46 and 4.48 can be gaged by plotting the current-inductance relation obtained through the use of the coefficients. This information is contained in equation 4.48 and results in

$$i = \frac{N}{3}\left(\frac{1}{L_i} + \frac{2}{L_o}\right)\sqrt{\frac{N}{3a_3}\left(\frac{1}{L_i} - \frac{1}{L_o}\right)} \qquad (4.49)$$

If a hysteresigram were taken, the fit of the current-flux relation given by equations 4.42, 4.46, and 4.48 to the saturation line could be judged readily as a second check.

### 4.13.1   Second Approximation

The current flux relation, to a second approximation, is given by

$$i = a_1\phi + a_3\phi^3 + a_5\phi^5 \tag{4.50}$$

The incremental inductance is once more determined as shown in equation 4.43 and results in

$$L_i = \cfrac{L_o}{1 + 3\phi^2 \cfrac{a_3}{a_1} + 5\phi^4 \cfrac{a_5}{a_1}} = \cfrac{L_o}{1 + 4m_3\phi^2 + 8m_5\phi^4} \tag{4.51}$$

where $m_3 = \dfrac{3a_3}{4a_1}$, and $m_5 = \dfrac{5a_5}{8a_1}$.

This expression can be rewritten

$$U_i \stackrel{\Delta}{=} \left(\frac{L_o}{L_i} - 1\right) = 4m_3\phi^2 + 8m_5\phi^4 \tag{4.52}$$

from which the flux is given by

$$\phi = \sqrt{\frac{m_3}{4m_5}\left(\sqrt{1 + \frac{2m_5 U_i}{m_3{}^2}} - 1\right)} \tag{4.53}$$

If this expression is substituted into equation 4.50, the following relation results:

$$i = a_1 \sqrt{\frac{m_3}{4m_5}\left(\sqrt{1 + \frac{2m_5 U_i}{m_3{}^2}} - 1\right)}$$
$$\times \left[\left(1 + \frac{U_i}{5}\right) + \frac{2m_3{}^2}{15m_5}\left(\sqrt{1 - \frac{2m_5 U_i}{m_3{}^2}} - 1\right)\right] \tag{4.54}$$

Theoretically, $m_3$ and $m_5$ are determined by two simultaneous equations resulting from two points on the curve of $U_i$ versus current. It can be seen that an explicit solution is likely to be a rather complex expression. However, it should be noted that the higher order coefficients become important only for the high values of flux, hence of current. Thus, if a point is chosen near the knee of the curve of $U_i$ versus current, the second coefficient is given to a sufficient approximation by equation 4.48. The other point is then taken near the high-current extreme of the curve, and equation 4.54 is solved for the third coefficient. Substitution of numerical values will result in considerable reductions in complexity due to approximations which then become obvious. However, generally speaking, the added accuracy does not appear to justify the added complexity. The following procedure may prove advantageous once the second coefficient is determined.

First the following substitution is made:

$$p \stackrel{\Delta}{=} \sqrt{1 + \frac{2m_5 U_i}{m_3{}^2}} \quad \text{hence} \quad m_5 = \frac{P^2 - 1}{2U_i} m_3{}^2 \quad (4.55)$$

Thus equation 4.54 becomes

$$\frac{i}{a_1} = \sqrt{\frac{U_i}{2m_3(P + 1)}} \left[ \left(1 + \frac{U_i}{5}\right) + \frac{4U_i}{15(P + 1)} \right] \quad (4.56)$$

This is a cubic equation in $(p + 1)$ which can be solved by trial and error or by the established methods. The third coefficient of equation 4.50 is then readily calculated from the expression given in equation 4.55.

Once all the coefficients are found a check on the fit of the curve can be obtained by evaluating the flux corresponding to selected values of $U_i$ from equation 4.53 and substituting the result into equation 4.49 to obtain the corresponding current.

## 4.14   Solution of a Nonlinear Circuit by Iteration Method

This very useful method can frequently be applied when circuits containing one or more nonlinear elements are to be analyzed. Duffing's method is applied to a second-order system, both with and without a resistive element (24). Only the periodic solution is selected, and the nonlinearity is assumed to be sufficiently small to make the resultant series solution converge.

Consider the parallel circuit shown in Figure 4.29 which is driven from a constant-current source. The response of the system is governed by the following relations:

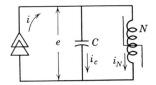

$$i = i_N + i_C \qquad i = I \cos \omega t$$

$$e = N\dot{\phi} \qquad i_C = C\dot{e} = CN\ddot{\phi} \quad (4.57)$$

$$i_N = a_1\phi + a_3\phi^3 + a_5\phi^5 \quad (4.58)$$

$$CN\ddot{\phi} + a_1\phi + a_3\phi^3 + a_5\phi^5 = I \cos \omega t \quad (4.59)$$

Figure 4.29.   Nonlinear loss-free second-order system containing a nonlinear inductor and a linear capacitor and driven from a constant-current source.

Through introduction of the symbols

$$\frac{1}{L_0 C} = \frac{a_1}{CN} \overset{\Delta}{=} \omega_0{}^2 \qquad \frac{a_3}{CN} \overset{\Delta}{=} \beta \qquad \frac{a_5}{CN} \overset{\Delta}{=} \gamma \qquad \frac{I}{CN} \overset{\Delta}{=} F \qquad (4.60)$$

equation 4.59 becomes

$$\ddot{\phi}_{01} = F \cos \omega t - \omega_0{}^2 \phi - \beta \phi^3 - \gamma \phi^5 \qquad (4.61)$$

If $\beta$ and $\gamma$ are sufficiently small, the linear periodic solution is a reasonable first guess. Thus let

$$\phi_{01} = A_{01} \cos \omega t \qquad A_{01} \overset{\Delta}{=} \frac{F}{\omega_0{}^2 - \omega^2} \qquad (4.62)$$

This solution is introduced on the right-hand side of equation 4.61, and with the aid of the trigonometric identity

$$(\cos x)^{2n+1} = \frac{1}{2^{2n}} \left[ \cos (2n+1)x + \cdots + \binom{2n+1}{k-1} \cos (2n-2k+3)x \right.$$
$$\left. \cdots + \cos x \right] \qquad (4.63)$$

there results, after suitable regrouping of terms,

$$\ddot{\phi}_1 = (F - \omega_0{}^2 A_{01} - \tfrac{3}{4}\beta A_{01}{}^3 - \tfrac{5}{8}\gamma A_{01}{}^5) \cos \omega t -$$
$$(\tfrac{1}{4}\beta A_{01}{}^3 + \tfrac{5}{16}\gamma A_{01}{}^5) \cos 3\omega t - \tfrac{1}{16}\gamma A_{01}{}^5 \cos 5\omega t$$
$$(4.64)$$

Double-integration of equation 4.64 results in the next approximation to the periodic solution:

$$\phi_1 = A_{11} \cos \omega t + A_{31} \cos 3\omega t + A_{51} \cos 5\omega t \qquad (4.65)$$

where $A_{11} = -\dfrac{1}{\omega^2}\left(F - \omega_0{}^2 A_{01} - \dfrac{3}{4}\beta A_{01}{}^3 - \dfrac{5}{8}\gamma A_{01}{}^5\right)$

$$A_{31} = \frac{1}{9\omega^2}\left(\frac{1}{4}\beta A_{01}{}^3 + \frac{5}{16}\gamma A_{01}{}^5\right) \qquad (4.66)$$

$$A_{51} = \frac{1}{400\omega^2}\gamma A_{01}{}^5$$

Equation 4.65 could now be substituted for $\phi$ in the right-hand side of equation 4.59 and the procedure repeated. Before proceeding, however, the following important consideration is introduced: since $\beta$ and $\gamma$ are small, it follows that $A_{11}$ must be very nearly equal to $A_{01}$, as assumed in equation 4.62. Thus, from equation 4.66, a significant relation results:

$$\omega^2 = \omega_0^2 + \frac{3}{4}\beta A_{11}{}^2 + \frac{5}{8}\gamma A_{11}{}^4 - \frac{F}{A_{11}} \qquad (4.67)$$

This expression for $\omega^2$ can now be used in equation 4.66 to define $A_{31}$ and $A_{51}$ further, and the iteration can be continued, with the resulting,

$$\phi_2 = A_{12}\cos\omega t + A_{32}\cos 3\omega t + A_{52}\cos 5\omega t \qquad (4.68)$$

Following the steps leading to equation 4.67, we might assume $A_{12}$ to be very nearly equal to $A_{11}$ of equation 4.66, yielding an improved relation between $\omega^2$ and the amplitude of the fundamental response component.

The relation between $\omega^2$ and $A_{11}$ defined by equation 4.67, or the improved relation resulting from higher iterations, is an important one and deserves closer attention:

Equation 4.67 can be rewritten as follows:

$$S = \frac{-F}{A_{11}\omega_0^2} + m_3 A_{11}{}^2 + m_5 A_{11}{}^4 \qquad (4.69)$$

Upon introduction of the symbols

$$S \overset{\Delta}{=} \frac{\omega^2}{\omega_0^2} - 1 \qquad m_3 \overset{\Delta}{=} \frac{3a_3}{4a_1} \equiv \frac{3\beta}{4\omega_0^2} \qquad m_5 \overset{\Delta}{=} \frac{5a_5}{8a_1} = \frac{10\gamma}{16\omega_0^2} \qquad (4.70)$$

or $S = S_1 + S_3 + S_5$ where

$$S_1 \overset{\Delta}{=} \frac{-F}{A_{11}\omega_0^2} \qquad S_3 \overset{\Delta}{=} m_3 A_{11}{}^2 \qquad S_5 \overset{\Delta}{=} m_5 A_{11}{}^4 \qquad (4.71)$$

A plot of the four relations of equations 4.71 results in Figure 4.31.

It is interesting, and important, to note that the curve $(S_3 + S_5)$ degenerates into the axis of ordinates as the nonlinearity coefficients $\beta$ and $\gamma$ (hence $m_3$ and $m_5$) are made to vanish. Conversely, the greater the nonlinearity, the more significant the contribution of $(S_3 + S_5)$ to the composite curve $S$, and the latter leans far away from the ordinate at $S = 0$ (i.e., at $\omega = \omega_0$).

Of further interest is the observation that the curve for $(S_3 + S_5)$ is not dependent upon the value of the driving force $F$ nor upon any of the system parameters outside the nonlinear element. Thus the shape of the composite curve $S$ is manipulated by altering the curve of $S_1$ alone for a given nonlinear element in the system. The manner in which $S_1$ varies, with variation of amplitude of the driving force or of system parameters, may be assumed to be well known, since it represents the familiar linear case.

It might be desirable to omit consideration of the sign of $A_{11}$ in Figure 4.30 and to plot its absolute value only. This procedure results in the curves of Figure 4.31.

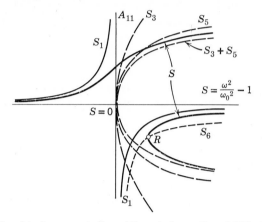

**Figure 4.30.** Graphical representation of the set of equations 4.35 in the $A_{11}$–$S$-plane

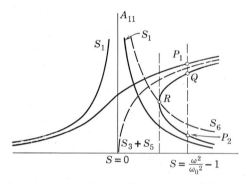

**Figure 4.31.** Variation of the fundamental component of flux in the nonlinear inductor of Figure 4.5.

The results shown in Figure 4.31 will be modified slightly if higher iterations are used. However, the deforming effect of the nonlinearity contributions is clearly visible.

If one or more of the nonlinearity coefficients are negative, the corresponding curve $(S_3 + S_5)$ may be related to negative values of $S$ only and will result in a deformation of the $A_{11}$ versus $S$ curve to the left of the linear case.

Consideration of the response curves of Figure 4.31 demonstrates that for a given value of $\omega$ there may exist as many as three possible values of amplitude $A_{11}$, indicated by the operating points $P_1$, $P_2$, and $Q$. In the physical case point $Q$ is found to be unstable, so that the device of Figure 4.29 can be made bistable.* If the nonlinearity is reduced by the addition of a linear inductor, for example, the section $P_2Q$ can be made arbitrarily steep. Thus this device can be used as a sensitive indicator of a variation of frequency, driving force, or nonlinearity coefficient. The last can be affected by magnetic bias or by temperature in many ferromagnetic materials and by electric field or by temperature in the case of ferroelectrics. In some materials, other circuit parameters such as the capacitance can be altered by external influences such as light, heat, or other radiation.

Point $R$ in Figures 4.30 and 4.31 shows that for any given value of driving force $F$ there may exist a point of discontinuity as the source

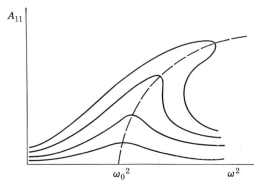

**Figure 4.32.** Variation of the fundamental component of flux in the nonlinear inductor of Figure 4.8 with amplitude of driving force as a parameter.

frequency (hence $S$) is reduced from some arbitrarily large value. The relation between flux amplitude $A$ and the frequency factor $S$ at such a point $R$ is found by differentiating equation 4.69 with respect to $A$ and equating the result to zero. Thus there follows

$$\frac{dS}{dA} = 0 = \frac{F}{A_{11}{}^2\omega_0{}^2} + 2m_3 A_{11} + 4m_5 A_{11}{}^3 \tag{4.72}$$

This can be rewritten as

$$S = \tfrac{3}{2}S_1 - S_5 \tag{4.73}$$

This expression is shown as $S_6$ in Figures 4.30 and 4.31. As might be expected, the trigger point $R$ is seen to be a function of the amplitude

* This phenomenon is known as "ferroresonance."

and frequency of the driving source as well as the linear system parameter $\omega_0$.

If the circuit dissipation is assumed small compared to the capacitive reactance at all frequencies under consideration, the response curves relating $A_{11}$ to $\omega^2$ for various values of $F$ will not differ much from those of the dissipation free case given by Figure 4.31 over a wide range of frequencies. However, just as in the linear case the presence of resistance precludes an increase of $A_{11}$ without limit. Thus a response as shown in Figure 4.32 may be anticipated. This is similar to Figure 4.31, except that the curves are rounded off rather than open due to the effect of dissipation in the circuit.

### 4.15  References

1. Bean, C., and D. Rodbell, "Kinetics of Magnetization in Some Square-Loop Magnetic Tapes," *J. Appl. Phy.*, **26**, No. 1, January 1955, pp. 124–125.
2. Wylen, J., "Pulse Response Characteristics of Rectangular Hysteresis Loop Material," *Trans. AIEE*, Part 1, **72**, 1953, p. 648.
3. Kikuchi, R., "On the Minimum of Magnetization Reversal Times," *J. Appl. Phy.*, **27**, No. 11, November 1956, p. 1352.
4. Menyuk, N., and J. B. Goodenough, "Magnetic Materials for Digital Computer Components; I. A Theory of Flux Reversal in Polycrystalline Ferromagnetics," *J. Appl. Phy.*, **26**, No. 1, January 1955, pp. 8–18.
5. Menyuk, N., "Magnetic Materials for Digital Computer Components," *J. Appl. Phy.*, **26,** No. 6, June 1955, p. 692.
6. Kornetzki, H., "A Note on Rectangular Magnetization Loop of Ferrite Cores," *Frequencz*, **9**, No. 3, March 1955, p. 81.
7. Brown, E. A., D. Buck, and N. Menyuk, "A Comparison of Metals and Ferrites for High Speed Pulse Operation," *Trans. AIEE*, Communications and Electronics, No. 16, January 1955.
8. Thompson, L. G., and C. F. DeVenny, Jr., "Ferromagnetic Computer Cores," *Electronic Inds. Tele-Tech*, **14**, September 1955, p. 58.
9. Friedlaender, F. J., "Flux Reversal in Magnetic Amplifier Cores," *Trans. AIEE*, *Paper No. 56–219*, January 1956.
10. McConnell, H. M., "Eddy Current Phenomena in Ferromagnetic Materials," *Trans. AIEE*, **73**, Part 1, 1954, pp. 226–235.
11. Blois, M. S., Jr., "Preparation of Thin Magnetic Films and Their Properties," *J. Appl. Phy.*, **26**, No. 8, August 1955, pp. 975–981.
12. Merz, W. J., "Switching Time in Ferroelectric $BaTiO_3$ and its Dependence on Crystal Thickness," *J. Appl. Phy.*, **27**, August 1956, pp. 938–943.
13. ————, "Domain Formation and Domain Wall Motion in Ferroelectric $BaTiO_3$ Single Crystals," *Phys. Rev.*, **95**, No. 3, August 1954, p. 690.
14. Little, C. A., "Dynamic Behavior of Domain Walls in $BaTiO_3$," *Phys. Rev.*, **98**, No. 4, May 1955, p. 978.
15. Landauer, R., "Electrostatic Considerations in $BaTiO_3$ Domain Formation During Polarization Reversal," *J. Appl. Phy.*, **28**, No. 2, February 1957.
16. Wieder, H. H., "Retarded Polarization Phenomena in $BaTiO_3$ Crystals," *J. Appl. Phy.*, **27**, No. 4, April 1956, pp. 413–417.

17. Feldman, C., "Time Changes in Thin Films of BaTiO₃," *J. Appl. Phy.*, **27**, August 1956, pp. 870–73.
18. Smith, D. O., "Magnetic Relaxation in Thin Films," *Proc. Conf. on Magnetism, AIEE*, Boston 1957, p. 625. "Magnetization Reversal in Thin Films," *Phys. Rev.*, **104**, No. 5, December 1, 1956.
19. Blois, M. S., "Thin Magnetic Films," *J. Appl. Phy.*, **26**, August 1955, p. 975.
20. Conger, R. L., "Magnetization Reversal in Thin Films," *Phys. Rev.*, **98**, No. 6, June 15, 1955, p. 1752.
21. Wolf, I. W., and V. P. McConnell, "Nickel Iron Electrodeposits for Magnetic Shielding," *Proc. Am. Electroplaters' Soc.*, 1956.
22. Duinker, S., "An Approximate Graphical Analysis of the Steady-State Response of Nonlinear Networks," *Philips Research Repts.*, **8**, April 1953, pp. 133–147.
23. Pipes, L. A., "Applications of Integral Equations to the Solution of Nonlinear Electric Circuit Problems," *Trans. AIEE*, Communications and Electronics, September 1953, pp. 445–450.
24. Stoker, J. J., *Nonlinear Vibrations*, Interscience Publishers, Inc., New York, 1950.
25. Pipes, L. A., *Applied Mathematics for Engineers and Physicists*, McGraw-Hill Book Company, New York, 1946.
26. Salihi, J. T., "Reactors with Rectangular Hysteresis Loop Core Materials," *Trans. AIEE*, Communications and Electronics, July 1956, pp. 296–305.
27. Ku, Y. H., "Acceleration Plane Method for Analysis of a Circuit with Nonlinear Inductor and Capacitor," *Trans. AIEE*, Communications and Electronics, January 1955, pp. 619–626.
28. Skalnik, J. G., "Transient Behaviour in a Ferroresonant Circuit," *J. Appl. Phy.*, May 1956, pp. 508–513.
29. ————, "Limiting Conditions in a Ferroresonant Trigger Circuit," *Tenth Technical Report, Navy Research Project*, Nonr. 433(00), October 1955.

# Chapter five

# Electromechanical Applications

## 5.0 Introduction

Chapter 3 describes several arrangements of polarized ferroelectric ceramic bars in which elementary ring and transverse sections are physically joined to form two basic four-terminal devices, the ring-type and the transverse-type transformer, shown in Figures 5.1 and 5.2. The application of a periodic electric field to the left half of each bar causes mechanical vibration of the whole bar by the converse piezoelectric effect. At specific frequencies which are integrally related for "long thin bars" resonant modes of vibration occur along the length and result in standing-wave distributions of large amplitude of elastic strain and stress. The resonantly amplified strain in the right half of each bar produces an electric field distribution by the direct piezoelectric effect, which results in a potential difference appearing across the output terminals. A voltage step-up of considerable magnitude may be obtained by these means.

## / DESIGN OF CERAMIC POWER TRANSFORMERS

### 5.1   Ceramic Transformer

Available ceramics, such as barium titanate modified with additions of calcium and lead titanate, can be made permanently piezoelectric by a simple polarization process (1). The remanent polarization can be maintained to a large degree up to operating temperatures of approximately 90° C. These modified titanates have low mechanical and dielectric losses, e.g., electrical $Q_e > 100$, mechanical $Q_m > 200$. They can withstand large electric gradients (50,000 to 100,000 volts per inch) and are chemically inert and mechanically strong. Because of low intrinsic losses it is possible by suitable design to operate a ceramic transformer as a power-handling device with high operating efficiency and at moderate power levels (several watts). The mechanical strength permits large amplitudes of strain to be developed when operated at resonance without physical fracture. Thus an electric field of large magnitude may be produced piezoelectrically. The ability of the material to withstand such fields without electrical breakdown or depolarization permits operation at output levels greater than a thousand volts, rms, with bars no longer than 5 to 6 inches. At present the most serious limitation is the rapidly rising loss when the ceramic transformer is operated at high levels. It has been found empirically that the loss becomes prohibitive when the generated field strength exceeds 500 volts rms per inch, averaged over the length of the generating portion of the transformer. The rise in temperature caused by operation beyond this limit causes depolarization of those areas subjected to the largest vibrational or electric strain.

Although the relative dielectric constant of suitable piezoelectric ceramics is quite high (approximately 1000), the input and output impedance levels are high when compared with conventional magnetic transformers. The ceramic transformer is thus best suited for operation at high-voltage, low-current levels, which are the requirements for some high-voltage supplies, e.g., cathode-ray tubes and Geiger-Mueller tubes. Conventional magnetically operated transformers, resonantly operated r-f transformers, and fly-back type pulse transformers all require many well-insulated turns of copper wire for their operation at high output voltages. The size, simplicity, and absence of high-voltage windings make the ceramic transformer potentially attractive for these applications.

By suitable electroding it is possible to operate the ceramic transformer in the fundamental resonant mode, the second harmonic, or in even higher harmonic modes. The electroding shown in Figures 5.1

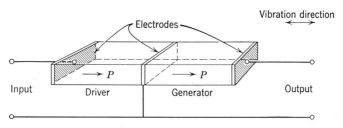

Figure 5.1. Ring-type piezoelectric transformer.

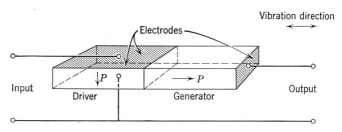

Figure 5.2. Transverse-type piezoelectric transformer.

and 5.2 is suitable for operation in the fundamental and second harmonic modes. It is found more practicable to operate in either the fundamental or second harmonic modes due to the greater simplicity of electroding and polarization and the availability of driving sources operating at relatively low frequencies. The choice between fundamental and second harmonic mode operation is predicated primarily on the impedance level requirements for matching driving source and electrical load and the possible nuisance value of audible output if the lower frequency of the fundamental mode falls below 20 kc.

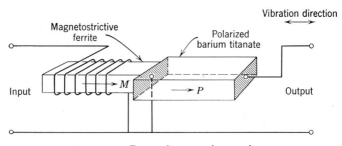

Figure 5.3. Composite ceramic transformer.

Another arrangement which falls in the class of ceramic power transformers is shown in Figure 5.3. A magnetostrictive slab (magnetostrictive ferrite, for example) is mechanically bonded to a polarized ferroelectric ceramic slab (barium titanate, for example). The principle of operation for this composite transformer is similar to that of the all-piezoelectric transformer. The ferrite must be optimally biased magnetically to obtain favorable conversion from electrical to mechanical energy. This may be done by means of a permanent magnet, by direct current flowing through the driving coil (or via a separate coil), or by remanent magnetization. The low input impedance possible with this arrangement and the availability of a d-c conductive path through the input coil may make this arrangement preferable for some applications.

It has been found in practice that this type is, in general, less desirable than the all-piezoelectric transformers for the following reasons:

1. The effective electromechanical coupling coefficient of available magnetostrictive ferrites is approximately 10 per cent, compared with approximately 40 per cent for titanates. It is thus more difficult to transform from electrical to mechanical forms of energy.

2. Larger electrical losses are usually encountered because of the electrical resistance of the driving coil. A more effective magnetic drive can be designed by greatly reducing the large air gap shown, but this entails a more complex structure.

3. Available ferrites have low saturation flux densities which limit the operating power level to smaller values than in the comparable all-piezoelectric system.

4. The composite transformer is more difficult to construct; it usually requires d-c magnetizing bias, a wound driving coil supported free of contact from the bar, and, finally, a careful physical bonding of ferrite to the piezoelectric ceramic.

Of the two types of all-piezoelectric transformers shown, the most versatile and useful is the transverse type used as a step-up high-voltage transformer. The open-circuit voltage amplification of the ring type, unlike the transverse type, is independent of the geometry, being a function only of the mechanical $Q_m$ and electromechanical coupling coefficient $k_{33}$. Typical values of open-circuit voltage amplification range from approximately 15 to 30 for available materials. Furthermore, the range of input impedance relative to the output impedance is limited because of the symmetrical geometry, and the level of the input impedance is high compared to that of the transverse type. Since the present practicable use of ceramic transformers is limited to those applications in which the power level, the voltage amplification, and the electrical terminations are specified, the availability to the designer of the additional variables due to the geometry of the bar is usually essential.

For the reasons given above the transverse type all-piezoelectric transformer has been selected for detailed analysis and the development of a method of design. It is important to note that the design for efficient voltage amplification is based on the assumption that the *electrical terminations* are specified.

## 5.2 Modified Equivalent Circuit of the Transverse Type Ceramic Transformer

Illustrated in Figure 5.4 is a transverse-type transformer composed of a rectangular slab of ceramic barium titanate. Pertinent dimensions are shown here in more specific detail than in Figure 5.2. This transformer is composed of driver and generator sections polarized as indicated by the vector **P**. It is assumed that the whole bar is operated in the fundamental longitudinal mode as a half-wave resonator (total length equals one half wavelength). Since its width and thickness are less than one eighth wavelength, it may be assumed that it vibrates as a "long thin bar." The whole bar is mechanically supported at a vibration node which occurs at the junction of driver and generator segments. The ends are mechanically free. It should be noted that the bottom electrode of the driver segment can also serve as the common ground electrode of the generator segment with little change in performance.

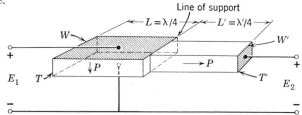

Figure 5.4. Transverse piezoelectric transformer.

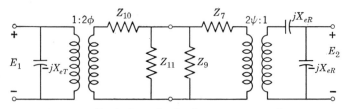

Figure 5.5. Equivalent circuit of transverse transformer.

The equivalent circuit for this arrangement is shown in Figure 5.5. It has been obtained from the equivalent circuits for side-plated (transverse section) and end-plated (ring section) bars shown in Figures 3.21 and 3.20, with the following modifications:

1. The impedances $Z_E{}^{LC}$ are replaced by lossless capacitive reactances $-jX_{eT}$ and $-jX_{eR}$. These approximations are quite valid, as the electrical $Q_e$ of available titanate compositions is quite high (in the neighborhood of 100).

2. The two segments have slightly different widths and lengths. Choice of proper values of $W'$ and $L'$ with respect to $W$ and $L$ permits exact matching of the acoustic impedance of the two segments and ensures that each segment represents a quarter-wave resonator with a node at the junction of the two segments. This modification greatly simplifies the analysis yielding a symmetrical mechanical network.

The equivalent circuit parameters are redefined in equations 5.1 to 5.12 inclusive, with the foregoing modifications noted.

Driver Section          Generator Section

$$Z_{10} = \frac{2Z_0}{\tanh \dfrac{\gamma L}{2}} \qquad (5.1) \qquad Z_7 = \frac{2Z_0{}'}{\tanh \dfrac{\gamma' L'}{2}} \qquad (5.7)$$

$$Z_{11} = 2Z_0 \tanh \frac{\gamma L}{2} \qquad (5.2) \qquad Z_9 = 2Z_0{}' \tanh \frac{\gamma' L'}{2} \qquad (5.8)$$

$$Z_0 = WT(\rho Y_1{}^E)^{\frac{1}{2}} \qquad (5.3) \qquad Z_0{}' = W'T'(\rho Y_3{}^D)^{\frac{1}{2}} \qquad (5.9)$$

$$\phi = W d_{31} Y_1{}^E \qquad (5.4) \qquad \psi = \frac{k_{33}{}^2}{g_{33}} \cdot \frac{W'T'}{L'} \qquad (5.10)$$

$$\gamma = j\omega \left(\frac{\rho}{Y_1{}^E}\right)^{\frac{1}{2}} = \alpha + j\beta \qquad (5.5) \qquad \gamma' = j\omega \left(\frac{\rho}{Y_3{}^D}\right)^{\frac{1}{2}} = \alpha' + j\beta'$$
$$(5.11)$$

$$X_{eT} = \frac{1}{\omega \epsilon_{33}{}^T (1 - k_{31}{}^2)} \cdot \frac{T}{WL} \quad (5.6) \quad X_{eR} = \frac{1}{\omega \epsilon_{33}{}^T (1 - k_{33}{}^2)} \cdot \frac{L'}{T'W'}$$
$$(5.12)$$

In order to match acoustic impedances of the two segments,

$$Z_0 = Z_0{}' \qquad (5.13)$$

and to make each segment a quarter-wave section

$$\beta L = \beta' L' \qquad (5.14)$$

Assuming $Y_1{}^E$ is real for this approximation, from equations 5.5 and 5.11

$$\left[\frac{\rho}{Y_1{}^E}\right]^{\frac{1}{2}} L = \left(\frac{\rho}{Y_3{}^D}\right)^{\frac{1}{2}} L' \tag{5.15}$$

It can be shown that

$$Y_3{}^D = \frac{Y_3{}^E}{1 - k_{33}{}^2} \tag{5.16}$$

and it may be assumed that

$$Y_1{}^E \simeq Y_3{}^E \ * \tag{5.16a}$$

Using equations 5.15, 5.16, and 5.16a

$$L' = \frac{L}{(1 - k_{33}{}^2)^{\frac{1}{2}}} \tag{5.17}$$

Using equations 5.3, 5.9, 5.13, 5.16, and 5.16a,

$$W'T' = WT(1 - k_{33}{}^2)^{\frac{1}{2}} \tag{5.18}$$

Thus the sectional area of the generator segment is reduced by the factor $(1 - k_{33}{}^2)^{\frac{1}{2}}$, and its length is increased by $1/(1 - k_{33}{}^2)^{\frac{1}{2}}$ over the corresponding quantities of the driver. For a typical good piezoelectric ceramic $(k_{33}{}^2 \simeq 0.2)$ these factors are approximately 0.89 and 1.11, respectively.

Using relations 5.13, 5.14, 5.17, and 5.18, equations 5.7 to 5.12 now become

$$Z_7 = \frac{2Z_0}{\tanh \dfrac{\gamma L}{2}} \tag{5.19}$$

$$Z_9 = 2Z_0 \tanh \frac{\gamma L}{2} \tag{5.20}$$

$$Z_0' = Z_0 = WT(\rho Y_3{}^E)^{\frac{1}{2}} \tag{5.21}$$

$$\psi = \frac{k_{33}{}^2(1 - k_{33}{}^2)}{g_{33}} \cdot \frac{WT}{L} \tag{5.22}$$

---

* Since the elastic moduli $Y_1{}^E$, $Y_3{}^E$ are both specified at constant electric field, it might be expected that they would be equal if the material were isotropic. However, permanent polarization causes the bulk material to assume a net polar axis (along the 3-axis), with consequent anisotropy along this axis. Recent measurements made by Moseley (9) indicate that

$$S_{33}{}^E/S_{11}{}^E = 1.045 \qquad \text{hence} \qquad Y_1{}^E/Y_3{}^E = 1.045$$

for polarized pure barium titanate ceramic. No measurements of modified barium titanate are known to have been reported.

$$\gamma'L' = \gamma L = j\omega \left(\frac{\rho}{Y_3{}^E}\right)^{\frac{1}{2}} \cdot L \tag{5.23}$$

$$X_{eR} = \frac{1}{\omega\epsilon_{33}{}^T(1 - k_{33}{}^2)^2} \frac{L}{TW} \tag{5.24}$$

Using relation 5.16, relations 5.4 and 5.5 become

$$\phi = Wd_{31}Y_3{}^E \tag{5.25}$$

$$\gamma = j\omega \left(\frac{\rho}{Y_3{}^E}\right)^{\frac{1}{2}} \tag{5.26}$$

## 5.3 Simplified Mechanical Circuit

With the foregoing simplifications the mechanical part of the equivalent circuit reduces to the symmetrical $T$, shown in Figure 5.6.

Performing a $T$ to $\pi$ transformation results in the circuit shown in Figure 5.7. By expanding the functions tanh $\gamma L/2$, tanh $\gamma L$ in power series about a value of $\beta L = \pi/2$ corresponding to the fundamental mode it is shown in Section 3.12 that for high $Q_m$

$$\tanh \frac{\gamma L}{2} \simeq j \tag{5.27}$$

$$\tanh \gamma L \simeq \frac{4Q_m}{\pi} \cdot \frac{1}{1 + j2Q_m r} \tag{5.28}$$

where

$$r = \frac{\omega - \omega_0}{\omega_0} = \frac{\Delta\omega}{\omega_0} \tag{5.29}$$

where $\omega_0$ is the angular resonant frequency of the fundamental mode.

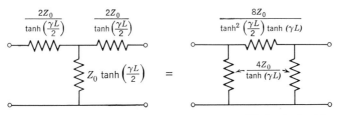

Figure 5.6. Mechanical equivalent circuit "$T$."

Figure 5.7. Mechanical equivalent circuit "$\pi$."

Expansions about $\beta L$ for higher modes can similarly be made to obtain the requisite approximations valid for higher mode operation.

By substituting equations 5.27, 5.28, and 5.29 in the $\pi$ equivalent circuit a simplified equivalent circuit (Figure 5.8) is obtained which holds to a high degree of precision for mechanical $Q_m$'s greater than 100 and frequency deviations $\Delta\omega/\omega_0$ of greater magnitudes than encountered in the range of operation of a practical transformer.

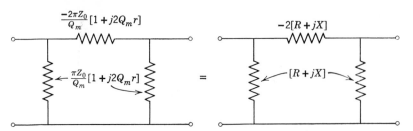

Figure 5.8. Approximate mechanical circuit "$\pi$."

Figure 5.9. Simplified mechanical circuit.

To simplify the algebraic manipulations which follow, let us introduce the parameters $R$ and $X$ for the resistive and reactive parts of these branch impedances.
Thus

$$R = \frac{\pi Z_0}{Q_m} \tag{5.30}$$

$$X = 2\pi Z_0 r \tag{5.31}$$

It should be carefully noted that although $R$ is not a function of frequency $X$ is proportional to the frequency deviation $r = \Delta\omega/\omega_0$ and can thus be a capacitive or an inductive reactance dependent on the algebraic sign of $\Delta\omega$. The mechanical circuit thus simplifies to that shown in Figure 5.9.

### 5.4 Complete System, Transformer Driven by Generator and Electrically Terminated

Using the mechanical circuit of Figure 5.9, the equivalent circuit of a complete system is shown in Figure 5.10. This consists of a generator source $E_g$, with specified internal resistance $R_g$ driving the transformer, which is terminated with a resistive load $R_L$. To be completely general $R_g$ and $R_L$ should be impedances. However, the additional complexity would serve only to obscure the method of analysis, and the network may readily be modified to include such a case, if necessary.

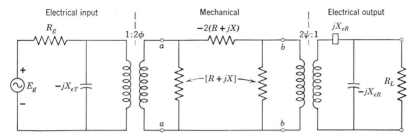

**Figure 5.10.** Simplified equivalent circuit for terminated transverse transformer.

The above circuit has been divided into three parts: electrical input, mechanical, and electrical output sections.

In the following paragraphs transformations of the electrical input and output sections into the mechanical section permit the determination of the effect of load and generator resistances on the performance.

### 5.4.1 Transformation of Electrical Input and Output into Mechanical Sections

By use of suitable network transformations both the electrical input and output sections can be transformed to the mechanical section. Analysis of the complete system is thereby greatly simplified when all quantities are referred to one section. These transformations are shown progressively in Figure 5.11 for the input section and Figure 5.12 for the output section. The final resistive and reactive quantities for input and output sections, in terms of the original quantities shown in Figure 5.10; then become

$$E_1 = E_g X_{eT} \frac{X_{eT} - jR_g}{R_g{}^2 + X_{eT}{}^2} \cdot 2\phi \qquad (5.32)$$

$$R_1 = \frac{R_g X_{eT}{}^2}{R_g{}^2 + X_{eT}{}^2} \cdot 4\phi^2 \qquad (5.33)$$

$$X_1 = \frac{R_g{}^2 X_{eT}}{R_g{}^2 + X_{eT}{}^2} \cdot 4\phi^2 \qquad (5.34)$$

$$R_2 = \frac{R_L X_{eR}{}^2}{R_L{}^2 + X_{eR}{}^2} \cdot 4\psi^2 \qquad (5.35)$$

$$X_2 = \frac{X_{eR}{}^3}{R_L{}^2 + X_{eR}{}^2} \cdot 4\psi^2 \qquad (5.36)$$

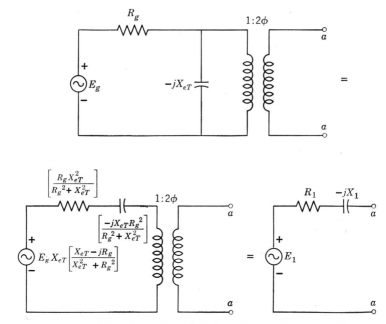

**Figure 5.11.** Transformations of the input into mechanical sections.

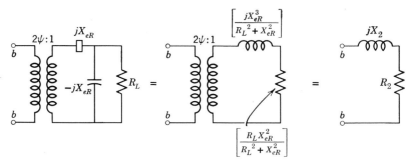

**Figure 5.12.** Transformations of the output into mechanical section.

### 5.4.2 Special Cases of Terminations

It is useful to examine the foregoing transformations for the special input conditions for constant voltage and constant current drive and for the special output conditions for open and short-circuit load terminations. Figures 5.13a and 5.13b show the transformed input parameter values for constant voltage and constant current generators, respectively. For the constant voltage case $R_g$ becomes zero and equations 5.32 to 5.34 reduce to

$$E_1 = E_g \cdot 2\phi$$
$$R_1 = 0 \qquad (5.37)$$
$$X_1 = 0$$

For the constant current case in which the current $I_g$ is defined

$$I_g = \lim_{\substack{E_g \to \infty \\ R_g \to \infty}} \left(\frac{E_g}{R_g}\right) \qquad (5.38)$$

the equations become

$$E_1 = -jX_{eT}I_g \cdot 2\phi$$
$$R_1 = 0 \qquad (5.39)$$
$$X_1 = X_{eT} \cdot 4\phi^2$$

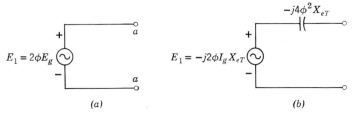

$E_1 = 2\phi E_g$       (a)

$E_1 = -j2\phi I_g X_{eT}$     $-j4\phi^2 X_{eT}$     (b)

Figure 5.13. (a) Transformed input for constant voltage drive; (b) transformed input for constant current drive.

For open- and short-circuit conditions of electrical loading, i.e., where $R_L = \infty$ and $R = 0$, respectively, equations 5.35 and 5.36 for the open-circuit case become

$$R_2 = 0$$
$$X_2 = 0 \qquad (5.40)$$

and for the short-circuit case

$$R_2 = 0$$
$$X_2 = 4\psi^2 X_{eR} \qquad (5.41)$$

Thus for an electrically open-circuited transformer the mechanical system is terminated by a short-circuited load, and for the electrical short-circuited case the mechanical system is terminated by a lossless mass reactance.

### 5.4.3 Thevenin Equivalent of Combined Input and Mechanical Sections

The efficiency, voltage transformation, and power transfer character-istics can most readily be obtained by making use of the Thevenin equivalent of the combined electrical input and mechanical sections which have been developed and simplified heretofore. Combining the equivalents shown in Figures 5.9, 5.11, and 5.12, we obtain Figure 5.14.

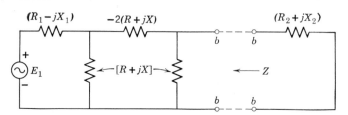

**Figure 5.14.** Combined input, output, and mechanical sections referred to the mechanical section.

The Thevenin equivalent of the input and mechanical sections is obtained by determining the input impedance $Z$ looking into the ter-minals $b$–$b$ with generator $E_1$ short-circuited and the open-circuited voltage appearing at terminals $b$–$b$. The result of these manipulations is shown in Figure 5.15.

## 5.5 Efficiency, Power Transfer, Frequency Shift

It should be recalled that the generator $E_1$ in the simplified equivalent circuit (Figure 5.14) is a function of $X_{eT}$ (see equation 5.32). For small deviations from the resonant frequency $\omega_0$, however, it may be assumed to be constant. The condition for maximum output voltage corresponds to the condition of maximum current in the foregoing equivalent, and this requires a shift in operating frequency such that the total series reactance reduces to zero. The same condition applies for maximum power transfer to the load *for a given load*.

The frequency shift is determined by applying the condition

$$2X - X_1 + X_2 = 0 \tag{5.42}$$

From equation 5.31 $X = 2\pi Z_0 r$, and from equation 5.29, $r = \Delta\omega/\omega_0$.

$$\Delta\omega = \omega_0 \frac{X_1 - X_2}{4\pi Z_0} \tag{5.43}$$

It is interesting to note that the frequency deviation $\Delta\omega$ is zero when the transformer is operated from a constant voltage source with an open-circuited output so that both $X_1$ and $X_2$ are zero (see equations 5.37 and 5.40). Thus one may define the condition of "fundamental resonance" of the composite bar under these operating conditions.

With a frequency shift set by equation 5.43, the condition for maximum power transfer to a given load is now simply derived and consists of making

$$R_2 = 2R + R_1 \qquad (5.44)$$

The efficiency for the general case can also be seen to be simply

$$\eta = \frac{R_2}{2R + R_1 + R_2} \qquad (5.45)$$

The efficiency for maximum power transfer, using equations 5.44 and 5.45, is 50 per cent.

The maximum possible efficiency $\eta_m$ *for a given load* can be seen to occur when the transformer is so designed that $R_2$, the transformed real part of the electrical load, is a maximum. Differentiating $R_2$ with respect to the electrical load $R_L$ in equation 5.35, the condition for maximum $R_2$ becomes

$$X_{eR} = R_L \qquad (5.46)$$

and for this condition

$$R_2 = 2\psi^2 R_L = 2\psi^2 X_{eR}$$
$$X_2 = 2\psi^2 X_{eR} \qquad (5.47)$$

Substituting condition 5.47 into 5.45, the maximum efficiency $\eta_m$ for a given electrical load $R_L$ becomes

$$\eta_m = \frac{2\psi^2 X_{eR}}{2R + R_1 + 2\psi^2 X_{eR}} \qquad (5.48)$$

## 5.6   Voltage Amplification General Case of Terminations

The voltage amplification $A_v$ for the general case can be arrived at most simply by making use of energy relations. For the condition of operation which yields the maximum voltage output, as described in preceding paragraphs, the power $W$ dissipated in the load is

$$W = |I_2|^2 R_2 \qquad (5.49)$$

where $I_2$ is the series resonant current of the equivalent circuit in Figure 5.15. But

$$|I_2| = \frac{|E_1|}{2R + R_1 + R_2} \tag{5.50}$$

Therefore,

$$W = \left(\frac{|E_1|}{2R + R_1 + R_2}\right)^2 R_2 \tag{5.51}$$

this power is dissipated in the actual electrical load $R_L$. Thus

$$W = \frac{|E_L|^2}{R_L} \tag{5.52}$$

where $E_L$ is the electrical output voltage.

Therefore,

$$E_L = \frac{|E_1|}{2R + R_1 + R_2} \cdot (R_2 R_L)^{\frac{1}{2}} \tag{5.53}$$

From 5.32

$$|E_1| = \frac{2\phi |E_g| X_{eT}}{(R_g{}^2 + X_{eT}{}^2)^{\frac{1}{2}}}$$

and the voltage amplification $A_v$ is

$$A_v = \left|\frac{E_L}{E_g}\right| = \frac{2\phi X_{eT}}{2R + R_1 + R_2}\left(\frac{R_2 R_L}{R_g{}^2 + X_{eT}{}^2}\right)^{\frac{1}{2}} \tag{5.54}$$

It serves little purpose to make the appropriate substitutions for the various terms in equation 5.54, as the resulting expression becomes quite complex and yields little physical insight into the operation of the transformer. However, when special operating conditions are chosen, as in the following section, simplified expressions result which are useful in practical design.

## 5.7  Transformer Characteristics.  Constant Voltage Drive

In practice it is usually difficult to approximate a constant voltage source to drive a transformer. This approximation, however, makes it possible to assess the effects of various material physical properties and the geometry on the operating characteristics, as well as to serve as a basis of comparison with other methods of high voltage generation.

Using simplifying relations in equation 5.37 and the equivalent circuit shown in Figure 5.15, we obtain the simple equivalent circuit of Figure 5.16.

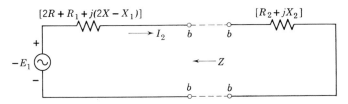

Figure 5.15. Thevenin equivalent of input and mechanical sections shown with output section, referred to mechanical section.

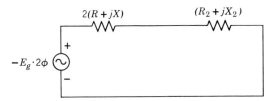

Figure 5.16. Equivalent circuit referred to mechanical section, constant voltage drive.

### 5.7.1 Voltage Amplification. Constant Voltage Drive

Using equation 5.54 and recalling that $R_g = R_1 = 0$ for this condition,

$$A_v = \frac{2\phi}{2R + R_2} (R_2 R_L)^{1/2} \tag{5.55}$$

There are three cases of interest: the electrically open-circuit voltage amplification, the voltage amplification for maximum power output, and the voltage amplification for maximum efficiency.

### 5.7.2 Case (1): Voltage Amplification Electrically Open-Circuited

For this case $R_L$ is assumed to become infinite.
From equation 5.35

$$R_2 = \frac{4\psi^2 R_L X_{eR}^2}{R_L^2 + X_{eR}^2}$$

Therefore,

$$[R_L R_2]^{1/2} = \left( \frac{4\psi^2 R_L^2 X_{eR}^2}{R_L^2 + X_{eR}^2} \right)^{1/2} \tag{5.56}$$

as $R_L \to \infty$

$$(R_L R_2)^{1/2} = 2\psi X_{eR} \qquad \text{and} \qquad R_2 = 0 \tag{5.57}$$

Inserting equation 5.57 into 5.55,

$$A_{vo} = \frac{2\psi\phi X_{eR}}{R} \qquad (5.58)$$

where $A_{vo}$ is the voltage amplification for the transformer electrically open-circuited.

In terms of more fundamental properties $A_{vo}$ may be evaluated as follows:

Substituting for $\psi$, $\phi$, $X_{eR}$, $R$ in equation 5.58 from equations 5.22, 5.4, 5.24, and 5.30, and using 5.16,

$$A_{vo} = \frac{2Q_m d_{31} Y_3{}^E k_{33}{}^2}{\pi\omega Z_0 \epsilon_{33}{}^T (1 - k_{33}{}^2)} \cdot W \qquad (5.59)$$

Substituting in equation 5.59 for $Z_0$ from equation 5.21 and from the auxiliary relations,

$$\omega = 2\pi f = \frac{2\pi c^E}{\lambda} = \frac{\pi c^E}{2L} \qquad (5.60)$$

where $c^E$ is velocity of propagation at constant field.

$$c^E = \left(\frac{Y_3{}^E}{\rho}\right)^{1/2}, \qquad k_{33}{}^2 = g_{33} d_{33} Y_3{}^E, \qquad d_{33} = \epsilon_{33}{}^T g_{33} \qquad (5.61)$$

The following result is obtained:

$$A_{vo} = \frac{4Q_m}{\pi^2} \cdot \frac{Y_3{}^E g_{33} d_{31}}{(1 - k_{33}{}^2)} \cdot \frac{L}{T} \qquad (5.62)$$

The foregoing result indicates very clearly the effects of geometry, mechanical $Q$, and piezoelectric properties of the material and serves as a first guide in designing a step-up transformer.

### 5.7.3 Case (2): Voltage Amplification for Condition of Maximum Power Transfer

For this case equation 5.44 yields for constant voltage drive.

$$R_2 = 2R \qquad (5.63)$$

since $R_1 = 0$; and from equation 5.35,

$$R_2 = \frac{4\psi^2 R_L X_{eR}{}^2}{R_L{}^2 + X_{eR}{}^2}$$

Let us assume $X_{eR} \ll R_L$. Then $R_2 = 2R \simeq \dfrac{4\psi^2 X_{eR}^2}{R_L}$ or

$$R_L \simeq \frac{2\psi^2 X_{eR}^2}{R} \tag{5.64}$$

The ratio $X_{eR}/R_L$, using 5.30, then becomes

$$\frac{X_{eR}}{R_L} \simeq \frac{\pi Z_0}{2 X_{eR} \psi^2 Q_m} \tag{5.65}$$

Using relations 5.21, 5.22, and 5.24 for $Z_0$, $\psi$, $X_{eR}$ and auxiliary relations 5.60 and 5.61,

$$\frac{X_{eR}}{R_L} \simeq \frac{\pi^2}{4 Q_m k_{33}^2} \tag{5.66}$$

For barium titanate type materials, values of $Q_m \geq 200$, $k_{33}^2 \geq 0.2$ are typical, and 5.66 approximates

$$X_{er} \leqq \tfrac{1}{16} R_L \tag{5.67}$$

Thus for these materials we can assume with little error that equation 5.35 reduces to

$$R_2 \simeq \frac{4\psi^2 X_{eR}^2}{R_L} \tag{5.68}$$

and equation 5.56, for $X_{eR} \ll R_L$, reduces to

$$(R_2 R_L)^{1/2} \simeq 2\psi X_{eR} \tag{5.69}$$

Inserting equations 5.69 and 5.63 into equation 5.55,

$$A_v \simeq \frac{\psi \phi X_{eR}}{R} \simeq \frac{1}{2} A_{vo} \tag{5.70}$$

Comparing this result with equation 5.58, we see that the voltage amplification for maximum power transfer is approximately one half the open-circuit amplification.

### 5.7.4   Case (3): Voltage Amplification for Maximum Efficiency Operation

The condition for maximum efficiency with a given load has been developed in general in Section 5.5, and the relations 5.46 and 5.47 hold for this condition.

Inserting conditions 5.46 and 5.47 into condition 5.55,

$$A_v = \frac{\sqrt{2}\, \phi \psi X_{eR}}{R + \psi^2 X_{eR}} \tag{5.71}$$

A comparison of the foregoing amplification with the open-circuit amplification $A_{vo}$ of equation 5.58 yields

$$\frac{A_v}{A_{vo}} = \frac{1}{\sqrt{2}\,[1 + (\psi^2 X_{eR}/R)]} \tag{5.72}$$

Evaluating the quantity $\psi^2 X_{eR}/R$ in more fundamental quantities, as previously done in equation 5.65,

$$\frac{\psi^2 X_{eR}}{R} = \frac{2}{\pi^2} \cdot k_{33}{}^2 Q_m \tag{5.73}$$

Thus

$$\frac{A_v}{A_{vo}} = \frac{1}{\sqrt{2}\,[1 + (2k_{33}{}^2 Q_m/\pi^2)]} \tag{5.74}$$

For materials with a $Q_m \simeq 200$, $k_{33}{}^2 \simeq 0.2$,

$$\frac{A_v}{A_{vo}} \simeq \frac{1}{12.9} \tag{5.75}$$

which represents a considerable reduction in voltage amplification and may be too large a reduction for practical design.

### 5.7.5 Optimization of Maximum Efficiency

As can be seen in condition 5.48, the maximum efficiency occurs for the case of constant voltage drive, i.e., when $R_1 = 0$ and then becomes

$$\eta_m = \frac{\psi^2 X_{eR}}{R + \psi^2 X_{eR}} = \frac{1}{1 + (R/\psi^2 X_{eR})} \tag{5.76}$$

Substituting from equation 5.73,

$$\eta_m = \frac{1}{1 + (\pi^2/2Q_m k_{33}{}^2)} \tag{5.77}$$

Thus for a typical material with $Q_m \simeq 200$, $k_{33}{}^2 \simeq 0.2$

$$\eta_m \simeq \frac{1}{1 + \frac{1}{8}} \simeq 89 \text{ per cent}$$

Examination of equation 5.77 indicates, of course, that higher maximum efficiencies may be obtained by increasing the mechanical $Q$, i.e., by use of materials with decreased mechanical loss or by increasing the electromechanical coupling coefficient $k_{33}$.

## 5.8   Input Impedance

In sub section 5.4.3, Figure 5.14, and indicated in Figure 5.15 the impedance $Z$ was determined for purposes of obtaining a Thevenin equivalent.   By symmetry the impedance looking into the net to the right at points $a - a$ transforms from Figure 5.17 to Figure 5.18.

The simplified network of output and mechanical sections referred to the mechanical section shown in Figure 5.18 is now transformed by the perfect input electromechanical transformer and is referred to the electrical input shown in Figure 5.19.

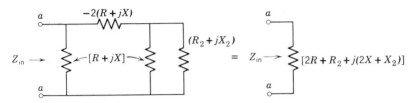

Figure 5.17.   Output section referred to me-chanical section.

Figure 5.18.   Simplified combined output and mechanical sections.

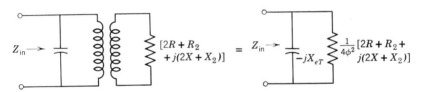

Figure 5.19.   Transformed system referred to electrical input.

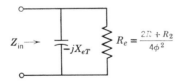

Figure 5.20.   Electrical input impedance.

When the transformer is operated at a frequency such that $2X + X_2 = 0$ the extreme right-hand branch of Figure 5.19 reduces to an equivalent resistor $R_e$, as shown in Figure 5.20.   With the transformer output open-circuited, i.e., $R_L \rightarrow \infty$, resistance $R_e$ becomes

$$R_e = \frac{R}{2\phi^2},   \text{since } R_2 = 0,   \text{for } R_L = \infty \text{ (see equation 5.40)} \quad (5.78)$$

Using equations 5.30, 5.4, 5.21, 5.61, and 5.16,

$$R_e = \frac{\pi}{2c^E Q_m Y_3{}^E d_{31}{}^2} \cdot \frac{T}{W} \qquad (5.79)$$

It should be noted that for the case of short-circuited output $R_e$ is the same value as in equation 5.79, since $R_2 = 0$ for $R_L = 0$ (see equation 5.41).

It can be shown that for other special load resistances of interest, $R_L$, the values of $R_e$ become as shown below.

*For maximum power transfer $R_2 = 2R$ (equation 5.63).*

$$R_e = \frac{\pi}{c^E Q_m Y_3{}^E d_{31}{}^2} \cdot \frac{T}{W} \qquad (5.80)$$

This is a value twice the open-circuited case.

*For maximum efficiency $R_2 = 2\psi^2 X_{eR}$ (equation 5.47).*

$$R_e = \frac{R}{2\phi^2}\left(1 + \frac{\psi^2 X_{eR}}{R}\right) \qquad (5.81)$$

The factor $\psi^2 X_{eR}/R$ has been encountered in equation 5.73 and was shown to be $2k_{33}{}^2 Q_m/\pi^2$, which for a typical material was approximately equal to 8. Thus for this case the value of $R_e$ is approximately nine times the value for the open-circuited transformer.

It is also instructive to compare the value of the resistance $R_e$ under open-circuited conditions to the value of reactance $X_{eT}$.

From equations 5.78 and 5.30 $R_e = R/2\phi^2 = \pi Z_0/2\phi^2 Q_m$. Using relations 5.21, 5.6, 5.60, and 5.61,

$$\frac{X_{eT}}{R_e} = \frac{4Q_m}{\pi^2(1 - k_{31}{}^2)} \cdot \frac{d_{31}{}^2 Y_3{}^E}{\epsilon_{33}{}^T}$$

Therefore,

$$\frac{X_{eT}}{R_e} = \frac{4Q_m}{\pi^2} \cdot \frac{k_{31}{}^2}{1 - k_{31}{}^2} \qquad \text{since} \qquad \frac{d_{31}{}^2 Y_3{}^E}{\epsilon_{33}{}^T} = k_{31}{}^2 \qquad (5.82)$$

For $Q_m \simeq 200$, $k_{31}{}^2 \simeq 0.03$ for a typical barium titanate material.

$$\frac{X_{eT}}{R_e} \simeq 2.5 \text{ for the open-circuited transformer} \qquad (5.83)$$

Thus the input impedance may have a relatively high reactive component which would lead to high over-all losses if uncompensated. For operation at maximum efficiency $R_e$ was found to be approximately nine times that of the open-circuited value. For this case, therefore, the reactive component is quite small.

## 5.9   Resonating Input Inductance

In practice, the reactive part of the input impedance may be resonated out by use of an appropriate inductor in series with the transformer input and usually yields an increased voltage amplification.   As an example, let us obtain the value of inductance and resulting voltage step-up due to this inductance for a transformer with termination chosen for maximum power transfer.   The simplified equivalent circuit is shown in Figure 5.21.   It is assumed there is negligible loss in the inductance, which has a reactance $jX_L$.

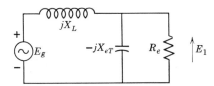

**Figure 5.21.** Simplified circuit with resonating input inductance.

The equivalent impedance of $-jX_{eT}$ and $R_e$ in parallel

$$Z_e = \frac{X_{eT}^2 R_e}{R_e^2 + X_{eT}^2} - j \cdot \frac{R_e^2 X_{eT}}{R_e^2 + X_{eT}^2} \tag{5.84}$$

Thus

$$X_L = \frac{R_e^2 X_{eT}}{R_e^2 + X_{eT}^2} = \frac{X_{eT}}{1 + (X_{eT}/R_e)^2} \tag{5.85}$$

From Section 5.8 a typical value for the ratio $X_{eT}/R_e$ is approximately 2.5 for the open-circuited case.   For maximum power transfer it was shown that $R_e$ is $\frac{1}{2}$ the value for the open-circuited case, thus $X_{eT}/R_e \simeq 5$.   A typical value for $X_L$ would therefore be

$$X_L \simeq \frac{X_{eT}}{26} \tag{5.86}$$

which usually results in a rather small inductance.

To obtain the voltage amplification due to the addition of the inductance, power delivered to the equivalent real part of impedance is equated to power delivered to the actual load $R_e$.

Thus,

$$\frac{|E_g|^2}{X_{eT}^2 R_e/(R_e^2 + X_{eT}^2)} = \frac{|E_1|^2}{R_e} \tag{5.87}$$

or

$$\left|\frac{E_1}{E_g}\right| = \frac{(R_e^2 + X_{eT}^2)^{1/2}}{X_{eT}}$$

$$\left|\frac{E_1}{E_g}\right| = \frac{[1 + (X_{eT}/R_e)^2]^{1/2}}{X_{eT}/R_e} \tag{5.88}$$

For a typical case $X_{eT}/R_e \simeq 5$.

Thus in this case the voltage amplification resulting from the compensating coil alone is barely greater than unity, but we are operating at unity power factor.

With the transformer operated in the maximum efficiency mode, $R_e$ was shown, typically, to be approximately nine times the open-circuit value and thus, typically, $X_{eT}/R_e \simeq 0.27$. For this case we obtain a voltage amplification of approximately 3.7, due to the resonating inductance which offsets the relatively poor voltage amplification of the transformer itself under these operating conditions. In fact, if we compare the over-all voltage amplification for conditions of maximum power transfer and maximum efficiency (see equations 5.70 and 5.75), the former is larger than the latter by a factor of only 1.75.

## 5.10  Transformer Design Procedure

At this writing there is one serious limitation to the extended use of available ferroelectric ceramics as voltage step-up transformers. At high levels of drive highly nonlinear effects, accompanied by increased loss with subsequent heating and depolarization of the ceramic, become evident. For a barium-titanate ceramic with nickel or cobalt additives the safe working generated field in the generating portion of the transformer is approximately 0.5 volt rms per mil averaged over the whole length of the generating portion. Thus, with the output voltage specified, the minimum length of the transformer is fixed, as is the maximum operating drive frequency.

To illustrate the foregoing analysis a typical design procedure is shown for a step-up transformer driven from a constant voltage source under the condition of maximum power transfer. Suppose the load resistance $R_L$, the voltage amplification $A_v$, and the rms output voltage $E_2$ are specified. The steps in the design are as follows with the necessary relations indicated:

### Step 1

The minimum length $L$ is set by the operating field of 0.5 volt per mil or approximately 20,000 v/m. Thus

$$L = \frac{E_2}{20,000} \text{ m} \tag{5.89}$$

### Step 2

The no-load voltage amplification $A_{vo}$ is determined from equation 5.62 and, together with relation 5.70, then yields the required thickness $T$. For this case of maximum power transfer relation 5.70 yields

$$A_{vo} = 2A_v \tag{5.90}$$

where $A_v$ is specified, and, using 5.62,

$$T = \frac{4Q_m Y_3{}^E g_{33} d_{31}}{\pi^2(1 - k_{33}{}^2)} \cdot \frac{L}{A_{vo}} \tag{5.91}$$

Using values obtained for $L$ and $A_{vo}$ from steps 1 and 2, the thickness $T$ is determined.

### Step 3

The width $W$ is determined by making use of relations 5.24, 5.60, and 5.66 to obtain a single expression.

Thus from

$$\frac{X_{eR}}{R_L} \simeq \frac{\pi^2}{4Q_m k_{33}{}^2} \tag{5.66}$$

$$X_{eR} = \frac{L}{\omega \epsilon_{33}{}^T(1 - k_{33}{}^2)^2 T \cdot W} \tag{5.24}$$

$$\frac{1}{\omega} = \frac{2L}{\pi c^E} \tag{5.60}$$

Combining the above and solving for $W$,

$$W = \frac{8Q_m k_{33}{}^2}{\pi^3 c^E (1 - k_{33}{}^2)^2 \epsilon_{33}{}^T} \cdot \frac{L^2}{R_L T} \tag{5.92}$$

where $L$, $T$ are determined from steps 1 and 2, and $R_L$ is specified.

### Step 4

Using relations 5.17 and 5.18, corrections to the area and length $T'W'$, $L'$ of the generator portion are determined.

**Step 5**

The operating frequency is determined from equation 5.60:

$$f = \frac{c^E}{4L} \tag{5.93}$$

**Step 6**

The input impedance parameters are computed

$$X_{eT} = \frac{1}{\omega \epsilon_{33}{}^T (1 - k_{31}{}^2)} \cdot \frac{T}{WL} \tag{5.6}$$

and

$$R_e = \frac{\pi}{c^E Q_m Y_3{}^E d_{31}{}^2} \cdot \frac{T}{W} \tag{5.80}$$

**Step 7**

The resonating inductance $L_e$ is computed from equation 5.85:

$$L_e = \frac{X_L}{\omega} = \frac{1}{\omega} \cdot \frac{X_{eT}}{1 + (X_{eT}/R_e)^2} \tag{5.94}$$

## 5.11 Performance of Transverse Type Ceramic High Voltage Transformer

Figures 5.22, 5.23, 5.24, and 5.25 show the performance of a typical ceramic high-voltage transformer, constructed as shown in Figure 5.2. A modified barium titanate ceramic having the following properties was used:

| | |
|---|---|
| Over-all Length | $2L = 0.1463$ m |
| Over-all Width | $W = 0.0254$ m |
| Over-all Thickness | $T = 0.0061$ m |

$\rho = 5390$ Kg/m$^3$      $g_{33} = 1.113 \times 10^{-2}$ volt m/newton

$Y_3{}^E = 9.5 \times 10^{10}$ newton/m$^2$      $k_{31}{}^2 = 0.0352$

$c^E = 4200$ m/sec      $k_{33}{}^2 = 0.17$

$\epsilon_{33}{}^T = 1.443 \times 10^{-8}$ farad/m      $Q_m = 185$

$d_{31} = 0.73 \times 10^{-10}$ m/volt      $Q_E > 400$

$d_{33} = 1.605 \times 10^{-10}$ m/volt      $f_0 = 14{,}332$ cps (open-circuited)

The theoretical performance curves shown for comparison in Figures 5.22 and 5.23 were corrected for the effects of stray capacitance due to leads and to stray flux emanating from the electrodes but not passing through the ceramic body. The effects of these corrections have been shown by Rosen (21).

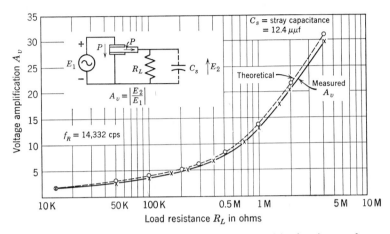

Figure 5.22.   Relation between voltage amplifications and load resistance for transverse ceramic transformer with constant voltage drive = 0.09 volt.

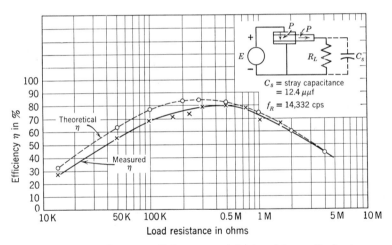

Figure 5.23.   Relation between efficiency $\eta$ and load resistance $R_L$ for transverse ceramic transformer; constant voltage drive = 0.09 volt.

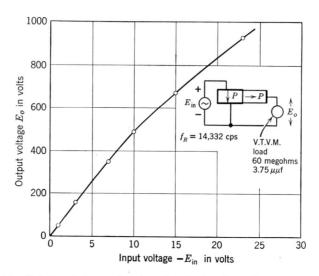

**Figure 5.24.** Relation between input and output voltage for transverse ceramic transformer operating with very light load.

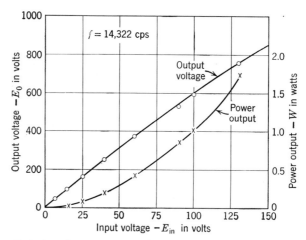

**Figure 5.25.** Relations between input voltage $E_{in}$ and (1) output voltage $E_o$, (2) power output $W$ for transverse ceramic transformer operating with resistive load of 330 KΩ.

Although the measured voltage amplification and efficiency are consistently smaller than the theoretical values, the correspondence between the curves is reasonably good. It should be noted that several sources of error which have not been factored into the theoretical curves are

1. The bar used had a uniform section for both driven and driver sections; there is, therefore, some mismatch between these segments.

2. The measured values of the physical properties can represent only "average" properties of the whole ceramic bar, since it cannot be assumed that the bar is homogeneous.

3. A common ground fired-on silver electrode was used instead of two separate electrodes. Thus a small but relatively important area in the middle of the bar had a distorted pattern of flux considerably different from that assumed in the analysis.

4. Examination of Figure 5.24 indicates that there is some degree of nonlinearity at higher output voltage levels, even with light electrical loading. It is interesting to note that this departure from linearity occurs at about the same output voltage for both loaded and unloaded cases (see Figure 5.25) suggesting that the effect is primarily due to high electric fields.


## / CERAMIC FILTER ELEMENTS


### 5.12   Introduction

Ceramic transformers as voltage step-up devices are described in Design of Ceramic Power Transformers. The analysis is based on obtaining maximum voltage step-up with high efficiency, and it is clear that these conditions can be met only when the bars are operating at frequencies at or near mechanical resonance. Thus large energy transfer from input to output terminals is restricted to narrow frequency bands, a property common to a large class of conventional radio filters.

Two-terminal electromechanical filter elements using single crystals of quartz, Ethylene Diamine Tartrate (EDT), Dipotassium Tartrate (DKT), are in wide use both for precise frequency control and in more elaborate multisection filters (6). The use of divided electrodes on single slabs of quartz to provide four-terminal filters has been investigated by Watanabi (10), by a group at Tufts College (11), and by Mason (6). More complex assemblies of multisection mechanical elements to which input and output magnetostrictive transducers are mechanically coupled for use as precise pass-band filters have been described by Roberts and Burns (12) and Adler (13). Magnetostrictive electromechanical filters using ferrite toroids in which magnetic coupling is balanced out have been described by Roberts (14). This section contains a qualitative description of the use of polarized ferroelectric ceramics and magnetostrictive ferrites as simple filter elements and a detailed analysis of several configurations consisting of polarized ferroelectric ceramics only. The advantages that may be foreseen include

1. The ease of molding ceramics in many shapes of relatively inexpensive materials.

2. A wide variety of electrical and mechanical properties of these ceramics can be obtained by an appropriate choice of additives and control of process variables, and new materials are continually being developed which extend the range of operation and improve the stability with age, temperature, and field.

3. Large slabs may be fabricated at little extra cost, as compared with with the rapidly rising cost of large single crystals of quartz or synthetic crystals.

4. It is possible to polarize ferroelectric ceramics in any desired direction and even in several different directions in sections of the same bar.

5. Composite filters made of both ferroelectric and magnetostrictive materials permit isolation of electrical input from electrical output, the coupling being entirely mechanical. Since the elastic moduli and densities are quite similar in both types of ceramics, the physical joining of the two materials does not require elaborate mechanical matching sections to prevent acoustic reflection, slight changes in the relative sectional areas being adequate to ensure exact matching of mechanical impedance.

6. Low-frequency filter elements (20 cps to 10 kc) using ceramic reeds can be made inexpensively with an effective electrical $Q$ greater than 100. The performance and size compare favorably with lumped constant $L$-$C$ type filter sections at these frequencies.

## 5.13 Physical Arrangements

The simplest mode of operation consists in driving long thin bars in longitudinal mechanical resonance. For frequencies above approximately $\frac{1}{2}$ mc and below 10 kc the length of the assembly becomes inconveniently small or large, respectively. Bimorph type construction permits operation below 10 kc to a few cycles per second; shear operation permits operation up to about 5 mc per second.

Figure 5.26 shows several arrangements of longitudinal mode filters; the principle of operation of this type is described in Section 5.0. The bimorph arrangements shown in Figure 5.27 are generally adaptations of the same principle used in thermal bimetallic strips and similar to the constructions used for ceramic phonograph pickups, microphones, loudspeakers, etc., in which amplification of displacement is effected by the physical arrangement. Briefly (Figure 5.27a), one polarized element tends to change its length on application of a field but is restrained by being firmly bonded to another element of equal flexural compliance. The net result is that the reedlike assembly bends in flexure, motion occurring at right angles to the forced extension in length. The actual lateral displacement may be many times the displacement along the length. The resulting stress, by the direct piezoelectric effect, produces an electrical field in the polarized second member, a potential difference appearing across its terminals. The center conductor bonded to both polarized elements serves several purposes: as common ground electrode, as electrostatic shield between both elements, and as a metallic strengthener greatly increasing its resistance to mechanical shock. Large energy transfer occurs when the assembly is driven at frequencies corresponding to mechanical resonance in flexure. These frequencies have been determined by Rayleigh (15); the resonant frequencies $f$ for a bar fixed at one end and free at the other, vibrating in flexure, are

$$ f = \frac{m^2 T}{2\pi \sqrt{12} \, L^2} \left( \frac{Y}{\rho} \right)^{\frac{1}{2}} \tag{5.95} $$

where $Y$ is Young's modulus,
  $\rho$ is the density,
  $T$ is the thickness,
  $L$ is the length,
  $m$ is a pure number.

The value of $m$ depends on the mode of vibration and is given for the fundamental as $m_1 = 1.875$. For higher modes $m_2 = 4.694$, $m_3 = 7.855$, $m_4 = 10.995 \cdots$.

For very low frequencies (100 cycles and below) either the thickness of the bimorph may be decreased or its length increased to an impracticable degree. For these frequencies the mass-loaded bimorph shown in Figure 5.27b is more suitable. This assembly behaves like a lumped

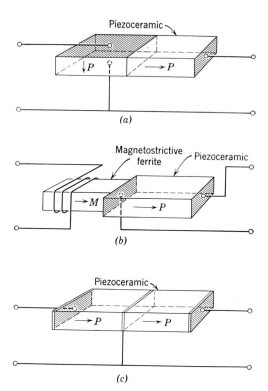

Figure 5.26.  Long bar elements: ($a$) transverse; ($b$) composite; ($c$) ring type.

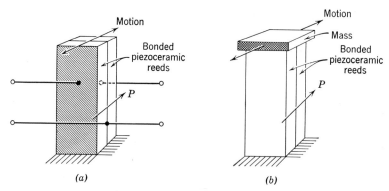

Figure 5.27.  Bimorph elements: ($a$) titanate bimorph; ($b$) titanate bimorph, mass-loaded.

constant mass-spring combination, and if the reed mass can be neglected the resonant frequency is given approximately by

$$f = \frac{1}{2\pi} \left( \frac{1}{KM} \right)^{\frac{1}{2}}$$ (5.96)

where $M$ is the mass, and

$$K = \frac{L^3}{3YI}$$ (5.97)

where $K$ is the compliance and $I$ is the moment of inertia given by

$$I = \frac{WT^3}{12}$$ (5.98)

where $W$ is the width,
 $T$ is the thickness,
 $L$ is the length,
 $Y$ is modulus of elasticity.

Thus

$$f = \frac{1}{4\pi} \left( \frac{YWT^3}{ML^3} \right)^{\frac{1}{2}}$$ (5.99)

Figures 5.28$a$ and 5.28$b$ illustrate ring-type shear and transverse-type shear filters. Application of an electric field at right angles to the

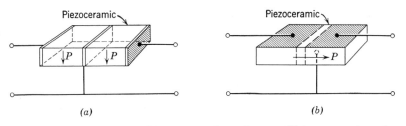

**Figure 5.28.** Shear elements: ($a$) ring-type shear element; ($b$) transverse-type shear element.

direction of polarization in the driver section induces shear through the $d_{15}$ piezoelectric coefficient, causing diamond-shaped deformation. Electrical output from the driven section results by the inverse piezoelectric effect through the $g_{15}$ coefficient. For operation in thickness shear where the thickness is much smaller than the other dimensions the resonant frequency is given approximately by Cady (1):

$$f = \frac{1}{2T}\left[\frac{Y}{\rho} \cdot \frac{1}{2(1+\sigma)}\right]^{1/2} \tag{5.100}$$

where $T$ is the thickness,
  $Y$ is the modulus of elasticity,
  $\rho$ is the density,
  $\sigma$ is Poisson's ratio.

More exact expressions, involving corrections functionally related to the other dimensions, are also given by this reference (1).

## 5.14 Simplified Equivalent Circuits for Ring-Type and Transverse-Type All-Piezoelectric Filter Elements

The matrix representation of a piezoelectric four-terminal electromechanical filter is described in Chapter 3. This representation, which is simple in form, contains within it all the essential information that determine performance. In multielement filters with parallel, cascade, or other operation, with or without additional electrical or mechanical elements, such representation permits formal analysis by using the techniques of matrix algebra. Many of the terms in the matrix are, however, hyperbolic functions with complex arguments, and an array of such terms is in general difficult to visualize without some familiar physical model. Such models, which can be simplified equivalent circuits, are usually essential to the practicing engineer to permit intelligent application, development, or invention.

In this section simplified equivalent circuits are developed for several configurations of moderate complexity representative of the whole class of electromechanical filter elements previously described. The network transformations for every configuration are quite similar, since all four-terminal electromechanical filter elements have in common a mechanical resonating system coupled electromechanically to input and output electrical circuits. The simplifying approximations used must, however, be examined for each separate configuration to determine the range of validity. The configurations chosen are the piezoelectric ring type shown in Figure 5.26c and the piezoelectric transverse type shown in Figure 5.26a. Both are operated as second harmonic resonators, i.e., the total effective length equals one wavelength, and are considered to be "long thin bars." Simplified equivalent circuits are developed, the effects of input and output circuit loading are explored, and design criteria are obtained to permit their use as filter elements. It is beyond the scope of this book to present the treatment of multielement filters (7) which may make use of such individual four-terminal elements.

The representations in Figure 5.29a and 5.29b show the principal features of the filters to be analyzed. It is assumed that the widths $W$ and $W'$ and thicknesses $T$, $T'$ will in all cases be small relative to a wavelength (less than $\lambda/8$) so that "long thin bar" equivalent circuits

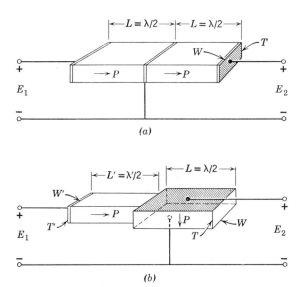

(a)

(b)

Figure 5.29. (a) Ring-type titanate filter operating at second harmonic response; (b) transverse-type titanate filter element operating at second harmonic response.

will apply. It may be noted that although the ring-type filter has a constant cross section the transverse type is shown with a stepped-down cross section for the same reasons described in Section 5.2. This leads to simplified analysis, for in practice a uniform bar is used with little change in observed performance.

The complete equivalent circuits for the two configurations (Figures 5.30a and 5.30b) are obtained by joining the appropriate equivalent circuits for ring and transverse sections shown in Figures 3.20 and 3.21. For the transverse case the necessary adjustments in length $L'$ and section $T'W'$, as defined by equations 5.17 and 5.18, have been made so that the mechanical section for this case is a symmetrical $T$ (see Figure 5.6). No such modification is necessary for the ring type, since input and output sections are identically polarized and thus operate with the same value of effective modulus of elasticity.

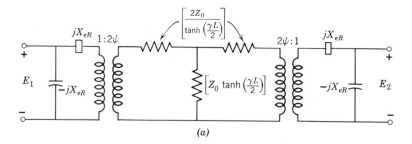

*(a)*

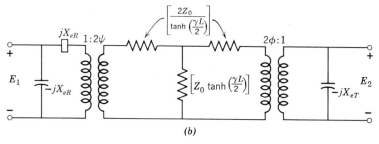

*(b)*

**Figure 5.30.** *(a)* Complete equivalent circuit-ring-type filter; *(b)* complete equivalent circuit-transverse-type filter.

For convenience the various quantities of the equivalent circuits are redefined below:

**Transverse Filter**

$$Z_0 = WT(\rho Y_1^E)^{1/2} \qquad (5.101)$$

$$\gamma = j\omega \left(\frac{\rho}{Y_1^E}\right)^{1/2} \qquad (5.102)$$

$$\psi = \frac{k_{33}^2(1 - k_{33}^2)}{g_{33}} \frac{WT}{L} \qquad (5.103)$$

$$\phi = W d_{31} Y_1^E \qquad (5.104)$$

$$X_{eR} = \frac{L}{\omega \epsilon_{33}^T (1 - k_{33}^2)^2 TW} \qquad (5.105)$$

$$X_{eT} = \frac{T}{\omega \epsilon_{33}^T (1 - k_{31}^2) WL} \qquad (5.106)$$

**Ring Filter**

$$Z_0 = WT(\rho Y_3^D)^{1/2} \qquad (5.101a)$$

$$\gamma = j\omega \left(\frac{\rho}{Y_3^D}\right)^{1/2} \qquad (5.102a)$$

$$\psi = \frac{k_{33}^2}{g_{33}} \cdot \frac{WT}{L} \qquad (5.103a)$$

$$X_{eR} = \frac{L}{\omega \epsilon_{33}^T (1 - k_{33}^2) TW} \qquad (5.105a)$$

It is to be noted that the shunt electrical losses in the input and output sections have been assumed negligibly small so that the pure reactances $-jX_{eR}$ and $-jX_{eT}$ may be used in the equivalent circuits ($\epsilon_{33}^T$ is assumed real). It is further assumed that all the mechanical losses are distributed in the mechanical system, there being no loss involved in either the transformation constants $\psi$ and $\phi$ or in the piezoelectric coefficients $d_{33}$, $d_{31}$, $g_{33}$, $g_{31}$, $k_{31}$, and $k_{33}$. (These quantities are assumed real.)

## 5.15   The Mechanical System

Both filter types have the same mechanical system shown in Figure 5.31. In a range of frequency centered about that for which $L = \lambda/2$,

$$\tanh \frac{\gamma L}{2} \simeq \frac{4Q_m}{\pi} \frac{1}{1 + j2Q_m r} \qquad (5.107)$$

See equation 5.28, noting that in this case $L$ represents $\lambda/2$ instead of $\lambda/4$ where $Q_m$ is the mechanical $Q$ of the bar and

$$r = \frac{\omega - \omega_0}{\omega_0} = \frac{\Delta\omega}{\omega_0} \qquad (5.108)$$

With this approximation, the circuit of Figure 5.31 becomes that of Figure 5.32.

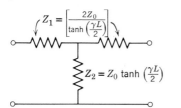

Figure 5.31. Mechanical equivalent circuit.

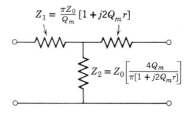

Figure 5.32. Approximate mechanical equivalent circuit near second harmonic resonance.

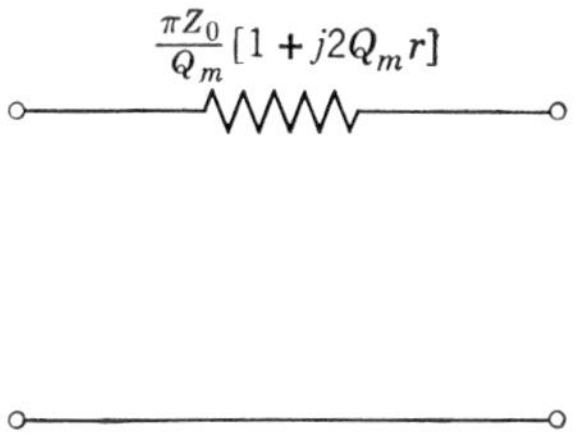

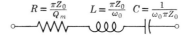

Figure 5.33. Approximate mechanical equivalent circuit.

Figure 5.34. Lumped constant representation of mechanical equivalent circuit.

The ratio of the absolute magnitude of the middle branch impedance to the absolute magnitude of either side branch impedance

$$\left| \frac{Z_2}{Z_1} \right| = \frac{8Q_m{}^2}{\pi^2(1 + 4Q_m{}^2 r^2)} \qquad (5.109)$$

At resonance where $r = 0$ it can be seen that for large $Q_m$ (greater than 100) the middle branch impedance is of the order of $10^4$, the magnitude of each side branch impedance, and effectively the equivalent circuit reduces very closely to the sum of the two side branch impedances. Even for rather large values of deviation from the resonant frequency this approximation holds rather well. If we assume a $Q_m$ of 100, it requires a deviation represented by $r \simeq 4$ per cent to obtain as small a ratio of $\left| \dfrac{Z_2}{Z_1} \right|$ as 100:1 and $r \simeq 14$ per cent for a ratio of $\left| \dfrac{Z_2}{Z_1} \right|$ of 10:1. Thus for $Q_m$'s larger than 100 and for frequency ranges extending up to $\pm 5$ per cent on either side of the resonant frequency we may safely omit the middle branch with little error, and the configuration of Figure 5.32 simplifies to that of Figure 5.33.

It is instructive to note that a more familiar lumped constant representation would be that of Figure 5.34 where

$$R = \frac{\pi Z_0}{Q_m} \qquad (5.110)$$

$$L = \frac{\pi Z_0}{\omega_0} \qquad (5.111)$$

$$C = \frac{1}{\omega_0 \pi Z_0} \qquad (5.112)$$

as readily verified by substitution in well-known relations

$$Q_m = \frac{\omega_0 L}{R} = \frac{1}{\omega_0 C R}$$

where $\qquad (5.113)$

$$\omega_0{}^2 = \frac{1}{LC}$$

## 5.16   Transformations of the Electrical Input and Output Circuits into the Mechanical Circuit

In vacuum tube and transistor circuits the electrical load of the single element filter is usually the input impedance of a tube or transistor stage which can be represented in most cases of interest by a shunt combination of resistance and capacitance. The output impedance of the tube or transistor driver can also usually be represented by an appropriate arrangement of resistance and capacitance. It is convenient to assess the loading effects of the driver impedance and the electrical load impedance on filter operation by referring (or transforming) the input and output terminations to the mechanical system.

### 5.16.1   Transformations of Input and Output Sections

Figure 5.35 illustrates a typical driver consisting of a constant voltage source $E_g$, with internal resistance $R_g$ and shunt capacitive reactance $-jX_g$, operating into a longitudinally polarized segment. This segment, as shown, may represent the driver or input section of either ring-type filter or an input section of a transverse-type filter which has a transverse output section. The two shunt reactances $X_g$ and $X_{eR}$ are combined into a single reactance $X_{e1}$, which is

$$X_{e1} = \frac{X_g X_{eR}}{X_g + X_{eR}} \tag{5.114}$$

Shown in Figures 5.36a and 5.36b are output sections, ring and transverse, respectively, loaded with typical electrical loads. Here again for convenience the single reactance $X_{e2}$ is defined as

$$X_{e2} = \frac{X_L X_{eR}}{X_L + X_{eR}} \tag{5.115}$$

for the ring section and

$$X_{e2} = \frac{X_L X_{eT}}{X_L + X_{eT}} \tag{5.116}$$

for the transverse section.

As in the case of the high voltage transformer, with the aid of network theorems the input and output electrical sections are transformed into the mechanical section and are shown in Figure 5.37 for both ring-type and transverse-type filters: use of the simplified mechanical circuit developed in Figure 5.33 is made.

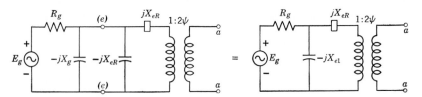

**Figure 5.35.** Input ring section with typical electrical load.

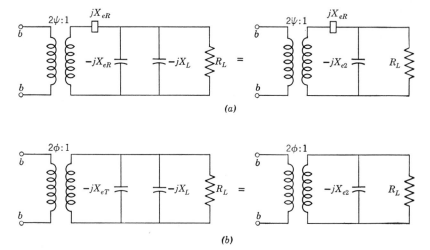

*(a)*

*(b)*

**Figure 5.36.** (*a*) Ring output section with typical electrical load; (*b*) transverse output section and typical electrical load.

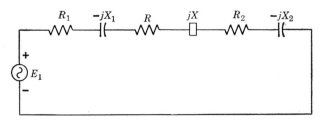

**Figure 5.37.** Simplified equivalent circuit of filter element referred to mechanical system.

The various quantities are defined for the two types of filter:

For the Ring-Type Filter
(ring input and output sections)

For the Transverse Type Filter
(ring input and transverse output
sections)

$$E_1 = 2\psi E_g \left( \frac{X_{e1}^2 - jR_g X_{e1}}{R_g^2 + X_{e1}^2} \right) \quad (5.117)$$

$$E_1 = 2\psi E_g \left( \frac{X_{e1}^2 - jR_g X_{e1}}{R_g^2 + X_{e1}^2} \right) \quad (5.117)$$

$$R_1 = 4\psi^2 \left( \frac{X_{e1}^2 R_g}{R_g^2 + X_{e1}^2} \right) \quad (5.118)$$

$$R_1 = 4\psi^2 \left( \frac{X_{e1}^2 R_g}{R_g^2 + X_{e1}^2} \right) \quad (5.118)$$

$$X_1 = 4\psi^2 \left( \frac{X_{e1} R_g^2}{R_g^2 + X_{e1}^2} - X_{eR} \right) \quad (5.119)$$

$$X_1 = 4\psi^2 \left( \frac{X_{e1} R_g^2}{R_g^2 + X_{e1}^2} - X_{eR} \right) \quad (5.119)$$

$$R_2 = 4\psi^2 \left( \frac{X_{e2}^2 R_L}{R_L^2 + X_{e2}^2} \right) \quad (5.120)$$

$$R_2 = 4\phi^2 \left( \frac{X_{e2}^2 R_L}{R_L^2 + X_{e2}^2} \right) \quad (5.122)$$

$$X_2 = 4\psi^2 \left( \frac{X_{e2} R_L^2}{R_L^2 + X_{e2}^2} - X_{eR} \right) \quad (5.121)$$

$$X_2 = 4\phi^2 \left( \frac{X_{e2} R_L^2}{R_L^2 + X_{e2}^2} \right) \quad (5.123)$$

and for the mechanical system in common

$$R = \frac{\pi Z_0}{Q_m} \quad (5.124)$$

$$X = 2\pi Z_0 r \quad (5.125)$$

where $Z_0$ is defined by equation 5.101a for the ring-type filter and by equation 5.101 for the transverse-type filter. In the latter case the length and width of the ring section have been slightly altered as described in Section 5.2, equations 5.17 and 5.18.

### 5.16.2   Resistive Loading on Mechanical System

In the later development of design criteria it is necessary to specify the degree to which the resistive part of the input and output electrical circuit loads the mechanical circuit. It is convenient to develop the necessary formulas in detail for the case of a ring filter loaded electrically, as shown in Figures 5.35 and 5.37. Thus let

$$R_1 = aR \quad (5.126)$$

where $a$ is a dimensionless design parameter.

Substituting for $R_1$ from equation 5.118,

$$a = \frac{4\psi^2}{R}\left(\frac{X_{e1}{}^2 R_g}{R_g{}^2 + X_{e1}{}^2}\right) \tag{5.127}$$

The quantity $4\psi^2/R$ may be expanded with the aid of equations 5.103$a$, 5.124, and 5.101$a$:

$$\frac{4\psi^2}{R} = 4\left(\frac{k_{33}{}^2 WT}{g_{33}L}\right)^2\left(\frac{Qm}{\pi WT(\rho Y_3{}^D)^{1/2}}\right) \tag{5.128}$$

From equation 5.105$a$

$$X_{eR} = \frac{1}{\omega\epsilon_{33}{}^T(1 - k_{33}{}^2)} \cdot \frac{L}{TW} \tag{5.105a}$$

but

$$\omega = \frac{2\pi c^D}{\lambda} = \frac{\pi c^D}{L} \tag{5.129}$$

where $c^D$ is velocity of propagation at constant electric displacement $D$. Thus

$$\frac{TW}{L^2} = \frac{1}{X_{eR}} \cdot \left(\frac{1}{\pi c^D \epsilon_{33}{}^T(1 - k_{33}{}^2)}\right) \tag{5.130}$$

Introducing equation 5.130 into equation 5.128 and using the auxiliary relations already defined,

$$c^D = \left(\frac{Y_3{}^D}{\rho}\right)^{1/2} \tag{5.131}$$

$$k_{33}{}^2 = g_{33}{}^2 \epsilon_{33}{}^T Y_3{}^E \tag{5.132}$$

$$Y_3{}^D = \frac{Y_3{}^E}{1 - k_{33}{}^2} \tag{5.133}$$

Equation 5.128 becomes

$$\frac{4\psi^2}{R} = \frac{4k_{33}{}^2 Q_m}{\pi^2} \cdot \frac{1}{X_{eR}} \tag{5.134}$$

Let us define for the ring-type transformer,

$$\frac{4k_{33}{}^2 Q_m}{\pi^2} = k_R \tag{5.135}$$

Thus

$$\frac{4\psi^2}{R} = \frac{k_R}{X_{eR}} \tag{5.136}$$

With the aid of equation 5.114, the quantity $X_{e1}^2 R_g / R_g^2 + X_{e1}^2$ may be expanded and simplified:

$$\frac{X_{e1}^2 R_g}{R_g^2 + X_{e1}^2} = \frac{R_g X_{eR}^2 X_g^2}{R_g^2 (X_g + X_{eR})^2 + X_{eR}^2 X_g^2} \tag{5.137}$$

Introducing equations 5.137 and 5.136 into equation 5.127,

$$a = k_R \left( \frac{R_g X_{eR} X_g^2}{R_g^2 (X_g + X_{eR})^2 + X_{eR}^2 X_g^2} \right) \tag{5.138}$$

The reactances $X_{eR}$, $X_g$ may be replaced by $1/\omega C_{0R}$, $1/\omega C_g$, respectively, where $C_{0R}$, $C_g$ are the relevant capacitances, with some simplification, equation 5.138 becomes

$$a = k_R \left( \frac{\omega R_g C_{0R}}{\omega^2 R_g^2 (C_{0R} + C_g)^2 + 1} \right) \tag{5.138a}$$

We have thus arrived at an expression which yields the degree of resistive loading on the mechanical system in terms of the external input electrical load, a material constant $k_R$ given by equation 5.135 and the reactance $X_{eR}$ of the clamped input capacitance. For design purposes it will be convenient to specify the value of the parameter $a$ and for specified generator internal resistance and capacitive reactance, $R_g$ and $X_g$, to determine the reactance $X_{eR}$ which with equation 5.105a will then yield the necessary dimensional relations.

Expanding and rearranging the terms of equation 5.138,

$$X_{eR}^2 + \frac{R_g X_g (2a R_g - k_R X_g)}{a(R_g^2 + X_g^2)} \cdot X_{eR} + \frac{R_g^2 X_g^2}{R_g^2 + X_g^2} = 0 \tag{5.139}$$

Solving this quadratic and simplifying,

$$X_{eR} = \frac{R_g}{2a \left[ 1 + \left( \frac{R_g}{X_g} \right)^2 \right]}$$

$$\times \left\{ k_R - 2a \left( \frac{R_g}{X_g} \right) \pm \left[ k_R^2 - 4a^2 - 4a k_R \left( \frac{R_g}{X_g} \right) \right]^{\frac{1}{2}} \right\} \tag{5.140}$$

Of the two solutions shown, it is usually found that one value of $X_{eR}$ corresponds to width and thickness dimensions which are impracticable or are larger than $\lambda/8$, the condition for which these formulas apply, and can therefore be rejected. With the aid of equation 5.130, the relationship between the dimensions $TW/L^2$ may be computed from equation 5.140.

The input resistive loading in the case of the transverse filter can be determined by the same method. It is necessary, however, to use the appropriate values of $Z_0$, $X_{eR}$, $\psi$, as defined by equations 5.101, 5.106, and 5.104, respectively, and the auxiliary relations:

$$\omega = \frac{\pi c^E}{L} \tag{5.141}$$

where $C^E$ is the velocity of propagation at constant electric field.

$$Y_3{}^E \simeq Y_1{}^E \ * \tag{5.16}$$

$$c^E \simeq \left(\frac{Y_3{}^E}{\rho}\right)^{\frac{1}{2}} \tag{5.142}$$

It can be shown that equations 5.138 and 5.140 hold for this case, provided that the quantity $X_{eR}$ is computed from equation 5.105 for the transverse filter.

The method for the determination of the loading due to the electrical load on the output filter section is identical with that shown above. In this case a design parameter $b$ is defined by

$$R_2 = bR \tag{5.143}$$

For the ring-type transformer we may arrive at the following design equations immediately by symmetry by substituting $X_L$ and $R_L$ for $X_g$ and $R_g$, respectively, in equations 5.138 and 5.140.

$$b = k_R \left(\frac{R_L X_{eR} X_L{}^2}{R_L{}^2 (X_L + X_{eR})^2 + X_L{}^2 X_{eR}{}^2}\right) \tag{5.144}$$

In terms of the clamped capacitance $C_{0R}$ (where $X_{eR} = 1/\omega C_{0R}$) and the load capacitance $C_L$, equation 5.144 may be written

$$b = k_R \left(\frac{\omega R_L C_{0R}}{\omega^2 R_L{}^2 (C_{0R} + C_L)^2 + 1}\right) \tag{5.144a}$$

$$X_{eR} = \frac{R_L}{2b \left[1 + \left(\dfrac{R_L}{X_L}\right)^2\right]}$$

$$\times \left\{k_R - 2b\left(\frac{R_L}{X_L}\right) \pm \left[k_R{}^2 - 4b^2 - 4bk_R\left(\frac{R_L}{X_L}\right)\right]^{\frac{1}{2}}\right\} \tag{5.145}$$

where $X_{eR}$ is as defined by equation 5.105a.

* See equation 5.16 and footnote.

For the transverse-type transformer it can be shown that

$$b = k_T \left( \frac{R_L X_{eT} X_L{}^2}{R_L{}^2 (X_L + X_{eT})^2 + X_L{}^2 X_{eT}{}^2} \right) \qquad (5.146)$$

In terms of the clamped capacitance $C_{0T}$ (where $X_{eT} = 1/\omega C_{0T}$) and load capacitance $C_L$ equation 5.146 may be written as

$$b = k_T \left( \frac{\omega R_L C_{0T}}{\omega^2 R_L{}^2 (C_{0T} + C_L)^2 + 1} \right) \qquad (5.146a)$$

$$X_{eT} = \frac{R_L}{2b \left[ 1 + \left( \dfrac{R_L}{X_L} \right)^2 \right]}$$

$$\times \left\{ k_T - 2b \left( \frac{R_L}{X_L} \right) \pm \left[ k_T{}^2 - 4b^2 - 4b k_T \left( \frac{R_L}{X_L} \right) \right]^{1/2} \right\} \qquad (5.147)$$

where $k_T$ is defined

$$k_T = \frac{4 Q_m}{\pi^2} \cdot \frac{k_{31}{}^2}{1 - k_{31}{}^2} \qquad (5.148)$$

and $X_{eT}$ is defined by equation 5.106.

### 5.16.3  Use of Compensating Inductors

It is evident from equations 5.139a, 5.144a, and 5.146a that the magnitude of the loading factors $a$ and $b$ are reduced if there is appreciable external capacitive loading $C_g$ or $C_L$. It is also seen (Section 5.17 and following) that in some cases it is desirable to maximize $a$ and $b$ and in others to be able to specify the values of these parameters when the filter terminations are given. A considerable latitude in design may be obtained by the use of auxiliary inductances which are preferably connected in shunt with either or both the input and output circuits. A typical example is shown in Figure 5.38, in which the auxiliary inductance $L_a$ is connected in shunt with the output of a transverse filter element.

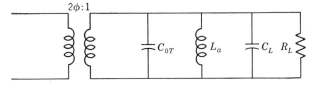

**Figure 5.38.**  Use of an auxiliary inductance $L_a$.

Referring to equation 5.146a, if $L_a$ is chosen to resonate with the combined capacitances $(C_{0T} + C_L)$, then to a good approximation the loading factor $b$ becomes

$$b_{mc} \cong k_T \omega R_L C_{0T} \qquad (5.149)$$

This condition represents the maximum loading when the ceramic material, the geometry, and electrical terminations are specified. Within the limitations that the width and thickness do not exceed $\lambda/8$, control of geometry permits an additional range of loading control. Since $\omega$ is proportional to $1/L$ and $C_{0T}$ is proportional to $(W/T)L$, the maximum loading with full compensation is proportional to $W/T$.

A large range of values of $b$ smaller than $b_{mc}$ may be obtained by using a smaller auxiliary inductance than required for the condition of full compensation or, in extreme cases, by the use of an auxiliary capacitance. More details regarding the use of compensation are shown in reference 21.

For the ring-type filter similar considerations show that with full compensation

$$b_{mc} \cong k_R \omega R_L C_{0R} \qquad (5.150)$$

and that with a given material and electrical terminations $b_{mc}$ is proportional to $WT/L^2$.

### 5.16.4 Maximum Loading. No Compensation

When engineering or economic considerations do not permit the use of compensating inductors it is useful to be able to determine rapidly the maximum values of loading $a_m$ or $b_m$ without compensation for specified input and output electrical terminations. By maximizing the expression in equation 5.138 with respect to $X_{eR}$ it may be shown that

$$a_m = \frac{k_R}{2} \left( \frac{X_g}{R_g + (R_g{}^2 + X_g{}^2)^{1/2}} \right) \qquad (5.151)$$

and for this condition the geometry is specified by

$$X_{eR} = \frac{R_g X_g}{(R_g{}^2 + X_g{}^2)^{1/2}} \qquad (5.152)$$

or

$$C_{0R} = \left( C_g{}^2 + \frac{1}{\omega^2 R_g{}^2} \right)^{1/2} \qquad (5.152a)$$

Similar expressions obtainable for the transverse-type filter and for output terminations are given in Tables 5.1 and 5.2.

## Table 5.1

### Design Formulas for Ring-Type Filter Elements

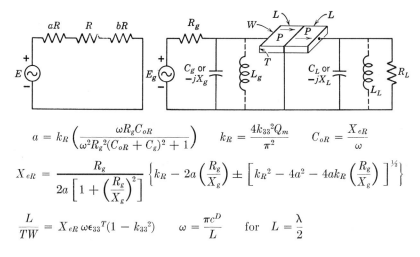

$$a = k_R \left( \frac{\omega R_g C_{oR}}{\omega^2 R_g^2 (C_{oR} + C_g)^2 + 1} \right) \qquad k_R = \frac{4k_{33}^2 Q_m}{\pi^2} \qquad C_{oR} = \frac{X_{eR}}{\omega}$$

$$X_{eR} = \frac{R_g}{2a \left[ 1 + \left( \frac{R_g}{X_g} \right)^2 \right]} \left\{ k_R - 2a \left( \frac{R_g}{X_g} \right) \pm \left[ k_R^2 - 4a^2 - 4ak_R \left( \frac{R_g}{X_g} \right) \right]^{1/2} \right\}$$

$$\frac{L}{TW} = X_{eR} \, \omega \epsilon_{33}^T (1 - k_{33}^2) \qquad \omega = \frac{\pi c^D}{L} \qquad \text{for} \quad L = \frac{\lambda}{2}$$

Maximum Loading

Without compensation, $L_g = 0$

$$a_m = \frac{k_R}{2} \left( \frac{X_g}{R_g + (R_g^2 + X_g^2)^{1/2}} \right)$$

$$C_{oR} = \left( C_g^2 + \frac{1}{\omega^2 R_g^2} \right)^{1/2}$$

With full compensation, $L_g = \dfrac{1}{\omega^2 (C_{oR} + C_g)}$

$$a_{mc} \simeq k_R \, \omega R_g C_{oR}$$

The same design formulas apply for output loading, with $b$ replacing $a$, $R_L$, $X_L$ replacing $R_g$, $X_g$, $L_L$ replacing $L_g$, respectively.

## Table 5.2

### Design Formulas for Transverse-Type Filter Elements

$$a = k_R \left( \frac{\omega R_g C_{oR}}{\omega^2 R_g^2 (C_{oR} + C_g)^2 + 1} \right) \qquad k_R = \frac{4k_{33}^2 Q_m}{\pi^2} \qquad C_{oR} = \frac{X_{eR}}{\omega}$$

$$b = k_T \left( \frac{\omega R_L C_{oT}}{\omega^2 R_g^2 (C_{oT} + C_L)^2 + 1} \right) \qquad k_T = \frac{4k_{31}^2 Q_m}{\pi^2 (1 - k_{31}^2)} \qquad C_{oT} = \frac{X_{eT}}{\omega}$$

$$X_{eR} = \frac{R_g}{2a \left[ 1 + \left( \frac{R_g}{X_g} \right)^2 \right]} \left\{ k_R - 2a \left( \frac{R_g}{X_g} \right) \pm \left[ k_R^2 - 4a^2 - 4ak_R \left( \frac{R_g}{X_g} \right) \right]^{1/2} \right\}$$

$$X_{eT} = \frac{R_L}{2b \left[ 1 + \left( \frac{R_L}{X_L} \right)^2 \right]} \left\{ k_T - 2b \left( \frac{R_L}{X_L} \right) \pm \left[ k_T^2 - 4b^2 - 4bk_T \left( \frac{R_L}{X_L} \right) \right]^{1/2} \right\}$$

$$\frac{L}{T} = \left[ \frac{X_{eR}}{X_{eT}} \cdot \frac{(1 - k_{33}^2)^2}{1 - k_{31}^2} \right]^{1/2} \qquad L' = \frac{L}{(1 - k_{33}^2)^{1/2}} \qquad W'T' = WT(1 - k_{31}^2)^{1/2}$$

### Maximum Loading

Without compensation, $L_g = 0$

$$L_L = 0$$

$$a_m = \frac{k_R}{2} \left( \frac{X_g}{R_g + (R_g^2 + X_g^2)^{1/2}} \right) \qquad b_m = \frac{k_T}{2} \left( \frac{X_L}{R_L + (R_L^2 + X_L^2)^{1/2}} \right)$$

$$C_{oR} = \left[ C_g^2 + \frac{1}{\omega^2 R_g^2} \right]^{1/2} \qquad C_{oT} = \left[ C_L^2 + \frac{1}{\omega^2 R_L^2} \right]^{1/2}$$

With full compensation, $L_g = \dfrac{1}{\omega^2 (C_{oR} + C_g)}$

$$L_L = \frac{1}{\omega^2 (C_{oT} + C_L)}$$

$$a_{mc} = k_R \omega R_g C_{oR}$$

$$b_{mc} = k_T \omega R_L C_{oT}$$

### 5.16.5  Summary of Electrical Loading

In the previous sections expressions have been developed for the effective mechanical impedances which are transformed from input and output electrical circuits into the common mechanical circuit. The reactive components of these impedances tend only to alter the resonant frequency; the resistive or real components, however, have a profound effect on the effective electrical $Q$ of the whole filter element, the degree of matching from driving generator to electrical load in terms of power transfer, and the power loss in the filter itself in relation to the power transferred. Thus expressions have been developed for a large number of cases of interest which permit accurate assessment and design of the resistive loading effects on the mechanical system. For convenience these cases are summarized in Tables 5.1 and 5.2. The simplified schematic at the top of each table represents the complete simplified circuit all referred to the mechanical system at resonance. This occurs, to a close approximation, when the sum of all reactances (mechanical and transformed input and output) is zero.

## 5.17  Filter Response

The major characteristics which describe the over-all performance of the filter driven by a generator with specified internal impedance and terminated by a given load are the variations of output voltage magnitude and phase with frequency, referred to the driving generator voltage.

It is convenient to present the foregoing in the form of (a) normalized resonance curves showing relative change of magnitude and phase with frequency, and (b) the absolute magnitude of the voltage amplification for at least one frequency, usually chosen to be that for which the response is maximum.

### 5.17.1  Frequency and Phase Response

From the complete equivalent circuit shown in Figure 5.37 it is seen that if $E_1$ is considered to remain constant over a small frequency range (see equation 5.117) the series current will be maximized *with respect to frequency* when the circuit is series resonant, i.e., when

$$X - X_1 - X_2 = 0 \qquad (5.153)$$

where

$$X = 2\pi Z_0 \left( \frac{\omega - \omega_0}{\omega_0} \right) \qquad (5.154 \text{ *})$$

* See equations 5.125 and 5.108.

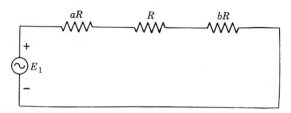

**Figure 5.39.** Simplified equivalent circuit at resonance.

Maximum output voltage $E_0$ for a fixed load resistance $R_L$ corresponds to the condition of maximum power loss in the load $R_L$ and, therefore, to maximum power loss in the transformed real part $R_2$ of the complex load. But maximum power loss in $R_2$ occurs for maximum current flowing through $R_2$. Thus it is concluded that the maximum output voltage $E_0$ occurs for the condition of series resonance.

In practical filter designs the controlling reactance at resonance is preponderantly that due to the mechanical branch, namely $jX$, the coupled-in reactances $-jX_1$, $-jX_2$ usually being relatively small and causing a slight frequency shift from the mechanical resonant frequency. Thus the shape of the over-all frequency response curve is primarily determined by the reactance $jX$ and the sum of the resistive parts $(R_1 + R + R_2)$. Since over the small frequency range centered around series resonance $R_1$ and $R_2$ will vary only slightly with frequency (see equations 5.118, 5.120, 5.122, and Figure 5.34), the response closely resembles that of a single-tuned $R$-$L$-$C$ lumped constant circuit with an over-all effective electrical $Q_E$ of

$$Q_E \simeq \frac{\omega_0 L}{R_1 + R + R_2} \tag{5.155}$$

where

$$L = \pi Z_0/\omega_0. \tag{5.111}$$

If $R_1$ and $R_2$ are designed to be $aR$, $bR$, respectively, then

$$Q_E \simeq \frac{\omega_0 L}{R(1 + a + b)} \tag{5.156}$$

Therefore,

$$Q_E \simeq \frac{Q_m}{1 + a + b} \tag{5.157}$$

For any given value of $Q_E$, as defined by 5.157, the frequency and phase response can be obtained from universal response curves for a series resonant circuit such as given by Terman (16). Equation 5.157 thus can be used to determine the sum of $(a + b)$ for materials with known effective mechanical $Q_m$'s to satisfy the designer's requirement for a specified electrical $Q_E$.

### 5.17.2 Magnitude of Response

As described in the previous section, the output voltage will be maximum at a frequency which is approximately equal to the series resonant frequency determined by the mechanical reactance $jX$ alone. At this frequency the equivalent circuit simplifies, to a close approximation, to that illustrated in Figure 5.39.

It should be recalled that $aR$ and $bR$ represent, respectively, the real parts of the effective generator and load impedances, referred to the mechanical system, and $R$, the internal mechanical resistance of the filter. In an ideal case when the mechanical loss $R$ is assumed to approach zero optimal design requires maximum power transfer from the generator to the load, and thus

$$aR = bR \qquad \text{or} \qquad a = b \qquad (5.158)$$

For this ideal condition, with half the total power delivered to the load $R_L$ and half dissipated in the effective generator resistance $R_e$ (the electrical equivalent of the mechanical resistance $aR$), it can easily be shown that the voltage amplification $A_{vo}$ is given by

$$A_{vo} = \frac{1}{2}\sqrt{\frac{R_L}{R_e}} \qquad (5.159)$$

For the general case in which $R$ is not negligible the voltage amplification $A_v$ can be determined with the aid of Figures 5.40$a$ and 5.40$b$.

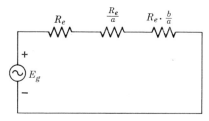
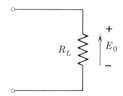

Figure 5.40$a$. Equivalent circuit referred to the input at resonance.  Figure 5.40$b$. Load circuit.

Since all the resistances shown in Figure 5.39 are on the same basis, i.e., referred to the mechanical system, all will be transformed to the input electrical circuit with the same relative magnitude. Thus the mechanical resistance $R$, when transformed into the electrical input, is $1/a$ the effective generator resistance $R_e$, and the load resistance $bR$ is $(b/a)R_e$. The total power $W_T$ delivered by the generator is

$$W_T = \frac{|E_g|^2}{R_e[1 + (1/a) + (b/a)]} = \frac{|E_g|^2}{R_e} \cdot \frac{a}{1 + a + b} \qquad (5.160)$$

The power $W_L$ delivered to the load $bR_e/a$ is

$$W_L = \frac{bR_e/a}{R_e[1 + (1/a) + (b/a)]} \cdot W_T = \frac{b}{1 + a + b} \cdot W_T \qquad (5.161)$$

but $W_L = |E_0|^2/R_L$ (see Figure 5.40$b$). Then

$$\frac{|E_0|^2}{R_L} = \frac{b}{1 + a + b} \cdot \frac{a}{1 + a + b} \cdot \frac{|E_g|^2}{R_e}$$

$$A_v = \left| \frac{E_0}{E_g} \right| = \frac{\sqrt{ab}}{1 + a + b} \cdot \sqrt{\frac{R_L}{R_e}} \qquad (5.162)$$

Equations 5.162 and 5.157 constitute the two major expressions which are used to determine the shape and absolute magnitude of the filter response. From equation 5.157 the quantity $(1 + a + b)$ is determined by the value of the known effective mechanical $Q_m$ of the material and the desired electrical $Q_E$ of the filter element and is therefore fixed. Since $R_L$ and $R_e$ are also fixed by the external circuitry, the voltage amplification $A_v$ is maximized when the quantity $\sqrt{ab}$ is a maximum under the condition that $(a + b)$ is constant. For these conditions

$$a = b \qquad (5.163)$$

With the values of $a$ and $b$ thus specified, the relations developed in Section 5.16 may be used to determine the geometry of the filter for given load and generator impedances. It may not always be possible within the limitations of the theory presented to obtain a solution, or the filter may be found to be physically impracticable. It may then be necessary to choose unequal values of $a$ and $b$ which conform to the requirement of equation 5.157 for $Q_E$, but not of equation 5.163, and which would result in a smaller voltage amplification than is optimally realizable.

### 5.17.3  Effect of Mechanical $Q_m$ on Performance

It was seen that the largest voltage amplification was obtained for equal values of $a$ and $b$. For this condition equations 5.157, 5.162, and 5.163 yield

$$Q_E \simeq \frac{Q_m}{1 + 2a} \qquad (5.164)$$

$$A_v = \frac{a}{1 + 2a} \sqrt{\frac{R_L}{R_e}} \qquad (5.165)$$

Thus it is seen that the voltage amplification $A_v$ will approach the maximum value $A_{vo} = \frac{1}{2} \sqrt{\frac{R_L}{R_e}}$ (equation 5.159) as $a$ gets large; but for a desired value of electrical $Q_E$ equation 5.164 indicates that $a$ can become large only if $Q_m$ becomes large. This simply demonstrates the need for materials with low intrinsic mechanical loss and care in the design of the support of the electromechanical filter to minimize mechanical damping.

## 5.18  Response of Ring-Type Ceramic Filter Element

Shown in Figures 5.41 and 5.42 is the response of a typical ring-type ceramic filter element as a function of electrical load. The element consisted of a rectangular uniform section bar made of Brush * Ceramic "B" operating in the second harmonic mode (over-all length = $\lambda$).

The variation of bandwidth with resistive load $R_L$ is clearly shown in Figure 5.41. Also plotted in this figure for the curve corresponding to $R_L = 76k\Omega$ are superimposed points obtained from the universal curves in Terman (16) for a resonant $R$-$L$-$C$ circuit indicating good agreement with the assumed simplified equivalent circuit.

The variation in effective bandwidth, with load $R_L$ and the theoretical value of $Q_E$ as calculated from equations 5.157, 5.144, and 5.135, is shown more clearly in Figure 5.42. The stray capacitance $C_s$ was determined by a separate measurement and added to the load capacitance $C_L$ in this calculation. The agreement between calculated and measured values is reasonably good, considering that published values for the material constants were used in the calculation.

* Clevite Corp., Cleveland, Ohio.

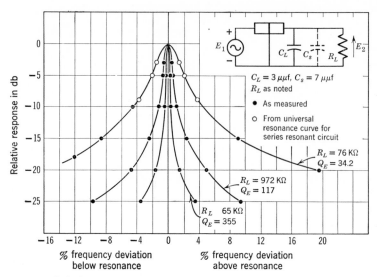

**Figure 5.41.** Relative response as a function of frequency deviation for a ring-type ceramic filter with various loads.

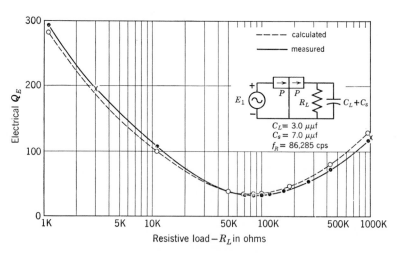

**Figure 5.42.** Electrical "$Q_E$" versus load resistance $R_L$ element operating at harmonic mechanical resonance.

## 5.19 Spurious Response

Filters are generally designed to have a specific pass band with a prescribed shape of response curve. Transmission of energy through the filter at frequencies other than within the pass band is known as spurious response. Since it is generally impossible to suppress the transmission of such undesired energy completely, it is usual to specify the ratio of peak power level of spurious response relative to the peak power level of response in the pass band in decibel units.

Spurious response may be divided into two major groups: unwanted response due to direct electrical coupling from input to output and that due to undesired resonant modes of vibration which are then electromechanically transformed into electrical output signals.

### 5.19.1 Spurious Response Due to Direct Electrical Coupling

Direct electrical coupling usually consists of capacitive coupling through air or other path from input to output electrode or from the input driving coil of a composite filter element to the output electrode. This problem is usually much severer when input and output sections are both made of piezoelectric ceramics as compared with the composite magnetostrictive-piezoelectric filter, since in the latter case the input coil is usually operated at a low impedance level and all turns are essentially at ground potential. The leakage paths for the all-piezoelectric case, in which the effective capacitive coupling is of a distributed nature and is represented by equivalent lumped capacitors $C_1$, $C_2$, and $C_3$, are shown in Figure 5.43. The capacitors $C_1$ and $C_2$* shunt the

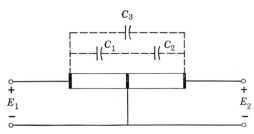

Figure 5.43. Ring filter with direct capacitive leakage paths.

input and output sections, respectively, and can be treated as small additions to the clamped input and output capacitances of the two

---

* $C_1$ and $C_2$ represent capacitive coupling due to leakage flux which do *not* have paths entirely in the ceramic material.

sections. Their effect on response is usually negligible. The capacitor $C_3$, however, represents a direct electrical coupling between input and output. Although it may be relatively small, it may easily raise the level of a response curve 20 to 30 db at frequencies outside but close to the desired pass band. Electric shielding usually provides a satisfactory reduction of such direct coupling and may simply consist of a conducting plate which effectively provides a large ground plane interposed between input and output sections or more elaborate shield cans almost entirely enclosing these sections. These arrangements are shown in Figure 5.44.

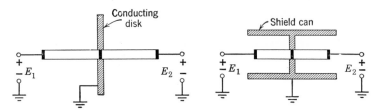

**Figure 5.44.** Shielding arrangements to minimize direct electrical feed-through.

### 5.19.2 Spurious Response Due to Mechanical Vibration Modes

The problem of suppression of spurious response due to mechanical vibration in electromechanical filters is severe, since in a distributed constant vibrating system many discrete modes of vibration are possible, each giving rise to the generation of appreciable undesired output. A careful choice of the geometry, mounting, excitation, electrical termination, and the design of staggered filter sections is often required to obtain a sufficiently low level of spurious response. In the following sections the major principles involved are explored qualitatively, and some general methods of suppression which apply particularly to piezo-electric ceramic filters are shown.

### 5.19.3 Effects of Geometry

Because of Poisson coupling strain in any given direction in an elastic body is always accompanied by strain induced along the other coordinates of the system. Such mechanical coupling, which may be extensional, shear, flexural, or in combinations thereof, gives rise to complex coupled modes of vibration for which no exact closed forms of solution have been evolved. Approximate methods yielding solutions to a high degree of accuracy have been devised by McSkimin (17) for rectangular plates with all surfaces free and adapted to metal plates by Lapin and Niederman (18). Their results may be illustrated by taking the relatively simple case of coupled extensional modes of vibration of a thin rectangular plate, i.e., where the principal "resonant" modes of vibration occur in length $L$ and width $W$ due to compressional waves only.

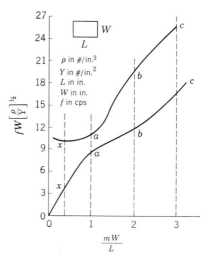

Figure 5.45. Curve showing extensional coupled modes of vibration for rectangular plates.

The curve in Figure 5.45, taken from Reference 18, shows the normalized frequencies at which such a plate will have strong resonant modes of vibration plotted as functions of multiples of the ratio of width to length $mW/L$, where $m$ can take on integral values only. Thus for a square plate in which $W = L$ the modes that are possible occur when $m = 1, 2, 3$, etc., and give rise to corresponding pairs of "resonant frequencies." These are labeled $a$-$a$, $b$-$b$, $c$-$c$, etc. A number of important points should be noted:

1. The frequencies corresponding to each pair are not integrally related.

2. There is no integral relation between frequencies of two pairs.

3. As $W$ becomes small relative to $L$, the two frequencies of the first pair of coupled modes (shown as $x$-$x$) diverge very rapidly. The lower curve is essentially linear, so that for a given width $W$ there are integral relations between resonant frequencies defined by successive integral values of the parameter $m$. This case corresponds to the vibrations of a "long thin bar" which has formed the basis of the previous analysis. Although the higher frequencies represented by the intersections with the upper curve exist, the vibration amplitudes are small, and the electrical terminations of the filter are usually such as to minimize their transmission.

Similar curves may be developed for other modes of coupling, such as shear-flexure and extensional-shear, each giving rise to multiple pairs of "resonant frequencies" which are all classed as spurious response. If plates are to be used as the mechanical resonators, careful choice of dimensions, excitation, and cascading of elements must be made to minimize spurious response. It is far simpler, however, to use elements which are essentially "long thin bars," since it is assumed that only harmonically related extensional modes of vibrations are involved. If the width and thickness of such bars are smaller than $\frac{1}{8}$ wavelength, as determined by vibration in length, long thin bar formulas hold to a satisfactory degree of precision.

### 5.19.4 Resonant Modes in Long Thin Bars

Shown in Figures 5.46a, 5.46b, and 5.46c are the sinusoidal distributions of the standing waves of displacement and strain along the length of the free-free bars for the first three resonant modes of vibration, assuming no mechanical losses. The strain curves are derived from the displacement curves by taking the slope of the displacement curve at each point ($S_X = \partial\mu/\partial X$). The internal stress distributions will, of course, be identical in form with the strain distributions, since they are linearly related. In each case particle displacement $\mu$ and strain $S_x$ are assumed present in the longitudinal ($x$) direction only, the amplitudes of particle displacement and strain being shown as functions of position along the $x$-axis. For the lossless case these diagrams represent the distributions at one instant of time, e.g., that instant when each particle has reached its maximum displacement, since all displacements are in time phase.

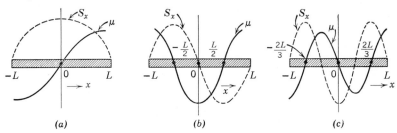

**Figure 5.46.** Particle displacement and strain distribution for first three resonant modes of a long thin bar: (a) fundamental resonance; (b) second harmonic resonance; (c) third harmonic resonance.

The free or natural vibration patterns shown are, of course, affected by constraints, such as the physical mounting and the application of periodic driving forces.

### 5.19.5 Effect of Mounting on Response

Theoretically, the free vibration patterns will be unchanged in each case if the bar is clamped immovably at nodal points, i.e., at points where the displacement is zero. Clamping at loops or points of maximum displacement of a particular mode tends to suppress that mode completely. Thus the positioning of the clamp or clamps will favor one or more particular modes. The use of clamping for suppression of spurious response is particularly effective when either the fundamental or second harmonic resonant mode of operation is desired. For example, a very rigid clamp at $x = 0$ will permit free vibration in the fundamental mode but will impose a rigid constraint at a position of maximum displacement for the second harmonic mode and tend to suppress vibration in this mode. The degree of suppression depends entirely on the degree of rigidity achievable by a clamp of small dimensions. Clamping at $x = 0$ will not suppress the third, fifth, seventh, etc., harmonic modes, but other factors such as method of excitation tend to suppress these higher order modes. Rigid clamps at $x = \pm L/2$ tend to suppress the fundamental and permit unrestricted vibration in the second harmonic mode. Some suppression of the third harmonic mode will also be obtained in this case (nodes are at $\pm 2L/3$), and again additional suppression can be obtained by the choice of the method of excitation.

In the use of clamps for spurious response control several important factors should be considered:

1. At a loop the actual particle motion is large in the longitudinal direction but the longitudinal strain is vanishingly small. The Poisson-coupled particle motion in the other coordinate directions are small, not having been enhanced by resonant effects. To be effective the clamp must therefore be designed to prevent longitudinal motion, and the provision of additional constraints in thickness or width will be of little use.

2. Ideally the clamp should be infinitely thin in the longitudinal direction at the line of contact with the ceramic, if it is not to interfere with the desired mode of vibration, and yet have very low compliance (or high stiffness) in this direction. A wedge-shaped clamp made of

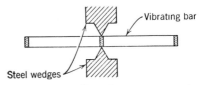

Figure 5.47. Clamping arrangements for fundamental mode operation.

material with a high modulus of elasticity satisfies these criteria to a considerable degree. A typical arrangement is shown in Figure 5.47.

### 5.19.6 Effect of Excitation on Response

If a bar is driven piezoelectrically by the application of a periodic electric field *along its whole length,* then the direct applied stress at any instant of time has the same sign at every point along the length, i.e., either a compressive or tensile applied stress. Referring to Figure 5.46a, it is seen that in free vibration the internal strain (therefore stress) also has the same sign at every point along the bar length for the fundamental mode of vibration, and thus the applied stress causes the reinforcement of particle motion at every point. The strain distribution for free vibration in the second harmonic mode (Figure 5.46b) is positive over one half the length and negative over the second half. Thus the applied stress tends to reinforce vibration in one half and interfere with vibration in the other half. The net result is that the second harmonic mode will not be excited at all. Under the same conditions of excitation the third harmonic mode (Figure 5.46c) will be weakly excited because of destructive interference over one third of the bar. Proceeding in this manner, it can be seen that higher even harmonics will not be excited and odd harmonics will be excited in a progressively weaker manner.

The application of an electric field to only part of the length of a piezoelectrically driven bar has been treated in detail by Cady (1). For the particular case in which the driving field is applied over the left half of the bar from $x = 0$ to $x = -L$ examination of Figures 5.46a, 5.46b, and 5.46c indicates that the fundamental and second harmonic modes will be strongly excited but that partial cancellation will occur for the third harmonic mode which will be relatively weakly excited. It can be shown that for the same applied field to the left half of the bar the open-circuit output voltage of the right half of the bar is the same for both fundamental and second harmonic modes if the mechanical $Q_m$ remains constant with frequency. In practice, it is found that $Q_m$ may vary considerably with frequency dependant on the frequency range of interest, and it is not uncommon to obtain 10 to 25 per cent higher output with the second harmonic mode. Proper clamping at the appropriate nodes is thus essential for selecting either fundamental or second harmonic operation, and such clamping together with excitation of one half the bar length tends to suppress the third harmonic and, even more so, the higher harmonic responses.

Excitation by application of a periodic magnetic field to a magnetostrictive driver has essentially the same effects on the vibration patterns as described for the piezoelectric case. The situation is often more complex, since the applied field is usually much less uniform throughout the bar than in the piezoelectric case due to considerable magnetic flux leakage, which can be serious in an unclosed magnetic path.

## 5.20    Miscellaneous Methods of Spurious Response Control

When a large reduction of spurious response is required a number of arrangements are available which usually involve more complex methods than we have outlined. In many cases an increased insertion loss of the filter in the desired frequency pass-band results, and the analytical design problem becomes much more involved. Empirical methods can often be used to supplement initial analytical designs. Several such methods are outlined in the following sections.

### 5.20.1    Control by Electrical Terminations

The simplest method of reduction of the second and higher harmonics is the use of external shunt capacitance across either the input or the output terminals of the filter element. Since the reactance of such a shunt path varies inversely with frequency, a considerably lower impedance shunting path is available for second and higher harmonic currents than for the fundamental. In the usual circuit application capacitive loading is already present (such as the input capacitance of a vacuum tube), but it may be augmented, if necessary, at the expense of reduced power transfer through the filter element.

This principle may, of course, be extended by providing a termination composed of a lossy filter section resonant at the unwanted frequency. Such a section may be composed of lumped circuit elements or, indeed, a simple two-terminal electromechanical element such as a fully electroded barium titanate vibrator operating with its fundamental mode at the undesired frequency.

### 5.20.2    Control by Mechanical Coupling

Examination of the displacement and strain curves of Figures 5.46a and 5.46b indicates that at the center of the bar the mechanical impedance of the fundamental mode is very high and for the second harmonic mode, very low. This can be qualitatively derived from the definition of mechanical impedance, viz., $Z_m = F/v$, where $F$ is the force and $v$, the particle velocity. For the fundamental mode internal strain and stress are high at $x = 0$, and therefore the force $F$ is high; on the other hand, displacement $\mu$ and, therefore, velocity $v$ is low. The opposite conditions obtain for the second harmonic mode. The introduction of a coupling element with high mechanical compliance between both halves of the filter element greatly favors second harmonic mode operation over the fundamental mode operation, since its low mechanical impedance tends to match the mechanical impedance of both halves of the bar to which it is mechanically attached, yet offers a considerable mismatch for operation at the fundamental mode. This coupling section must be quite small in length compared to a wavelength and may consist of a necked-down sectional area of the ceramic itself. Shown in Figures 5.48a and 5.48b are arrangements which would tend to suppress fundamental and third harmonic modes without greatly affecting the second harmonic mode.

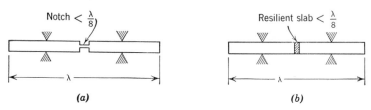

(a)         (b)

**Figure 5.48.** Spurious response control by (a) notching and (b) matching sections.

### 5.20.3 Control by Staggering of Coupled-Mode Elements

If the condition for long thin bar vibrations is departed from to a small degree, such that coupled modes occur as described in Section 5.19.3, it is possible to design several elements which have identical fundamental resonant frequencies with appreciably different frequencies for higher coupled modes of vibration. Use can be made of a curve similar to that shown in Figure 5.45 to choose slightly different widths and lengths for the two elements such that the intersections on the lower curve (in the region where it is almost linear) represent the same frequency; but the intersections with the upper curve (which is quite nonlinear in this region) represent quite different coupled-mode frequencies. A filter composed of two or more such elements, separated by active elements (vacuum tubes, transistors, etc.), will pass the required fundamental frequency and progressively reject the staggered spurious response.

## 5.21 Summary

Based on electrical equivalent circuits representing the electrical and mechanical behavior of long thin bars made of piezoelectric ceramic materials, two classes of device have been analyzed and design criteria developed. These classes are ceramic high-voltage transformers and ceramic filter elements.

The high-voltage transformer has limited utility at present, due to the lack of suitable ceramic materials capable of operating at very high output voltage levels (10 kv) with a bar of reasonable size. The range of utility would also be greatly increased if improved or new materials could be fabricated with considerably larger dielectric permittivities without sacrificing the large electromechanical coupling coefficient or mechanical $Q_m$ now obtainable. The subsequent lowering of operating impedance levels might permit application in many moderately powered power supplies with economic and performance advantages over existing supplies. It is not thought probable, however, that even extensive materials development would result in making the ceramic transformer competitive with existing magnetic transformers for most power applications. It is far more likely that the extensive ferrite development now in progress will enhance the present formidable advantages of the conventional transformer.

The piezoelectric ceramic filter element is now being developed for use in a wide variety of filters. Its small size, simplicity, and high effective electrical $Q_E$ are known advantages over the conventional lumped-constant filter elements. The simple principle of combining the two transducers and the resonator functions in a single piezoelectric bar yields far simpler filter elements when compared with existing electromechanical filters. Finally, it is probable that there will be developed stable piezoelectric ceramics capable of maintaining essential electrical and mechanical properties at elevated temperatures (500° C), thus greatly extending the working range of presently used filters. At present much materials development is aimed at producing stable, uniform ceramic bodies with high mechanical $Q_m$ and high electromechanical coupling coefficients. Mason and Wick (20) have reported tests made on a barium titanate ceramic with additives of lead and calcium titanates which after a simple aging process has sufficient temperature stability and other essential properties suitable for immediate use in some commercial applications.

Further development is needed in the analytical treatment of more complex geometries, especially those involving several coupled modes of vibration. Such geometries, which are now being empirically developed, yield performance advantages over "long thin bar" resonators, especially in the wider range of impedance levels available for design purposes. Further work is indicated in the improvement of methods of suppression of spurious response and in the analysis of cascaded filter elements.

## 5.22 References

1. Cady, W. G., *Piezoelectricity*, McGraw-Hill Book Company, New York, 1946.
2. von Hippel, A., "Piezoelectricity, Ferroelectricity and Crystal Structure," ONR Contract N5-OR1-07801 and N5-OR1-07858, March 1952.
3. "Standards on Piezoelectric Crystals, 1949," *I.R.E. Standard*, 49 *I.R.E.* **14.** S1; also *Proc. I.R.E.*, **37,** 1949; *I.R.E. Standard*, 58 *I.R.E.* 14.S1.
4. Haskins, J. F., and J. S. Hickman, *J. Acoust. Soc. Am.*, **22,** 1950, p. 584.
5. von Hippel, A., "Ferroelectricity, Domain Structure and Phase Transitions of Barium Titanate," *Revs. Modern Phy.*, **22,** 1950, p. 229.
6. Mason, W. P., *Piezoelectric Crystals and Their Applications to Ultrasonics*, 2nd ed., D. Van Nostrand Company, Princeton, N. J., 1948, p. 40.
7. ————, *Electromechanical Transducers and Wave Filters*, D. Van Nostrand Company, Princeton, N. J., 2nd ed., 1948, p. 203.
8. Tehon, S. W., "Piezoelectric and Magnetostrictive Transducers," Ph.D. dissertation, University of Illinois, 1958.
9. Moseley, D. S., *J. Acoust. Soc. Am.*, **27,** 1955, pp. 947–950.
10. Watanabe, Y., "Piezoelectric Resonator in High Frequency Oscillation Circuits," *Proc. I.R.E.*, **18,** 1930, pp. 695–717, 862–893.
11. Research Laboratory of Physical Electronics, "An Investigation of the Characteristics of Electromechanical Filters," C. R. Mingins, et al., Tufts College Final Report, Contract DA 36-039-SC 5402, Signal Corps Project 33-862A-5.
12. Roberts, W. van B., and L. L. Burns, "Mechanical Filters for Radio Frequencies," *R C A Rev.*, **10,** 1949, p. 348.
13. Adler, R., "Compact Electromechanical Filter," *Electronics*, **20,** No. 4, April 1947, p. 100.
14. Roberts, W. van B., "Some Applications of Permanently Magnetized Ferrite Magnetostrictive Resonators," *R C A Rev.*, **14,** 1953, p. 3.
15. Lord Rayleigh, *The Theory of Sound*, Vol. 1, 2nd ed., Dover Publications, Inc., New York, 1945.
16. Terman, F. E., *Radio Engineers Handbook*, 1st ed., McGraw-Hill Book Company, New York, 1943.
17. McSkimin, H. J., "Theoretical Analysis of Modes of Vibration for Isotropic Rectangular Plates Having All Surfaces Free," *Bell System Tech. J.*, **23,** 1944, p. 151.
18. Lapin, S. P., and B. Niederman, "Low Frequency Electro-Mechanical Filters," First Quarterly Progress Report, Signal Corps Contract No. DA-36-039-SC 15535, 1952.
19. Gerber, E. A., "A Review of Methods for Measuring the Constants of Piezoelectric Vibrators," *Proc. I.R.E.*, **41,** 1953, pp. 1103–1112.
20. Mason, W. P., and R. F. Wick, "Ferroelectrics and the Dielectric Amplifier," *Proc. I.R.E.*, **42,** 1954, p. 1606.
21. Rosen, C. A., "Ceramic Transformers and Filters," Ph.D. thesis, Syracuse University, 1956.

# Chapter six

# Small Signal Applications

## 6.0 Introduction

The area covered in the following sections encompasses what might be termed the more conventional applications of ferrite materials. In other words, we envision the magnetic material as part of a high-permeability, linear, and low-loss system. As such, the ferrite can be considered as a direct substitute for various metallic alloys for use in inductors and transformers, particularly at high frequencies. The applications which have been chosen as illustrations are for the most part those which have enjoyed the widest commercial use. In this class antenna rods, radio-frequency inductors (fixed and variable), television deflection transformers, and yokes are included as representative devices. The magnetic ferrite delay line is also described as a practical application which utilizes the dielectric properties of ferrites.

Though this chapter is devoted almost exclusively to magnetic applications, the final section is concerned with two applications of dielectric materials to small signal problems.

## 6.1  Antenna Rods 1–7

An extruded ferrite rod wound with a solenoidal coil is a particularly simple configuration used widely as an antenna for broadcast receivers. A low-loss, high-permeability, magnetic-core antenna offers the advantage of an over-all reduction in size compared to the usual air core coils. Moreover, a magnetic antenna usually has a better signal-to-noise ratio than one which responds primarily to electric field radiation. This is due to the fact that local sources of noise (i.e., induction fields) have much larger electric field components than the comparable sources of magnetic field noise.

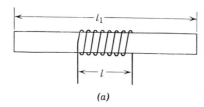

*(a)*

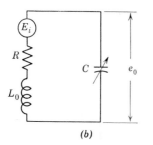

*(b)*

**Figure 6.1.** (*a*) Ferrite antenna rod; (*b*) antenna equivalent circuit.

Though the magnetic antenna is a rather straightforward application, there are several interesting features to the problem which are worth noting. In practice the antenna must provide a maximum output signal at a specified effective $Q$ and with certain restrictions on maximum size. A simple formula can be developed which relates the output voltage to the geometric parameters and the material properties.

Figure 6.1a shows an antenna rod of length $l_1$ with a winding whose linear turn density is $n$ and whose length is $l$. Since the $Q$ of the tuned circuit is relatively high (100 to 300), the output voltage is

$$E_0 = QE_i \tag{6.1}$$

where $E_i$ is the induced emf due to the incoming plane wave.

$$E_i = \omega n H A l \mu_r = n\frac{d\phi}{dt} \tag{6.2}$$

where $H$ is the received magnetic field intensity,

$A$ is the cross-sectional area of the rod, and

$\mu_r$ is the effective rod permeability when placed in a uniform magnetic field.

If the antenna had been in the shape of an ellipsoid, it would be simple to calculate $\mu_r$ in terms of the true permeability.* However, the value of $\mu_r$ for cylindrical rods of different length to diameter ratios can be obtained to a good approximation from the curves of Figure 6.2. The apparent permeability $\mu_r$ has been obtained experimentally by measuring the induction $B$ at the center of the rod when it is placed in a uniform external field $H_a$ (i.e., $\mu_r = B/H_a$). It is observed that because of surface demagnetization effects the full permeability of the ferrite can be utilized only for large rod length-to-diameter ratios.

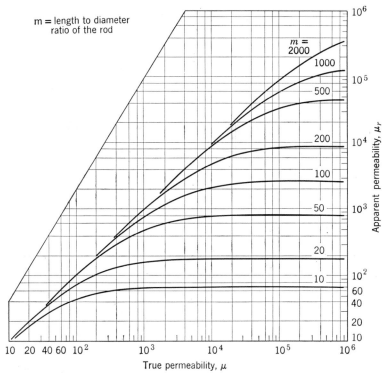

**Figure 6.2.** Apparent rod permeability as a function of length to diameter ratio. (Bozorth, *Ferromagnetism*, 1951.)

For a given value of the tuning capacitor the required antenna inductance $L_0$ is fixed.

$$L_0 = n^2 l A \mu_l \tag{6.3}$$

where $\mu_l$ = effective permeability of rod when wound as an inductance.

* See Section 1.8, Chapter 1.

The value of $\mu_l$ is in general different from that of $\mu_r$. This is due to the fact that $\mu_r$ is determined for the rod when it is placed in a uniform applied field. Under these conditions the field in the ferrite is almost uniform over the length $(l_1)$. However, when a winding of length $l$ is placed on the core the current in the winding produces a very nonuniform field along the length of the ferrite. A sketch of the variation of $\mu_l$ with winding length obtained experimentally where $n$ was adjusted to maintain $L_0$ constant is shown in Figure 6.3. It is seen that the effective $\mu_l$ increases with increasing winding length and would approach the material permeability for a sufficiently large $l$ and $l_1$. For an extremely long rod wound uniformly over the entire length $\mu_l = \mu_r =$ the true ferrite permeability.

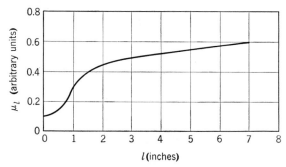

**Figure 6.3.** Effective rod permeability as a function of winding length.

By substituting $n$ from equation 6.3 into equation 6.1 and using 6.2, we obtain

$$E_0 = K l^{\frac{1}{2}} \mu_r / \mu_l^{\frac{1}{2}} \tag{6.4}$$

where

$$K = \omega H A^{\frac{1}{2}} L_0^{\frac{1}{2}} Q \tag{6.5}$$

Hence for maximum output voltage we should use the largest practical length to diameter ratio rod with a uniform winding over almost its entire length. The maximum volume of ferrite must be compromised against the total cost of the rod. A typical antenna rod is about 7 inches long with a diameter of about $\frac{1}{4}$ inch.

Another aspect of the magnetic antenna for broadcast receivers is its directional property. Since the transmitted wave has its magnetic vector in the horizontal plane, the antenna is also mounted in this plane. Hence the received signal is a minimum when the rod is pointed directly toward the transmitter and is a maximum at 90° to this direction.

## 6.2   Radio Frequency Inductors (8-12)

In general, magnetic cores are used with inductors for the following reasons:

1. Since the inductance is proportional to the square of the number of turns, the permeability, and the volume occupied by inductor, it is evident that a core of higher permeability will permit a decrease of the required volume and the amount of copper for a given inductance.

2. A certain amount of magnetic shielding between coils may be obtained by proper shaping of the magnetic structure.

The toroidal form theoretically utilizes these advantages to the greatest degree. With a uniform winding about the circumference of the

Figure 6.4. Typical ferrite geometries used as inductors. (Courtesy General Electric.)

toroid, leakage flux is reduced to a minimum, and the full material permeability of the ferrite is approached. However, there are decided practical disadvantages, since toroids are usually very expensive to wind in comparison to winding a coil directly onto a rod. More commonly used equivalent configurations are shown in Figure 6.4. These include cup cores with a center rod and $C$- or $E$-shaped frames. In these cases the windings are first placed on hollow cylinders and then slipped over one of the straight portions of the structure. In each of these configurations an unavoidable air gap is introduced. However, there is considerable advantage to be derived from the use of a carefully controlled air gap, as shown in Section 6.2.2.

### 6.2.1 Complex Permeability

The characteristics of ferrite materials for this application are sometimes given in terms of a "complex" permeability. If the copper losses can be appropriately accounted for,* then the impedance of a wound toroid is given as

$$Z = R + j\omega L \tag{6.6}$$

where $R$ represents the effect of core losses. This can be rewritten as

$$Z = j\omega\mu L_0 \tag{6.7}$$

where $L_0$ represents the inductance of the toroid without a magnetic core, and $\mu$ is the complex permeability $\mu' - j\mu''$. Hence

$$Z = \omega\mu''L_0 + j\omega\mu'L_0 \tag{6.8}$$

Therefore, the core losses are represented by $\omega\mu''L_0$ and the small signal permeability by $\mu'$. The material $Q$ is then defined as $\mu'/\mu''$. The same property is sometimes given in terms of a loss factor $\tan \delta = 1/Q$.†

### 6.2.2 Effect of an Air Gap on $\mu$ and $Q$

If a small air gap is now introduced into the structure so that all of the flux is still in a well-defined path (Figure 6.5), we can recalculate the effect of the air gap on the effective permeability and also the change in the measured $Q$.

Let $l$ = path length in the magnetic circuit,
$k$ = ratio of air gap length to core path length,
$H_f$ = magnetic field in the ferrite,
$H_a$ = magnetic field in the air gap,
$A$ = cross-sectional area of the core.

* See Chapter 11.
† The loss factor is sometimes given as $1/\mu Q$.

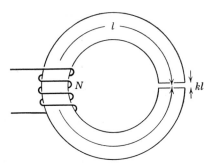

**Figure 6.5.** Toroid with air gap.

Since $\oint \mathbf{H} \cdot d\mathbf{l} = NI$, then

$$H_f(l - kl) + H_a kl = NI \tag{6.9}$$

Also $\oint \mathbf{B} \cdot d\mathbf{s} = 0$, then *

$$\mu' H_f = H_a \tag{6.10}$$

From equations 6.9 and 6.10

$$H_f = \frac{NI}{(1 - k)l + \mu' kl} \tag{6.11}$$

Since the inductance is defined as $NBA/I$, then

$$L = \frac{\mu' \mu_0 N^2 A}{(1 - k)l + \mu' kl} \tag{6.12}$$

In terms of the air core inductance $L_0 = \mu_0 N^2 A/l$, equation 6.12 becomes

$$L = \frac{\mu' L_0}{1 - k + \mu' k} \tag{6.13}$$

A new effective permeability $\mu_e$ can now be defined as $L = \mu_e L_0$ where

$$\frac{1}{\mu_e} = \frac{1 - k}{\mu'} + k \tag{6.14}$$

For the usual case when $k \ll 1$, then

$$\mu_e = \frac{\mu'}{1 + \mu' k} \tag{6.15}$$

In other words, the permeability has been reduced by the factor $(1 + \mu k)$.

* $\mu'$ is the relative permeability; $\mu_0$, free-space permeability.

In order to see the effect on the losses, replace $\mu'$ in equation 6.15 by $\mu' - j\mu''$, and let

$$\mu_e = \mu_e' - j\mu_e'' \tag{6.16}$$

Therefore, from equation 6.15

$$\frac{\mu_e'}{(\mu_e')^2 + (\mu_e'')^2} + \frac{j\mu_e''}{(\mu_e')^2 + (\mu_e'')^2} = \frac{\mu'}{\mu'^2 + \mu''^2} + \frac{j\mu''}{\mu'^2 + \mu''^2} + k \tag{6.17}$$

For most materials which could be considered of any utility for high quality inductors we can assume $\mu_e' \gg \mu_e''$ and $\mu' \gg \mu''$.

Therefore,

$$\frac{1}{\mu_e'} + \frac{j\mu_e''}{\mu_e'^2} = \frac{1}{\mu'} + \frac{j\mu''}{\mu'^2} + k \tag{6.18}$$

As before,

$$\mu_e' = \frac{\mu'}{1 + \mu'k} \tag{6.19}$$

In addition, the new $Q = Q_e$; from equation 6.18

$$\frac{1}{Q_e} = \frac{\mu_e''}{\mu_e'} = \frac{\mu_e'\mu_e''}{\mu_e'^2} = \frac{\mu_e'\mu''}{\mu'^2} \tag{6.20}$$

Substituting $\mu_e'$ from equation 6.19, we obtain

$$Q_e = Q(1 + \mu'k) \tag{6.21}$$

Therefore, the $Q$ of the toroid with an air gap is greater than that of the original toroid. It is also instructive to consider the effect of a small air gap from an energy viewpoint.

Consider a closed toroid shown in Figure 6.5 ($k = 0$). The maximum energy stored per cycle is $\mu_o H B V_c / 2$, where $V_c$ is the volume of the core. The energy lost in the core per cycle is a fixed fraction $F$ of the stored energy. Therefore, the energy loss per cycle is $(F\mu_o H B / 2)V_c$. Therefore the $Q$ of the core is

$$Q = \frac{HBV_c}{FHBV_c} = \frac{1}{F} \tag{6.22}$$

If the same voltage is applied, but an air gap of length $l_a$ is introduced, then $B$ remains the same and $H$ changes to a new $H'$. The energy stored is now the sum of the energy in the core $\mu_o H' B V_c'$, where $V_c'$ is the new core volume, plus the energy in the air gap which equals

$$\frac{\mu_o H_a B_a V_a}{2} = \frac{B^2 V_a}{2} \tag{6.23}$$

since $\mu_o H_a = B$.

However, the energy dissipated in the core is still $F$ times the stored energy in core. The loss, therefore, equals $F\mu_o H'BV_c'$. The new $Q_e$ is

$$Q_e = \frac{\mu_o H'BV_c' + B^2 V_a}{F\mu_o H'BV_c'} \tag{6.24}$$

$$Q_e = \frac{1}{F}\left(1 + \frac{B}{\mu_o H'}\frac{V_a}{V_c}\right) \tag{6.25}$$

However, $B/\mu_o H' = \mu'$, and $V_a/V_c' = l_a/l_c = k$. Therefore,

$$Q_e = Q(1 + \mu'k) \tag{6.26}$$

which is the same result that was obtained in equation 6.21. We may, therefore, interpret the air gap as a means of introducing a large amount of stored energy with no attendant loss. Thus an appreciable portion of the total inductance comes from the air gap, whereas the losses are still the same fixed fraction of the remaining energy stored in the core.

From equations 6.19 and 6.21 we obtain the interesting result that

$$\mu_e'Q_e = \mu'Q \tag{6.27}$$

In other words, the $\mu Q$ product of a material is an excellent figure of merit, since its value is independent of the length of air gap as long as

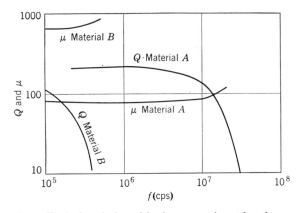

**Figure 6.6.** Typical variation of ferrite properties at low frequencies.

the leakage flux is small. The increase in $Q$ is obtained by a proportionate sacrifice in effective permeability. If an inductor of given $Q$ and $L$ is required, then a larger number of turns will be necessary. This increases the copper losses and the distributed capacitance and therefore reduces the available $Q$. Copper losses, however, are difficult to evaluate, since they are a function of the winding geometry and the dielectric constant and the permeability of the ferrite.

A typical increase in $Q$ that can be obtained is shown in the following example. A material with a $\mu' = 500$ is likely to have a $Q = 50$. Hence, if $k$ is assumed as 0.01, then $1 + \mu'k = 6$. This yields an effective $Q_e = 300$. Figure 6.6 illustrates the usual frequency dependence of $\mu$ and $Q$ for a ferrite with a high permeability and one with a rather low permeability. The large material permeabilities are normally obtained at the expense of a reduced $Q$.

### 6.2.3 Effect of an Air Gap on Temperature Stability

The effect that an air gap has on the over-all temperature stability can be found by differentiating equation 6.19 with respect to temperature $T$.

$$\frac{1}{(\mu_e')^2}\frac{d\mu_e'}{dT} = \frac{1}{(\mu')^2}\frac{d\mu'}{dT} \tag{6.28}$$

The air gap length is not assumed to vary with temperature. Therefore,

$$\frac{d\mu_e'}{dT} = \left(\frac{\mu_e'}{\mu'}\right)^2\frac{d\mu'}{dT} = \frac{1}{(1+\mu'k)^2}\frac{d\mu'}{dT} \tag{6.29}$$

In other words, variations in the permeability of the original material with temperature is reduced by the factor $1/(1 + \mu'k)^2$. The percentage change in $\mu_e'[(1/\mu_e')(d\mu_e'/dT)]$ is reduced by $1/(1 + \mu'k)$.

Before completing the discussion of r-f inductors it might be well to review the assumptions made in the derivation of these equations.

1. The system was assumed to be linear with respect to signal strength. The hysteretic character of ferrites indicates that this was not true at very large signals. If the signal excursions over the hysteresis loop were maintained as small as feasible, this would not only reduce the nonlinear behavior, but the losses due to hysteresis would also be reduced. For a given applied voltage and cross-sectional area, a minimum value to the number of turns at a given frequency is set.

2. As long as the leakage flux is at a minimum the equations derived are very accurate. However, for other structures, such as rods, for example, the form of the equations is still valid, but there is an empirical factor dependent on geometry which must be included.

A more complete analysis of cup-core design is given in the references (8). The authors give a more detailed account of the losses associated with the particular ferrite material. This leads to optimum design parameters, depending on which losses are greater, hysteresis, eddy current, or residual.

## 6.3 Ferrite Transformers (13, 14)

The introduction of ferrites essentially adds no new problems to transformer design. The criteria for a good transformer material remain in a standard form. These conventional standards may be enumerated very briefly:

### Low Core Loss

Eddy current losses are negligible in ferrite. The major loss is the hysteresis component due to its high dynamic coercive force, even though the saturation flux density is low.

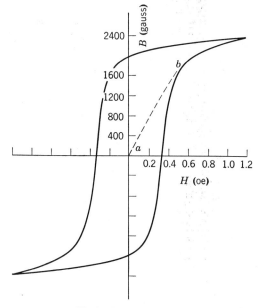

Figure 6.7*a*. Typical ferrite transformer material.

### High Effective Permeability

A typical *B-H* loop for ferrite transformer material is shown in Figure 6.7*a*. It is desirable that the slope *a–b* be as large as possible. However, an interesting problem arises in the case of pulse transformers. When used as the output transformer in a vacuum tube circuit the current flow in the primary circuit is unidirectional. Hence after several initial pulses the core material is not operating from the origin of the *B-H* loop as a starting point but rather from one of the remanent points on the major loop. If the transformer material of Figure 6.7*a* were used, the effective core permeability would be very small. A more desirable material (Figure 6.7*b*) would have a low remanent value and a large slope at this point. Oscillations with the distributed capacitance of the transformer tends to reset the cores to a value of flux density somewhat below the remanent value.

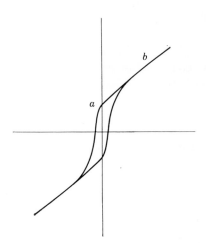

**Figure 6.7***b***.** Desired core characteristic for pulse transformer which passes undirectional pulses.

### High Saturation Flux Density

In present ferrites the usual range is of saturation flux density from 3000 to 5000 gauss. This factor tends to limit its usefulness at very low frequencies unless we can tolerate the use of large volumes of material. In certain specialized applications the large space factor may be justified.

### Temperature Stability

Since ferrites have a rather low Curie temperature (150 to 300° C), the saturation flux density and incremental permeability tend to decrease with increasing temperature. For those applications in which the operating or ambient temperature approaches 80 to 100° C, these characteristics have become troublesome. However, it has been possible to minimize the temperature variation through proper control of chemical constituents and firing schedules.

Ferrites are universally used as the core materials for television deflection transformers (Figure 6.8). The two main functions of this transformer are

1. To match the relatively high driver tube plate impedance to the relatively low deflection yoke impedance. The deflection yoke current wave shape is a modulated sawtooth with peak currents varying from 1 to 7 amp.

Figure 6.8. Ferrite television deflection transformer. (Courtesy General Electric.)

2. To generate high voltage (10 to 20 kv) in a "tertiary winding" for use with the cathode-ray tube by utilizing the sudden reversal in deflection current during "flyback."

The high-frequency content of the modified sawtooth current would produce large eddy current losses in conventional laminated metal cores as compared to the low-loss ferrite. Figure 6.8 is a photograph of a typical *TV* transformer. The basic construction consists of two *C*-frames separated by a suitable air gap spacer. The large unused window area is inefficient from a design point of view, but in order to prevent high-voltage breakdown the tertiary winding must be kept away from the chassis. The high narrow coil is the tertiary winding, wound directly over the primary to obtain maximum magnetic coupling.

Several other functions are performed by this transformer in addition to the one of impedance matching. A detailed circuit analysis is not warranted here; but suffice to say that the rapid reversal of the deflection current during the flyback time is utilized to generate the high voltage through a tertiary winding for accelerating the electron beam (10 to 20 kv). In addition a B+ boost circuit is added to obtain an additional 300-v d-c supply. The high-frequency content in the sawtooth waveform makes the use of ferrite ideal as compared to the laminated metal structures.

## 6.4   TV Deflection Yoke

The electron-beam deflection system in modern television receivers is of the magnetic type rather than the electrostatic. In the latter it is extremely difficult to obtain large angular deflections without severe defocusing of the beam. For cathode-ray tubes utilizing a single beam the deflection yoke is required to produce a nearly uniform magnetic field across the neck of tube.* Two sets of coils in the form of saddles are placed over the neck of the tube to provide the horizontal and vertical deflection. The outer surface of the coils is surrounded by four ferrite segments to increase the magnitude of the magnetic field inside the tube. A photograph of the entire structure is shown in Figure 6.9.

Figure 6.9.   Ferrite television deflection yoke. (Courtesy General Electric.)

Though the function of the ferrite in this application is rather straight-forward, it is interesting to calculate the exact expressions for the magnetic field in terms of the dimensions and the permeability of the ferrite.

* For color tubes the electron-optics usually require a somewhat different field configuration.

The method of solution provides a practical illustration of the field concepts developed in the earlier chapters.

Figure 6.10 is an idealized cross section of the deflection yoke. The circle of radius $R_1$ represents the neck of the tube. Along the neck are shown the conductors with their respective current directions which produce a vertical magnetic field. In order to produce a uniform field it is necessary to vary the turn density along the circumference in a

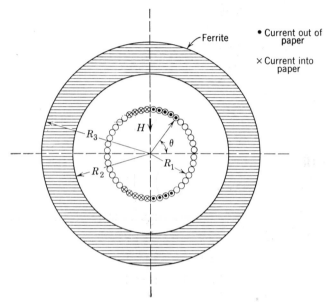

**Figure 6.10.** Idealized cross section of TV deflection yoke.

sinusoidal fashion. A second set of conductors for the horizontal field has been omitted from this calculation. The inner and outer radii of the ferrite yoke are represented by $R_2$ and $R_3$. Because of the method of construction the ferrite yoke is displaced somewhat from the windings. The ferrite is shown as a continuous ring, although in actual practice it is formed with two or four separate sectors. It can be seen that the effect of the resultant small air gap is small compared to the larger air gap of length $2R_2$. The analysis is further simplified by assuming an infinitely long structure and thus neglecting the end effects of a finite yoke.

The formal solution is carried out in two parts. The first part is to calculate the field due to the distribution of currents on the circle of radius $R_1$. The second part is to superimpose the field due to the ferrite. The arbitrary constants in the second are evaluated through the appropriate boundary conditions.

### Field Due to Current $H_I$

The field is most directly calculated from the vector potential $\mathbf{A}$, which in cylindrical coordinates yields

$$\mathbf{H}_I = \nabla \times \mathbf{A} = \frac{1}{r}\frac{\partial A_z}{\partial \theta}\mathbf{i}_r - \frac{\partial A_z}{\partial r}\mathbf{i}_\theta \tag{6.30}$$

$\mathbf{A}$ has only a $z$-component.

The current is assumed to be distributed according to

$$i = I \cos \theta \tag{6.31}$$

For any arbitrary distribution of current on the circumference of a circle the vector potential can be expanded in an infinite series of sines and cosines (1).

$r \leq R_1$

$$A_z = R_1 C_0 \ln R_1 + \frac{R_1}{2}\sum_{n=1}^{\infty}\left(\frac{1}{n}\right)\left(\frac{r}{R_1}\right)^n (C_n \cos n\theta + D_n \sin n\theta) \tag{6.32}$$

$r \geq R_1$

$$A_z = R_1 C_0 \ln R_1 + \frac{R_1}{2}\sum_{n=1}^{\infty}\frac{1}{n}\left(\frac{B_1}{r}\right)^n (C_n' \cos n\theta + D_n' \sin n\theta) \tag{6.33}$$

Because of the symmetry of the assumed current distribution the only coefficient which remains is $C_1$:

$$C_1 = I \cos \theta = C_1'$$

$$C_n = 0 \qquad n \neq 1 \tag{6.34}$$

Therefore,

$$r < R_1$$

$$A_z = \frac{rI}{2}\cos\theta \tag{6.35}$$

$$r > R_1$$

$$A_z = \frac{R_1{}^2 I}{2r}\cos\theta \tag{6.36}$$

The field can then be calculated from equation 6.30.

For $r < R_1$

$$H_{I_r} = -\frac{I}{2}\sin\theta \tag{6.37}$$

$$H_{I_\theta} = -\frac{I}{2}\cos\theta \tag{6.38}$$

For $r > R_1$

$$H_{I_r} = -\frac{R_1{}^2}{2r^2} I \sin \theta \tag{6.39}$$

$$H_{I_\theta} = \frac{R_1{}^2}{2r^2} I \cos \theta \tag{6.40}$$

Figure 6.11 is a sketch of the resultant field which is uniform inside the neck of the tube ($|H| = I/2$).

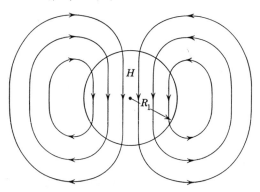

Figure 6.11.   Field due to coils.

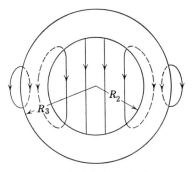

Figure 6.12.   Field due to ferrite yoke.

### Field Due to Ferrite ($\mathbf{H}_f$)

Since the ferrite produces a magnetostatic field as a result of its surface poles, this portion of the problem reduces to a solution of Laplace's equation, $\nabla^2 \phi = 0$. In cyclindrical coordinates the potential $\phi$ can be expressed in a infinite series (2).

$$\phi = \sum_{m=1}^{\infty} (a_1 r^m + a_2 r^{-m})(f_m \sin m\theta + g_m \cos m\theta) \tag{6.41}$$

Because of the symmetry of the current distribution it is necessary only to take the case for $m = 1$. From $\mathbf{H}_f = -\nabla\phi$ we can calculate the components of $\mathbf{H}_f$ in the various regions.

For $r < R_2$

$$H_{f_r} = -(f_1 \sin\theta + g_1 \cos\theta) \qquad a_1 = 1 \tag{6.42}$$

$$H_{f_\theta} = -(f_1 \cos\theta - g_1 \sin\theta) \tag{6.43}$$

For $R_2 < r < R_3$

$$H_{f_r} = -\left(a_1' - \frac{a_2'}{r^2}\right)(f_1' \sin\theta + g_1' \cos\theta) \tag{6.44}$$

$$H_{f_\theta} = -\left(a_1' + \frac{a_2'}{r^2}\right)(f_1' \cos\theta - g_1' \sin\theta) \tag{6.45}$$

For $r > R_3$

$$H_{f_r} = \frac{1}{r^2}(f_1'' \sin\theta + g_1'' \cos\theta) \tag{6.46}$$

$$H_{f_\theta} = -\frac{1}{r^2}(f_1'' \cos\theta - g_1'' \sin\theta) \tag{6.47}$$

After applying the boundary conditions on $\mathbf{H}$ at $R_2$ and $R_3$, we can evaluate all the constants.

The results are

$$g_1 = g_1' = g_1'' = 0 \qquad \text{and} \qquad f_1' = 1 \tag{6.48}$$

$$f_1 = a_1' + a_2'/R_2^2 \tag{6.49}$$

$$f_1'' = R_3^2\left(a_1' + \frac{a_2'}{R_3^2}\right) \tag{6.50}$$

$$f_1'' = R_3^2 \frac{\left[\left(\dfrac{2\mu f_1}{B}\right)\left(\dfrac{R_2}{R_3}\right)^2 - (\mu - 1)K_2\right]}{1 + \mu L} \tag{6.51}$$

$$f_1 = \left(\frac{(\mu L + 1)(\mu - 1)B - 2(\mu - 1)(R_2/R_3)^2}{(\mu L + 1)^2 B^2 - 4\mu^2(R_2/R_3)^2}\right)BK_1 \tag{6.52}$$

where

$$K_1 = \frac{R_1^2}{2R_2^2}I \qquad \text{and} \qquad K_2 = \frac{R_1^2}{2R_3^2}I \tag{6.53}$$

$$B = 1 - \left(\frac{R_2}{R_3}\right)^2 \tag{6.54}$$

$$L = \frac{1 + (R_2/R_3)^2}{1 - (R_2/R_3)^2} \tag{6.55}$$

The only constant of interest is $f_1$, since it yields the field contributed by the ferrite inside the neck of the tube. A sketch of the ferrite field is shown in Figure 6.12.

The important point is that since a constant permeability was assumed the ferrite field is produced by the resultant surface poles on the inner and outer radii.* For $r < R_2$ the field is uniform and in the same direction as that produced by the current. However, for $r > R_2$ the **H** field is opposed to the field produced by the current. In order to obtain a quantitative measure of this result, we can add the two fields. The total field inside the neck is

$$H_T = \frac{I}{2} + \frac{I}{2}\left(\frac{R_1}{R_2}\right)^2 N \tag{6.56}$$

where $N = f_1/K_1$.

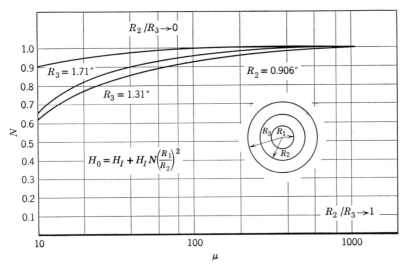

**Figure 6.13.** Effect of wall thickness and permeability on deflection sensitivity.

The second term is the contribution due to the ferrite. For the optimum conditions the various parameters would take on the following values:

$$R_1 = R_2$$
$$\mu \to \infty \tag{6.57}$$
$$R_3 \to \infty$$

Under these conditions $N$ approaches one. In this case the ferrite pro-

* Section 1.12, Chapter 1.

duces a field just equal to the original field inside the neck and reduces the field **H** everywhere else to zero. For practical parameters $N$ is plotted as a function of permeability in Figure 6.13. It is seen that for $\mu$ greater than 1000 the ideal conditions are almost reached. This was experimentally verified by removing the ferrite segments from the yoke and noting that the picture width and height decrease by almost 50 per cent.

The problem of losses in the ferrite for this application is not too significant. The copper losses far exceed the ferrite losses for ordinary TV application.

## 6.5 Magnetic Core Delay Lines (15)

Distributed constant delay lines utilizing ferrites afford another interesting application for ferrite materials. The basic properties which appear attractive are again the high permeability and low-loss characteristics at video frequencies. In addition, since the small signal permeability is a function of d-c bias fields, it is possible to vary the delay by electrical means. This implies that a ferrite delay line allows for small adjustments of delay while the component is in an operating circuit.

A standard air-core delay cable usually consists of a uniformly wound solenoid as the distributed inductance $(L)$ and a metallic sheath placed over the solenoid to provide the distributed capacitance $(C)$. For this type of line the time delay per unit length $(T_d)$ is given at low frequencies by

$$T_d = \sqrt{LC} \tag{6.58}$$

The characteristic impedance is given by

$$Z_0 = \sqrt{L/C} \tag{6.59}$$

The inclusion of a ferrite core as part of the inductance has as its purpose the increase of the inductance per unit length. This has the effect of miniaturizing the delay cable and also of increasing the characteristic impedance. A similar result may be obtained by increasing the number of turns per inch length. However, this procedure increases the over-all attenuation.

There are two fundamental criteria to be considered in the design of video delay cables. The first is the constancy of the time delay as a function of frequency. The second is the attenuation as a function of frequency. The latter problem is mainly characteristic of the type of materials used and is partly due to the geometric arrangement of the conductors. However, it is the former problem which provides some of the basic limitations in the use of ferrites for this application.

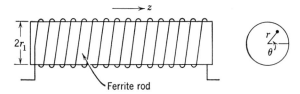

**Figure 6.14.** Uniformly wound infinite solenoid on a ferrite rod.

Consider the configuration shown in Figure 6.14. A ferrite rod is inserted into a uniformly wound solenoid. The second conductor is not shown, but let us assume that a wave has been propagated along the line so that the current per unit length is distributed along wire according to

$$I = I_0 e^{j(\omega t - \beta z)} \tag{6.60}$$

Hence the time delay per unit length is

$$T_d = \beta/\omega \tag{6.61}$$

The desired characteristic is that the propagation constant increase linearly with frequency. In order to determine how $\beta$ varies, or, more precisely, how the inductance of a small segment of line varies with frequency, it is necessary to solve the field equations for the assumed current distribution. Since the algebraic details are somewhat lengthy, only the broad outlines are presented.

The following assumptions are made in order to simplify the analysis:

1. The turns are close wound.
2. There are no circumferential variations in current in the frequency range of interest.
3. The line is lossless and infinitely long.

With these assumptions, it is necessary only to solve the differential equation for the vector potential **A** in cylindrical coordinates.

$$\nabla^2 \mathbf{A} = \mu\epsilon \frac{\partial^2 \mathbf{A}}{\partial t^2} \tag{6.62}$$

Since **A** has a vector component only in the $\theta$ direction,

$$\mathbf{A} = A(r)e^{-j\beta z}e^{j\omega t}\mathbf{i}_\theta \tag{6.63}$$

Equation 6.56 therefore reduces to

$$\frac{1}{r}\frac{d}{dr}\left(r\frac{dA_\theta}{dr}\right) - k^2 A_\theta - \frac{A_\theta}{r^2} = 0 \qquad (6.64)$$

where

$$k^2 = \beta^2 - \omega^2 \mu\epsilon = (T_d{}^2 - \mu\epsilon)\omega^2 \qquad (6.65)$$

The solution to equation 6.58 is of the form (5)

$$A_\theta = aI_1(kr) + bK_1(kr) \qquad (6.66)$$

where $I_1$ and $K_1$ are modified Bessel functions of the first and second kind and of the first order. The solution, however, must be divided into two parts. One solution is for the region inside the rod ($0 < r < r_1$), the second, for the region outside ($r > r_1$). Therefore,

$$A_\theta = aI_1(kr) \qquad 0 < r < r_1 \qquad (6.67)$$

$$A_\theta = bK_1(kr) \qquad r > r_1 \qquad (6.68)$$

since $K_1(kr)$ is undefined for $r = 0$, and $I_1(kr)$ is undefined for $r \to \infty$.

After matching the appropriate boundary conditions at $r = r_1$, the following values of $a$ and $b$ are found:

$$a = \frac{ni}{k\mu[I_1(kr_1)K_0(kr_1)/K_1(kr_1)] + kI_0(kr_1)} \qquad (6.69)$$

$$b = \mu a \frac{I_1(kr_1)}{K_1(kr_1)} \qquad (6.70)$$

where $\mu$ is now the relative permeability of the ferrite rod.* The current $I_0$ has been replaced by $ni$ where $n$ is the number of turns per unit length and $i$ is the current per turn.

It is now possible to calculate the inductance per unit length from

$$L = \frac{n\phi}{i} \qquad (6.71)$$

The total flux $\phi$ linking a single turn can be shown to be

$$\phi = 2\pi r_1 \mu A_\theta|_{r=r_1} \qquad (6.72)$$

* In general there is a $k$ inside the rod different from the $k$ outside the rod. However, the boundary conditions indicate that the $\beta$ is the same for each region. In addition, when we are concerned with large time delays per unit length $\beta^2/\omega^2 > \mu\epsilon$ (equation 6.65). Therefore, it is a satisfactory approximation to take $k$ as the same in both regions.

The resulting expression for $L$ is then

$$L = \frac{\mu\mu_0 n^2 2\pi r_1 I_1(kr_1)}{\dfrac{k\mu I_1(kr_1) K_0(kr_1)}{K_1(kr_1)} + k I_0(kr_1)} \qquad (6.73)$$

At very low frequencies equation 6.67 reduces to

$$L_0 = \mu\mu_0 n^2 \pi r_1^2 \qquad (6.74)$$

the familiar formula for the low-frequency inductance. A more useful form for equation 6.73 is obtained by normalizing $L$ to its low frequency value:

$$\frac{L}{L_0} = \frac{2 I_1(\beta r_1)}{\beta r_1 \left( \dfrac{\mu I_1(\beta r_1) K_0(\beta r_1)}{K_1(\beta r_1)} + I_0(\beta r_1) \right)} \qquad (6.75)$$

In this equation $k$ has been replaced by $\beta$, since for most applications $\beta^2 \gg \omega^2 \mu\epsilon$. The significant feature of equation 6.75 lies in the manner in which the permeability of the ferrite enters into the problem, If one chooses $\beta r_1$ as a variable, it is then possible to plot the variation of $L/L_0$ with $\mu$ as a parameter. In addition, it is instructive to replace $2\pi/\lambda$ by $T_d\omega$. Hence

$$\beta r_1 = 2\pi f T_d r_1 = \pi T_d D f \qquad (6.76)$$

where $D$ is the diameter of the rod.

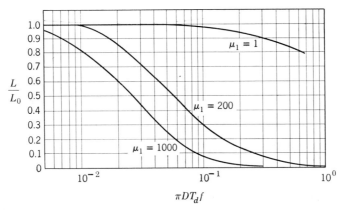

**Figure 6.15.** Variation of normalized inductance of infinite solenoid with permeability as a parameter.

Figure 6.15 is a plot of equation 6.75 for two different values of $\mu$. The case for $\mu = 1$ is that of an air core line previously derived by

Blewett. One obtains the characteristic decrease of inductance with increasing frequency. The interpretation of this fall off can be seen by noting that the total inductance of a single turn is due to the flux produced by the current in that turn, plus the flux produced by all the neighboring turns. At low frequencies all the currents along the line are in phase and thus produce the maximum value of inductance. However, at higher frequencies the currents in neighboring turns become out of phase due to the time delay of the signal. Hence the inductance per unit length decreases. From Figure 6.14, however, we see that although the use of a ferrite rod increases the low-frequency inductance the rate of decrease of inductance is much greater than for the air-core line. In fact, the effect becomes worse as we increase the permeability. This is due fundamentally to the mismatch in the radial component of the magnetic field at the boundary between the ferrite rod and the outside region.

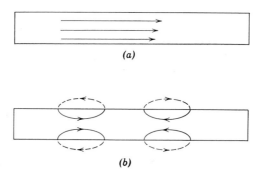

(a)

(b)

Figure 6.16. Magnetic field distribution along delay line: (a) long wavelengths; (b) short wavelengths.

At very low frequencies the field is almost completely confined to the ferrite rod due to its large length-to-diameter ratio. However, at higher frequencies where there are several wavelengths on the line the magnetic field is partially inside the ferrite and partially outside (Figure 6.16). Hence the effective permeability is reduced by the introduction of an air path at higher frequencies. In order to obtain a frequency response at least equal to that of the air-core delay line, equation 6.69 suggests that the outside region should also be filled with a ferrite of the same permeability as that of the rod.

The simplest configuration which embodies this principle is shown in Figure 6.17. The ferrite rod is surrounded with a ferrite sleeve whose outside is coated with silver to form the second conductor.

The analysis for this configuration is somewhat lengthy, but it follows the same procedure as outlined for the rod. However, since the second conductor is included, it is now possible to obtain an explicit expression for time delay as a function of frequency rather than as a function of the generalized parameter $(\pi D T_d f)$. This is done by taking into account the longitudinal as well as the circumferential component of current.

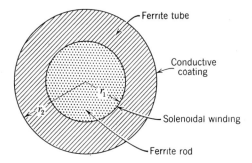

**Figure 6.17.** Cross section of improved ferrite delay line.

The solutions for each component of the current are tied together by the boundary condition that the electric field tangential to the solenoid winding must vanish.

The following expressions are the results of such a calculation:

$$T_d = \frac{\sqrt{\mu\epsilon}}{\alpha} \sqrt{\mu_0\epsilon_0} \sqrt{M/Q} \tag{6.77}$$

where

$$M = I_1{}^2(kr_1)\left(\frac{K_1(kr_1)}{I_1(kr_1)} - \frac{K_1(kr_2)}{I_1(kr_2)}\right) \tag{6.78}$$

$$Q = \frac{I_0(kr_1)}{I_0(kr_2)}[K_0(kr_1)I_0(kr_2) - I_0(kr_1)K_0(kr_2)] \tag{6.79}$$

$$\alpha = \text{pitch angle of solenoid}$$

$$k^2 = (T_d{}^2 - \mu\epsilon\mu_0\epsilon_0)\omega^2 \tag{6.80}$$

$$Z_0 = \frac{T_d Q}{2\pi\epsilon\epsilon_0} \tag{6.81}$$

At very low frequencies equations 6.76 to 6.80 reduce to the following simple form:

$$T_d = \sqrt{L_0 C_0}$$

$$Z_0 = \sqrt{L_0/C_0} \tag{6.82}$$

where

$$L_0 = \mu\mu_0 \left[ 1 - \left(\frac{r_1}{r_2}\right)^2 \right] \pi r_1{}^2 n^2 \qquad (6.83)$$

$$C_0 = \frac{2\pi\epsilon\epsilon_0}{\ln r_2/r_1}$$

Numerical calculations can be carried out for a given value of $r_1$, $r_2$, $u$, $\epsilon$ and $\alpha$. A value of $k$ is assumed from which we can calculate the value of $T_d$ (equation 6.77). For this value of $T_d$ we then calculate the corresponding value of $a$ from the expression for $k^2$ (equation 6.80).

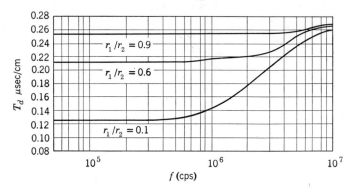

Figure 6.18. Variation of time delay with frequency for configuration of Figure 6.17.

A typical calculation was carried out for the following parameters: $\mu = 200$; $\epsilon = 200$; $r_1 = 0.25$ cm. The results are plotted in Figure 6.18. This particular configuration is thus seen to yield a time-delay characteristic which rises rather than falls with frequency. There are two factors which account for this. One is the use of ferrite both inside and outside the coil. The other is essentially due to the capacitive coupling that exists between neighboring turns through the outer conducting sheath. The amount of capacitive correction is determined by the thickness of the outer wall. We can view this compensation as the insertion of a leading component of current into a winding to oppose the lagging current due to the time delay.

The actual performance of this type of line is markedly dependent on both the mechanical tolerances involved and the properties of the ferrite. As the analysis shows, larger time delays per unit length and a wide bandwidth require thin rods and thin-walled tubes. Furthermore, we are also utilizing the ferrite not only for its magnetic characteristic but for its properties as a dielectric material. Experimental lines with the proper material have been constructed with delays of the order of 0.2 $\mu$sec/in. and a bandwidth (at the 3-db point) of 6 mc.


## 6.6  Electrically Controlled Inductors

The devices discussed in the present and the following sections are essentially linear systems with respect to the a-c signals but are nonlinear in the sense that an external parameter varies the operating point.

For the frequency range of several kilocycles to 60–70 mc there are several commercially available, electrically controllable ferrite inductors. Figure 6.19 shows sketches of a few of the configurations used by C.G.S. Laboratories. The small signal inductance of the signal winding is controlled by the current in the control winding. If a bias is required, it can be supplied by a direct current through bias winding. In the case of the Vari-L-Inductor the bias is supplied by a permanent magnet (Figure 6.20). A typical characteristic curve for this type is shown in Figure 6.21. The winding arrangements on the core are such as to decouple the a-c signal from the control circuit impedance.

Hysteresis effects are present in each of these devices in addition to a nonlinear inductance versus control current characteristic. The degree to which these inductors depart from linearity is determined by the portion of the curve over which operation takes place. The manufacturer's literature should be consulted for more exact specifications.

The electrical $Q$ of these inductors varies somewhat over the operating range, as shown, for example, in Figure 6.21. The average value of $Q$ for an electrically controlled inductor is somewhere between 15 and 125, depending on the characteristics of the core material and the frequency of operation. The temperature coefficient depends largely on the type of core material used and the value of control flux. In the commercially available models temperature coefficient varies from about 0.02 to about 0.6 per cent per degree centigrade. When a permanent magnet is included in the assembly care must be taken not to demagnetize the magnet by an excessively large a-c signal accidentally applied to the control winding.

The following is a list of the possible applications:

1. Remote frequency control of oscillators (16).
2. Variable electrical filter elements (16).
3. Sweep frequency oscillators (16).
4. Automatic frequency control (17).

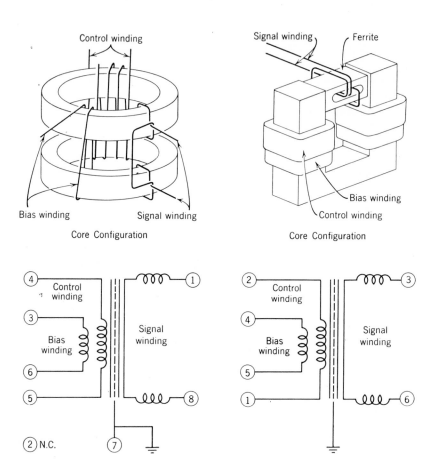

Core Configuration

Core Configuration

Circuit Diagram

Circuit Diagram

**Figure 6.19.** "Increductor"

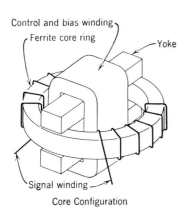

Control and bias winding
Ferrite core ring
Yoke
Signal winding

Core Configuration

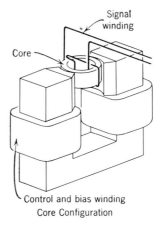

Signal winding
Core
Control and bias winding

Core Configuration

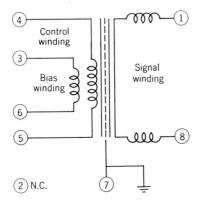

Circuit Diagram

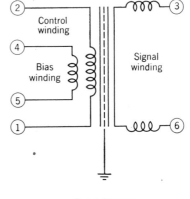

Circuit Diagram

configurations.   (C.G.S. Laboratories.)

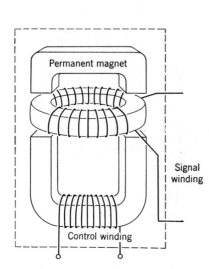

Figure 6.20. Vari-L-Inductor. (Courtesy Vari-L-Corporation.)

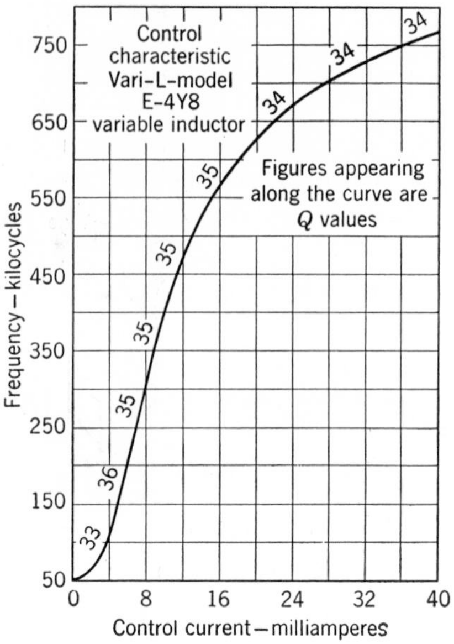

Figure 6.21. Vari-L-characteristic. (Courtesy Vari-L-Corporation.)

### 6.6.1 Ferrite Delay Line. Phase Modulation (31)

This device involves both the variable permeability of the ferrite discussed above and the ferrite delay line discussed in Section 6.5. An additional solenoidal winding is inserted over the delay line of Figure 6.16 so that a d-c current through this winding would electrically control the time delay of the line. This becomes a particularly useful feature for the production of phase or frequency modulation directly at the carrier frequency.* Most PM or FM modulation systems perform the modulation at a relatively low frequency, and thus several stages of frequency multiplication are employed in order to obtain the several hundred degrees of phase shift that are required.

With the present system the carrier frequency (10 to 30 mc) is the delay-line input, whereas the audio modulation, together with a d-c bias, is applied directly to the additional winding. Experimental lines of this type have been constructed (approximately 4 inches long) in which a variation in time delay of ±0.1 μsec was obtained at 10 mc.

---

* If the same type of line was used as a video delay line, then the auxiliary modulation winding permits the time delay of the output pulse to be adjusted electrically while the delay line is in an operating circuit.

This corresponds to $\pm 360°$ of phase variation. The resulting distortion due to the nonlinearity of the ferrite was less than 5 per cent, and the modulation power was of the order of 50 milliwatts.

The conversion of phase modulation to frequency modulation requires no additional circuitry, since it occurs directly in the modulation winding. If a low-impedance audio source is used, the audio current will vary inversely at the audio frequency due to the inductive nature of the modulation winding. This is exactly the deemphasis required for frequency modulation.

## 6.7   Electrically Controlled Capacitors

A controlled static electric field applied to a ferroelectric material can be used in a similar manner to vary the incremental permittivity of a capacitor. Since ceramic ferroelectric materials have become commercially available, a number of investigations have been made pertaining to the usefulness of these materials in practical voltage-controlled capacitors (18, 19). A dielectric constant-temperature-electric field ($\epsilon$-$T$-$E$) surface obtained on a commercially available ferroelectric ceramic is shown in Figure 6.22 (20). The points indicated on the surface are a plot of dielectric constant versus increasing applied field. The large temperature sensitivity of the material at low applied fields is obvious from the sketch. Additional data for this material also indicates that the capacitor $Q$ is lowest for high frequencies and small fields and that it increases rapidly with both increasing field and decreasing temperature. Thin layers of dielectric material are required to permit operation with relatively low control voltages. Similar to the controllable inductor is the fact that hysteresis occurs when the capacitance is varied with the control voltage.

Some of the electronic frequency control applications to which the electrically controlled capacitor has been put are controlled filters, oscillators, sweep-frequency generators, and spectrum analyzers. An application in which an electrically controlled capacitor was used to good advantage was the dielectric tuned panoramic receiver (21).

The amount of development work on applications of the electrically controlled capacitor will undoubtedly increase as better nonlinear dielectric materials become available. The problems concerning these materials at present are aging, temperature, and frequency sensitivity of the dielectric constant (wide variations in properties from one batch to another [or even within a batch] of any given material when manufactured).

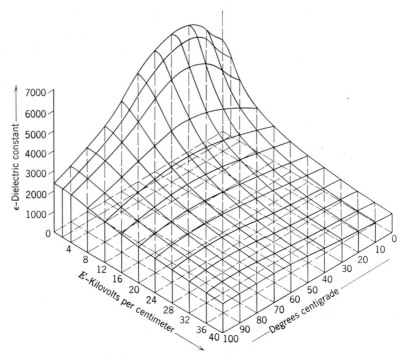

**Figure 6.22.** $\epsilon$-$T$-$E$ surface for Aerovox Hi-Q 41. (Butler, et al., 1955.)

## 6.8 Temperature Compensating Capacitors

The wide range of temperature coefficients of the many available dielectric materials has made possible the temperature compensation of some electrical circuits without elaborate environmental controls. Figure 6.22 shows the characteristics of some Erie Resistor Corporation temperature-compensating ceramicon capacitors. Capacitors which have temperature coefficients ranging from $+100$ ppm/° C to $-2500$ ppm/° C are available commercially. The temperature coefficients of these nonferroelectric ceramic materials are varied by mixing titania with other metallic oxides (22).

An example of this type of application is the use of a temperature-sensitive capacitor in place of the local oscillator d-c blocking capacitor in most modern superheterodyne home radio receivers. The function of the temperature-sensitive capacitor is to increase the temperature range over which reasonable tracking of the receiver tuner can be maintained. It does this by compensating relatively accurately for the

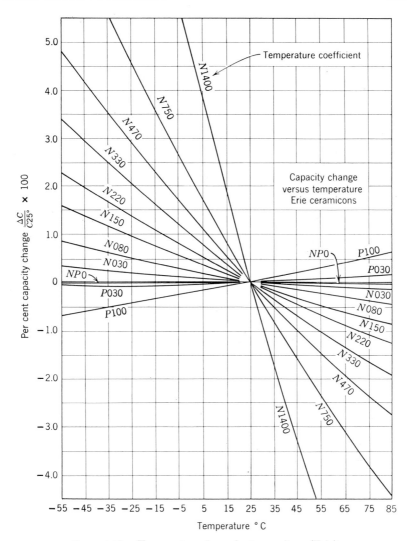

**Figure 6.23.** Temperature dependent capacitors (Erie).

collective effect of all the other elements in the tuner as temperature varies.

In addition to the dielectric materials shown in Figure 6.23, there are available many ferroelectric dielectrics which can be utilized in temperature-sensitive capacitors. Materials such as the titanates have exceptionally high temperature coefficients of permittivity just below and just above the Curie temperature (see Figure 2.16). The temperature coefficients of some strontium-barium titanate capacitors over a temperature range beginning about 15° C above the Curie temperature is approximately +4 per cent per degree centigrade. The variation of dielectric constant with temperature generally follows a Curie-Weiss law. The temperature range over which these materials are highly sensitive can be arranged to fall almost anywhere between 0 and 130° C, depending on the ceramic mixture used, as shown in Figure 2.16.

Below the Curie point the temperature sensitivity of these ferroelectric materials is also quite high. However, the temperature characteristic curves for these materials, obtained with increasing temperatures, do not coincide with corresponding curves obtained with decreasing temperatures. Above the Curie point this "hysteresis" effect with temperature is present to a much smaller degree. On the other hand, below the Curie point the temperature coefficient is positive, whereas above Curie the temperature coefficient is negative. Thus these materials provide temperature-compensating capacitors where negative temperature coefficients are required.

The main disadvantage of these materials at present is that the degree of reproducibility of dielectric constants is very poor. Where tolerances closer than ±10 per cent are required, capacitors utilizing these materials become relatively expensive.

## 6.9 References

1. Blok, H., and J. J. Rietveld, "Inductive Aerials in Modern Broadcast Receivers," *Philips Tech. Rev.*, **16**, No. 7, January 1955, pp. 181–194.
2. Grimmett, C. A., "Ferrite Cored Antennas," *I.R.E. Convention Record*, Part 7, Vol. 2, 1954, pp. 5–7.
3. Belrose, J. S., "Ferro-Magnetic Loop Aerials," *Wireless Engineer*, **32**, February 1955, pp. 41–46.
4. Suchtelen, H. van, "Ferroxcube Aerial Rods," *Electronics Application Bulletin*, No. 6, **13**, 1952, p. 88.
5. Everden, W. A., "Ferrite Rod Aerials," *Wireless World*, **60**, 1954, p. 440.
6. Dupuis, J., "Frame Aerials Using Ferrites," *L'Onde Elect.*, **35**, March–April 1955, p. 379.
7. Page, L., "Magnetic Antennas," *Phys. Rev.*, **69**, No. 11, June 1946, p. 12.
8. Stone, H. A., "Ferrite Core Inductors," *Bell System Tech. J.*, **32**, March 1953, pp. 265–291.
9. Duncan, R. S., and H. A. Stone, "Survey of the Application of Ferrites to Inductor Design," *Proc. I.R.E.*, **44**, No. 1, January 1956, pp. 4–13.
10. Suchtelen, H. van, "Losses in Ferroxcube Rods and Tubes," *Electronics Application Bulletin*, No. 6, **13**, July 1952, pp. 109–14.
11. ———, "Tolerances and Temperature Coefficients of Coils with Ferroxcube Slugs," *Electronics Application Bulletin*, **14**, January–February 1953, pp. 27–32.
12. Arrazan, J., "Calculations for Ferroxcube Pot-Cored Coils," *L'Onde Elect.*, **36**, March 1956, pp. 256–267.

13. Yukiaki, H., "Very Wide Band Radio Frequency Transformer Using Ferrite Core and Permalloy Tape Wound Core," *Elec. Commun.* (Tokyo), **3**, September 1955, p. 7.
14. O'Meara, T. R., "Wide Band Ferrite-Core Transformer for High Frequencies," *Tele-Tech.*, **14**, No. 4, April 1953, p. 73.
15. Katz, H. W., and R. E. Schultz, "Miniaturized Ferrite Delay Lines," *I.R.E. Convention Record*, Part 2, Circuit Theory, 1955, p. 78.
16. Increductor Bulletin, C. G. S. Laboratories, Stamford, Conn.
17. Venema, H. J., M. F. Schlecht, B. Silverman, "Pulse Control of a Variable Frequency Oscillator Using Saturable Reactors," *Proc. Nat. Electronics Conf.*, **11**, 1955.
18. Apstein, M., H. H. Wieder, "Capacitor-Modulated Wide Range FM Systems," *Electronics*, **26**, October 1953, p. 190.
19. Jenkins, J. L., "Ferroelectric Dielectrics Used in Voltage Sensitive Capacitors," *Elec. Mfg.*, **54**, No. 1, July 1954.
20. Butler, T. W., Jr., H. Diamond, L. W. Orr, "Sub-Miniature Non-Linear Capacitors for Applications to VHF Wide Range Tuning Devices," *Proc. Nat. Electronics Conf.*, **11**, 1955, p. 839.
21. Butler, T. W., Jr., W. J. Lindsay, L. W. Orr, "Application of Dielectric Tuning to Panoramic Receiver Design," *Proc. I.R.E.*, **43**, No. 9, September 1955, p. 1091.
22. Lewis, B. G., "Non-Linear Condensers," *Radio and Television News*, **49**, No. 5, May 1953.
23. Owens, C. D., "A Survey of Ferrites Below Microwave Frequencies," *Proc. I.R.E.*, **10**, No. 44, October 1956, p. 1234.
24. Lescroel, Y., "Ferromagnetic Ferrites," *Cables et Transmission*, **7**, October 1953, p. 273–92.
25. Suchtelen, H. van, "Introduction to the Application of Ferroxcube," *Electronics Applications Bulletin*, No. 2, **11**, 1950, p. 27.
26. Stiber, S., "Use of Ferromagnetic Materials in Electronic Tuning of RF Components," *Proc. Nat. Electronics Conf.*, **8**, 1952, pp. 462–468.
27. Uibert, Legrand G. van, "Dielectric Properties of and Conductivity in Ferrites," *Proc. I.R.E.*, **44**, No. 10, October 1956, p. 1294.
28. Koops, C. G., "On the Dispersion of Resistivity and Dielectric Constant of Some Semiconductors at Audio Frequencies," *Phys. Rev.*, **83**, 1951, p. 121.
29. Proceedings of I.R.E., **44**, No. 10, October 1956, "Ferrites Issue."
30. I.R.E. Standards on Radio Receivers: "Methods of Testing Receivers Employing Ferrite Core Loop Antennas," **55**, *I.R.E.* 17.S1, 1955.
31. Katz, H. W., "High Frequency Ferrite Delay Line for Phase Modulation," *Proc. Electronic Components Symposium*, *I.R.E.*, 1957, Chicago; also *Electronic Design*, September 1957.
32. "Use of Ferroxcube Pot Cores as Variable Inductors," *Matronics*, No. 6, June 1954.
33. "Calculating Coils in Ferroxcube Pot Cores," *Matronics*, No. 4, October 1953.
34. Gourary, B. S., "Dispersion Relations for Tensor Media and Their Application to Ferrites," *J. Appl. Phy.*, **28**, No. 3, March 1957.
35. Harrison, R. J. "Realizability of a Prescribed Frequency Variation of Dielectric Constant," *Proc. I.R.E.*, **45**, No. 3, March 1957.

Chapter seven

# Ferrites at Microwave Frequencies

## 7.0 Introduction

It is in the microwave region that some of the most interesting properties of ferrites occur. Ferrites are the first materials to be developed which exhibit nonreciprocal propagation characteristics of sufficient magnitude to make them useful to the communications art.* Although nonreciprocal propagation of plane-polarized visible light was first observed by Faraday (1845) in certain liquids, these effects are so small or else accompanied by such high attenuations as to be of very limited significance. In the ferrites, however, relatively small applied magnetic fields will produce nonreciprocal effects large enough to make practicable a number of unique microwave components.

These nonreciprocal phenomena arise from the interaction of the electron's spin with a magnetic field. When the ferrite is saturated by an applied magnetic field the spin axes of these electrons are, on a classical basis, aligned in the direction of this field. These spinning particles will react to a perturbing force at right angles to their spin by precessing about the spin axis, just as a spinning top does when disturbed from its "sleeping" position. This perturbing force is supplied by an r-f

* See Appendices 1 and 2.

wave of suitable frequency. The closer this r-f frequency is to the precessional frequency, the more marked is the interaction, and resonance effects can be observed when these two are near coincidence. Ferromagnetic resonance was first observed by Griffiths in 1946 and is the electronic counterpart of the nuclear-spin resonance effect discovered by Purcell, Torrey, and Pound (1) and Bloch (2) in the same year.

Macroscopically, these spin effects manifest themselves in the r-f permeability of the ferrite. It will be shown quantitatively that a component of magnetic induction is set up at right angles to both the incident

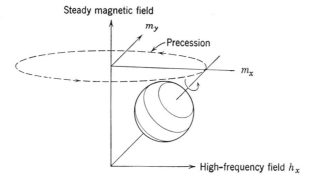

Steady magnetic field

$m_y$

Precession

$m_x$

High-frequency field $h_x$

Figure 7.1. Electron precession under the influence of a steady and high-frequency magnetic field.

r-f wave and the applied d-c field. Referring to Figure 7.1, the precessing total magnetization vector will have a component $m_y$ in time quadrature at right angles to the applied r-f field $h_x$. This means that a component of r-f flux density has been generated at right angles to the direction of the applied r-f field. Bloch's nuclear induction experiment consisted in measuring this component. The existence of such a component implies the existence of a tensor r-f permeability for the ferrite, instead of the usual scalar permeability.

## 7.1  Tensor Permeability *

Polder, in a thorough analysis of ferromagnetic resonance (3) first derived the tensor and showed that its antisymmetry could be utilized to realize nonreciprocal microwave elements. This tensor can be developed from the equations of motion for a spinning electron. The

* In this chapter the cgs system has been used, since the microwave literature on ferrites is almost exclusively in this system.

equation of undamped motion of the spinning electron, of angular momentum $\mathbf{J}$, magnetic moment $\mathbf{M}$, in a magnetic field $H$, is

$$\frac{d\mathbf{J}}{dt} = \mathbf{T} \tag{7.1}$$

where $\mathbf{T}$ is the torque exerted by the magnetic field.

However,

$$\mathbf{T} = \mathbf{M} \times \mathbf{H} \quad \text{and} \quad \mathbf{J} = \mathbf{M}/\gamma \tag{7.2}$$

hence

$$\frac{d\mathbf{M}}{dt} = \gamma \mathbf{M} \times \mathbf{H} \tag{7.3}$$

where $\gamma$, the magnetomechanical ratio, is $ge/2mc$,* in which $g$ is the Landé $g$-factor, and $M$ is the magnetization per unit volume.

Let

$$\mathbf{M} = \mathbf{M}_0 + \mathbf{m} \tag{7.4}$$

and

$$\mathbf{H} = \mathbf{H}_0 + \mathbf{h} \tag{7.5}$$

where $M_0$ and $H_0$ represent the d-c values and $m$ and $h$, the r-f values. For r-f fields very small compared to the d-c values (so that we need consider only first order terms in $m$ and $h$) we obtain

$$j\omega m_x = \gamma(m_y H_0 - M_0 h_y) \tag{7.6}$$

$$j\omega m_y = \gamma(M_0 h_x - m_x H_0) \tag{7.7}$$

$$m_z = 0 \; \dagger \tag{7.8}$$

We have assumed the time dependence as usual to be $e^{j\omega t}$ and $M_0$ and $H_0$ to lie along the $z$-direction. The solution of these equations for $m_x$ and $m_y$ yields

$$m_x = \frac{\gamma^2 M_0 H_0}{\gamma^2 H_0{}^2 - \omega^2} h_x - \frac{j\omega\gamma M_0}{\gamma^2 H_0{}^2 - \omega^2} h_y \tag{7.9}$$

$$m_y = \frac{\gamma^2 M_0 H_0}{\gamma^2 H_0{}^2 - \omega^2} h_y + \frac{j\omega\gamma M_0}{\gamma^2 H_0{}^2 - \omega^2} h_x \tag{7.10}$$

* See Sec. 2.7. Note $\gamma$ is negative for an electron.

† Actually, $m_z = 0$ is only approximate. A closer investigation reveals that $m_z$ varies with time according as $e^{2j\omega t}$. This dependence has been utilized (Ayres, Vartanian, and Melchor, *J. Appl. Phy.*, **27**, February 1956, p. 188) to obtain frequency doubling. Since this is a second order effect, large r-f powers have to be used to observe the phenomenon.

Since $\mathbf{b} = \mathbf{h} + 4\pi\mathbf{m}$, we obtain from equations 7.9 and 7.10

$$b_x = \mu h_x - j\kappa h_y \tag{7.11}$$

$$b_y = j\kappa h_x + \mu h_y \tag{7.12}$$

$$b_z = h_z \tag{7.13}$$

where

$$\mu = 1 + \frac{\gamma^2 4\pi M_0 H_0}{\gamma^2 H_0^2 - \omega^2} = 1 - \frac{4\pi M \gamma \omega_0}{\omega_0^2 - \omega^2} \tag{7.14}$$

$$\kappa = \frac{\omega \gamma 4\pi M_0}{\gamma^2 H_0^2 - \omega^2} = \frac{\omega \gamma 4\pi M_0}{\omega_0^2 - \omega^2} \tag{7.15}$$

and where

$$\omega_0 = -\gamma H_0 \tag{7.16}$$

Equations 7.11 to 7.13 can be written operationally as

$$\mathbf{b} = \mu_T \mathbf{h}$$

where $\mu_T$ can be given the matrix or tensor representation

$$\mu_T = \begin{bmatrix} \mu & -j\kappa & 0 \\ j\kappa & \mu & 0 \\ 0 & 0 & 1 \end{bmatrix} \tag{7.17}$$

We naturally ask if there is any particular type of r-f wave for which this new complication of a tensor permeability is reduced to the more familiar case of the usual scalar permeability. This simplification is, in fact, achieved in the case of circularly polarized waves. Consider a positively circularly polarized r-f wave given by

$$h_y = -jh_x \tag{7.18}$$

Substituting this into equations 7.11 and 7.12, we obtain

$$b_x = h_x(\mu - \kappa) \tag{7.19}$$

$$b_y = -jh_x(\mu - \kappa) \tag{7.20}$$

Therefore,

$$b_y = -jb_x \tag{7.21}$$

Similarly, for a negatively circularly polarized r-f wave

$$h_y = jh_x \tag{7.22}$$

we obtain

$$b_x = h_x(\mu + \kappa) \tag{7.23}$$

$$b_y = jh_x(\mu + \kappa) \tag{7.24}$$

Therefore,

$$b_y = jb_x \tag{7.25}$$

Thus we see that in each case the flux density $b$ is also circularly polarized in the same sense as the magnetic fields and related to the latter through the respective scalar permeabilities $\mu - \kappa$ and $\mu + \kappa$. We may write these relationships as

$$\mathbf{b}^+ = \mu_{\text{eff}}^+ \mathbf{h}^+ \tag{7.26}$$

where

$$\mu_{\text{eff}}^+ = \mu - \kappa \tag{7.27}$$

and

$$\mathbf{b}^- = \mu_{\text{eff}}^- \mathbf{h}^- \tag{7.28}$$

where

$$\mu_{\text{eff}}^- = \mu + \kappa \tag{7.29}$$

From equations 7.14 and 7.15 we find

$$\mu_{\text{eff}}^+ = 1 - \frac{4\pi\gamma M_0}{\omega_0 - \omega} \tag{7.30}$$

$$\mu_{\text{eff}}^- = 1 - \frac{4\pi\gamma M_0}{\omega_0 + \omega} \tag{7.31}$$

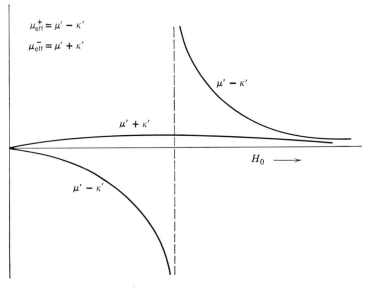

**Figure 7.2.** Variation of $\mu_{\text{eff}}^+$ and $\mu_{\text{eff}}^-$ with $H_0$ for circularly polarized waves.

The qualitative variation of $\mu_{\text{eff}}^+$ and $\mu_{\text{eff}}^-$ with applied magnetic field $H_0$ are shown in Figure 7.2. According to equation 7.30, an infinite value of $\mu_{\text{eff}}^+$ occurs for $H_0 = \omega/|\gamma|$. However, as we shall see, damping which has not so far been taken into account will limit $\mu_{\text{eff}}^+$ to finite values.

## 7.2    Demagnetization Corrections

Equations 7.30 and 7.31 must be generalized in two particulars before they are useful for interpreting experimental data. The first is with regard to the field $H_0$. From the manner of its introduction it is evident that $H_0$ represents the total d-c field acting upon the precessing electrons and will equal the applied field only for an infinite isotropic medium. Otherwise, it is given more generally by

$$\mathbf{H}_0 = \mathbf{H}_{\text{app}} + \mathbf{H}_D + \mathbf{H}_{\text{anis}}$$

The second term on the right is the demagnetizing field due to the finite geometry of the ferrite, and the third term is the effective field due to crystalline anisotropy.* The latter, although quite small, plays a role in broadening the resonance line and in producing low-frequency resonances for small or zero applied fields.

Since there are also demagnetizing effects for the r-f fields, the internal fields become

$$h_x{}^i = h_x - N_x m_x \tag{7.32}$$

$$h_y{}^i = -N_y m_y \tag{7.33}$$

$$H_z{}^i = H_z - N_z M_z \tag{7.34}$$

where the d-c field is in the $z$-direction and the applied r-f field is in the $x$-direction.

A derivation analogous to that which resulted in equations 7.14, 7.15 and 7.16 yields the new resonant frequency

$$\omega_0 = |\gamma| \left\{ [H_z + (N_y - N_z)M_z][H_z + (N_x - N_z)M_z] \right\}^{\frac{1}{2}} \tag{7.35}$$

The term within the curly brackets defines an effective field $H_{\text{eff}}$. This shows that it is imperative that the geometry be considered in interpreting experimental results. Table 7.1 gives $\omega_0$ for various commonly encountered configurations.

It will be understood that the magnetic field occurring below in the expressions for the tensor components is the effective field. The preceeding derivations also assume that both the r-f and d-c fields are uniform over the sample cross-section.

* See Chapter 2, Section 2.8.

## Table 7.1

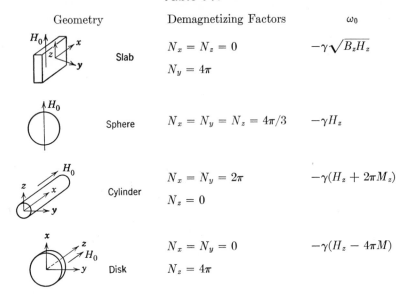

| Geometry | | Demagnetizing Factors | $\omega_0$ |
|---|---|---|---|
| | Slab | $N_x = N_z = 0$ $N_y = 4\pi$ | $-\gamma\sqrt{B_z H_z}$ |
| | Sphere | $N_x = N_y = N_z = 4\pi/3$ | $-\gamma H_z$ |
| | Cylinder | $N_x = N_y = 2\pi$ $N_z = 0$ | $-\gamma(H_z + 2\pi M_z)$ |
| | Disk | $N_x = N_y = 0$ $N_z = 4\pi$ | $-\gamma(H_z - 4\pi M)$ |

## 7.3 Damping Terms

The second alteration in the expressions for the tensor components is brought about by the introduction of damping terms into the equation of motion. A loss term must exist, since a damping force is required to prevent the precessional motion from increasing without limit if the applied frequency equals the resonant frequency.

However, there is yet no completely satisfactory method of introducing such a term. There are two types currently in use whose forms are based on heuristic arguments rather than rigorous derivations. The first (chronologically), due to Landau and Lifshitz (4) (LL-type), is given by

$$\frac{d\mathbf{M}}{dt} = \gamma(\mathbf{M} \times \mathbf{H}) - \frac{\alpha\gamma}{|\mathbf{M}|}\mathbf{M} \times (\mathbf{M} \times \mathbf{H}) \qquad (7.36)$$

where $\alpha$ is the damping parameter.

The damping term is in such a direction as to bring $\mathbf{M}$ into coincidence with $\mathbf{H}$. By taking the scalar product of both sides with $M$ it follows that $M$ is constant in time:

$$\mathbf{M} \cdot \frac{d\mathbf{M}}{dt} = \frac{1}{2}\frac{d|\mathbf{M}|^2}{dt} = \gamma\mathbf{M} \cdot (\mathbf{M} \times \mathbf{H}) - \frac{\alpha\gamma}{|\mathbf{M}|}\mathbf{M} \cdot [\mathbf{M} \times (\mathbf{M} \times \mathbf{H})] \equiv 0 \qquad (7.37)$$

With this modification of the equation of motion, equations 7.14 and 7.15 become (36).

$$\mu' = \frac{1 + 4\pi\gamma H_z[M_0\gamma(1 + \alpha)^2(\gamma^2 H_z'^2 - \omega^2) + 2\gamma M_0\alpha^2\omega^2]}{(\gamma^2 H_z'^2 - \omega^2)^2 + 4\omega^2\alpha^2\gamma^2 H_z^2} \tag{7.38}$$

$$\mu'' = -\frac{4\pi M_0\gamma\omega\alpha(\gamma^2 H_z'^2 + \omega^2)}{(\gamma^2 H_z'^2 - \omega^2)^2 + 4\omega^2\alpha^2\gamma^2 H_z^2} \tag{7.39}$$

$$\kappa' = \frac{4\pi M_0\gamma\omega(\gamma^2 H_z'^2 - \omega^2)}{(\gamma^2 H_z'^2 - \omega^2)^2 + 4\omega^2\alpha^2\gamma^2 H_z^2} \tag{7.40}$$

$$\kappa'' = \frac{8\pi\omega^2\alpha\gamma^2 H_z M_0}{(\gamma^2 H_z'^2 - \omega^2)^2 + 4\omega^2\alpha^2\gamma^2 H_z^2} \tag{7.41}$$

where

$$\mu = \mu' - j\mu'' \tag{7.42}$$

$$\kappa = \kappa' - j\kappa'' \tag{7.43}$$

$$H_z' = H_z(1 + \alpha^2)^{\frac{1}{2}} \tag{7.44}$$

The denominators show that the damping term will shift the resonant frequency from $|\gamma|H_z$ to $|\gamma|H_z'$. However, since $\alpha$ is small, this shift will be very slight. Figures 7.3 and 7.4 show a plot of $\mu_{eff}^-$ and $\mu_{eff}^+$ (real and imaginary parts, as defined in equations 7.26 and 7.27), which utilizes equations 7.38 to 7.41.

The second type of damping term proposed is due to Bloch (5) and Bloembergen (6) and is expressed in the form

$$\frac{d\mathbf{M}_{x,y}}{dt} = \gamma(\mathbf{M} \times \mathbf{H})_{x,y} - \frac{\mathbf{M}_{x,y}}{T_2} \tag{7.45}$$

$$\frac{dM_z}{dt} = \gamma(\mathbf{M} \times \mathbf{H})_z - \frac{(M_z - M_0)}{T_1} \tag{7.46}$$

where the $T$'s are relaxation times. $T_2$ is the spin-spin relaxation time and is the time constant for interactions between electron spins. It is of the order of $10^{-9}$ sec. $T_1$ is the spin-lattice relaxation time of the order of $10^{-6}$ sec. Since we are interested only in the $x$, $y$ components of $M$, and since $1/T_2$ is much greater than $1/T_1$, we shall say no more about $T_1$.

In this formulation $M$ is not constant in time as it was for the $L$-$L$-type damping. For a saturated medium it would be expected that $M$ would be constant and, for this reason, that the $L$-$L$ mechanism would give

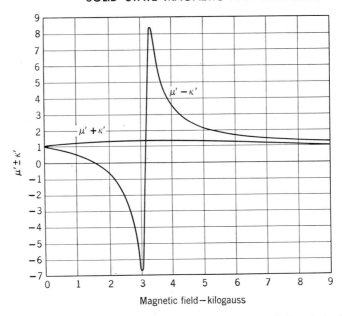

**Figure 7.3.** The real parts of the effective permeabilities for circularly polarized waves.

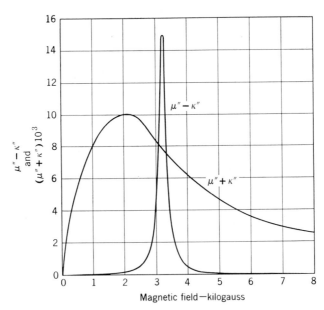

**Figure 7.4.** The imaginary parts of the effective permeabilities for circularly polarized waves.

results in closer accord with the experiment. However, such is actually not the case.

Both experimental (7) and theoretical (8) work have indicated that constancy of the magnetization is not preserved. The precise reasons for this behavior, however, are not clearly understood at the present time.

If equations 7.45 and 7.46 are solved in the same manner as before, we find

$$\mu' = 1 + \frac{4\pi M_0 \gamma^2 H_z (\gamma^2 H_z^2 - \omega^2 + 1/T_2^2)}{(\gamma^2 H_z^2 - \omega^2 + 1/T_2^2)^2 + 4\omega^2/T_2^2} \tag{7.47}$$

$$\mu'' = \frac{8\pi M_0 \omega \gamma^2 H_z/T_2}{(\gamma^2 H_z^2 - \omega^2 + 1/T_2^2)^2 + 4\omega^2/T_2^2} \tag{7.48}$$

$$\kappa' = \frac{4\pi M_0 \omega \gamma (\gamma^2 H_z^2 - \omega^2 - 1/T_2^2)}{(\gamma^2 H_z^2 - \omega^2 + 1/T_2^2)^2 + 4\omega^2/T_2^2} \tag{7.49}$$

$$\kappa'' = \frac{M_0 \gamma T_2^{-1} (\gamma^2 H_z^2 + \omega^2 + 1/T_2^2)}{(\gamma^2 H_z^2 - \omega^2 + 1/T_2^2)^2 + 4\omega^2/T_2^2} \tag{7.50}$$

We find, by comparing the tensor components given by $L$-$L$-type damping with those of the $B$-$B$-type damping, that if $1/T_2$ is set equal to $\alpha\gamma H_z$ then the $\mu''$s and $\kappa''$s are identical, to the first order in $\alpha$, for all $H_z$'s. However, the $\mu'''$s and $\kappa'''$s are equal only at resonance. Thus the two types of damping lead to differently shaped loss curves, and we should in principle be able to see which better fits the experimental data. However, the differences are slight, and additional measurements are needed to make the comparison. Young and Uehling (9) concluded that the $B$-$B$ damping gave results in closer agreement with experiment, although still not completely satisfactorily. From a practical viewpoint neither of these formulations is accurate in all respects. Further theoretical work is required to produce a damping mechanism which adequately explains a wide range of experimental data.

## 7.4 Solution of Maxwell's Equations for an Infinite Medium

A plane wave solution of Maxwell's equations can be obtained for an infinite medium for the general case in which the direction of propagation makes an angle $\theta$ with the magnetization (9). This solution may then be particularized for the two specific cases which are important in practice.

With field quantities in lower case letters, Maxwell's equations are

$$\nabla \times e = \frac{-1}{c} \frac{\partial b}{\partial t} \tag{7.51}$$

$$\nabla \times h = \frac{4\pi\sigma e}{c} + \frac{1}{c} \frac{\partial d}{\partial t} \tag{7.52}$$

The field vectors for a plane wave have the following form:

$$e = e_0 \exp \left[ j\omega t - \Gamma(n \cdot r) \right] \tag{7.53}$$

$$h = h_0 \exp \left[ j\omega t - \Gamma(n \cdot r) \right] \tag{7.54}$$

$$b = b_0 \exp \left[ j\omega t - \Gamma(n \cdot r) \right] \tag{7.55}$$

$$d = \epsilon e \tag{7.56}$$

where $\Gamma$ is the propagation constant, $n$ is the wave normal, and $r$ the position vector to a point in the wave front. Substituting equations 7.53 and 7.56 into 7.51, we obtain

$$\Gamma(e_0 \times n) = -j\omega \frac{b_0}{c} \tag{7.57}$$

Similarly, substituting equations 7.54 and 7.56 into 7.52 yields

$$\Gamma(h_0 \times n) = \left( \frac{4\pi\sigma}{c} + j \frac{\epsilon\omega}{c} \right) e_0 \tag{7.58}$$

Expressing $b_0$ and $e_0$ in terms of $h_0$, we obtain

$$\lambda b_0 = \Gamma^2 [n(n \cdot h_0) - h_0] \tag{7.59}$$

$$\lambda e_0 = -j \frac{\omega}{c} \Gamma(h_0 \times n) \tag{7.60}$$

where $\lambda = -j \dfrac{\omega}{c^2} (4\pi\sigma + j\omega\epsilon)$.

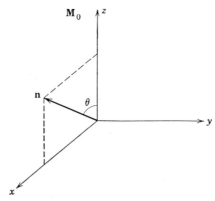

Figure 7.5. Relationship between $M_0$ and $n$.

For convenience, the subscript 0 will henceforth be omitted. We shall assume that the saturation magnetization $M_0$ of the ferrite is in the $z$-direction. The wave propagates in the $n$-direction, which is in the $x$-$z$-plane. $\mathbf{n}$ makes an angle $\theta$ with $M_0$, (Figure 7.5), i.e.,

$$n_x = \sin \theta \tag{7.61}$$

$$n_y = 0 \tag{7.62}$$

$$n_z = \cos \theta \tag{7.63}$$

Equation 7.59 then gives the three scalar equations:

$$\lambda b_x = \Gamma^2[\sin \theta(\sin \theta\, h_x + \cos \theta\, h_z) - h_x] \tag{7.64}$$

$$\lambda b_y = \Gamma^2(-h_y) \tag{7.65}$$

$$\lambda b_z = \Gamma^2[\cos \theta(\sin \theta\, h_x + \cos \theta\, h_z) - h_z] \tag{7.66}$$

Substituting for the $b$'s from equations 7.11 to 7.13, we obtain three linear homogeneous equations for the three $h$'s. For nontrivial solutions the determinant of the coefficients must vanish:

$$\begin{vmatrix} \lambda\mu + \Gamma^2 \sin^2 \theta & -jk\lambda & -\Gamma^2 \sin \theta \cos \theta \\ jk\lambda & \lambda\mu + \Gamma^2 & 0 \\ -\Gamma^2 \sin \theta \cos \theta & 0 & \lambda + \Gamma^2 \sin^2 \theta \end{vmatrix} = 0 \tag{7.67}$$

The solution of this equation results in two possible values for $\Gamma$.

$$\Gamma_{1,2} = \sqrt{-\lambda}\left[\frac{\left\{[\sin^2 \theta(\mu^2 - k^2 - \mu) + 2\mu]\right.}{\left. \pm [\sin^4 \theta(\mu^2 - k^2 - \mu)^2 + 4\kappa^2 \cos^2 \theta]^{1/2}\right\}}{2[(\mu - 1) \sin^2 \theta + 1]}\right]^{1/2} \tag{7.68}$$

### 7.4.1  Faraday Effect

There are two cases of equation 7.68 of particular interest. First, for $\theta = 0$, as in the Faraday effect, and second, for $\theta = \pi/2$, as in the Cotton-Mouton effect, we obtain, respectively,

$$\text{(Faraday)} \qquad \Gamma_\pm = \frac{j\omega\sqrt{\epsilon}}{c}(\mu \mp \kappa)^{1/2} \tag{7.69}$$

$$\text{(Cotton-Mouton)} \qquad \Gamma_1 = \frac{j\omega\sqrt{\epsilon}}{c}\left(\frac{\mu^2 - \kappa^2}{\mu}\right)^{1/2} \tag{7.70}$$

$$\Gamma_2 = \frac{j\omega\sqrt{\epsilon}}{c} \tag{7.71}$$

We now show explicitly that the two permeabilities $\mu \pm \kappa$, occurring in equation 7.69, are associated with oppositely circularly polarized waves, hence lead to the Faraday rotation. This is most easily done by returning to equations 7.59 and 7.60. If the wave is assumed to propagate in the direction of the d-c magnetization ($n_x = n_y = 0$, $n_z = 1$), the resultant calculation yields

$$\frac{h_x}{h_y} = \frac{e_y}{e_x} = \pm j \qquad (7.72)$$

Equation 7.72 shows that the waves are circularly polarized, since the $x$- and $y$-components are equal in magnitude and 90° in time-phase. The positive circularly polarized wave is defined as the one whose rotation is in the same sense as the positive electric current which produces the d-c axial field. By this definition it is the positive wave ($\Gamma_+$) with effective permeability $\mu - \kappa$, which displays resonance characteristics. It can be seen in equation 7.69 that the two circularly polarized waves have different effective permeabilities. Hence rotation of the plane of polarization will occur for a wave propagating through the medium. For just as a circularly polarized wave is composed of two linearly polarized vibrations 90° out of phase, so one linearly polarized wave can be regarded as being comprised of two contrarotating circularly polarized vibrations. If one of these circular components alters its phase constant with respect to the other, so that it travels with a different speed through the medium, the plane of polarization of the resultant vibration will gradually rotate as the waves progress through the medium (Figure 7.6.)

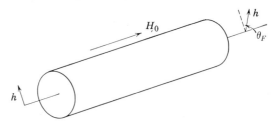

**Figure 7.6.** Schematic of Faraday rotation.

Specific rotation and phase shift are given, respectively, by

$$\theta_F = (\beta_+ - \beta_-)/2 \qquad (7.73a)$$

and

$$\phi_F = (\beta_+ + \beta_-)/2 \qquad (7.73b)$$

Since $\mu$ and $\kappa$ are complex, we can obtain the real and imaginary parts of the propagation constant by observing that, generally,

$$(a + jb)^{\frac{1}{2}} = \left(\frac{\sqrt{a^2 + b^2} + a}{2}\right)^{\frac{1}{2}} + j\left(\frac{\sqrt{a^2 + b^2} - a}{2}\right)^{\frac{1}{2}} \quad (7.74)$$

Applying this to equation 7.69 and setting $\Gamma_{\mp} = \alpha_{\mp} + j\beta_{\mp}$, we obtain

$$\beta_{\mp} = \frac{\omega}{c} \sqrt{\frac{|\epsilon| + \epsilon'}{2}} \left[\frac{[(\mu' \pm \kappa')^2 + (\mu'' \pm \kappa'')^2]^{\frac{1}{2}} + (\mu' \pm \kappa')}{2}\right]^{\frac{1}{2}} \quad (7.75)$$

$$\alpha_{\mp} = \frac{\omega}{c} \sqrt{\frac{|\epsilon| + \epsilon'}{2}} \left[\frac{[(\mu' \pm \kappa')^2 + (\mu'' \pm \kappa'')^2]^{\frac{1}{2}} - (\mu' \pm \kappa')}{2}\right]^{\frac{1}{2}} \quad (7.76)$$

If, for a given value of the applied field, both the real and imaginary parts of $\mu - \kappa$ are near zero, $\alpha_+$ is very small and most of the incident wave is reflected. (This is analogous to the approach of cutoff in a waveguide.) If the imaginary part of $\mu - \kappa$ is always appreciable, then propagation will take place at all values of the applied magnetic field.

By substituting the values already found for the tensor components, explicit expressions for the propagation constants can be written in terms of the magnetization, applied field, and frequency of the r-f wave. However, the expressions are cumbersome, and some approximations will be made. The Faraday rotation per unit length for a lossless sample is given from equation 7.69 by

$$\theta_F = \frac{\omega\sqrt{\epsilon}}{2c} \left|\sqrt{\mu_{\text{eff}}^-} - \sqrt{\mu_{\text{eff}}^+}\right| \quad (7.77)$$

$$= \frac{\omega}{2c} \sqrt{\frac{|\epsilon| + \epsilon'}{2}} \left|\sqrt{\mu' - \kappa'} - \sqrt{\mu' + \kappa'}\right| \quad (7.78a)$$

Using the simplified forms (equations 7.14 and 7.15) for the permeability terms, the term within the bars becomes

$$\left(1 - \frac{4\pi M\gamma}{\omega_0 - \omega}\right)^{\frac{1}{2}} - \left(1 - \frac{4\pi M\gamma}{\omega_0 + \omega}\right)^{\frac{1}{2}} \quad (7.78b)$$

If $\omega \gg \omega_0$ (in terms of varying $H_0$ this means well below resonance) and if the saturation magnetization is sufficiently low so that $4\pi M|\gamma| \ll \omega$, the expression simplifies further to $4\pi M|\gamma|/\omega$.

Hence

$$\theta_F = \frac{1}{2c} \sqrt{\frac{|\epsilon| + \epsilon'}{2}} (4\pi M |\gamma|) \qquad (7.78c)$$

a value independent of frequency. However, the requirement $4\pi M |\gamma| \ll \omega$ is fulfilled in practice only for very small fields and, therefore, is not generally valid/(28).

## 7.5 Solutions of Maxwell's Equations for a Finite Medium

Maxwell's equations may also be solved for the case of a finite medium. Expressions containing the propagating constant have been obtained (Kales (10), Gamo (11), Suhl and Walker (12)) for the cases of a circular waveguide filled with ferrite and also for the practical case of a cylindrical rod along the axis of the waveguide. However, these expressions are so unwieldy that explicit forms for the propagation constants cannot be extracted without laborious computations. Perturbation treatments (Suhl and Walker (13), Berk (14)) have yielded explicit expressions which have proved useful for certain simplified calculations. This treatment yields (Berk (14))

$$\beta_{\pm} \approx \beta_e \left\{ 1 + \frac{CS_f}{S_w} \left[ (\mu' \pm \kappa' - 1) - \frac{\beta_0^2}{\beta_e^2} (\epsilon - 1) \right] \right\} \qquad (7.79a)$$

where $\beta_e$ = propagation constant of the empty guide,
   $\beta_0$ = propagation constant of free space,
   $S_f$ = cross-sectional area of the ferrite,
   $S_w$ = cross-sectional area of the waveguide,
   $C$ = numerical constant ($= 1.04$ for circular waveguide).

Suhl and Walker give another form:

$$\beta_{\pm} = \beta_e \left[ 1 + A \frac{Sf}{S_w} \left( \frac{\mu_{\pm} - 1}{\mu_{\pm} + 1} - \frac{\beta_0^2}{\beta_0^2} \frac{\epsilon - 1}{\epsilon + 1} \right) \right] \qquad (7.79b)$$

where $A = 3.2$.

Far from resonance, equation 7.79$b$ reduces substantially to equation 7.79$a$. There is, however, a further important point of distinction between 7.79$a$ and 7.79$b$ (Berk and Lengyel). In the derivation of the latter the field within the ferrite is actually calculated and used in the perturbation expressions. Therefore, the permeability in 7.79$a$ is in the nature of an "effective" or "observed" permeability, whereas that in

7.79*b* is the intrinsic permeability. The domain of applicability of either of these expressions is limited, as mentioned before, to very small diameter ferrites. Suhl and Walker state that the diameter of the rod must be small enough so that over a circle whose radius is several times that of the rod the transverse r-f magnetic field must be essentially constant. Since the radial component of the r-f field is

$$H_r \sim J_1{}'(kr)$$

where $J_1$ is the first order Bessel function, we can determine a maximum rod diameter for a given waveguide by postulating that $H_r$ should not vary by more than 10 per cent over the ferrite cross section. For 0.9375-inch I.D. waveguide the upper limit of the ferrite diameter is about 0.090 inch.

Measurements have been made on rods of this diameter in round waveguide and the permeability tensor components deduced therefrom by using 7.79*a* (15). Experimental plots obtained are similar to those shown in Figures 7.3 and 7.4. A discussion on measurement techniques is given in Chapter 11.


## 7.6 Summary

Maxwell's equations have been solved for the case of plane waves propagating through a magnetized ferrite medium of infinite extent. There are two cases of particular interest. The first is that for which the direction of propagation coincides with the magnetization. We showed that each of the two circularly polarized components of the plane wave possessed a scalar permeability, and the fact that these differed led to the Faraday rotation of the plane of polarization. The second case is that for which the magnetization is perpendicular to the direction of propagation. There are two subcases here: (a) the magnetization is parallel to the r-f magnetic field; (b) the magnetization is perpendicular to the r-f magnetic field. In case (a) there is no interaction between the precessing electrons and the r-f field, hence the material presents only the free-space permeability to the wave (equation 7.71). In the second case there is an interaction, and the permeability is a function of the diagonal and off-diagonal terms of the permeability tensor. The propagation constants for the first case were examined in some detail and the amount of the Faraday rotation deduced. These constants were given for a more practical case, viz., that of a thin ferrite rod in a waveguide.

The material presented here is fundamental to a qualitative understanding of all microwave ferrite devices. The behavior of the waves for the simple cases considered will be found to form the basis of all the devices subsequently described.

## /FERRITES IN CIRCULAR WAVEGUIDES

### 7.7 Losses and Ellipticity

Before turning to considerations of practical devices utilizing the Faraday effect we shall deal with some general problems that the microwave engineer encounters in using such devices.

For many applications low loss is of prime importance. The physical mechanisms contributing to the losses in ferrites at microwave frequencies have been described earlier. Figure 7.7a shows the field pattern

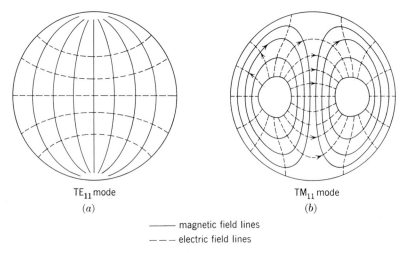

$TE_{11}$ mode          $TM_{11}$ mode

(a)             (b)

——— magnetic field lines
— — — electric field lines

**Figure 7.7.** $TE_{11}$ and $TM_{11}$ modes in circular waveguide.

in a round guide excited by the dominant $TE_{11}$ mode. In a small region about the center we can consider the wave to be plane-polarized.

Rotation of the plane of polarization will take place as the wave propagates through the longitudinally magnetized ferrite. In practice, the emergent wave is elliptical rather than plane-polarized, especially for larger values of the applied magnetic field. This occurs because the circularly polarized (positive component) wave undergoes greater attenuation through the ferrite than the negative component when the applied magnetic field approaches the resonant value. The ellipticity will depend upon a number of factors. At resonance the positive component will be almost completely absorbed, and a circularly polarized (negative component) wave will result. The diameter of the ferrite has an important bearing on the ellipticity. It is found that if the diameter of the ferrite exceeds about one quarter of the guide higher modes will be excited. Fox and Weiss (16) have shown that there is a tendency for the $TM_{11}$ mode (Figure 7.7b) to be excited when the diameter of the ferrite cylinder exceeds about one quarter of the waveguide diameter. Since the dielectric constant of the ferrite is still quite high at microwave frequencies (10 to 15), higher modes (in particular the $TM_{11}$ mode) will propagate if excited. These higher modes manifest themselves in anomalous behavior of the rotation and in increased loss and ellipticity. Examination of the $TM_{11}$ mode configuration (Figure 7.7b) indicates that this mode will be excited if there is an agency in the waveguide tending to introduce a 180° phase shift between the central and peripheral regions of the $TE_{11}$ mode. A ferrite rod which produces phase shift is just such an agent.

As in any waveguide device, the ferrite section must be "matched" to its neighbors. Mismatching will result in reflections from the ends which will compound the harmful effects mentioned above. The easiest way to overcome this feature is to taper the ends of the rod, particularly if broadband operation is desired. One must be certain, however, that the rod diameter is sufficiently small so that the $TM_{11}$ mode is beyond cutoff, for the tapered rod tends to excite this mode.

## 7.8   Figure-of-Merit for Faraday Effect

To compare relative efficiencies of ferrites to be used in a Faraday rotator device we can introduce a figure-of-merit $F$, defined by the ratio of rotation to loss (degrees/db). Lax has shown how this may be done theoretically (17). From equations 7.69 and 7.47 to 7.50 he shows that for $\omega \gg |\gamma| H_0$ or $\omega \ll |\gamma| H_0$, and assuming small losses, $F$ takes the simple form

$$F = 6.6\omega T_2 \text{ (degrees/db)} \tag{7.80}$$

This expression holds for the two limiting cases of an infinite ferrite medium and a very thin rod in a circular waveguide. This formula is more valuable in setting a lower frequency limit for a given $F$ than in examining the more detailed dependence of $F$ on ferrite size and geometry within a waveguide. For a given ferrite that value of the rod diameter which maximizes $F$ should be chosen.

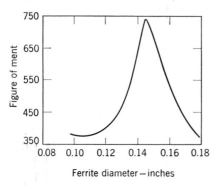

From the perturbation formular 7.79$a$ and equation 7.73$a$ we can see that for small ferrite diameters the rotation is proportional to the cross-sectional area. As the area increases beyond a certain value, the rotation increases at a faster rate, due to an increased concentration of r-f energy within the ferrite. A larger percentage of the power flowing through the waveguide passes through the ferrite instead of the surrounding space. However, this increase continues only until the difference in the phase constants of the two circular components is a maximum. The cross-sectional area which is effective for rotation will decrease beyond

**Figure 7.8.** Ferrite rotation per db loss as a function of ferrite diameter. (From "Behavior and Applications of Ferrites," Fox, Miller, and Weiss, *Bell System Tech. J.*, **34**, 1955, p. 5.)

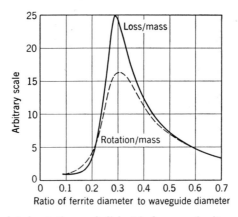

**Figure 7.9.** Calculated rotation and dielectric loss per ferrite mass versus ferrite diameter. (From "Behavior and Applications of Ferrites," Fox, Miller, and Weiss, *Bell System Tech. J.*, **34**, 1955, p. 5.)

that point. That this decrease must take place can be seen from the fact that the outer portions of the ferrite become less and less effective as they approach the guide walls to which the r-f magnetic field must be tangential. This dependence of $F$ on geometry is shown in Figures 7.8 and 7.9.

Even though some of the transverse magnetic field does not contribute to the rotation effect, it still is effective in causing losses. The aforementioned increase in energy concentration also contributes to the increased loss with increasing diameter. From these qualitative arguments we can conclude that for each type of ferrite axially located in a circular waveguide propagating the $TE_{11}$ mode there exists an optimum ratio of ferrite diameter to waveguide diameter for which $F$ is a maximum. We have neglected here any contributions to the rotation or loss of the rather large dielectric constant. That there are contributions to both is certain, but quantitative information is lacking (18).

## 7.9   Frequency Dependence of Faraday Effect

It was shown, for the infinite medium, that if we operate at magnetic field strengths far below the resonant value the rotation is independent of frequency. Unfortunately, this does not hold true in a waveguide for two reasons. First, the impedance of the $TE_{11}$ mode (or any TE mode) decreases with increasing frequency. Therefore, the transverse magnetic field, hence the rotation, increases.* Second, at higher frequencies there is a greater concentration of the r-f energy in the ferrite rod, and this, as above, leads to greater rotations. Rowen has shown that surrounding the ferrite rod with a high dielectric material will result in increased bandwidth, since under these conditions the guide wavelength is more nearly linearly related to frequency (19). We can also deliberately mismatch the ends of the ferrite rod so that multiple reflections are set up in such a way as to enhance the rotation at the lower frequencies where it would otherwise fall off.

### 7.9.1   Temperature Dependence

Since all ferromagnetic properties disappear when the Curie point is reached, we should like to work with specimens with a sufficiently high Curie point so that even at high r-f power levels the heating is not sufficient to bring the ferrite to this temperature.

However, this change of the magnetization with temperature is but one aspect of the problem. In addition, there can be changes in the

---

* For given input power the lower the characteristic impedance, the greater the r-f magnetic field; hence the larger the induced field and the greater the Faraday rotation.

gyromagnetic ratio and in the complex dielectric constant. As a consequence, the gyromagnetic resonance frequency will be temperature-dependent, and this will be important in those high-power devices utilizing resonance absorption. Duncan and Swern (20) give curves that show that the field necessary for resonance decreases or increases with temperature according to the location of the ferrite in a rectangular waveguide (with transverse field) or in a circular waveguide (with a longitudinal field). They also give curves which show the variation in phase.

### 7.9.2   R-F Power Dependence

The theory developed for the permeability tensor components, hence for all phase, rotation, and attenuation phenomena, was based on a "small signal" theory. By "small-signal" is meant that the ratio of the r-f magnetic field to the applied d-c field is very small. Under ordinary laboratory circumstances this is indeed so, but for radar applications, in which r-f power levels can reach the megawatt region, this is no longer true. For standard $X$-band waveguide (0.900 × 0.400 inch) an r-f power level of 50 kw for the frequency 9375 mc/sec corresponds to a transverse field of about 10 oersteds. Thus it is evident that we have an r-f field that is beginning to compare with the applied d-c field for ordinary rotations. The question naturally arises as to the effect of this "large-signal." A theoretical treatment poses grave difficulties, for the equations of motion are no longer linear. Some experimental work has been done which indicates that although the attenuation increases with r-f power level the rotation is not appreciably altered. This increased loss is not due to heating effects, as the sample was purposely kept relatively cool, but is rather an intrinsic-large-signal phenomena.

Sakiotis, Chait, and Kales (21) give experimental data showing the variation in absorbed power for positive and negative circularly polarized waves as a function of r-f power, with the applied magnetic field and ferrite rod diameter as parameters. The power absorbed increased with the r-f level, with increasing applied field, and with increasing ferrite diameter. The increases were more marked for the negative component than for the positive.

### 7.9.3   Zero Field Loss (34)

It has often been observed that certain ferrites have rather large losses at small values of the applied field (Figure 7.10). A number of explanations has been advanced to explain this phenomenon and, although differing in detail, they are in substantial agreement that domain-wall effects are involved. Since the position of the resonance peak as a function of applied field shifts to lower fields at lower frequencies, a practical lower limit of useable frequency arises because of the overlap of the main resonance with the zero field loss portion of the characteristic. An analysis of this problem indicates that the loss can be decreased

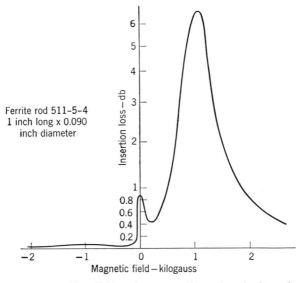

Figure 7.10. Zero-field and resonance losses in a ferrite rod.

by a reduction of the saturation magnetization and a reduction of the magneto-crystalline anisotrophy. This can be accomplished by changes in the ferrite composition.

## / APPLICATIONS OF THE FARADAY EFFECT

### 7.10  Isolators

At present the most widespread application of the Faraday rotation properties of ferrites is in isolator devices.* If a microwave source operates directly into a mismatched line, there is a tendency for the oscillator frequency to be pulled. In practice, heretofore, we placed

* The Faraday effect has also been utilized as a very sensitive magnetometer. The unknown d-c magnetic field is measured by the amount of rotation it produces in the ferrite (22).

an attenuator after the source so that reflections would undergo sufficient attenuation to minimize this undesirable effect. However, the forward power would also suffer this same attenuation, and unless sufficient power were available this effect could be very troublesome in some applications. The Faraday rotation effect, since it is nonreciprocal, enables us to construct a device which is essentially a one-way transmission line. A schematic for such a device is shown in Figure 7.11. A wave traveling

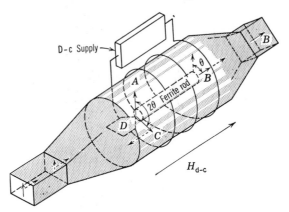

Figure 7.11. Microwave isolator utilizing Faraday rotation in a ferrite rod.

from left to right experiences a 45° rotation through the ferrite section and emerges through the rectangular waveguide section with the indicated polarization. A wave traveling in the reverse direction is rotated through 45° in the same direction as before, and since the wave is now oriented at 90° to the narrow side of the waveguide it cannot be transmitted. Absorbing vane D attenuates this wave sufficiently so that a negligible portion is re-reflected and emerges from the right-hand part. In practice, there are additional waveguide twist sections so that the output orientation is the same as that of the input. Commercially available devices at X-band have typical characteristics of 0.1 db or less forward loss, and minimum backward loss over the band of 15 db. By operating a number of such units in series a number of valuable effects can be obtained. First, if the forward loss requirements are not too stringent and high backward loss is desirable, $n$ units in series will give only 0.1 $n$ db forward loss for 15 $n$ db backward loss. By this method one can achieve a broadband device and also reduce the temperature sensitivity. For, if each section is designed to produce its 45° rotation at a somewhat different temperature or frequency from its neighbor, the total effect should be a relative insensitivity to temperature or frequency change over the range.

## 7.11   Switches

A simple change in the waveguide configuration of the isolator described above yields a single-pole, double-throw switch (Figure 7.12). The two rectangular waveguides at right angles will, with care, be decoupled by about 40 db. A positive 45° rotation will couple the input

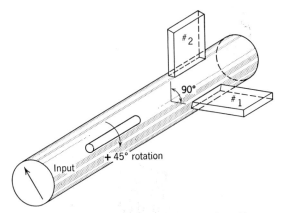

**Figure 7.12.**   A ferrite controlled "single-pole, double-throw" waveguide switch.

energy to terminal No. 1, provided it is suitably terminated. A negative 45° rotation will send the energy to terminal No. 2. Switches can be designed to work with microsecond speeds so that the action can be very rapid. In radar this type of component could be used to switch electrically between two antennas (e.g., sequential lobing).

## 7.12   Circulator

An additional modification of this switch is shown in Figure 7.13a. Here we have two pairs of rectangular waveguides, the members of each pair being at right angles and the second pair derived from the first by a 45° rotation. The device, with the ends of the circular guide properly terminated, constitutes a "circulator" and is schematically represented in Figure 7.13b. The arrows represent the sense of energy propagation from terminal to terminal.

If the end $E_1$ of the waveguide is properly matched, power incident through waveguide $A$ will propagate down the guide toward $E_2$. (None will be transferred to guide $C$ under ideal conditions because of the decoupling existing between guides $A$ and $C$.) Since the wave undergoes

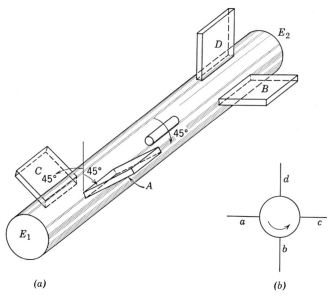

(a)                                    (b)

**Figure 7.13.**  A circulator utilizing the Faraday rotation in circular waveguide.

a 45° rotation through the ferrite, the wave can be accepted by guide $B$ (again assuming proper termination at $E_2$).   On the other hand, a wave incident from $B$ will travel toward $E_1$ and because of the additional 45° rotation will be accepted by $C$.   Similarly, a wave incident at $C$ will be accepted by $D$ and a wave incident at $D$ will emerge at $A$, completing the cycle.

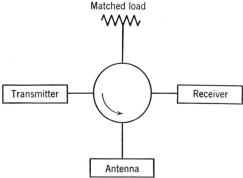

**Figure 7.14.**  Circulator as a radar duplexer.

A possible use of the circulator is in radar duplexing.   Figure 7.14 shows the positions of transmitter, antenna, and receiver.   However, the isolations presently obtainable are not comparable with those obtained for TR and ATR tubes. An additional disadvantage is due to the existence of unavoidable mismatch at the antenna which directs some of the transmitter energy into the receiver. Certain refinements can reduce this leakage to lower values.

## 7.13  Rectangular Waveguide

It is evident that in rectangular waveguide the Faraday rotation cannot occur (except in the special case of square waveguide), so that phase and attenuation present the simplest possibilities for field-controlled effects. The Cotton-Mouton effect (equation 7.70) has long been known as a phenomenon somewhat related to the Faraday effect, and we shall show its applicability to the case of ferrites in rectangular waveguide.

In Section 7.4 we showed that for an infinite ferrite medium magnetized transversely to the direction of propagation a constant permeability is obtained for a wave whose magnetic vector is parallel to the d-c magnetization, whereas a field-dependent permeability is obtained for a wave whose magnetic vector is perpendicular to the magnetization. These relative permeabilities are given, respectively, by

$$\mu_{\parallel} = 1 \tag{7.81a}$$

$$\mu_{\perp} = \left(\frac{\mu^2 - \kappa^2}{\mu}\right)^{\frac{1}{2}} \tag{7.81b}$$

Nonreciprocal phase and attenuation characteristics result when a ferrite slab, located off the central axis, extends for a distance along the guide, as shown in Figure 7.15. If the ferrite is subjected to the trans-

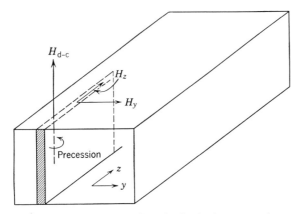

**Figure 7.15.**  Transverse magnetization of a ferrite in rectangular waveguide.

verse field indicated, the electron precession within the ferrite will be in the sense depicted. It is well known that the transverse and longitudinal components of the magnetic field, although varying relatively in magnitude across the waveguide, maintain a constant 90° phase difference. For the $TE_{01}$ mode we have for the spatial components

$$h_z = h_0 \cos \pi y / a \qquad (7.82a)$$

$$h_y = j h_0 \left[ \left( \frac{2a}{\lambda} \right)^2 - 1 \right]^{\frac{1}{2}} \sin \pi y / a \qquad (7.82b)$$

where $a$ and $y$ are as indicated in Figure 7.15.

Thus, at positions in the guide where $|h_z| = |h_y|$ circular polarization in the $Y$-$Z$ plane of the r-f wave will exist, i.e., where $\tan \pi y / a = \left[ \left( \frac{2a}{\lambda} \right)^2 - 1 \right]^{-\frac{1}{2}}$. For a given frequency $y$ may easily be calculated. For standard $X$-band waveguide (0.900 × 0.400 inch) at $f = 9375$ mcps $y/a = 0.24$ or 0.76, i.e., about one quarter of the guide width in from the walls. Assuming that the ferrite does not perturb the empty waveguide field appreciably, this circular polarization will exist in the ferrite slab and in the sense indicated in the figure. If the frequency of the r-f wave is near that of the precessional motion of the electrons, coupling of the energy can take place in the manner described.

Note particularly that if the wave propagates in the $-Z$-direction the sense of the circular polarization reverses. Since the precession stays the same, there will no longer be coupling between the wave and ferrite and, therefore, no marked attentuation or phase effects. Hence we have a nonreciprocal unit which can produce differential phase shifts or attenuations as functions of the applied magnetic field. We may designate the permeabilities for the two directions as $\mu_\perp^+$ and $\mu_\perp^-$, where plus indicates coupling between the electron spins and the d-c magnetic field and minus indicates no coupling.

In practice, we wish to use slabs as thick as possible in order to enhance the nonreciprocal effects. An upper limit is set, of course, by the onset of undesired effects, such as the appearance of higher order modes and mismatching. Much attention, both experimental and theoretical, has been given to the problem of maximizing the differential phase shift for the two directions of propagation within these constraints. Although Suhl and Walker (13) showed that for an infinitely thin slab (i.e., unperturbed empty waveguide mode) maximum differential phase shift obtains when the slab is one quarter of the guide width from a side wall; this no longer holds true when the slab is of practicable thickness. For thicker ferrites the optimum position moves closer to the side wall. Figure 7.16 shows some data on phase shift versus ferrite position for

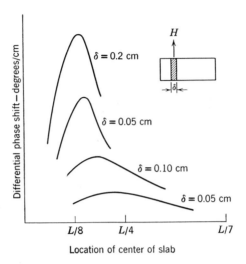

Location of center of slab

**Figure 7.16.** Differential phase shift as a function of ferrite position. (From Lax, Button, and Roth, *J. Appl. Phy.*, **25**, November 1954, p. 1413.)

the two directions of propagation. For a slab in the center of the waveguide a reciprocal device results. Figure 7.17 shows calculated electric field intensities for a typical ferrite as a function of position in

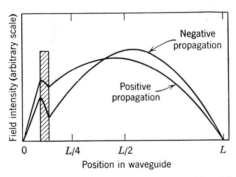

Position in waveguide

**Figure 7.17.** Electric field intensity in rectangular waveguide with transversely magnetized ferrite. (From Lax, Button, and Roth, *J. Appl. Phy.*, **25**, November 1954, p. 1413.)

the waveguide. Figure 7.18 shows the phase shift for each direction of propagation as a function of ferrite position in the waveguide. The curves verify the theory that as the frequency is decreased the differential phase shift diminishes and the peak moves towards the center of the waveguide.

The differential phase shift can be increased by the addition of another ferrite slab symmetrically situated with respect to the first (Figure 7.19a). If the applied field direction differs for each, it follows, from what was said previously, that a wave propagating in the $+Z$-direction sees $\mu_\perp^+$ for each ferrite but a returning wave sees $\mu_\perp^-$ for each. An

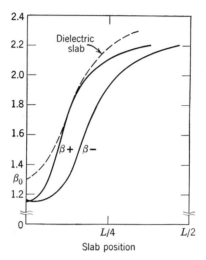

**Figure 7.18.** Nonreciprocal phase shift in ferrite-loaded rectangular waveguide. (From Lax, Button, and Roth, *J. Appl. Phy.*, **25**, November 1954, p. 1413.)

example of the electric field distribution is given in Figure 7.19b. The symmetry of this arrangement should aid in matching such a section to an empty waveguide. Figure 7.19c shows the variation of the phase constants as a function of slab position.

Numerical solutions of the wave equation in a rectangular waveguide (23) have disclosed the existence of additional modes which have no empty waveguide counterparts. They are shown as $C$ and $D$ in Figure 7.20, wherein $A$ and $B$ are the previously described modified empty waveguide modes. $C$ and $D$ cannot propagate simultaneously. $D$ is cut off until the guide is nearly filled with ferrite, and then $C$ is cut off. This rather curious behavior is attributed to a type of "dielectric" propagation treated by Schelkunoff (24). The $C$ and $D$ curves calculated on this basis were in good agreement with those obtained from a numerical solution of the field problem.

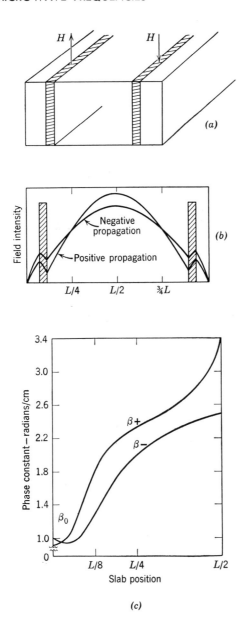

**Figure 7.19.** Symmetrical nonreciprocal phase shift in rectangular waveguide. (From Lax, Button, and Roth, *J. Appl. Phy.*, **26**, 1955, p. 1184.)

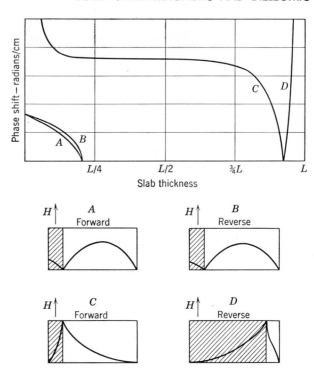

**Figure 7.20.** Ordinary and "anomalous" modes in ferrite-loaded rectangular waveguide. (From Lax, Button, and Roth, *J. Appl. Phy.*, **26**, September 19, 1956, p. 1186.)

### 7.13.1 Rectangular Waveguide Applications

Other factors being equal, we prefer to use ferrite elements in a rectangular waveguide rather than in a circular waveguide. First, the use of rectangular waveguide is much more widespread, and, second, the effects of strain on a rectangular waveguide are unimportant; but for a round waveguide distortion can lead to coupling between orthogonal $TE_{11}$ modes.

The first application to suggest itself is that of phase shifting. In certain cases the ability to produce a phase shift very rapidly in a waveguide is quite important. The automatic phase balancing of r-f bridges in certain radar schemes can be accomplished in this way. In these cases the phase shift need not be nonreciprocal. Practically, we cannot obtain large phase shifts without suffering attenuation. The maximum phase shift obtainable in a given case is set by the tolerance on the loss.

The main interest, however, lies in the nonreciprocal properties of ferrites in rectangular waveguides. Many of the applications given for circular waveguides with axial ferrite rods can be duplicated in rectangular waveguides.

The "gyrator" which produces a differential phase shift of 180° can be realized quite readily in rectangular waveguide by simply adjusting the length of ferrite and/or the applied magnetic field until this value is obtained. This structure is simpler than the circular waveguide analogue.

The circulator can be realized in a number of ways, one of which is shown in Figure 7.21. $A$ and $B$ are each 3-db short-slot-couplers. The ferrite produces 180° differential phase shift, and the dielectric slab is a "dummy" to give the same phase shift as the reciprocal contribution from the ferrite. The 3-db couplers have the property of introducing a 90° phase lag into that component which is coupled through the aperture, and the power is also equally split. It is readily shown by making use of these properties that this configuration is indeed a circulator in the sense previously defined.

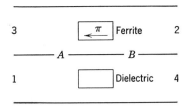

Figure 7.21. Circulator in rectangular waveguide.

Matched loads at terminals 3 and 4 result in an isolator. By putting a transmitter at terminal 1, an antenna at 2, a matched load at 3, and a receiver at 4 a duplexer results. This device suffers from the same disadvantages mentioned in the case of the circular waveguide analogue. It can be made less frequency- or temperature-sensitive by cascading elements with specified coupling ratios. For $n$ sections the leakage power into the undesired terminal is proportional to $\Delta^{2n}$ where $\Delta$ is the phase error (i.e., the departure from 180°) in each ferrite section (16).

Another type of isolator is easily realized by adjusting the magnetic field to produce resonance. The concomitantly large attenuation will occur for only one direction of propagation. Figure 7.22 shows attenuation and phase shift as a function of field for a typical ferrite. Since the field required to produce resonance is a function of the frequency, this device may readily be broadbanded by using a nonuniform d-c field along the length of the ferrite. As in the case of maximizing differential phase shift, the ferrite thickness and position in the guide are important factors in determining not only the maximum attenuation at resonance but also the maximum ratio of forward to backward loss. Clavin (25) describes such a device which has 50-db isolation for 0.5-db insertion loss and at least 30-db isolation over a 25 per cent bandwidth. Resonance isolators are limited to frequencies for which permanent

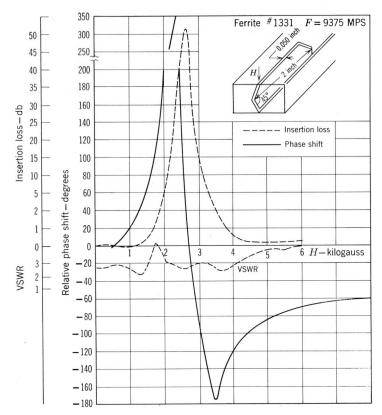

**Figure 7.22.** Phase shift and absorption of centered ferrite plate in rectangular waveguide.

magnets of the requisite strength are not inconveniently large. Since the magnetic field required to produce resonance is roughly proportional to the frequency, this type of isolator would be most useful at $X$-band and below.

Reference to Figure 7.17 suggests another type of isolator. Since the position of maximum field depends upon the direction of propagation and can be made to occur close to the edge of the ferrite by proper choice of the thickness of the slab, it is evident that if a resistance card is placed along the side of the ferrite there will be appreciable attenuation for one direction of propagation and a negligible amount for the other. This property of maximum field displacement can be utilized to build isolators and circulators.

It is instructive to compare the "efficiencies" of a Faraday rotator in circular waveguide and a phase shifter in rectangular waveguide. One criterion of efficiency is the magnitude of the external magnetic field required to produce the desired effect. Since the effects are not identical, there is some arbitrariness involved, but we may take as a representative case that of a circulator. A 45° rotation is required in the circular waveguide, and 180° phase shift is required in the rectangular guide.

For the former case we had

$$\theta_F = \frac{\omega}{2c} \sqrt{\epsilon} \left( \sqrt{\mu^-} - \sqrt{\mu^+} \right) \tag{7.78a}$$

and for the latter, from 7.70 and 7.71, we have

$$\frac{\phi}{l} = \frac{\omega}{2c} \sqrt{\epsilon} \left[ \left( \frac{\mu^2 - \kappa^2}{\mu} \right)^{\frac{1}{2}} - 1 \right] \tag{7.83a}$$

If we were dealing with an infinite medium, the $\mu$'s would be the intrinsic permeabilities of the medium; for a finite medium they are understood to be given by the ratio of the effective field to the internal flux density. The effective field was previously defined by

$$\mathbf{H}_{\text{eff}} = \mathbf{H}_{\text{app}} + \mathbf{H}_D + \mathbf{H}_{\text{anis}}$$

If in the case under consideration we make the radically simplifying assumptions that

$$|\gamma| H \ll \omega$$

$$4\pi M |\gamma| \ll \omega$$

then, as shown in equation 7.78c,

$$\theta_F = \frac{1}{2c} \sqrt{\epsilon} \cdot 4\pi M |\gamma|$$

Similarly, it can be shown with the same assumption that for rectangular waveguide the phase shift per unit length is given by

$$\frac{\phi}{l} = \frac{1}{2c} \frac{\sqrt{\epsilon}}{\omega} (4\pi M |\gamma|)^2 \tag{7.83b}$$

In view of the second assumption, the specific phase shift will be much smaller than the specific rotation. However, as pointed out before, the second assumption is not too good in practice, so that the result for the specific phase shift is only qualitative. In practice, it is usually observed that larger fields are required when ferrites are used in rectangular waveguide than when they are put into circular waveguides to obtain similar results.

## 7.14   Transverse Field in Circular Waveguide

Although the use of transverse fields for ferrite structures in circular waveguide has not enjoyed the popularity accorded to the use of longitudinal fields, Fox, Miller, and Weiss (16), in their excellent article, describe some configurations and principles of the former type which may prove important in the future. They give to these the name "magnetically bi-refringent," a designation whose suitability will become apparent. Referring to Figure 7.23, we note that if a $TE_{11}$ mode which

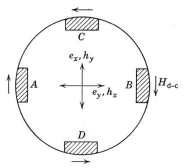

has as its magnetic vector $h_x$ propagates into the paper the ferrites $A$ and $B$ will exhibit only a dielectric effect, since $h_x$ is parallel to the applied field. However, for the orthogonal mode, with $h_y$ as shown, the phase relations between the transverse and longitudinal $h$ are such as to give positive elliptical polarization in $A$ and $B$; hence there will be coupling between the r-f field and the precessing electrons which will result for low applied fields in a permeability less than 1 (equations 7.30 and 7.31 and Figure 7.2). Thus the ferrite presents two different permeabilities, and, therefore, phase velocities, to two orthogonal $TE_{11}$ modes (i.e., it is "birefringent").

**Figure 7.23.** Transverse magnetic field in ferrites in circular waveguide. (From Fox, Miller, and Weiss, *Bell System Tech. J.*, **34**, January 1955, p. 82.)

To eliminate the dielectric effect and enhance the magnetic effect fields are applied to $C$ and $D$ as indicated. Relative to $h_y$ and the fields on $A$ and $B$, the fields on $C$ and $D$ are reversed with respect to $h_x$. Hence $h_x$ will see a permeability greater than 1. In waves propagating out of the paper the situation is reversed: $h_y$ sees permeability 1 in $A$ and $B$ and $h_x$ sees a permeability less than 1 in $C$ and $D$. Hence a wave whose magnetic vector is at 45° to $h_x$ and $h_y$ would become circularly polarized in the negative sense when propagating into the paper and circularly polarized in the positive sense when propagating out of the paper if the length of the section were chosen so that it was a quarter-wave plate.

Alternate configurations to that of Figure 7.23 are given in Reference 16. As in a rectangular guide, the ferrite position for producing maximum nonreciprocal phase shift for a very thin nonfield-perturbing ferrite is the locus at which the product of transverse $h$ and longitudinal $b$ is a maximum. In circular guide this position is about one quarter of the waveguide diameter in from the wall. For thicker ferrites this position moves toward the guide wall.

## 7.15 Miscellaneous Applications

### Tuning of Klystrons

Cacheris, Jones, and Diehl (26) have discussed how the frequency of an $X$-band klystron with an external cavity is varied by applying a magnetic field to a ferrite within the cavity. A frequency deviation of 160 mc was obtained for a magnetic field of 400 oersteds. This frequency change, accomplished with less than 20 per cent change in power output, should be compared with about 15 mc obtained by conventional reflector tuning.

### Single Side-Band Modulators

One of the first applications of the birefringent effect discussed in Section 7.14 was the single side-band modulator developed by Cacheris (27). This was modeled after a previously developed mechanical device and consisted of a rotating half-wave section between two quarter-wave sections.

The rotating 180° section produces a continuous phase change which is equivalent to a frequency shift. Insertion loss of 1 db for a frequency shift of 20 kc with carrier and undesired side band suppression of 30 db or greater have been obtained.

### Ferrites in Traveling Wave Tubes

That the exploitations of microwave ferrite properties are not restricted to waveguides was demonstrated by Cook, Kompfner, and Suhl (28) and Rich and Webber (29). The first group showed that circumferentially magnetized ferrite rings or a helical ferrite surrounding the traveling wave tube helix produced isolator action. The second group used a longitudinally magnetized tubular ferrite over the helix. Such isolation action is particularly valuable in the case of a traveling wave tube, since there may not only be power reflections, but the tube may actually oscillate as a backward-wave oscillator. The ferrite isolator can minimize the first and entirely prevent the latter.

### High Speed Switches

LeCraw (30) has described a ferrite switch with a switching cycle of 0.025 $\mu$sec and recovery time of 0.012 $\mu$sec to the 1.5-db point. The insertion loss was less than 1 db, and isolation was greater than 35 db in the "off" position. In connection with this device, some interesting work has been described on the time delay and distortion of pulses in these high speed switches (31).

## 7.16  The Use of Ferrites at Other Microwave Frequencies

The initial investigations of the microwave properties of ferrite were carried out at $X$-band frequencies (ca. 10,000 mcps). The scaling of the geometry up or down for lower or higher frequencies, respectively, would immediately suggest itself as a design principle in extending the use of ferrites to other frequencies. Although this is true to some extent, there are numerous complicating factors which make the practical realization of certain devices at some other frequencies somewhat more difficult.

The fact that the permeability tensor components are also functions of frequency will have an effect on their variation with the applied magnetic field. Using the approximate expression (true for an infinite medium) that $f = 2.8H$,* we can see that a larger field will be required for resonance for a higher frequency. Thus, if a 2000-oersted field suffices for a particular geometry at $X$-band, about 4000 oersteds will be required for the same geometry at $K$-band. Fortunately, this same proportionality does not hold for the phase behavior in general or the Faraday rotation in particular. To a first approximation, the saturation Faraday rotation is independent of frequency so that approximately the same rotation is obtained for the same applied field at higher frequencies. Since the losses associated with resonance occur at higher fields, the figure-of-merit (rotation/loss) remains sensibly the same. As we move down in frequency this behavior holds to about 7 kmcps for a given type of ferrite. Below this frequency the losses start to rise appreciably and the figure-of-merit decreases. This increase in loss is attributable to the fact that for a given magnetization the applied field necessary to produce resonance decreases with decreasing frequency. This follows from Kittel's relation for a long thin rod

$$H_r = f/2.8 - 2\pi M \qquad (7.84)$$

---

* Note 2.8 = $\gamma/2\pi$ in megacycles/oersted.

Hence, with only a moderate field applied, a ferrite which was well below resonance at $X$-band might be suffering near-resonance field losses at one half the frequency. The remedy is the use of ferrites with smaller saturation magnetization. Such ferrites, with figures-of-merit at 4000 mc about equal to the best obtainable at 10 kmc, have been described by Van Uitert, Schafer, and Hogan (32).

Granting that ferrites with the requisite physical properties for operation at the lower microwave frequencies can be made, it is natural to enquire what the useful low-frequency limit might be for applications. At lower frequencies operation above ferromagnetic resonance becomes feasible because of the more moderate requirements on the applied magnetic field. Preliminary work reported by Fox (33) indicates that $45°$ rotation can be obtained for frequencies greater than 250 mcps with rods of the order of wavelength long. Calculations indicate that a $90°$ nonreciprocal phase shift can be obtained at 375 mcps with a slab 120 cm long and a field of 1000 oersteds. However, the figures are not given for the losses. Because of the inordinately large size of waveguide required at these frequencies this work would seem of academic interest only. However, the use of coaxial cable at these low frequencies seems to be feasible.

## 7.17   References

1. Purcell, E. M., H. C. Torrey, R. V. Pound, "Resonance Absorption by Nuclear Magnetic Resonance in a Solid," *Phys. Rev.*, **69**, 1946, p. 37.
2. Bloch, F., "Nuclear Induction," *Phys. Rev.*, **70**, 1946, p. 460.
3. Polder, D., "The Theory of Ferromagnetic Resonances," *Phil. Mag.*, **40**, 1949, p. 99.
4. Landau, L., L. Lifshitz, "On the Theory of the Dispersion of Magnetic Permeability in Ferromagnetic Bodies," *Phys. Z. Sowjet.* **8**, 1935, p. 153.
5. Bloch, F., W. W. Hansen, M. Packard, "The Nuclear Induction Experiment," *Phys. Rev.*, **70**, 1946, p. 474.
6. Bloembergen, N., "The Ferromagnetic Resonance in Nickel and Supermalloy," *Phys. Rev.*, **78**, 1950, p. 572.
7. Damon, R. W., "Relaxation Effects in Ferromagnetic Resonance," *Revs. Modern Phys.*, **25**, 1953, p. 239.
8. Van Vleck, J. W., "Concerning the Theory of Ferromagnetic Resonance Absorption," *Phys. Rev.*, **78**, 1950, p. 266.
9. Young, J. A., E. A. Uehling, "The Tensor Formulation of Ferromagnetic Resonance," *Phys. Rev.*, **94**, 1954, p. 544.
10. Kales, M. L., "Modes in Waveguides that Contain Ferrites," *J. Appl. Phy.*, **24**, 1953, p. 816.
11. Gamo, H. J., "Faraday Rotation of Waves in Round Waveguide," *J. Phys. Soc. Japan*, **8**, 1953, p. 176.
12. Suhl, H., L. R. Walker, "Topics in Guided Wave Propagation Through Gyromagnetic Media," *Bell System Tech. J.*, **33**, 1954, p. 579.

13. Op. cit., p. 1133.

14. Berk, A. D., "Cavities & Wave Guides with Inhomogeneous and Anisotropic Media," Thesis, Massachusetts Institute of Technology, 1954.

15. Mullen, E. B., E. R. Carlson, "Permeability Tensor Values from Wave Guide Measurements," *Proc. I.R.E.*, **44**, 1956, p. 1318.

16. Fox, A. G., M. T. Weiss, "Magnetic Double Refraction at Microwave Frequencies," *Revs. Modern Phys.*, **25**, 1953, p. 262.

17. Lax, B., "Figure-of-Merit for Microwave Ferrites at Low and High Frequencies," *J. Appl. Phy.*, **26**, 1955, p. 919.

18. Fox, A. G., S. E. Miller, M. T. Weiss, "Behavior and Application of Ferrites in the Microwave Range," *Bell System Tech. J.*, **32**, 1953, p. 1358.

19. Rowen, J. H., "Ferrites in Microwave Applications," *Bell System Tech. J.*, **32**, 1953, p. 1333.

20. Duncan, B. J., L. Swern, "Temperature Behavior of Ferromagnetic Resonance in Ferrites Located in Wave Guides," *J. Appl. Phys.*, **27**, March 1956, p. 209.

21. Sakiotis, H. G., H. N. Chait, M. L. Kales, "Non-Linearity of Propagation in Ferrite Media," *Proc. I.R.E.*, **43**, August 1955, p. 1011.

22. Allen, P. J., "Microwave Magnetometer," *Proc. I.R.E.*, **41**, 1953, p. 100.

23. Button, K. J., B. Lax, "New Ferrite Mode Configurations," *J. Appl. Phy.*, **26**, 1955, p. 1186.

24. Schelkunoff, S., *Electromagnetic Waves*, D. van Nostrand Company, Inc., Princeton, N. J., 1943, p. 428.

25. Clavin, A. J., "High Power Ferrite Load Isolators," *Trans. I.R.E.*, MTT, **3**, 1955, p. 38.

26. Cacheris, J. C., G. James, L. Diehl, "Magnetic Tuning of Klystron Cavities," *Proc. I.R.E.*, **43**, 1956, p. 1017.

27. Cacheris, J. C., "Microwave Single-Sideband Modulator Using Ferrites," *Proc. I.R.E.*, **42**, 1954, p. 1242.

28. Cook, J. R., R. Kompfner, H. Suhl, "Nonreciprocal Loss in Travelling-Wave Tubes Using Ferrite Attenuators," *Proc. I.R.E.*, **42**, 1954, p. 1188.

29. Rich, J. A., S. E. Webber, "Ferrite Attenuators in Helices," *Proc. I.R.E.*, **43**, 1955, p. 100.

30. LeCraw, R. C., "High Speed Magnetic Pulsing of Ferrites," *J. Appl. Phy.*, **25**, 1954, p. 678.

31. LeCraw, R. C., H. B. Bruns, "Time Delay in High Speed Ferrite Microwave Switches," *J. Appl. Phy.*, **26**, 1955, p. 124.

32. Van Uitert, L. A., J. P. Schafer, C. L. Hogan, "Low Loss Ferrites for Applications at 4 kmc," *J. Appl. Phy.*, **25**, 1954, p. 925.

33. Fox, R. H., "Extension of Non-Reciprocal Ferrite Devices to the 500–3000 Megacycle Frequency Range," *J. Appl. Phy.*, **26**, 1955, p. 126.

34. Polder, D., J. Smit, "Resonance Phenomena in Ferrites," *Revs. Modern Phys.*, **25**, 1953, p. 89.

35. Berk, A. D., B. A. Lengyel, "Magnetic Fields in Small Ferrite Bodies with Applications to Microwave Cavities," *Proc. I.R.E.*, **43**, 1955, p. 1587.

36. Hogan, C. L., "Ferromagnetic Faraday Effect at Microwave Frequencies and its Applications," *Revs. Modern Phys.* **25**, 1959, p. 253.

# Chapter eight

# Magnetic
# and Dielectric
# Amplifiers

## 8.0 Introduction

By definition, all devices using flux in magnetic cores as a gating or control medium may be classed as magnetic amplifiers. This definition includes the well-known saturable reactor which had been in commercial use long before the more recently developed regenerative types. Despite the many advantages of magnetic amplifiers over vacuum-tube power amplifiers from the viewpoints of stand-by power, reliability, and overall cost, intensive development of these devices was not started in this country until 1940. By that time considerable effort had been expended in Sweden, Germany, and Japan. Since then research and development in low coercive-force square-loop magnetic materials and the development of high efficiency rectifiers (such as Germanium power diodes) have contributed greatly to the improved performance of magnetic amplifiers. They are now beginning to find very wide application, indeed. In power levels they range from microwatts to megawatts output. Power amplification with control signals as low as $10^{-12}$ watt and power gains of $10^{+12}$ per stage have been obtained without instability, through the use of regeneration (11).

As power amplifiers, these devices are most frequently compared with vacuum tubes, although perhaps a more proper comparison is with thyratrons, with rotating amplifiers such as motor-generator sets or with some of the other more sophisticated rotating amplifier types in which positive feedback is used to increase the gain of the stage. Since magnetic amplifiers lack rotating parts, maintenance is negligible and compares in essence to the maintenance of transformers. In size and weight magnetic amplifiers are also comparable to transformers of the same power rating. In most applications unrectified a-c from the mains is used as a power source. The output of the magnetic amplifier can be a-c (for use with two-phase servo motors, for example) or d-c, depending upon the circuit used.

As a rule of thumb, magnetic amplifiers can deliver 10 to 15 watts output power per pound at 60 cycles and proportionately more at higher frequencies. Conventional magnetic amplifiers respond to a step function input within 3 to 8 cycles of the frequency of the power source (depending upon the gain of the stage). More recently developed circuits, the Ramey flux reset type (14) and the pulse relaxation type (16), respond within a half cycle per stage, regardless of gain. The permissible frequency of the carrier is limited by the core material, and operation of metallic cores above 2 megacycles generally becomes unsatisfactory. If ferrite cores are used, operation up to 10 megacycles has been shown to be feasible, although the power gain was only about 5 because of the relatively poor magnetic properties of the ferrite used (11). It is of interest to note that a small saturable reactor capable of operation with a carrier of 10 megacycles at 30 volts has recently been placed on the market under the trade name "Ferristor" (42).

## 8.1 Magnetic Cores and Core Types

Nearly all magnetic amplifiers used today employ metallic magnetic cores, and only a small number of special-purpose devices utilize ferrite, despite the fact that ferrite cores are far less expensive to manufacture than metallic cores. The principal reason for this is the relatively low saturation flux density of ferrites and their comparatively high coercive force.

For low-power, high-gain amplifiers special nickel-iron alloys are used because of their low coercive force. For high-power applications the coercive force is less important than the higher saturation flux density found in such materials as Permalloy. The metals used for cores are grain oriented in order to obtain the square-loop characteristics. According to one procedure, after final rolling (98 to 99 per cent reduction) the material is heated in a dry hydrogen atmosphere to 1000 to 1150° C. It is then superheated for two hours and cooled rapidly. By another method it is slowly cooled in a magnetic field of about 0.5 oersted. Such treatment results in relative differential permeabilities of 300,000 and higher.

As a result of the rectangular loop, the flux in such cores can change from one saturation value to the other in an exceedingly short time; hence eddy current losses in the core material can be considerable. It has been found desirable to raise the resistivity of the core material for some applications by the addition of molybdenum or chromium to the nickel-iron alloy. This procedure, however, seems to result in a reduction of saturation flux density.

As in the design of ordinary transformers, spiral-wound tape cores are superior to laminated cores. The cost of winding coils on such spiral

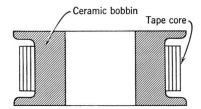

Figure 8.1. Spiral wound tape core.

cores is, of course, much higher than the cost of placing coils on the legs of laminated cores. On the other hand, tape cores are grain oriented everywhere, so that all parts of the material have the same orientation. (Figure 8.1). It has been observed that even slight bending of the rectangular-loop metallic material will round the corners and slope the sides of the hysteresis loops. Therefore, these tapes are usually wound on a ceramic or stainless steel bobbin and are heat-treated after placement. In other cases the spiral cores are first heat-treated and then placed in plastic troughs for protection. Thus it is virtually impossible to degrade the hysteresis loop through careless handling, as is easily the case with unprotected laminations. For these reasons low-power, high-gain amplifiers usually employ tape cores on bobbins. Tapes have been rolled as thin as 0.125 mil, although 0.5 mil is a more common thickness.

Because of the lower assembly cost laminated cores are used whenever possible, as in the case of high-power, low-gain amplifiers. For the usual materials, however, the direction of grain orientation cannot follow the circumference of the lamination in all four legs.* In order to minimize this disadvantage, the construction of Figure 8.2 is frequently used. Here the wedges are of different orientation from the rest of the lamination. Through proper stacking of the laminations these wedges provide

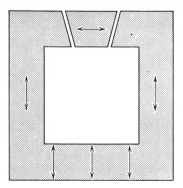

Figure 8.2. Grain oriented lamination and wedge.

the correct grain orientation over at least half of the cross section of the core. Laminations are stamped carefully so as to leave no burrs, and thicknesses down to 0.8 mil are employed.

## 8.2 Basic Magnetic Amplifier Circuits

The simplest circuit which describes the amplifying action of a selectively saturated core is shown in Figure 8.3. The power winding

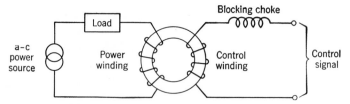

Figure 8.3. Basic one-core magnetic amplifier.

of a single nonlinear core is supplied from an a-c power source in series with the load. A direct current flows through the "control winding" and partially saturates the core. It is necessary to provide a blocking choke or a sufficiently large resistance in the control circuit to prevent the

* Westinghouse and General Electric have recently announced "cube-oriented" magnetic materials, i.e., the alloy has two easy directions of magnetization which are at right angles to each other.

low-impedance control signal source from short circuiting the load winding. The operating point on the magnetization curve is fixed by the specific value of control current used. Let it now be assumed that the a-c source voltage is of such amplitude that even for a complete half cycle the volt-time integral per turn is no greater than twice the saturation flux $\phi_s$. Hence a displacement of the operating point, from $O$ to $P$ in Figure 8.4, results in saturation of the core as soon as the volt-

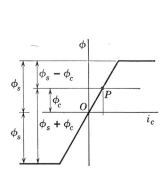

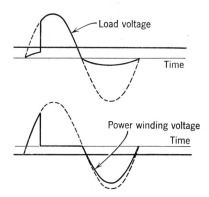

Figure 8.4. Magnetization line for a magnetic amplifier core.

Figure 8.5. Wave shapes of load voltage and power winding voltage for the amplifier of Figure 8.3.

time integral per turn reaches the value $(\phi_s - \phi_c)$. During the remainder of the half cycle the source current is limited only by the load, and the full source voltage appears across it. During the succeeding half cycle the entire volt-time area per turn is available to return the core to its operating point. The wave shapes of load voltage and of power winding voltage for such a case are shown in Figure 8.5. It might be noted that there can be no d-c component in any of the wave shapes of Figure 8.5. Hence a change of operating point results in a vertical displacement of the wave shapes shown. It is thus seen that the instant of "firing" is controlled by the control current, and the half-wave average value or the effective value of load current can be regulated. A nearly square magnetization line gives rise to an extremely sensitive magnetic amplifier.

A balanced arrangement of cores would eliminate the need for an impedance in the control circuit if the fundamental component of voltage induced in the control winding could be eliminated. How this is customarily achieved is shown in Figures 8.6 to 8.9.

In Figure 8.6 a load winding is placed on each of the two cores, and the two windings are connected in series opposition with respect to the

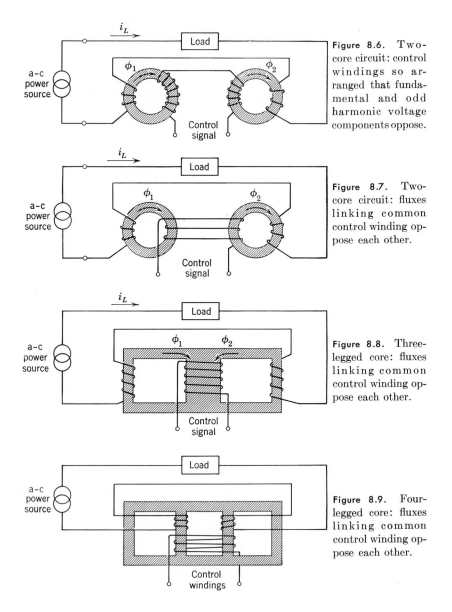

Figure 8.6. Two-core circuit: control windings so arranged that fundamental and odd harmonic voltage components oppose.

Figure 8.7. Two-core circuit: fluxes linking common control winding oppose each other.

Figure 8.8. Three-legged core: fluxes linking common control winding oppose each other.

Figure 8.9. Four-legged core: fluxes linking common control winding oppose each other.

series-connected control windings (a parallel arrangement is also often used for the load windings). In this manner the induced voltages are made to oppose each other, and the fundamental and all odd harmonic components of voltage induced in the control windings cancel if the cores and windings are identical.

Figure 8.7 also shows a two-core system, but here a common control winding links both cores. With respect to this control winding the load windings are connected in series opposition. (A parallel connection can also be used.) The fluxes in the two cores, both of which link the control winding, oppose each other, and no fundamental or odd harmonic voltage components are induced in the control winding as long as the two cores are of identical construction.

Figure 8.8 shows the common three-legged reactor. This system is, in effect, a simplification of the preceding one in that the two cores are merged together within the control winding. The method of operation is identical with that of the circuit of Figure 8.7.

Figure 8.9 is a four-legged reactor and operates similar to the two-core system of Figure 8.7. Again, the fluxes linking the common control winding oppose each other to prevent the presence of fundamental and odd harmonic voltage components in the control winding.

Table 8.1 shows a comparative listing of the advantages and disadvantages of the four core types.

Generally speaking, it must be remembered that the inductance of the control winding is usually of the order of $10^4$ or $10^5$ henrys (11). Thus even a slight unbalance of core or winding construction may give rise to extremely high fundamental or odd harmonic voltage components

## Table 8.1

| | Advantages | Disadvantages |
|---|---|---|
| I. Two-core, voltage opposition | (1) Low leakage flux<br>(2) Cores can be placed physically far apart<br>(3) Cores are assembled first, need not be handled or bent during winding | (1) High-voltage insulation needed in each control winding<br>(2) Placement of windings more costly than III or IV<br>(3) Control windings at different potentials with respect to ground<br>(4) Cores must be matched |

## Table 8.1 (Continued)

| | Advantages | Disadvantages |
|---|---|---|
| II. Two-core, flux opposition | (1) Low leakage flux<br>(2) Less costly to wind than I<br>(3) Control winding needs less protection against high voltage than I<br>(4) Cores are assembled first, need not be handled or bent during winding<br>(5) Control windings of same potential with respect to ground | (1) Placement of windings more costly than III or IV, more difficult than I for small cores<br>(2) Cores must be matched |
| III. Three-legged core, flux opposition | (1) Inexpensive assembly from laminations and preformed coils<br>(2) Control winding needs less protection against high voltage than I<br>(3) Control windings at same potential with respect to ground<br>(4) Single-core assembly avoids need for core matching | (1) Relatively high leakage flux<br>(2) Core properties likely to be deteriorated by handling during assembly<br>(3) Larger and heavier than I or II for same rating |
| IV. Four-legged core, flux opposition | (1) Inexpensive assembly from laminations and preformed coils<br>(2) Less leakage flux than III<br>(3) Control winding needs less protection against high voltage than I<br>(4) Control windings at same potential with respect to ground<br>(5) Single-core assembly avoids need for core matching | (1) Laminations more costly than III<br>(2) Core properties likely to be deteriorated by handling during assembly<br>(3) Larger and heavier than I or II for same rating |

in the control winding. The even harmonics do not cancel but rather add in the control winding, thus giving rise to very high terminal voltages even when the cores and windings are perfectly balanced.

## 8.3   Basic Magnetic Amplifier Operation with Feedback

It is pointed out in the introduction to this chapter that the simple saturable reactor (without feedback) is classed as a type of magnetic amplifier. However, since its importance appears to be diminishing in favor of the feedback types, this section is devoted primarily to the latter.

Feedback can be achieved in either of two ways:

1. A d-c signal is derived from the output circuit and is applied to a specially provided feedback winding or added to the signals already present at a control winding or bias winding. This method is defined as "external" feedback.

2. Rectifiers are placed in the load circuit so that they carry all, or a portion of, the load current and so that a d-c component is generated in the load windings. This method is defined as "internal" feedback.

The feedback signal can be made to aid or to oppose the control signal, as in other types of amplifiers, with essentially the same results.

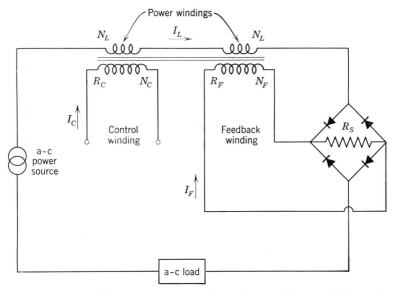

**Figure 8.10.**  External feedback circuit supplying a-c load.  $R_S$ is a stabilizing resistor controlling the effective feedback.

Regenerative connection results in higher gain, greater nonlinearity, and, with the exception of the flux reset type, reduced speed of response. The picture is somewhat complicated, of course, by the fact that mag-

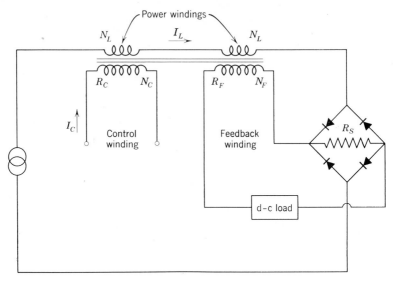

**Figure 8.11.** External feedback circuit supplying d-c load. $R_S$ is a stabilizing resistor controlling the effective feedback.

netic amplifiers are fundamentally modulators and that recovery of the signal wave shape necessitates demodulation. This is customarily achieved by rectifiers in the load circuit, which can thus be made to

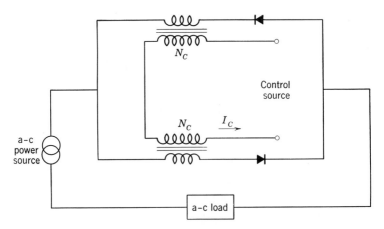

**Figure 8.12.** Internal feedback circuit supplying an a-c load.

serve double-duty by acting as the generator for the feedback signal and by providing the demodulated signal for the d-c load.

Figure 8.10 shows the diagram of a magnetic amplifier with external feedback, arranged for supplying an a-c load. If the load requires direct current, a separate bridge power rectifier can be provided or the circuit of Figure 8.11 can be used.

Figure 8.12 shows the diagram of a magnetic amplifier with internal feedback, arranged to supply an a-c load, and Figure 8.13 shows two diagrams of circuits supplying d-c loads. The circuit of Figure 8.14 is similar to that of Figure 8.13$a$, except that load current is controlled

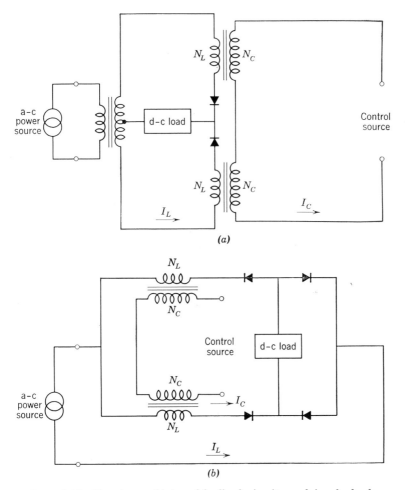

Figure 8.13. Two types of internal feedback circuit supplying d-c loads.

by a variation of the resistance shunting the feedback rectifiers, which thus controls the effective feedback.

If a sufficient amount of feedback is used, the circuits of Figures 8.10 and 8.11 can be made unstable. The unstable device can be converted

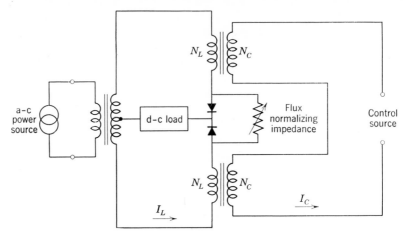

**Figure 8.14.** Load control by means of variation of a flux normalizing impedance.

to a bistable one by the use of a suitable amount of bias. This is shown in Figure 8.15, in which the input-output characteristic of an unstable magnetic amplifier is made to serve as the transfer characteristic of a bistable device or of a "one-shot multivibrator" (4).

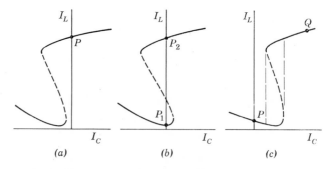

**Figure 8.15.** A suitable amount of d-c bias permits use of (a) the unstable magnetic amplifier, (b) as a bistable device, or (c) as a one-shot multivibrator.

Although the bistable amplifier is relatively independent of circuit parameters and external influences, the minimum value of control current at which triggering occurs may be strongly affected by such factors as changes in load impedance, rectifier leakage, a-c supply voltage, control-circuit resistance, or bias changes (3).

Bistable magnetic amplifiers can, of course, be used as switches or gates. A perhaps more sophisticated application is found in their use in a pulsed or in a continuously running, contact-free magnetic selector (4).

The instability resulting from excessive positive feedback should not be confused with the jump phenomenon resulting from inductive loads, a discussion of which is beyond the scope of this book (3, 6).

## 8.4  Voltage-Controlled Magnetic Amplifiers

Another type of amplifier has come into common use in recent years, primarily in applications in which rapid response is the major consideration, as, for example, high-speed computing machines. It is known as the flux reset, or Ramey, amplifier and carries the distinction of responding to a control signal in less than one cycle of the a-c power source (12, 13, 14). This is achieved by permitting the volt-time integral of the d-c power source or of a separate a-c reset source to return the core to its operating point during alternate half cycles. Thus, the control source is relieved of this task and it merely determines the operating point. In its very simple form this amplifier consists of a single-winding core in series with the a-c power source, the load, and the load rectifier. The last two elements are shunted by the control source and its series rectifier, as shown in Figure 8.16. Operation is based on the

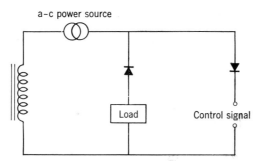

a–c power source

Load        Control signal

Figure 8.16.  Basic flux reset amplifier, using a single-winding core.

principle that during each half of the supply period the flux in the core is reset by the a-c power source itself, thus determining how much volt-time area must be absorbed by the core during the alternate half cycle before the core saturates and the entire source voltage appears across the load during the remaining portion of the cycle. The two rectifiers ensure that these two functions are properly separated. The two-winding reactor (Figure 8.17) results in a somewhat more flexible component, since the reset and gating functions are electrically insulated.

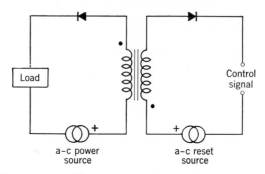

**Figure 8.17.** Flux reset amplifier, using a two-winding core. The a-c power source and the a-c reset source are in phase, and the a-c power source can perform both functions if the windings are properly designed.

The flux value following reset is determined by the combined volt-time area of power source and control source. A square-loop core material is desirable to avoid uncontrolled flux "fall-back" between start of the reset function and following the termination of flow of load current. This flux fall-back occurs in cores with a remanent flux value significantly different from the saturation value—an effect which can be brought about by material deficiency or by excessive leakage reactance due to core geometry or winding design. Its effect would be a reduction in available load current, hence gain, since part of the next half cycle of voltage would have to be absorbed by the core in order to build the flux back to the saturation value. A similar deleterious effect results from rectifier leakage and also produces uncontrolled reset. Both of these effects are demonstrated in Figure 8.18.

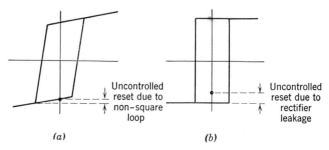

**Figure 8.18.** Uncontrolled reset caused by (a) non-square loop, and (b) by rectifier leakage.

The need for a near-perfect square-loop material is overcome in an extension of the reasoning which led to the flux-reset type. This modified circuit has been called the flux-preset magnetic amplifier and can operate successfully despite the fact that the remanent flux value may be but a fraction of the saturation value (15). Flux fall-back is compensated by application of an additional volt-time area of the same sign as that of the power half cycle and thus in opposition to the reset flux. This can be achieved in a single-winding core, as shown in Figure 8.19; the three functions can, of course, be electrically isolated once again, as shown in the three-winding amplifier of Figure 8.20.

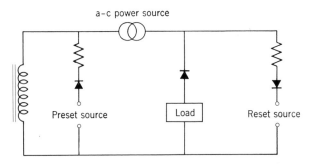

Figure 8.19. Basic flux-preset amplifier using a single-winding core.

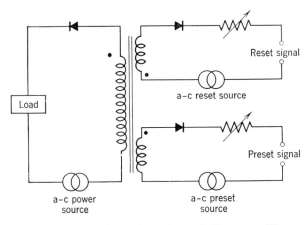

Figure 8.20. Flux preset amplifier, using a three-winding core. The a-c sources are in phase and can be replaced by a single source if the windings are properly adjusted.

All of the types of magnetic amplifier thus far discussed have the following characteristic in common. Because the power source is a sinusoidal low-impedance voltage supply the load current has the shape of a "gated" sine wave; that is, for a certain portion of the cycle all of the applied volt-time integral is absorbed by the power winding. When the flux in the core or cores reaches saturation level all of the remaining sine wave of voltage appears across the load, as discussed earlier (leakage reactance being neglected). The "firing angle," as shown in Figure 8.21, is determined by the amount of bias and control current in a given magnetic amplifier. The operation of the device can thus be likened to that of a thyratron.

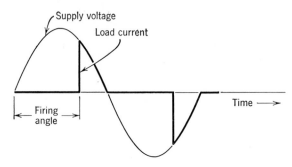

**Figure 8.21.** Wave shape of the current in each of the power windings of a magnetic amplifier supplying an a-c load.

### 8.4.1 Pulse Relaxation Amplifier

A slightly different device is the pulse relaxation amplifier (Figure 8.22). As can be seen, there are no rectifiers in the circuit, and a single core is used. If several such amplifiers are to be cascaded, stages of different design are used. Claims are made for a zero drift level of less than $10^{-16}$ watt over a temperature range from $-70$ to $+140°$ C (16). Conventional amplifiers, in comparison, have a stability of no less than $10^{-8}$ watt over this range, primarily because of the instability of the feedback rectifiers.

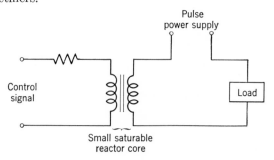

**Figure 8.22.** Simplified pulse relaxation amplifier input stage.

Instead of a sinusoidal a-c power source, a pulse source is used. Synchronized pulses are readily available from an a-c supply by the use of a saturable pulse transformer. Figure 8.23 shows the hysteresis loop which the core traverses. The numbers correlate to the voltage wave shape of Figure 8.24. Thus the control signal establishes the starting

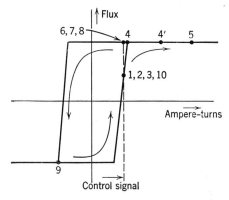

Figure 8.23. Hysteresis loop for the core of the amplifier of Figure 8.22. Numbers correspond to the points on the waveform shown in Figure 8.24.

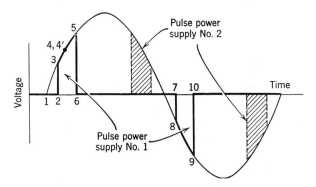

Figure 8.24. Voltage wave shapes.

point. As the power pulse across the winding persists, the operating point moves up on the loop until saturation is reached. If this occurs prior to the end of the power pulse (beyond point 4), load current will flow for the remainder of the power pulse (to point 5). Following the positive power pulse the control signal mmf dictates point 6. When the negative power pulse appears the core is reset (points 7, 8, 9) but essentially without causing the appearance of a negative pulse of load current. Following the negative power pulse the control-signal current resets the core to point 10. In the absence of any control-signal current operation takes place between points 4 and 9 of the loop, and essentially no load current flows during any part of the cycle.

If several stages are to be cascaded, the pulse output of one stage is used to "set"the core of the succeeding stage, somewhat in the manner of the flux-preset amplifier discussed earlier. This succeeding stage must be fed from a second pulse power source whose signals are phase-displaced with respect to the first source, as indicated in Figure 8.24. Successive stages are thus supplied from the two pulse power sources in alternation. For d-c output, the last stage must be followed by a rectifier discriminator as shown in Figure 8.25.

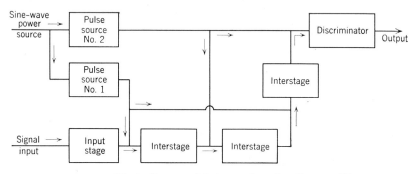

**Figure 8.25.** Block diagram of 4-stage pulse relaxation amplifier.

## 8.5 General Operating Problems

A serious problem can arise when the control signal current of a magnetic amplifier is derived from an a-c source by rectification. As discussed in Section 8.2, the power windings should be arranged so as to avoid the presence of induced voltages of fundamental (or all odd harmonic) frequencies at the control terminals of the amplifier. By the same token, however, the even harmonic induced voltages fail to cancel. That these induced voltages may be of rather high magnitude becomes obvious if it is considered that the control winding inductance is often in the order of 100,000 henrys (11). Thus, if the control circuit contains rectifiers, the current resulting from these induced voltages will be rectified and give rise to a "false" signal. A similar difficulty arises from cascading magnetic amplifiers, since, of necessity, the a-c output must be rectified to be suitable as a control signal for a succeeding stage (3). A ready solution is provided by the use of a low-pass filter. In the simplest case a suitable coil or resistor is placed in series with the control winding, or a capacitor is placed in parallel.

The gain of a magnetic amplifier is, of course, a function of the amount of feedback. Thus amplifiers deriving their high gain largely from the use of regeneration may be expected to be highly sensitive to all factors affecting the feedback signal, notably the variation of rectifier leakage resistance with temperature. Shunting the rectifiers with stable resistors of sufficiently low value will remedy this difficulty at the expense of amplifier gain. However, a suitable choice of resistor may avoid the need for using a separate bias (17). The effect of a change in winding resistance with temperature can be reduced by the use of a compensating series resistor with negative temperature coefficient for each of the affected windings (3).

## 8.6 Response Time and Figure-of-Merit

A simplified design method, based largely on empirical data, has been developed by Johnson and Rauch (20). Consider the curve of response time versus control power and of core volume versus output power, as shown in Figures 8.26 and 8.27, respectively, for various common core

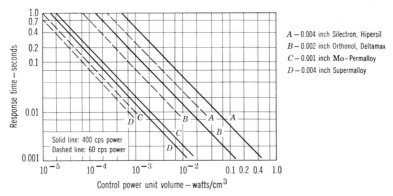

$A$ – 0.004 inch Silectron, Hipersil
$B$ – 0.002 inch Orthonol, Deltamax
$C$ – 0.001 inch Mo–Permalloy
$D$ – 0.004 inch Supermalloy

Solid line: 400 cps power
Dashed line: 60 cps power

Response time – seconds

Control power unit volume – watts/cm$^3$

**Figure 8.26.** Calculated response time versus control energy per cm$^3$ for various core materials. (After Johnson and Rauch.)

materials for 60 and 400 cycles. (Response time is defined as the time in which 63 per cent of the ultimate response is reached.) According to the authors, these curves have been successfully used in the design of many existing amplifiers. The only prerequisites are that the ratio of magnetic path length (in centimeters) to cross-sectional area (in square centimeters) shall be at least 15 and that the build up of the toroidal cores shall be one third of the core height. The charts do not apply to the flux-reset, preset-reset, or pulse-relaxation types of magnetic amplifier but only to those in which a current source is used as a control signal rather than a voltage source. Also, if a bias source is to be used, the power consumed by the bias windings should be considered as part of the total control power.

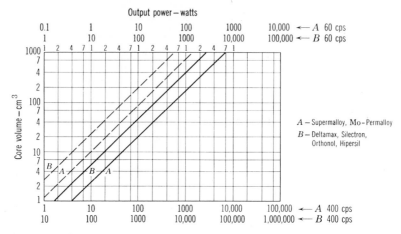

**Figure 8.27.** Continuous output power rating versus core volume for various core materials. The toroidal core configuration assumes a magnetic path length-to-cross-section ratio of 15/cm and a build up equal to the core height. (After Johnson and Rauch.)

## 8.7  Saturable Transformers

Amplifiers, generally speaking, act as controlled series impedances and thus permit or inhibit the flow of energy from the power source to the load in a conductive path. Saturable transformers, on the other hand, can be defined as elements in which the energy transfer from the power source to the load is influenced by a controlled change of the amount of effective magnetic flux linking the two circuits. The simplest type of saturable transformer is shown in Figure 8.28. Here the permeability of the magnetic path between power windings and load windings is affected by the control signal (6, 10).

A somewhat more elaborate version permits a gradual shift of power from one load to another as the control signal is varied. Figure 8.29 shows the corresponding circuit diagram (7, 22). Here control is effected by variation of the permeability of a magnetic shunt path. In the absence of control current the reluctance of the path linking the windings of load 1 is low, and maximum coupling to the a-c power source exists with only a small amount of flux linking the winding supplying load 2. If sufficient control current flows, however, the two legs holding the windings of load 1 are saturated, their reluctance is high, and minimum coupling to the a-c power source exists. All the flux in the primary winding is now forced to link the winding supplying load 2.

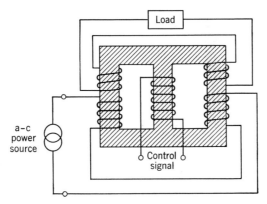

Figure 8.28. Saturable transformer with control of mutual inductance between power windings and control windings.

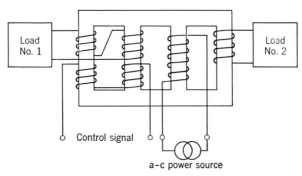

Figure 8.29. Saturable transformer with control of the reluctance of a magnetic shunt path.

The circuits of Figures 8.28 and 8.29 should be considered generic, and many variations of the two principles they illustrate are possible.

## 8.8 Cross-Field Operation

An interesting device for altering the effective magnetization characteristics of a core is illustrated in Figure 8.30. This saturable transformer shows not only the customary power, load, and control windings which are concentric to the cross section of the toroidal core but has in addition a so-called "agitating winding" concentric to the axis of the toroid (7, 23, 24). This winding supplies a cross magnetization at a frequency several times that of the a-c power source. It appears that in this manner the hysteresis losses can be supplied, at least in part, by the low-intensity agitating frequency, thereby increasing the gain of the device as viewed in terms of load power controlled divided by control power required (24). Figure 8.30 shows a single-core arrangement. Obviously, two-core circuits or multilegged circuits can be devised.

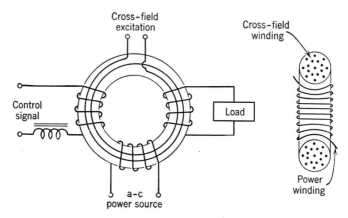

**Figure 8.30.** Saturable transformer with provisions for cross-field excitation.

The energy transfer from the power source to the load can also be affected by the use of a controlled low-frequency cross field (24). This is brought about by the rotation of the total magnetization vector under the influence of the cross field, with the result that the effective saturation flux density of the square-loop material, hence of firing angle, can be varied over a wide range (24, 25). Control of load power in this manner is characterized by an essentially constant average value of load voltage at any given cross-field control current regardless of the value of the load resistance (25).

A similar technique, in which crossed magnetic fields are utilized, can be employed to determine the state of a magnetic memory element without changing its state of magnetization (27). This is discussed further in Chapter 9.

The cross-field toroid has also been suggested for use as a second harmonic modulator with a lower power limit of $10^{-14}$ watt, negligible hysteresis effects, a modulation efficiency of nearly 100 per cent, and a time constant of 1.5 sec (28).

## 8.9    Voltage Stabilizers Utilizing Magnetic Amplifiers

A block diagram of a typical two-stage magnetic amplifier type stabilizer is shown in Figure 8.31.

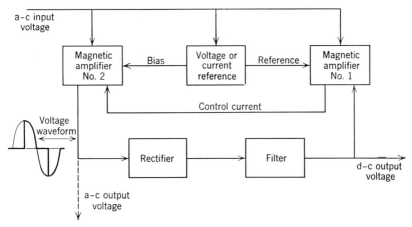

**Figure 8.31.**    Block diagram of a typical magnetic amplifier type voltage stabilizer.

The second stage provides a regulated, though distorted, output a-c voltage which can be rectified and filtered to provide a low ripple, well-regulated d-c output voltage to the load.    The load voltage delivers a signal current to one control winding of the first stage while the reference voltage source delivers current to another control winding magnetically opposing the first one.    The reference voltage source also provides proper biasing of the second stage.    If the voltage on the load decreases, an unbalance will exist within the first stage between the control ampere-turns delivered from the reference source and the load voltage.    The output current of the first stage adjusts so that it will control the second stage and bring the load voltage back to normal.

The a-c output voltage indicated in Figure 8.31 by dashed lines is regulated to have a constant area under the curve of the voltage waveform.    Thus the average a-c voltage output as well as the d-c voltage is regulated by this type of stabilizer when the a-c output voltage is rectified and filtered.

Obviously, the regulation of this stabilizer can be no better than the regulation obtainable from the voltage reference device.    (The voltage reference device, incidentally, can obtain its power for operation from the d-c output voltage of the stabilizer if it requires d-c input voltage, as in the case of gas-tube references.)

The magnetic amplifier type voltage stabilizer has relatively high output impedance and is relatively slow in response to load voltage changes. The more magnetic amplifier stages used, the higher the loop gain in the stabilizer, but, the poorer the time required to correct for error signals.

Several magnetic amplifier type a-c and d-c voltage stabilizers are commercially available. For example, a Sorensen magnetic amplifier type a-c voltage stabilizer, using a silicon diode operating in its Zener breakdown region as the reference voltage device, is available for handling 1000 va at an output voltage adjustable from 110 to 120. The regulation is ±0.5 per cent for about ±15 per cent line voltage variations and is ±0.5 per cent for load variations from zero to full load. Distortion of the output voltage wave is a maximum of 3 per cent at 60 cps but can be higher as the input signal frequency deviates from 60 cps. The response time is 0.2 sec. Output load power factor can be anywhere from unity to 0.7 lagging. The ambient temperature range is 0 to 40° C.

A magnetic amplifier type voltage stabilizer which provides a d-c output voltage is also available from Sorensen & Company. A silicon diode reference element is again used to provide the reference voltage. However, a transistor amplifier provides the control current for the magnetic amplifier. (The transistor amplifier is substituted in place of magnetic amplifier No. 1 in the block diagram shown in Figure 8.31. Power for the transistor operation could be derived from the d-c output power of the stabilizer.) The input voltage range of 105 to 125v, 60 cps produces a d-c output voltage continuously adjustable from 5 to 32 v. The output current available ranges from zero to 15 amp. Regulation of output voltage is ±0.5 per cent for the specified input voltage range and is ±0.5 per cent for load variations from zero to full load. Ripple is 1 per cent rms at 32 v d-c. Recovery time is, again, 0.2 sec.

Magnetic amplifier type voltage stabilizers when used with very good voltage reference devices provide excellent voltage regulation and are capable of handling reasonably large amounts of power with the utmost reliability. The main disadvantages are the inherent relatively high output impedance and the relatively slow response time.

## 8.10   Dielectric Amplifiers

Although there is little or no doubt today about the utility of the magnetic amplifier, the position of its dielectric counterpart, the dielectric amplifier, is nowhere nearly so well established. Whereas the input impedance of the magnetic amplifier to d-c signals is fixed by the resistance of the control winding, the dielectric amplifier has nearly infinite input impedance to d-c signals. This, of course, makes it desirable for many applications where loading of the signal circuit must be avoided. Also, the size and weight of the nonlinear element, as well as its cost, are much lower in the case of the dielectric amplifier than in the case of the magnetic amplifier, particularly for low-power applications. This, however, is offset at the present time by two very severe disadvantages:

1. Aging of the nonlinear dielectric material causes changes in operating characteristics. Several theories have been proposed for this phenomenon, which is only partially understood at the present time.

2. The dielectric is exceedingly temperature-sensitive at present. The reason for the latter follows from the consideration that the necessary nonlinearity can be obtained from two sources: (a) The Curie temperature has been found to be highly field-sensitive. Thus, if the ambient temperature is maintained slightly above the Curie temperature, a change in applied voltage will cause a relatively large change in "dielectric constant," although changes of the order of magnitude possible with magnetic biasing of ferromagnetic materials cannot be achieved by this method with existing dielectrics. A change in ambient temperature has the same effect as a change of control signal.

(b) Since ferroelectric materials possess hysteresis loops similar to those of ferromagnetic materials, we might also use the square loops found in single crystals of these dielectrics. Here, however, we are confronted with the fact that the per unit volume losses in existing materials are from one hundred to one thousand times as large as those of the best ferromagnetic materials. The self-heating which results from this deficiency causes such severe changes in the shape of the hysteresis loop, hence the operating characteristics, that suitable cooling equipment must be provided.

It must be remembered, however, that these remarks are predicated upon the existing materials. Since research in this field is quite intense, it may be expected that the situation will have improved materially within a few years.

With the discovery of ferroelectric materials, such as, for example, barium titanate or lead metaniobate, it was to be expected that many of the saturable magnetic devices would be translated into their dielectric analogs. One of the first, based on the availability of voltage-sensitive capacitors, was the dielectric amplifier. It is shown in Figure 8.32 in its simplest form, and is the dual of the basic one-core magnetic amplifier of Figure 8.3. A blocking capacitor prevents the a-c power source from short circuiting the control signal, and a choke (or resistor) prevents the control source from short circuiting the saturable element.

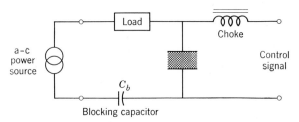

**Figure 8.32.** Basic single-capacitor dielectric amplifier.

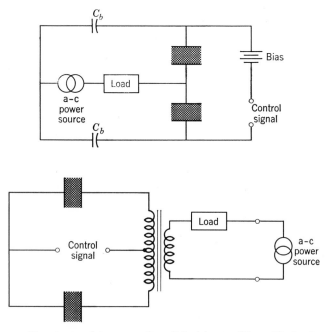

**Figure 8.33.** Two types of two-capacitor dielectric amplifier. No fundamental or odd harmonic voltage components appear in the control circuit, supplying a-c loads.

If the dielectric possesses a square hysteresis loop (such as is found in single crystals of the material), high-gain amplifiers can be built. Unfortunately, commercially available ferroelectrics developed to date have a rather high coercive field and relatively large hysteresis losses, besides being relatively temperature-sensitive (29, 30, 31). As a result, dielectric amplifiers have found very little acceptance thus far. On the other hand, their lower cost and much smaller size and weight may well become overwhelming arguments, once the material properties are adequate (31).

Just as in the case of the magnetic amplifier, blocking elements in the control circuit can be eliminated by the use of a balanced circuit, such as the one shown in Figure 8.33. Fundamental and odd harmonic voltage components are eliminated from the control circuits, but even harmonic components are present. If the less expensive polycrystalline ceramic ferroelectric is used rather than a single crystal of the material, the dielectric constant, though voltage-sensitive, generally cannot be varied over a sufficiently wide range. For this reason, it is usually necessary to augment the sensitivity of dielectric amplifiers by means of a resonating choke, described in Section 8.11.

Nonlinear capacitors can also be used in a variety of other applications, such as a ratio detector, bridge switching circuits, and bridged-T switching circuits (32). Although these devices suffer from the same temperature difficulties as the dielectric amplifier, this may not be an important consideration in certain applications.

## 8.11   Resonant Type Amplifiers

Magnetic and dielectric amplifiers should be considered basically as series reactances whose impedance is sensitive to a control signal. As such, the magnetic amplifier has its highest impedance when the control signal is zero (provided that the bias and control mmf aid each other) and its lowest impedance for some relatively large control signal. Its dual, the dielectric amplifier, has its largest impedance when full control voltage is applied and minimum impedance in the absence of any control signal. Clearly, the useful range is extended if the maximum impedance can be raised and the minimum impedance lowered. In the case of the magnetic amplifier, the zero-signal impedance is readily raised by paralleling the power winding terminals with a capacitor whose value is so chosen as to resonate the zero-signal reactance of the power winding at the frequency of the power source. In this manner the amplifier operates on the steep slope of a resonance characteristic, and the gain of the device can in general be raised considerably, although at the expense of linearity. This is seen from the phasor diagrams of Figure 8.34, which apply to the typical circuit of Figure 8.35. In the case of external regenerative feedback the gain of such a magnetic amplifier can be enhanced even further (see Figure 8.10, for example) if the regenerative action of nonlinear resonance is used to amplify the feedback signal.

(See Chapter 4 for a discussion of the phenomenon of nonlinear resonance.) One such circuit is shown in Figure 8.36, which combines off-resonance load control and nonlinear resonance in the feedback circuit (7, 33).

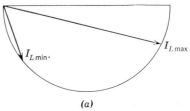

(a)

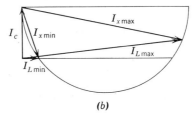

(b)

**Figure 8.34.** Phasor diagram for a magnetic amplifier before (a) use of $C_{res}$ and (b) after paralleling the power windings with a suitable capacitor $C_{res}$.

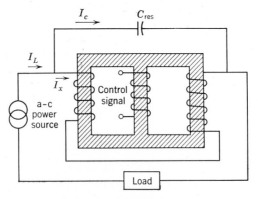

**Figure 8.35.** Magnetic amplifier with tuning capacitor $C_{res}$.

In somewhat similar fashion the minimum impedance can be lowered by the use of series capacitors, as Figure 8.37 shows (11).

Similar to the tuned magnetic amplifiers, resonant dielectric amplifiers have higher gain than the nonresonant types. Figure 8.38 shows the

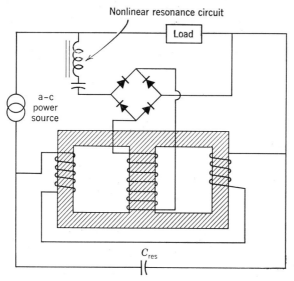

Figure 8.36. Magnetic amplifier circuit with off-resonance load control and non-linear resonance regeneration in the feedback circuit.

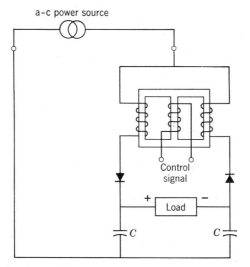

Figure 8.37. Magnetic amplifier supplying a d-c load; capacitors are used for series resonance.

simple, one-capacitor type (34, 35). Clearly, the two-capacitor circuits of Figure 8.33 can be tuned in analogous manner, with attendant gain increase.

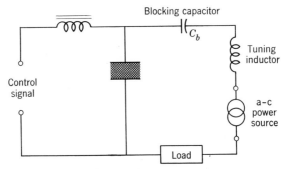

**Figure 8.38.** Dielectric amplifier with series tuning inductor.

## /NONLINEAR RESONANCE COMPUTER COMPONENTS

### 8.12  Introduction

It has been shown (see Chapter 4) that a suitable combination of linear and nonlinear energy storage elements can give rise to the bistability phenomena of nonlinear resonance. It is evident that devices with these properties might well be useful in digital computer applications. Some effort has been devoted to the design and development of such devices. At the time of this writing, however, no information has been made available regarding the assembly of an entire computer based on nonlinear resonance components. From a practical viewpoint the following comparative characteristics of nonlinear resonance elements may be of importance:

1. With a carrier frequency of 10 megacycles, operation at a trigger rate of 1 or even 2 megacycles appears feasible.

2. Temperature stability can be made fairly high, and high-temperature operation (above 100° C) might be practical.

3. Power consumption is small for well-designed components, but is likely to exceed somewhat the stand-by requirements of transistor trigger elements.

4. Size and weight requirements are comparable to transistor components at sufficiently high carrier frequencies but may exceed those of vacuum tube components at carrier frequencies in or below the audio range.

## 8.13   The Series Resonant Double-Branch Trigger Pair, Using Current Sensitive Inductors

The basic circuit of a nonlinear resonance trigger pair is shown in Figure 8.39.   This double-branch series circuit should be supplied from a constant-current a-c source which, in practice, is conveniently simulated by a constant-voltage source in series with a suitable capacitor.

A reasonably complete analysis and derivation of design expressions can be found in the literature (38).   The salient results are summarized here for the dissipation-free case only.

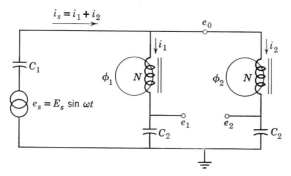

**Figure 8.39.**   Double-branch series resonant trigger pair using current-sensitive inductors.

Since the two nonlinear inductors are assumed to be identical, the two respective current-flux relations are given by

$$i_1 = a_1\phi_1 + a_3\phi_1^3 \qquad i_2 = a_1\phi_2 + a_3\phi_2^3 \qquad (8.1)$$

where $i_1$ and $i_2$ are the respective branch currents, $\phi_1$ and $\phi_2$, the corresponding core fluxes, and $a_1$ and $a_3$, the coefficients relating flux and current in each core.

For this circuit the following relations exist:

$$i_s = i_1 + i_2 \qquad (8.2)$$

$$N\dot{\phi}_1 + \frac{1}{C_2} \int i_1 \, dt = N\dot{\phi}_2 + \frac{1}{C_2} \int i_2 \, dt \qquad (8.3)$$

Considering fundamental components only, the following harmonic solutions are assumed:

$$\phi_1 = A \cos \omega t \qquad \phi_2 = B \cos \omega t \qquad (8.4)$$

The flux amplitudes $A$ and $B$ can be determined from a substitution of these expressions into the relations defined by equations 8.2 and 8.3. If the coefficients of the fundamental frequency terms are compared,

$$I_s = a_1(A + B) + \tfrac{3}{4}a_3(A^3 + B^3) \qquad (8.5)$$

$$0 = (A - B)\left(\frac{a_1}{C_2} - \omega^2 N\right) + \left(\frac{3a_3}{4C_2}\right)(A^3 - B^3) \qquad (8.6)$$

where $I_s$ is the peak value of source current. For convenience, the symbols used in Chapter 4 are again introduced here:

$$L_0 \triangleq \frac{N}{a_1} \qquad \omega_0{}^2 \triangleq \frac{1}{L_0 C_2} \qquad m \triangleq \frac{3a_3}{4a_1} \qquad S \triangleq \frac{\omega^2}{\omega_0{}^2} - 1 \qquad (8.7)$$

Thus equations 8.5 and 8.6 can be rewritten

$$\psi_1 \equiv 0 = -\frac{I_s}{a_1} + (A + B) + m(A^3 + B^3) \qquad (8.8)$$

$$\psi_2 \equiv 0 = -S + m(A^2 + AB + B^2) \qquad (8.9)$$

Equation 8.9 defines an ellipse $\psi_2$ with $A$ and $B$ as the variables. The intersection of this curve with the bell-shaped curve $\psi_1$ of equation 8.8 determines the operating point of the trigger pair, as illustrated in Figure 8.40. One limiting condition of intersection occurs if the two curves have a common tangent. Inspection of Figure 8.40 shows this to be the case when $A = B$, due to the symmetry of $\psi_1$ and $\psi_2$. From equation 8.9, this defines the point

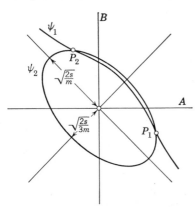

Figure 8.40. Graphical representation of the operating characteristics $\psi_1$ and $\psi_2$ of the trigger pair of Figure 8.39. Intersections $P_1$ and $P_2$ define the possible operating points.

$$A = B = \sqrt{\frac{S}{3m}} \qquad (8.10)$$

Substitution of this result into equation 8.8 yields the upper limit of source current if no more than two stable points are to exist:

$$I_s < 2a_1 \left(\frac{S}{3} + 1\right) \sqrt{\frac{S}{3m}} \tag{8.11}$$

If $I_s$ exceeds this value, four stable operating points may exist. This condition is not considered desirable in the use of the circuit as a binary element.

In the limit, when $\psi_1$ and $\psi_2$ osculate, the circuit ceases to be bistable. This will be the case if $\partial\psi_1/\partial A = \partial\psi_2/\partial A$ and $\partial\psi_1/\partial B = \partial\psi_2/\partial B$. Carrying out these indicated operations and dividing the resulting two equations by each other, there follows

$$\psi_3 \equiv 0 = A^2 + 3AB + B^2 - \frac{1}{3m} \tag{8.12}$$

This equation represents a hyperbola, which can be shown to intersect the operating ellipse $\psi_2$ only if

$$S > \tfrac{1}{5} \quad \text{or} \quad \omega^2 > 1.2\omega_0{}^2 \tag{8.13}$$

Thus equations 8.11 and 8.13 define the limiting conditions which permit operation of the circuit of Figure 8.39 as a binary trigger pair.

If ideal operation is to be achieved, one branch current must be very nearly equal zero while almost the entire source current flows in the other branch. Thus, permitting $B = 0$, there follows from equation 8.9

$$A = \sqrt{S/m} \tag{8.14}$$

The required source current under these conditions is found by substituting equation 8.14 into equation 8.8:

$$I_s = a_1(1 + S)\sqrt{S/m} \tag{8.15}$$

Since this entire source current flows through the branch that exists in the "high" state, the output voltages across the branch capacitors are

$$E_1 = I_s \frac{1}{\omega C_2} = \omega N \sqrt{S/m}$$
$$E_2 = 0 \tag{8.16}$$

If the resistance of the system is considered to be sufficiently small, the relations thus far derived are essentially unaltered. However, it can be shown that there exists a maximum permissible value of resistance for bistability (38):

$$R_{\max} = \frac{1}{\omega C_2}\sqrt{S} \tag{8.17}$$

It can be further shown that whereas in the ideal case the signal-to-noise ratio of the trigger pair is infinite the presence of resistance reduces it to

$$\text{Signal-to-noise ratio} = \frac{S - \omega^2 R^2 C_2{}^2}{\omega R C_2} \tag{8.18}$$

Thus the signal-to-noise ratio is seen to be independent of the nonlinearities of the system under the conditions assumed at the outset. However, a highly nonlinear system carries smaller currents (see equation 8.14) and triggers on lower source currents (see equation 8.15) than a system containing a nonlinear core with a gentle nonlinearity.

## 8.14 The Series Resonant Double-Branch Trigger Pair, Using Voltage-Sensitive Capacitors

It may be reasonably expected that a different nonlinearity than that due to use of ferromagnetic material may give rise to a similar trigger pair. This has been demonstrated to be the case, and Figure 8.41 shows a trigger pair in which the charge-voltage characteristic of the capacitors is nonlinear (39). Analysis of this type of circuit proceeds along lines similar to those of that previously described. The basic equations are, in this case,

$$q_s \equiv q_1 + q_2 \tag{8.19}$$

$$e_1 + L\dot{q}_1 = e_2 + L\dot{q}_2 \tag{8.20}$$

$$e_1 = a_1 q_1 + a_3 q_1{}^3 \tag{8.21}$$

$$e_2 = a_1 q_2 + a_3 q_2{}^3$$

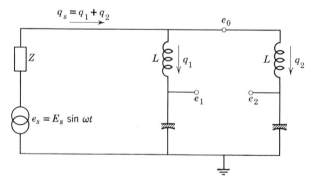

**Figure 8.41.** Double-branch series resonant trigger pair, using voltage-sensitive capacitors.

Once again, only fundamental components are considered, and upon substitution of equations 8.21 into equations 8.19 and 8.20, respectively, there results

$$\psi_1 \equiv 0 = -Q_s + A + B \tag{8.22}$$

$$\psi_2 \equiv 0 = -S + m(A^2 + AB + B^2) \tag{8.23}$$

where $A$ and $B$ are the amplitudes of the fundamental components of charge, $Q_s$ is the amplitude of the driving charge, and $m$ and $S$ are defined as in equation 8.7. Equations 8.22 and 8.23 can be represented graphically in a figure similar to Figure 8.40, except that the bell-shaped curve is now a straight line intersecting the $A$-axis at $(Q_s, 0)$ and the $B$-axis at $(0, Q_s)$. The intersection of $\psi_1$ and $\psi_2$ can be found analytically and occurs at

$$A = \frac{Q_s}{2} \pm \sqrt{(S/m) - \tfrac{3}{4}Q_s^2} \tag{8.24}$$

$$B = \frac{Q_s}{2} \mp \sqrt{(S/m) - \tfrac{3}{4}Q_s^2} \tag{8.25}$$

Obviously, no real intersection can exist when the radical in equations 8.24 and 8.25 becomes negative, which implies that bistability occurs only when

$$Q_s < \sqrt{4S/3m} \tag{8.26}$$

Again, the optimum trigger pair results when one of the branch charges is zero and the other is large. This occurs when

$$Q_s = \sqrt{S/m} \tag{8.27}$$

and results in

$$\begin{aligned} A &= Q_s \qquad B = 0 \\ A &= 0 \qquad B = Q_s \end{aligned} \tag{8.28}$$

Since a constant-current source may be impractical, a constant-voltage source of adequate impedance can once more be substituted. This is indicated in Figure 8.42, where a constant-voltage source in series with a sufficiently large impedance $Z$ substitutes for the constant-current source.

## 8.15   Example

One particular trigger pair utilized the following design constants:

$$\omega = 1.46 \times 10^6 \text{ rad/sec} \qquad N = 200 \qquad C_1 = C_2 = 500 \times 10^{-12} F$$
$$(8.29)$$

For the given magnetic ferrite core the current-flux relation was approximated on the basis of slopes and found to be

$$i = 0.2 \times 10^5 \phi + 20 \times 10^{14} \phi^3 \tag{8.30}$$

where $i$ is in amperes and $\phi$ in maxwells. The ideal operating system would then require a source voltage of

$$E_s = I_s \frac{1}{\omega C_2} = 333 \text{ v peak} \tag{8.31}$$

The maximum permissible resistance is $R_{max} = 4180$ ohms.

The remaining performance data are calculated as

$$I_1 = I_s = 0.14 \text{ amp peak}$$
$$E_1 = 333 \text{ v peak} \tag{8.32}$$
$$E_2 = 0$$

If the source requirements are too high, redesign is required. However, with some sacrifice in signal-to-noise ratio, a source voltage of 100 volts peak was found to be adequate, even without circuit redesign, and the following results were obtained:

$$E_s = 100 \text{ v peak}$$
$$I_1 = 0.1 \text{ amp peak}$$
$$I_2 = 0.005 \text{ amp peak}$$
$$E_1 = 80 \text{ v peak}$$
$$E_2 = 4 \text{ v peak}$$

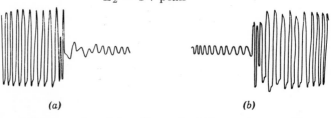

(a)                                    (b)

**Figure 8.42.** Response of $e_1$ of the trigger pair of Figure 8.39 to a trigger pulse: (a) change from the high state to the low state; (b) change from the low state to the high state.

The speed at which each branch of the trigger pair of Figure 8.39 responds to trigger pulses is shown in Figure 8.42, both for a change from the high to the low state and vice versa.

## 8.16   The Parallel Resonant Double-Branch Trigger Pairs

The principles of duality apply to nonlinear circuits, as they do to linear circuits.   Hence it is to be expected that the circuits of Figures

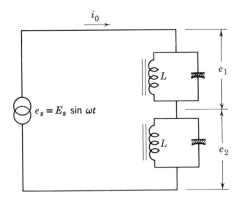

**Figure 8.43.**   Double-branch parallel resonant trigger pair, using voltage-sensitive capacitors.   This circuit is the dual of Figure 8.39.

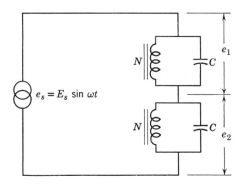

**Figure 8.44.**   Double-branch parallel resonant trigger pair, using current-sensitive inductors.   This circuit is the dual of Figure 8.41.

8.39 and 8.41 have duals which are capable of trigger action.   They are shown in Figure 8.43 and Figure 8.44.   An analysis of these two systems would follow the reasoning given.

### 8.16.1 Triggering Schemes

It has been demonstrated in the preceding discussions that by the use of nonlinear resonance various double-branch circuits can be made to perform as trigger pairs. In all cases the degree of nonlinearity of two identical elements determines whether or not the system is capable of bistability. It is clear, therefore, that a temporary change in the nonlinearity, even though it may last for only one cycle of the a-c source, may be adequate to alter the state of the system. It was suggested in Chapter 4 that this change in nonlinearity can be effected in a variety of ways, e.g., temperature changes, externally supplied electric or magnetic fields, and change of source frequency, voltage, or current. The effects of temperature changes are illustrated in Figure 8.45. If

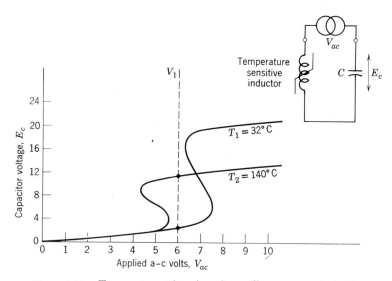

**Figure 8.45.** Temperature triggering of a nonlinear resonant circuit.

the system is operating at temperature $T_1$, then an applied voltage $V_1$ will produce a small current $I_1$. As the external temperature increases, the hysteresis loop of the material becomes narrower and the saturation flux density decreases. At a temperature $T_2 > T_1$ the operating characteristic shifts to the left, as shown in Figure 8.45. Hence the stable operating current suddenly increases to $I_2$. A ratio of $I_2/I_1 = 3$ was obtainable with a ferrite core operating at 400 cps.

## 8.17  Applications

For many applications, notably in digital-computer circuitry, electrical triggering is essential.  For example, in the so-called "negation," or "not," circuit the set pulse is applied to one terminal pair, and the "reset" pulse to another.  Such a system is shown in Figure 8.46 and is based on the double-branch series resonant trigger pair.

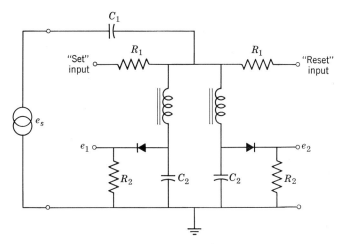

**Figure 8.46.**  "Not" circuit, using separate "set" and "reset" terminals, in the double-branch series resonant trigger pair using current-sensitive inductors.

One of the logic components, the "not" circuit, has already been discussed and is shown again in Figure 8.46.  Its function is to negate and to remove the output signal in the presence of a "set" pulse.  Thus in Figure 8.46 only output $e_1$ would be used unless an inversion is desired, in which case $e_2$ is used instead.

An "and" circuit is used to provide an output only in the presence of all inputs.  If an "and" circuit with two inputs is available, combinations of several such circuits can be used to form an "and" circuit with an arbitrary number of inputs.  This logic component, as well as the "exclusive or" circuit (an output appears if one or the other input is present, but not both), the "inclusive or" circuit (an output appears if one or the other or both inputs are present), and a shift register have been described in the literature (41).

## 8.18   Binary Counter

A binary counter is readily assembled by cascading circuits of the type of Figure 8.46 in such a way that each change from the low state to the high state develops a trigger signal for the next binary stage (37). Ring counters are equally readily constructed (42).   In a binary counter circuit it is desirable that successive like-polarity pulses applied to a single input terminal pair should flip the circuit alternately from one state to the other.   This can be achieved by providing a single inductively coupled trigger winding acting on both magnetic cores simul-

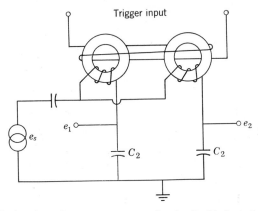

**Figure 8.47.**   Single-trigger input arrangement for the double-branch series resonant trigger pair, using current-sensitive inductors.

taneously.   However, it is essential that the coupling be loose or that other decoupling means be provided to prevent the trigger source from loading the nonlinear resonant circuit.   One method which achieves this aim is shown in Figure 8.47, where the plane of the trigger coil is at right angles to the plane of the toroidal flux path (40).   Consider one of the cores of the circuit, as shown in Figure 8.48.   As can be seen, the trigger flux aids the carrier flux in one half of the core and opposes it in the other half.   If the core under consideration belongs to the branch in the low state, then the carrier flux is negligible, and the trigger flux tends to saturate both halves of the core.   If the source current is suitably chosen, then this partial saturation due to the trigger flux will urge the low-current branch toward a change of state.   Simultaneously, the trigger flux acts on the other core, which was originally in the high state.   Here, the high carrier current has forced both core halves into saturation, and the additional effect of the trigger flux is negligible in that half of the core in which the fluxes aided each other. In the other core half they oppose, causing partial desaturation and thus urging the branch toward return to the "low" state.

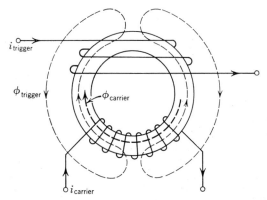

**Figure 8.48.** Flux paths for the flux due to the trigger current and the a-c carrier current in a nonlinear resonant trigger circuit.

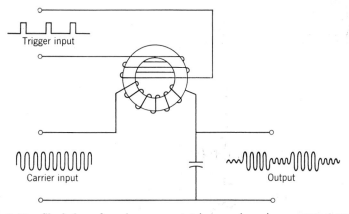

**Figure 8.49.** Single-branch series resonant trigger pair, using a current-sensitive inductor.

It may now be argued that a succession of like-polarity pulses applied to a trigger winding surrounding a single core should cause alternate state changes in a single-branch series resonant trigger circuit. This is indeed the case, and a corresponding arrangement is shown in Figure 8.49.

## / FREQUENCY CONVERTERS AND
## VOLTAGE REGULATORS

### 8.19   Introduction

Earlier in this chapter it has been shown that even the fastest magnetic amplifiers, namely the flux reset types, cannot respond to a change in control signal in less than one half cycle of the a-c supply. Clearly, then, if high-speed operation is essential, a higher frequency than the normally available 60 or 400 cycles is needed. Such a conversion can, of course, be performed electronically or with rotating machines. A third method, which is finding wide acceptance, uses the nonlinearity of reactors with ferromagnetic cores to generate suitably phased harmonic voltages, which then serve to supply magnetic amplifiers designed for this higher frequency.

This method of generating harmonic voltages was developed in the early days of radio transmission as a competitor to the rotating high-frequency generator, but both fell into disrepute with the development of vacuum tube transmitters. The revival of interest is due primarily to the aforementioned need for high-speed magnetic amplifiers and to the high degree of reliability under severe operating conditions of such transformerlike devices.

In some isolated applications in which a frequency below that of the source is needed the opposite procedure is desirable. This, too, can be achieved statically. It is the purpose of this section to discuss briefly both the harmonic and the subharmonic generator types.

### 8.19.1   Harmonic Generators

It was shown in Figures 8.4 and 8.5, and in the related discussion, that a given inductor can absorb only a volt-time area per turn equal to twice the saturation flux. Any source voltage remaining after this condition is reached must appear across the series-connected load. If the hysteresis loop is square, this switching occurs abruptly. Conversely, if the loop is gently rounded, then the voltage shifts more gradually from the reactor power winding to the load, as shown by the broken line. Since, in frequency multipliers, the higher frequency "sine wave" is assembled from such current pulses, a wave shape approximating a half sine wave results in lower distortion of the output signal (43).

Frequency doubling occurs in balanced saturable reactors and in magnetic amplifiers of the types shown in Figs. 8.6 to 8.14, and others. This is achieved, for example, by connecting the primaries of two identical inductors in series, or in parallel, and by connecting the secondaries in series opposition; this arrangement results in cancellation of the fundamental and all odd harmonics. Next, a d-c bias is provided, either through properly arranged bias windings or by making either the primaries or the secondaries serve a dual purpose. Suitable adjustment of the bias will cause the second harmonic to predominate over all other even harmonics, particularly if cores with gently rounded hysteresis loop are used (44).

Among the earliest frequency multipliers is the third harmonic generator, which results from the use of saturable transformers in a three-phase wye-delta connection. For more detailed information the reader is referred to the literature (45, 46, 47, 48, 49).

### 8.19.2 Subharmonic Generators

The topic of nonlinear resonance has been discussed in some detail in Chapters 4 and 8, where the criteria for bistability of the simple nonlinear $R$-$L$-$C$ series circuit and of the more complex parallel circuits were developed. These derivations do not suggest, however, that another type of response can exist whose fundamental frequency is an integral submultiple of the source frequency. A discussion and mathematical proof for this phenomenon can be found in the literature (50), but it is considered beyond the scope of this book. Suffice to say that such subharmonics have been observed experimentally by many different observers (51) and can be initiated in a variety of ways: by providing the capacitor of the nonlinear $R$-$L$-$C$ series circuit with a d-c charge prior to closing the circuit, by applying the a-c source voltage at the instant at which the voltage passes through zero, or by temporary alteration of one of the circuit elements. The source voltage must, in general, be lower than that required for nonlinear resonance if subharmonic response is to occur. Depending upon the boundary conditions at the instant of energizing the circuit, the lowest frequency component may be one half, one third, one fourth, etc., of the source frequency. The oscillation is then termed a subharmonic of the second, third, fourth order, etc.

It has been observed that the voltage across the nonlinear inductor of an $L$-$C$ series circuit with negligible resistance consists, essentially, of only two sinusoidal components: one of source frequency and one of subharmonic frequency. Thus, with suitable filtering, power can be extracted at a subharmonic frequency.

## 8.20   Voltage Stabilizers

Several aspects of the ferroresonant phenomena have been utilized in various forms of voltage regulators.* Two illustrations are discussed which show the application to power-handling transformers and to low-power voltage references.   Figure 8.50 is a schematic of a transformer

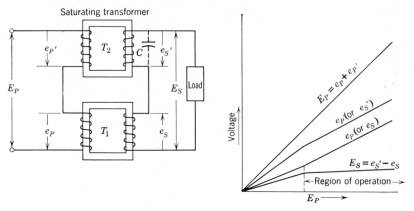

**Figure 8.50.**   Saturating-transformer voltage regulator.   (Terman, 1943.)

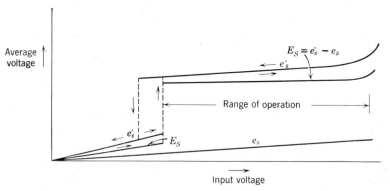

**Figure 8.51.**   Voltage characteristic of regulator.   (Terman, 1943.)

configuration which employs a saturable reactor $T_2$ in series with a standard transformer $T_1$.   The secondary windings are connected so that their output voltages oppose.   As the primary voltage $E_P$ increases, the transformer core $T_2$ tends to saturate and thus reduce the effective permeability.   The reduction in coupling reduces the output voltage from $T_2$.   By proper proportioning, the secondary voltage $E_S$ can be

* See Chapter 4.

made nearly constant over a large range of input voltage variations. Figure 8.50 indicates the variation in each of the circuit voltages.

The addition of capacitor $C$ across the secondary winding allows the circuit to operate as a ferroresonant system. Thus the turns ratio of transformer $T_2$ no longer tends to determine the amplitude of voltage across the secondary when the capacitor produces the nonsinusoidal oscillations. Figure 8.51 shows the voltage characteristics of this device, which displays the typical ferroresonant effect.

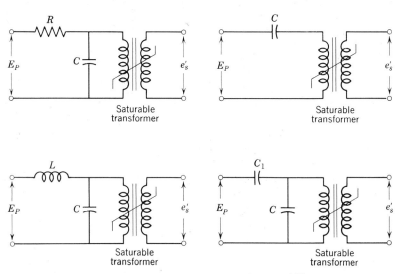

Figure 8.52. Basic ferroresonant voltage stabilizers.

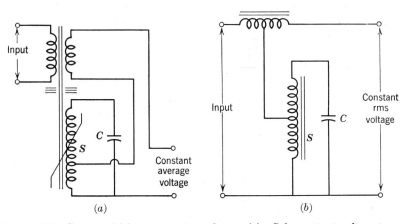

Figure 8.53. Commercial ferroresonant regulators: ($a$) a Sola constant voltage transformer; ($b$) a Sorensen MVR regulator. (Courtesy Sola Co. and Sorenson Co.)

Several circuit arrangements are used to obtain a relatively stable average voltage across a saturable inductor. Figure 8.52 shows the schematic diagrams of four basic ferroresonant voltage-stabilizer circuits. In two commercial models (Fig. 8.53) additional compensation is also provided. For ratings of a few kva to about 25 kva it is possible to obtain a voltage regulation of ±1 per cent for input voltage variations of ±15 per cent. Regulation under variable loads is not as good. When frequency compensation is added the output voltage regulation can be specified at ±3 per cent maximum for ±15 per cent line voltage fluctuation and ±5 per cent frequency variation.

### 8.20.1 Voltage Reference

Other adaptations of the ferroresonant circuit provide a rectified output reference voltage at a one-watt power level. The regulation is less than ±1 per cent over the temperature range of −55 to 85° C at a frequency of 400 cps ±5 per cent and an input voltage variation of ±10 per cent. The basic circuit of this specially designed reference device is shown in Figure 8.54. Temperature compensation is achieved by bucking the output voltages from two ferroresonant circuits by utilizing an Orthonol metallic tape core and a ferrite core.

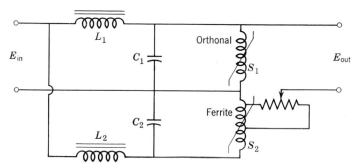

**Figure 8.54.** Temperature compensation circuits of ferroresonant reference device. (Manteuffel, 1955.)

### 8.21  References

1. Storm, H. F., "Series-Connected Saturable Reactor with Control Source of Comparatively High Impedance," *Trans. AIEE*, **69**, 1950.
2. ————, "Series-Connected Saturable Reactor with Control Source of Comparatively Low Impedance," *Trans. AIEE*, **69**, 1950.
3. Malick, Franklin S., "Magnetic Amplifier Application Problems," *AIEE Miscellaneous Paper* 50–207, August 1950.

4. Hislop, T. H., "Some New Applications of Transductors in Amplifying and Switching Circuits," *Telecommunications Research Establishment Technical Note, I.R.E.*, No. 119, May 1951.
5. Rosenstein, A. B., "160,000 Ampere High-Speed Magnetic Amplifier Design," *Trans. AIEE*, Communications and Electronics, No. 17, March 1955, pp. 90–99.
6. Sakamoto, M., "The Effect of Commutation on the Stability of Magnetic Amplifiers," *AIEE Miscellaneous Paper* 52–233, May 1952.
7. Miles, J. G., "Types of Magnetic Amplifiers—Survey," *Trans. AIEE*, Communications and Electrics, No. 1, July 1952, pp. 229–237.
8. ———, "Bibliography of Magnetic Amplifier Devices and the Saturable Reactor Art," *Trans. AIEE*, **70**, 1951, pp. 2104–23.
9. Finzi, I. A., G. F. Pittman, Jr., "Basic Methods of Analysis of Magnetic Amplifiers—A Critical Comparison," *Tech. Report No. 11*, Office of Naval Research, Contract N-7-ONR-30306 and 30308, Project Nos. 075–272 and 275, Carnegie Institute of Technology, Pittsburgh, Pa.; also *Proc. Nat. Electronics Conf.*, **8**, 1952.
10. Storm, H. F., *Magnetic Amplifiers*, John Wiley and Sons, New York, 1955.
11. Morgan, R. E. "The Fundamental Operation of the Amplistat," *AIEE Miscellaneous Paper* 49–183, May 1949.
12. Ramey, R. A., "On the Mechanics of Magnetic Amplifier Operation," Naval Research Laboratory *Report 3799;* also, *Trans. AIEE*, **70**, Part II, 1951, pp. 1214–23.
13. ———, "On the Control of Magnetic Amplifiers," *Trans. AIEE*, **70,** Part II, 1951, pp. 2124–48.
14. ———, "The Single-Core Magnetic Amplifier as a Computer Element," *Trans. AIEE*, Communications and Electronics No. 4, January 1953, pp. 442–446.
15. House, C. B., "Flux Preset High-Speed Magnetic Amplifiers," *Trans. AIEE*, Communications and Electronics, No. 10, January 1954, pp. 728–735.
16. Morgan, R. E., J. B. McFerran, "Pulse Relaxation Amplifier—A Low-level D-c Magnetic Amplifier," *Trans. AIEE*, Communications and Electronics, No. 13, July 1954, pp. 245–249.
17. Lowrance, J. L., and J. D. Dolan, Diode Shunting in Magnetic Amplifiers, *Trans. AIEE*, Communications and Electronics, November 1956, pp. 619–624.
18. Storm, H. F., "Theory of Magnetic Amplifiers with Square Loop Materials," *Trans. AIEE*, Communications and Electronics, No. 9, November 1953, pp. 629–640.
19. Carleton, J. T., W. F. Horton, "The Figure of Merit of Magnetic Amplifiers," *Trans. AIEE*, Communications and Electronics, No. 2, September 1952, pp. 239–245.
20. Johnson, L. J., S. E. Rauch, "Response Time of Magnetic Amplifiers," Phamplet published by Hufford Machine Works, Inc., Electronics Division, Los Angeles, Calif.; also *Elec. Mfg.*, September 1954.
21. Bowen, A. E., U.S. Patent 2,230,558, 1941.
22. Hines, C. M., U.S. Patent 2,215,820, 1940.
23. Hartley, R. V., U.S. Patent 1,287,982, 1918.
24. Kalb, R. M., W. R. Bennett, "Ferromagnetic Distortion of a Two-Frequency Wave," *Bell System Tech. J.*, **14**, April 1935, pp. 322–359.
25. Wakeman, C. B., F. J. Beck, "Superposed Magnetic Fields in Materials and Rectangular Hysteresis Loops," *Trans. AIEE*, Communications and Electronics, November 1956, pp. 562–569.

26. Beck, F. J., J. M. Kelly, "Magnetization in Perpendicularly Superposed Direct and Alternating Fields," *J. Appl. Phy.*, **19**, June 1948, pp. 551–562.

27. Buck, Dudley A., Werner I. Frank, "Nondestructive Sensing of Magnetic Cores," *Trans. AIEE*, Communications and Electronics, No. 10, January 1954, pp. 822–830.

28. Heartz, Robert A., Herbert Buelteman, Jr., "The Application of Perpendicularly Superposed Magnetic Fields," *Trans. AIEE*, Communications and Electronics, No. 21, November 1955, pp. 655–660.

29. Coffeen, W. W., "The Effect of Minor Constituents in High Dielectric Constant Titanate Capacitors," *Trans. AIEE*, Communications and Electronics, No. 9, November 1953, pp. 704–709.

30. Penney, G. W., J. R. Horsch, E. A. Sack, "Dielectric Amplifiers," *Trans. AIEE*, Communications and Electronics, No. 5, March 1953, pp. 68–79.

31. Vincent, A. M., "Dielectric Amplifier Fundamentals," *Electronics*, December 1951, pp. 84–88.

32. Jenkins, J. L., "Voltage-Sensitive Capacitors," *Elec. Mfg.*, December 1954, pp. 83–89.

33. Runaldue, L. R., U.S. Patent 2,278,151, 1942.

34. Penney, G. W., E. A. Sack, E. R. Wingrove, "Frequency Response of a Resonant Dielectric Amplifier," *Trans. AIEE*, Communications and Electronics, No. 12, May 1954, pp. 119–124.

35. Sack, E. A., G. W. Penney, "Voltage Gain of a Resonant Dielectric Amplifier," *Trans. AIEE*, Communications and Electronics, No. 20, September 1955, pp. 428–434.

36. Spitzer, C. F., et al., "Nonlinear Resonant Flip-Flop Circuit," Patent No. 2,653,256, 1953.

37. Isborn, C., "Ferroresonant Flip-Flops," *Electronics*, April 1952, pp. 121–123; also, C. Isborn, "Ferroresonant Ring Counter," Patent No. 2,697,178, 1954.

38. Spitzer, C. F., "The Ferroresonant Trigger Pair," *Trans. AIEE*, Communications and Electronics, No. 26, September 1956, pp. 407–416.

39. Gremer, C. E., "The Ferroelectric Resonant Trigger Pair," *Proc. Nat. Electronics Conf.*, 1955, **11**, pp. 828–838; also, *Trans. AIEE*, Communications and Electronics, No. 26, September 1956.

40. Spitzer, C. F., et al., "Nonlinear Resonant Trigger Circuits," Patent No. 2,723, 353, November 8, 1955.

41. Arborn, R. S., G. Phylip-Jones, "Ferroresonant Computing Circuits," *Wireless World (London)*, July 1956, pp. 324–330.

42. Electronic Design with Ferristors, Data File 110, Berkeley Division of Beckman Instruments, Inc., 2200 Wright Avenue, Richmond, Calif.

43. Johnson, L. J., C. E. Rauch, "Magnetic Frequency Multipliers," *Trans. AIEE*, Communications and Electronics, No. 15, November 1954, pp. 448–451.

44. Harriott, L. C., "Magnetic Frequency Conversion," *Proc. Nat. Electronics Conf.*, **9**, 1953, pp. 78–87.

45. Kerchner, R. M., G. F. Corcoran, *Alternating Current Circuits*, John Wiley and Sons, New York, 3rd ed., 1951, pp. 297–301.

46. Lawrence, R. R., *Principles of Alternating Current Machinery*, McGraw-Hill Book Company, New York, 3rd ed., 1940, pp. 277–307.

47. Smith, O. J. M., J. T. Salihi, "Analysis and Design of a Magnetic Frequency Multiplier," *Trans. AIEE*, Communications and Electronics, No. 17, March 1955, pp. 99–106.

48. Leonhard, W., "Characteristic Properties of a Magnetic Frequency Multiplier," Conference Paper No. 56–716, *AIEE, Summer General Meeting*, San Francisco, Calif., June 1956.
49. McMurray, W., "Magnetic Frequency Multipliers and Their Rating," Part I: Frequency Triplers, *Trans. AIEE*, Communications and Electronics, No. 26, September 1956, pp. 384–390; Part II: Frequency Sextuplers, *Trans. AIEE*, Communications and Electronics, No. 31, July 1957, pp. 289–293.
50. Stoker, J. J., *Nonlinear Vibrations*, Interscience Publishers, Inc., New York, 1950.
51. Spitzer, C. F., "Sustained Subharmonic Response in Nonlinear Series Circuits," *J. Appl. Phys.*, **16**, February 1945, pp. 105–111.
52. Terman, F. E., *Radio Engineers Handbook*, McGraw-Hill Book Company, New York, 1943, pp. 615–616.
53. Mannteuffel, E., and R. O. McCary, "Magnetic Voltage Reference," *Proc. Special Conf. Mag. Amp., AIEE*, 1956, pp. 200–210.

Chapter nine

# Digital Techniques
# Employing Square
# Loop Materials

## 9.0  Introduction

In the present chapter circuits are discussed which incorporate square-loop magnetic and ferroelectric (single-crystal) materials and which are designed for digital operation. They provide simple methods of obtaining many required functions, such as wave shaping, timing, gating, modulation, and information storage, which are used in computing, control, and communications systems.

Power gain is not the primary consideration in these devices but rather the utilization of the grossly nonlinear properties of the materials to effect the desired circuit operation. Frequently, however, these passive elements perform functions which heretofore have required active devices.

To date there has been a much greater application of square-loop magnetic materials in electronic equipment than square-loop ferroelectrics. Considered as two-terminal circuit elements, these devices are duals of each other. However, there is no dielectric dual of the transformer. Consequently, most digital circuitry employing single-crystal ferroelectrics has been more complicated than the analogous circuits using square-loop magnetic material (15, 19, 20). Furthermore, excellent magnetic materials (metallic tapes and ferrites) are available commercially, whereas the ferroelectrics are not. It has proved difficult to grow uniform single-crystal ferroelectrics in commercial quantities. On the other hand, many of the ferroelectric devices can be made smaller than their magnetic duals; also their fabrication can be simpler. Therefore, in each particular requirement both types of devices must be investigated.

## 9.1   Passive Binary Counter (1, 2)

The first class of devices to be considered is the digital counter. Counting requires essentially the addition and storage of discrete units of information. The many stable states of magnetization or polarization of square-loop materials provide an excellent means of accomplishing these functions in a passive manner. In particular, these materials are ideally suited for binary counting which requires only two identifiable stable states.

Figure 9.1 shows the circuit diagram of such a passive binary counter. It consists of a capacitor in series with a coil wound on a toroidal core of square-loop magnetic material. The input signal consists of uni-directional voltage pulses whose volt-time areas are all equal (see Figure 9.2a). The first pulse switches the core $L_1$ from state 1 to state 2 in Figure 9.2b. The voltage across the capacitor during this time interval ($t_1$ to $t_2$ in Figure 9.2a) is small. At the end of the pulse ($t_2$) the capacitor discharges through $L_1$ and $R_g$. However, the magnitude of this discharge current never exceeds the coercive current, and consequently there is no resetting of core flux. During the time interval of the next input signal the output is a relatively large voltage equal to the input minus the voltage across $R_g$. At the end of the second pulse the capacitor $C$ is charged to a value nearly equal to the input voltage. At the termination of the second pulse $C$ discharges through $L_1$ and the internal impedance of the input source $R_g$. This resets the core of $L_1$ to negative saturation in preparation for the next input pulse. Thus passive counting by two is accomplished. Without the capacitor a second source of energy is required to reset the core. In the present device, however, the energy is derived from the input signal itself.

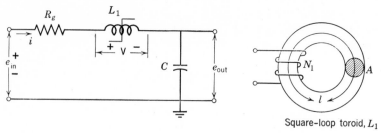

Square-loop toroid, $L_1$

**Figure 9.1.** Elementary passive counter. The symbol ⌐ indicates that the coil is wound on a core which has a square hysteresis loop.

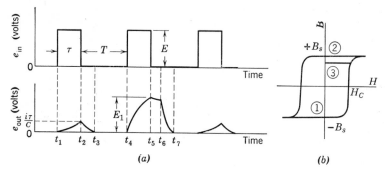

**Figure 9.2.** (*a*) Input and output of passive binary counter; (*b*) flux states in binary counter.

### 9.1.1 Design Parameters

The output voltage which results while switching the core from state 1 to state 2 in time $t_1$ to $t_3$ in Figure 9.2 represents an unwanted noise pulse. An essential figure-of-merit for this counter, as for any counter, is the ratio of the desired to the undesired output voltage or signal-to-noise ratio. This output noise voltage is determined by

1. The magnitude of the switching current.

2. Incomplete resetting. This allows the core to saturate before the termination of the next pulse.

3. Deviations of the material from the ideal square-loop character-istic.

Design criteria based on consideration of these factors may be established. Thus the volt-time area of the input pulses is adjusted so that the setting signal is sufficient to move the core only to point 3 in Figure 9.2*b* rather than to saturation. Over this vertical portion of the hysteresis loop the magnetizing current is small (and relatively constant), which limits the noise voltage. During this time interval $\tau$ the relationship between the applied voltage and the circuit current is given by the following equations: *

$$e = iR_g + \frac{1}{C} \int_0^\tau i \, dt + V \tag{9.1}$$

or

$$V = N_1 \frac{\Delta\phi}{\Delta t} = \frac{2N_1 A B_s K_1}{\tau}$$

$$V\tau = 2N_1 A B_s K_1 = N_1 \, \Delta\phi \text{ v-sec} \tag{9.2}$$

where $V$ is voltage across the winding $N_1$ in volts.

$i$ is the current in amperes during the switching. This can be obtained from the switching time data for the core (see Section 4.3.2).

$N_1$ is the number of turns on the core winding.

$A$ is the cross-sectional area of the core in square meters.

$B_s$ is the saturation flux density of the core in webers/square meter.

$K_1 = 0.7$ to $0.9$ for typical ferrite cores.

During the time $t_1$ to $t_2$ the output voltage, which is an unwanted noise voltage, is

$$e_0 = \frac{1}{C} \int_{t_1}^{t_2} i \, dt = \frac{1}{C} \int_0^\tau i \, dt \tag{9.3}$$

After the removal of the input voltage at time $t_2$, the small charge on the capacitor $C$ discharges through the core and $R_g$ during the time interval from $t_2$ to $t_3$. During this period the current must be less than that value which tends to reverse the magnetization of the core. In other words, the resistor $R_g$ must be large enough to limit the current to a value less than the d-c coercive current $I_c$. At time $t_2$ the voltage across the capacitor $C$ is from equation 9.3

$$e_0 = \frac{i\tau}{C} \tag{9.4}$$

where $i$ is considered as the average value of current during the time

* Rationalized MKS units are used in the equations in this chapter. However, much information is published in mixed systems of units. For complete tables of conversion of units the reader is referred to a standard text, e.g., *Electric Circuits*, M.I.T., Dept. of EE Staff (appendix C). Two useful relations are $H$ in ampere turns/meter $\times 4\pi(10)^{-3} = H$ in oersteds, $B$ in gauss $\times (10)^{-4} = B$ in webers/square meter.

$t_1$ to $t_2$. From $t_2$ to $t_3$ the current is limited only by $R_g$ if this current is less than $I_c$. This requires that

$$I_c > \frac{1}{R_g}\left(\frac{i\tau}{C}\right)$$

or

$$\frac{\tau}{R_gC} < \frac{I_c}{i} \tag{9.5}$$

When the next input voltage pulse is applied at $t_4$ the core is driven into saturation, and nearly all of the input signal appears across the capacitor because $R_g$ is small. During the interval $t_4$ to $t_5$ the capacitor charges to $E_1$, as shown in Figure 9.2. After the termination of the input pulse, the capacitor discharges through the core and $R_g$ from $t_5$ to $t_7$ before the occurrence of the next pulse. This opposite polarity current resets the core to negative saturation. Complete resetting is accomplished only if the energy stored in the capacitor is sufficient to supply the core losses and the loss in $R_g$. This requires that the following condition be satisfied:

$$\tfrac{1}{2}CE_1{}^2 \geq 2B_sH_c'lA + i_1{}^2R_gt' \tag{9.6}$$

where $E_1$ is the peak voltage across the capacitor at time $t_5$.

$i_1$ is the current during reset.

$H_c' = \dfrac{N_1i_1}{l}$ is the resetting field.

The magnitude of $i_1$ depends on the required resetting time ($t' = t_7 - t_6$).

Inequalities 9.5 and 9.6 and equation 9.2 determine the range of satisfactory circuit operation. Because the value of the field required to reverse the magnetization in the core is a function of the time of reversal, the currents appearing in inequalities 9.5 and 9.6 are different.

### 9.1.2 Noise Compensation

To improve the signal-to-noise ratio of this counter the circuit of Figure 9.3 is employed. The polarity and number of turns of the additional winding $N_2$ are adjusted so that no voltage appears across the capacitor $C$ while the core is being switched from negative to positive saturation. Under these conditions the following relationship must be satisfied:

$$N_2\frac{\Delta\phi}{\tau} + i_{C2}R = N_1\frac{\Delta\phi}{\tau} \tag{9.7}$$

Thus the switching current $i_{C2}$ flows through the winding $N_2$ rather than $N_1$ and the output capacitor $C$.

Furthermore, it is required that

$$(E - i_{C2}R_g) = N_1 \frac{\Delta\phi}{\tau} = 2N_1 \frac{AB_s}{\tau} K_1 \qquad (9.8)$$

Since it is again desired that the core should not quite reach positive saturation at the termination of the first pulse, $K_1$ is usually chosen approximately equal to 0.9. In addition, the value of the resistor $R$ should equal at least ten times $R_g$ in order that negligible current flows through winding $N_2$ during the reset period. Any current which does flow through $N_2$ during this time tends to oppose the resetting action. In order to permit complete resetting, it is necessary to satisfy an equation similar to equation 9.6, i.e., sufficient energy must be stored in the capacitor.

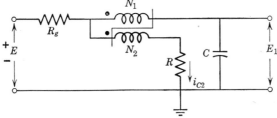

Figure 9.3.  Passive counter with improved signal-to-noise ratio.

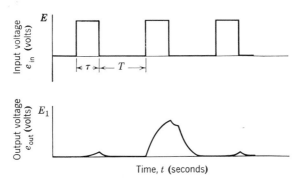

Figure 9.4.  Input and output of improved binary counter.

The output wave shown in Figure 9.4 for a properly designed compensated circuit utilizing ferrite cores has a signal-to-noise ratio of 30 to 40 db.  An uncompensated counter normally has only a 10 to 15 db signal-to-noise ratio.  This improved performance has been gained at the expense of the energy dissipated in the resistor $R$.

Another method for reducing the output noise voltage is discussed in the next section.

## 9.2    Counter of Arbitrary Order

If the minor hysteresis loops of the magnetic material are sufficiently square,* the devices shown in Figures 9.1 and 9.3 can be made to count to a base other than two.   In fact, by controlling the volt-time area of the input pulses to a prescribed fraction of the total saturation-to-saturation flux density of the core counting to an arbitrary base is obtained.   The required fixed volt-time area can be obtained from an arbitrarily shaped pulse by using a buffer transformer having a square loop core, as shown in Figure 9.5.

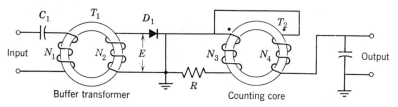

**Figure 9.5.**   Reliable passive counter (arbitrary base).

The volt-time area of every input pulse must be large enough to saturate this buffer core $(T_1)$ and must also store sufficient charge on $C_1$ to reset the core $T_1$ to negative saturation.   The resetting must be accomplished between input pulses.   This procedure gives a constant volt-time area output pulse from $T_1$.   Furthermore, if $T_1$ and $T_2$ are identical, effects of environmental changes on both cores are the same, and the accuracy of the counter is not affected by these changes.   The diode $D_1$ isolates $T_2$ from $T_1$ during the reset time of transformer $T_1$. Because of diode $D_1$ the resetting current of transformer $T_2$ must flow through winding $N_3$.

If it is desired to count in steps of $(n + 1)$ using identical cores, the voltage output of $T_1$ should be a pulse of amplitude $E$ and duration $\Delta t$ such that

$$E = N_2 \left(\frac{2B_sA}{\Delta t}\right) = \frac{1}{n} N_3 \left(\frac{2B_sA}{\Delta t}\right) + iR + V_{D1}$$

or

$$N_3 = nN_2 - \frac{\Delta t}{2B_sA}(iR + V_{D1}) \tag{9.9}$$

where $i$ is the current in $N_3$ when the pulses $E$ are present.

Although it is satisfactory to assume a fixed average switching current in the design of the binary counter, this assumption results in an un-

* See Section 4.4.

reliable counter which has a poor signal-to-noise ratio when the magnetization of the core is reversed in several discrete steps. This is caused by the curvature of the vertical portion of the hysteresis loop, which requires a different value of switching current $i$ in equation 9.9 for each succeeding change in the state of magnetization. This varying current produces a variable voltage across diode $D_1$ and resistor $R$. Consequently, for a fixed input ($E\ \Delta t$) the flux change in the core $T_2$ is not constant. Furthermore, the noise voltage cannot be eliminated uniformly throughout the counting cycle using the circuit configuration in Figure 9.5.

A more satisfactory method for improving the signal-to-noise ratio in a counter of arbitrary order is shown in Figure 9.6. When the core is

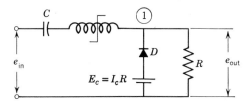

Figure 9.6. Improved digital counter.

not counting, the current through $R$ and diode $D$ is approximately equal to the largest value of switching current. If a positive pulse is applied at the input, the switching current now flows through $R$ and the core, since point 1 is slightly positive and diode $D$ does not conduct. Hence during the counting process the voltage at point 1 remains relatively constant. As the core goes into saturation, the voltage at point 1 rises to a large positive value, and the reset capacitor $C$ charges as in the previous counter. The increased signal-to-noise ratio has been obtained at the expense of a greater power requirement from generator $e_{in}$ and voltage source $E_c$.

## 9.3 Cascaded Counters

Direct coupling of several stages of the passive counter described does not result in a satisfactory composite counter. This can be seen by examining the circuit diagram for a two-stage passive counter shown in Figure 9.7. The case in which each stage is a binary counter is considered. If each stage of the circuit in Figure 9.7 functions the same way as the single-stage counter shown in Figure 9.3, $C_2$ must reset $T_2$ to a state of negative saturation at the same time that $C_1$ resets

$T_1$. Under these conditions the voltage across $T_2$ is the difference between the two capacitor voltages, i.e., $V_{T2} = V_{C2} - V_{C1}$. Since the two counters are identical, this value of $V_{T2}$ is too small to reset $T_2$.

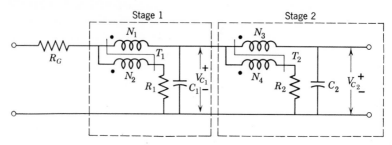

**Figure 9.7.** Two-stage passive counter.

The circuit parameters can be adjusted to allow satisfactory counting by four, but the performance is no better than a single-stage scale-of-four counter described in Section 9.2. Consequently, in practice, if two or more stages are cascaded, an additional source of energy is provided to reset the core. This also provides a method of regenerating the signal pulse which is propagated in the forward direction.

One method of accomplishing this is shown in Figure 9.8. In addition, the features of the circuits shown in Figures 9.3 and 9.5 have been in-

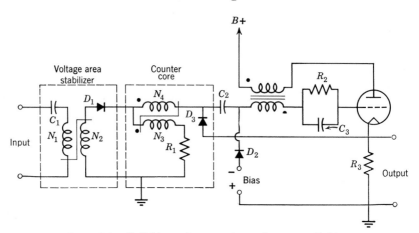

**Figure 9.8.** Reliable random counter or frequency divider.

corporated into this circuit. The output of the circuit labeled "voltage-area stabilizer" supplies unidirectional pulses of fixed volt-time area to the input of the counter core. These voltage pulses appear across $N_4$ until the counter core saturates. During saturation the output of the "voltage-area stabilizer" triggers the monostable blocking oscillator which comprises the remainder of the circuit. An output voltage is available across $R_3$, and the counter core is reset to negative saturation through $D_3$. Capacitor $C_2$ provides d-c isolation for the grid bias supply, and $R_2 - C_3$ prevents spurious high-frequency triggering of the blocking oscillator.

Figure 9.9 shows a reliable digital counter which uses a single transformer and fewer components than the one previously discussed and possesses additional desirable characteristics.

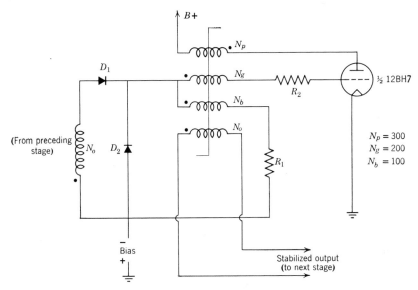

**Figure 9.9.** Single transformer random digital counter.

The stabilizing, counting, and regenerating functions performed by three separate transformers in Figure 9.8 can be performed by one transformer. The result is a simplified random-pulse counting circuit. Any arbitrary number of stages, counting by arbitrary integers, can be cascaded without degradation of information. Four separate windings are used: $N_p$ and $N_g$ provide regenerative action; $N_g$ and $N_b$ provide the counting action; and $N_0$ provides stabilized output pulses for the next stage. If transformers are identical from stage to stage, the ratio $N_o/N_g$ determines the integer by which the succeeding stage counts. Diode $D_1$ isolates negative pulses from the preceeding stage, and $D_2$ prevents grid current from reflecting back into this stage.

Nearly any value of plate supply voltage can be combined with nearly any commercial triode tube for a given transformer, and the count is not altered. Up to a scale of ten or so per stage, this counter has proved to be at least as stable as well-designed multivibrator binary chains. Typical design values are shown in Figure 9.9.

Figure 9.10 shows plate and grid waveforms.

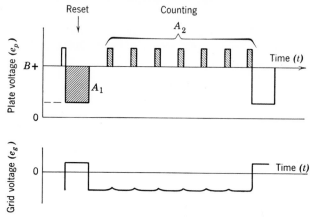

Figure 9.10. Plate and grid voltage waveforms (counting by seven). *Note:* $A_1 = A_2$.

## 9.4 Tachometer or Frequency Meter

An electronic tachometer can be constructed which utilizes the principles discussed in the previous sections. If unidirectional constant volt-time area pulses are fed into an integrator network, the d-c voltage output is proportional to the rate at which the pulses are generated. An embodiment of this principle is shown in Figure 9.11. The arbitrary

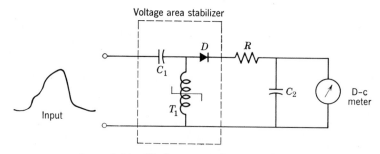

Figure 9.11. Tachometer or frequency meter.

input waveforms are shaped by core $T_1$ which produces the constant volt-time area pulses. Capacitor $C_1$ resets the core as in the previous circuits.

This type of circuit is useful in systems which produce output voltages whose frequency is proportional to speed, e.g., the distributor on a gasoline engine.  Under such conditions the speed of rotation can be determined by using an electrical connection only and not requiring mechanical coupling to a rotating shaft.

## 9.5   Nonlinear Stabilization of a Multivibrator

The nonlinear characteristic of magnetic materials can be used to improve the timing stability of multivibrators.  In a conventional circuit

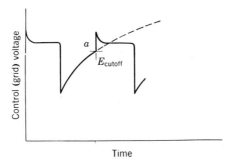

**Figure 9.12.**   Conventional timing waveform applied to grid of multivibrator.

the "off" tube of a multivibrator is turned on by an exponentially varying voltage applied to its grid (Figure 9.12).  The timing accuracy of the multivibrator is partially determined by the slope of the exponential curve at point $a$, the cutoff voltage of the tube.  In particular, the

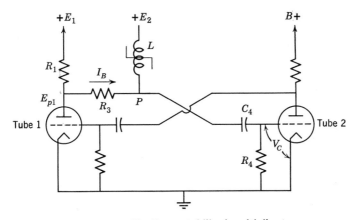

**Figure 9.13.**   Nonlinear stabilized multivibrator.

difficulty of maintaining timing accuracy is accentuated when the exponential curve has a long duration. One method of overcoming this is that of returning the grid to a high potential so that use is made of the steepest portion of the control curve. Another method uses a square-loop core $L$ as the timing element, as shown in Figure 9.13.

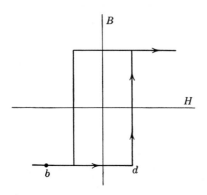

If tube 1 is in the "off" condition, a biasing current $I_b$ flows through the core so that its operating point is at $b$ (Figure 9.14). This occurs if $E_1 > E_2$ in Figure 9.13. When the grid of tube 1 reaches the conduction point the current through the core begins to decrease to zero and reaches some value $I_c$ (point $d$ in Figure 9.14). This current tends to remain constant while the core is switching. The waveforms at the plate of tube 1 ($E_{P1}$) and at point $P$ (Figure 9.13),

**Figure 9.14.** Flux states of timing reactor.

which is essentially the grid voltage of tube 2 since the $R_4 - C_4$ time constant is very large, are shown in Figure 9.15. Since the current $I_b$ cannot change instantaneously, the voltage at point $P$ drops below $E_{P1}$ by an amount $I_b R_3$. As the core current decreases and reverses direction ($b - d$, Figure 9.14), the grid voltage of tube 2, $V_C$, increases in the time

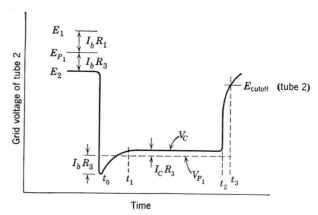

**Figure 9.15.** Timing waveform of nonlinear multivibrator (see Figures 9.13 and 9.14).

interval $t_0 - t_1$ (Figure 9.15) but then remains at a large negative value from $t_1$ to $t_2$. At $t_2$ the core saturates, the grid voltage rises very rapidly, and the intersection with $E_{cutoff}$ of tube 2 is extremely sharp. The slope at this point is a function of the rounding of the inner corner of the hysteresis loop as the core begins to saturate.

In a practical circuit utilizing square-loop ferrites it was possible to obtain a timing interval of 50 $\mu$sec with a 250-v supply. The slope of the timing waveform was 8v/ $\mu$sec. To achieve a comparable slope with a conventional $R$-$C$ circuit, it would be necessary to have the timing resistor returned to a 1000-v supply and a 500-v plate drop.

## 9.6 Memory Matrices (3, 4)

### 9.6.1 Introduction

One of the important subsystems of any computer is its memory, or storage function. During the various stages of the computation procedure it is necessary either to store temporarily computed results for use in later calculations or to store permanently information which must be referred to over long periods of time. Among the many physical possibilities which are available to perform these storage functions a few examples are magnetic tape, rotating magnetic drum, photographic film, recirculating delay lines, and thin magnetic films (6, 7). The degree to which each of these techniques adequately fulfills the memory function depends on its ability to meet the conflicting requirements of a modern computer. This conflict arises from the demands for larger capacity memories and higher speeds of operation.

Since most computers store information in binary form, each bit has a definite location in space. Hence, although it may be possible to store a high volume density of information in a given medium, the problem becomes essentially one of locating exactly where a particular bit is stored. Photographic film whose resolving power is of the order of 100 to 300 lines/mm is a good example of a high density storage medium which is deficient because of the difficulty of quickly and accurately locating a point on the film.

Besides the problems of access time to the storage system, an additional requirement of a good storage medium is that it be passive and reuseable. In other words, the maintenance of the information should not depend on the power source. In the event of power failure it would be costly and time consuming to replenish the original information.

### 9.6.2 Magnetic Core Memory

Of the many types of memory which have been tried, the use of magnetic cores has been the most successful at present for large-capacity, high-speed systems. The square-loop properties of these cores, particularly the ferrites, are admirably suited for this type of application. The binary information resides in the two stable states of magnetization of the cores. Furthermore, the existence of a coercive force allows the use of a threshold signal required for matrix operation. In addition, its switching time between the two states is of the order of a microsecond.

The basic method is illustrated in Figure 9.16 (8).* A square array

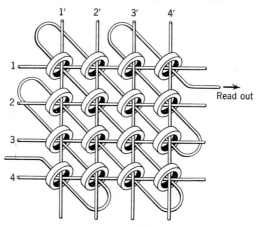

**Figure 9.16.** Basic ferrite toroid memory matrix. (Courtesy of *Proc. I.R.E.*)

of magnetic cores is arranged so that each one is threaded by three leads. The horizontal and vertical wires are used to set information into the core and to "interrogate" the core. The third lead which interweaves the matrix is used to read out information from the matrix. The idealized $B$-$H$ loop for each core is shown in Figure 9.17. The negative saturation state $(N)$ corresponds arbitrarily to a "zero"; the positive saturation state $(P)$ corresponds to a "one." In order to select a particular core in the matrix, it is merely necessary to excite the corresponding vertical and horizontal leads which intersect at the desired point. If a current corresponding to $+H_d/2 < H_c$ is placed on lines 3

---

* At the present writing new magnetic memory planes have been announced by RCA and Bell Telephone Laboratories which consist of sheets of ferrite perforated by many small holes. Part of the wiring of the system is accomplished through printed circuit techniques.

and 3', for example, none of the cores can change state except the one which is at the intersection point. Thus, if all the cores were originally in the $N$-state, core 3–3' will switch from $N$ to $P$. This is the procedure for reading in a "one." Conversely, in order to read out the information stored in a core, currents corresponding to $(-H_d/2)$ are applied to the selected lines. Again only the core at the intersecting point will receive a drive equal to $H_d$. If the core were in an $N$-state, there would be no change in flux. However, if the core had been in a $P$-state, the core would be reset to the $N$-state. The resultant output voltage would be picked up on the read-out winding which threads every core in the matrix.

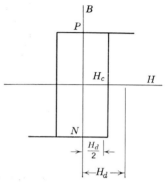

Figure 9.17. Magnetization cycle of memory core.

It should be noted that this method destroys the information stored in the core. Hence, if a "one" is stored, it is necessary to follow the read-out pulse with a positive current drive to reset the core from $N$ back to $P$. This, of course, is a time-consuming procedure. A great amount of effort has been concentrated on the problem of nondestructive sensing of the core. This is discussed in a later section.

### 9.6.3  Switching Matrix

This relatively simple process can be continued to incorporate a million-bit memory. However, it must be remembered that a separate driver is required for each line. Hence a $(10)^6$ matrix would require $2 \times (10)^3$ driving tubes. This is a prohibitively large number of tubes just for the memory function. The required number of sources can be considerably reduced by employing additional matrices for the selection process.

Figure 9.18 shows a $9 \times 9$ memory matrix driven by two $3 \times 3$ switching matrices. Each core of the latter matrix contains four windings, two of which are the usual horizontal and vertical selection wires. A third bias winding interlaces each core. The fourth winding is the output winding which drives all the cores in one row or column of the *memory* matrix. Hence each core of the switching matrix is being used as a transformer. For an $n \times n$ memory matrix there are two switching matrices each of size $\sqrt{n} \times \sqrt{n}$. Therefore, the total number of

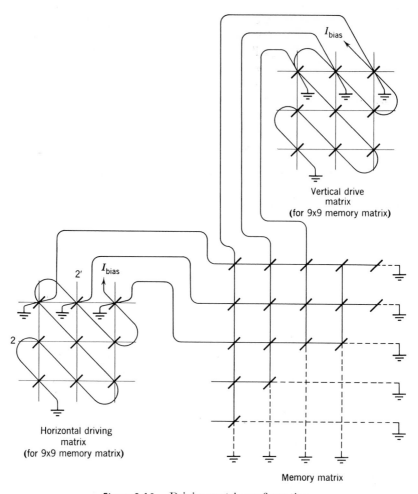

**Figure 9.18.** Driving matrix configuration.

driving sources is $4\sqrt{n}$ as compared to $2n$ for the original matrix. It should be noted that 4 instead of 2 sets of drive currents are required in order to select a given memory core under the new conditions.

It is rather interesting to follow the sequence of pulses through the switching matrix in order to set information into the memory. The difference in operation between the two types of matrix lies in the fact that the switching matrix need not store information but must always be ready to deliver a current pulse to the memory. Each core of the switching matrix is biased to point 1, Figure 9.19. Thus all the cores in the switching matrix are in the same state. The only requirement on the drive currents supplied on lines 2 and 2′, for example, is that the output current in the secondary of core 2–2′ is $H_d/2$. The coincident drive pulses overcome the bias and apply a driving $H$ corresponding to point 3 (Figure 9.19). The d-c bias resets each core after the removal of the drive pulses and produces a negative output current equal $H_d/2$.

It is assumed that the polarity of the output current is such as to drive the selected memory core from the $N$- to $P$-state. Hence to set the memory core to the $N$-state it is necessary to apply the simultaneous output currents from the switching matrix, as shown in Figure 9.20.

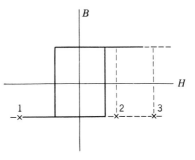

Figure 9.19. States of magnetization of cores in driving matrices.

At time $t_1$ the memory core is switched to the $P$-state. After time $t_2$ the output pulses from the two switching matrices due to the d-c bias, return the memory core to the $N$-state. The same result occurs if the memory core was originally in the $P$-state.

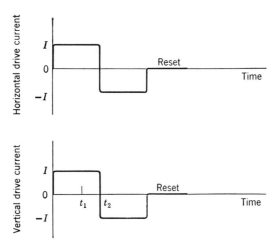

Figure 9.20. Drive currents for writing 0. Current $I$ produces $H_d/2$ in the output windings of the driver matrices. Note that bias current is not shown.

However, to set a memory core to the $P$-state requires a slightly different procedure. At time $t_1$ the drive currents to one of the switching matrices is removed, resulting in a reset current during time $t_1$ to $t_2$ (Figure 9.21). The memory core remains in the $P$-state during $t_1$ to

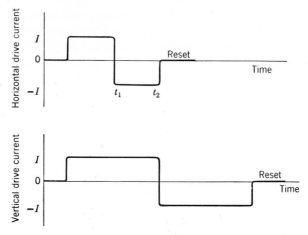

**Figure 9.21.** Drive currents for writing 1. The current $I$ produces $H_d/2$ in the output windings of the drivers. Note that the bias current is not shown.

$t_2$, since the net $H$ on the core is zero. After $t_2$ the reset pulse produces a current proportional only to $-H_d/2$. Hence the selected memory core remains at $P$.

### 9.6.4 Noise Problems

If one excludes the circuitry involved in driving the matrices, the major difficulties in the operation of these memories are due to the noise produced by the departure of ferrites from ideal squareness. A more typical loop is shown in Figure 9.22. The slope of the $B$-$H$ curve in the saturated region produces a noise pulse during read out upon application of $H_d/2$ in all the unselected cores of a given row and column. A measure of this slope is the squareness ratio for the core which is defined as $B_r/B_m$ (Figure 9.22), where $B_r$ is the remanent flux density after the application of pulses of $H_d$, followed by several pulses of $-H_d/2$. Hence this type of noise is first minimized by the proper choice of core material (squareness ratios of approximately 0.9 are possible). Further

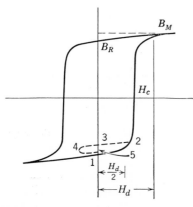

**Figure 9.22.** Hysteresis loop of memory core.

noise reduction is accomplished by threading the read-out winding through the matrix, as shown in Figure 9.16. Since all the cores in a given row and column are driven in the same direction, all the noise pulses tend to cancel except those from two cores. The total decrease in noise is thus a function of the similarity of all the cores. Advantage can also be taken of the fact that the noise pulses are of shorter

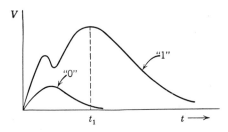

Figure 9.23.   Memory-matrix voltage output.

duration than the desired pulse (Figure 9.23). If the read-out winding is sampled at time $t_1$ in Figure 9.23, the signal-to-noise ratio is further increased.

### 9.6.5   Magnitude of Driving Current

The value of $H_d$ that is chosen for a given core is determined by two factors. Since it is desirable to switch the core in the minimum time, $H_d$ should be very large. However, since the squareness ratio as defined above should be close to unity, we use the switching time that corresponds to the maximum squareness ratio. Since the switching time is inversely proportional to $(H_d - H_c)$ and $H_d/2$ is slightly less than $H_c$, the difference $(H_d - H_c)$ increases for cores with larger $H_c$ and the switching time decreases. This usually results in large driving currents. At the present time most commercially available ferrite cores have been designed for memory-matrix application. However, for other square-loop applications in which the above restrictions on the driving fields are not applicable it would be desirable to have cores with smaller values of $H_c$.

One further restriction on $H_d$ is that successive applications of $H_d/2$ should not demagnetize the core, e.g., operation from 1–2–3 (Figure 9.22.). This problem is minimized in the case in which the memory matrix is driven by another core matrix. For the read-in method described, the reset current moves the core from 3–4–5, which leaves the core in a state of greater magnetization.

### 9.6.6 Magnetic Thin-Film Matrices (9, 10)

The magnetic core memories which were discussed in the previous sections are limited in two important aspects. If the total number of cores in the memory is large, the expense of threading each of the cores is appreciable. In addition, the present ferrite cores are limited to a switching speed of approximately 1 μsec when operated in the coincident current mode. Both of these objections can be overcome when the ferrite toroid is replaced by a thin magnetic metal-alloy film. As pointed out in Section 4.2.6, the thin film can be switched in as short a time as 20 mμsec. Furthermore, the thin-film geometry lends itself more suitably to printed circuit techniques for the entire matrix.

The operation of a thin-film memory is analogous to the ferrite-core memory except for the fact that the switching mechanism in the film is a much more rapid process. However, the minimum switching time of 20 mμsec is attainable only with pulses whose rise times are of the order of 1 mμsec. With rise times of this order of magnitude no domain walls are formed, and the switching process occurs almost entirely by rotation. More practical thin-film memories have been constructed whose switching speeds are in the range of 0.1 to 0.5 μsec.

Figure 9.24 is a schematic representation of one mode of operation. The thin films are deposited simultaneously on a glass substrate either

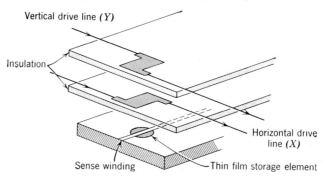

**Figure 9.24.** Magnetic thin-film memory element.

by vacuum evaporation or electrodeposition. The drive windings are printed or deposited in the form of thin, broad conductors. In this arrangement the $X$ and $Y$ conductors produce magnetic fields which are parallel to the easy direction of magnetization. A sense winding threads the memory in a manner similar to that of the ferrite memory.

Figure 9.25 represents another form of the same memory in which the $X$-drive line produces a magnetic field at right angles to the easy direction of magnetization. The $Y$-drive produces a magnetic field parallel to the easy direction. In this manner the irreversible switching proceeds primarily by a very rapid rotation process.

The size of the thin film is determined by several competing factors. A thicker film would produce a large output voltage. However, the long dimension of the film would have to be increased in order to minimize the demagnetization effect. A reasonable compromise appears to be a circular film approximately 0.4 cm in diameter and having a thickness

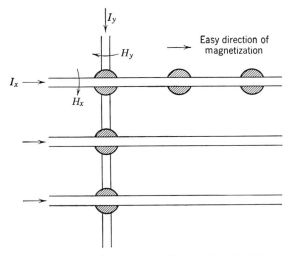

**Figure 9.25.** Thin-film matrix utilizing 180° and 90° fields.

of approximately 2000 A. Under these conditions an output voltage of about 4 mv is obtained with a switching time of 0.5 $\mu$sec ($H_c \approx$ 1oe).

The thin-film matrix appears to be one of the most promising techniques for high-speed memories. It should also be noted that the small volume of material involved and its large surface-to-volume ratio permit high-speed operation with very little heating of the element.

### 9.6.7  Twistor (11)

In the search for other memory configurations relative simplicity in the fabrication of the array has been one of the significant aspects in the evaluation of new matrices. Another illustration of this trend is exhibited in the "twistor" matrix which is comprised of interwoven wires. One set of wires (either the horizontal or vertical set) is composed of a Ni-Fe alloy which possesses a rectangular hysteresis loop. In addition, the magnetic material is magnetostrictive. This latter feature is distinctive in that most square-loop magnetic materials are designed to have almost zero magnetostriction.

As a result of the negative magnetostrictive coefficient, the easy direction of magnetization is along an axis which is determined by the direction of an applied strain. Figure 9.26 illustrates a small segment of the wire to which a torsional twist has been applied. The easy direc-

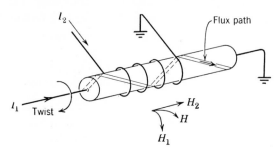

Figure 9.26. Coincident currents for "write" operation in a "twistor" with wire under torsion. (Courtesy of *BSTJ*.)

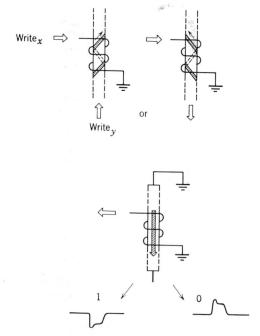

Figure 9.27. Read-write cycle for a twistor element when wire is not under torsion. (Courtesy of *BSTJ*.)

tion of magnetization is thus a helix of the same sense as the applied torsion. If a helical magnetic field is applied to the wire, the magnetization can be switched from one stable state along the helix to the second state which is oriented 180° along the same helix. This mode of operation is illustrated in Figure 9.26 where the helical magnetic field is produced by the combination of an axial field ($H_2$) and a solenoidal field ($H_1$).

Another mode of operation is illustrated in Figure 9.27 in which the wire is not under torsion. Therefore, the magnetization can be switched to either a right-hand or left-hand helix, depending on the direction of the coincident fields.

One read-out procedure for the first mode of operation is to reverse the sense of both coincident currents. The output voltage pulse would appear across the ends of the wire. For the second mode a coincident current need not be used for reading. A current applied only to the solenoidal coil will switch the magnetization from the helical direction to the longitudinal direction and will result in an output pulse across the nickel-iron wire.

A memory array constructed with the twistor mode was capable of switching times of the order of 1 $\mu$sec with drive currents of 2.3 ampere-turns on the solenoid and 130 ma through the magnetic wire. It is also possible to replace the solenoid coil with a single drive wire lying perpendicular to the magnetic wire.

### 9.6.8 Superconducting Memory Devices (12, 13, 14, 15)

The unique properties of superconductors have been utilized to construct passive bistable devices suitable for use in memory matrices. To date, twenty-one of the elements, in addition to many alloys and compounds, have been reported to exhibit properties of superconductivity. To understand the operation of the memory devices the following characteristics of superconductors should be recalled:

1. There is a transition temperature for each superconductor above which it exhibits a normal electrical resistivity and below which its electrical resistivity is identically zero. This latter property permits a current to flow in a closed coil for an indefinite period of time after the current has been established. The existence of this stable state forms the basis of a memory system.

2. Furthermore, this transition temperature is a function of the applied magnetic field. The characteristics of several elements are shown in Figure 9.28.

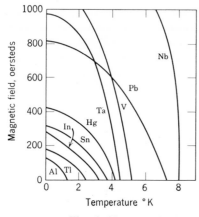
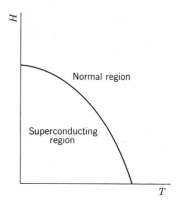

Temperature ° K

**Figure 9.28.** Threshold magnetic field versus temperature for several supercon-ductors. For a given element the area below the threshold curve represents the superconducting region as indicated by the general characteristic shown on the right.

3. In the superconducting state these materials are perfect diamag-netic materials ($\mu = 0$), i.e., the magnetic flux density $B$ inside super-conductors is identically zero. Although this property has been demon-strated experimentally, it gives rise to some unresolved questions about the exact behavior of superconductors (13).

In one application to computer logic the normally conducting and superconducting states are used as the two stable states of a binary logic element (31). However, in the memory application a different mode of operation is used. To illustrate this mode, consider the coil system of Figure 9.29 in which coil 2 is a superconductor, whereas coil 1 may be an ordinary conductor. If an increasing current $I_1$, as shown in Figure 9.30, is applied to coil 1, a current $I_2$ flows in coil 2 to maintain the flux density linking coil 2 equal to zero; since $\int E \cdot dl = 0$ around coil 2. At time $t_1$ the critical value of magnetic field is reached in coil 2, and it becomes a normal conductor. Under this condition there can be a change in flux linking coil 2, and the two loops are coupled magnet-ically, as in normal transformer action. The value of magnetic field drops at the surface of coil 2, which causes it to tend to return to its

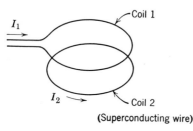

(Superconducting wire)

**Figure 9.29.** Experimental supercon-ducting device.

superconducting state. However, its temperature rises because the heat dissipation of current flowing in a normal conductor causes it to tend to remain in its normal conducting state. The predominant effect in a particular case is determined by the electrical and thermal time constants, the geometry, and the magnitudes of the currents. For example,

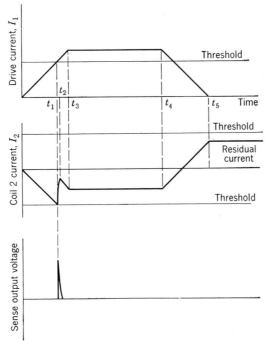

Figure 9.30. Waveforms of drive current, induced current, and sense voltage of experimental superconducting memory cell.

at time $t_1$ the current $I_2$ decreases much faster than $I_1$ increases, and the net magnetic field at coil 2 decreases. There is insufficient time in the interval $(t_1-t_2)$ for appreciable heating, and at $t_2$ coil 2 again becomes superconducting. At $t_3$ the current $I_1$ no longer increases; consequently $I_2$ remains constant, since coil 2 is still in its superconducting state. The current $I_1$ begins to decrease at $t_4$, and again this induces a change in current $I_2$. Note that the critical field is not attained in time interval $(t_4-t_5)$. When $I_1$ returns to zero there is a residual current flowing in superconducting coil 2. If the direction of $I_1$ is reversed in this example, a residual current of opposite polarity is stored in coil 2. These two stable states provide means for storing binary information.

It is interesting to compare the nature of the storage medium of the ferrite-core memory of Subsection 9.6.2 with that of the superconductor memory. In the former case the information is retained by the magnetization in the ferromagnetic core. In Chapter 1 (Section 1.18) it was pointed out that the same flux density could be established by an equivalent amperian solenoidal current around the toroid surface. In the superconducting case the information is stored by a circulating current which produces a magnetic field or "trapped flux" while the coil is in the superconducting state.

When coil 2 becomes normally conducting there is a change in the magnitude of the flux linking it. This results in an induced voltage which can be sensed (Figure 9.30). The pulse width of the voltage may be of the order of a few millimicroseconds. It should be noted that this pulse width is independent of the slope of leading edge of the drive current over a wide range of slopes. This differs from the other magnetic core memories in which the switching time is a function of the slope of the driving pulses for very fast switching times.

An elementary model of an experimental memory cell is shown in Figure 9.31a. Coil 2 is replaced by the crossbar which is electrically

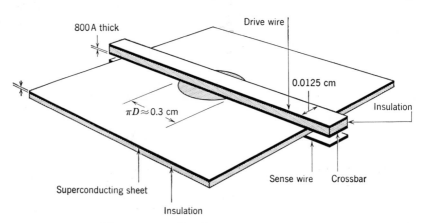

**Figure 9.31a.** Memory test cell. (Courtesy *I.B.M. Jour. of Res. and Dev.*)

connected to the superconducting sheet. However, the thickness of the cross bar is less than that of the superconducting sheet, so that the critical field for the crossbar is smaller than the critical field for the sheet. Hence during the operation of the memory cell the crossbar alone is driven in and out of the superconducting state. The memory array is formed by evaporating a layer of lead to form the sheet which contains the holes, and then a thinner layer of lead is evaporated across the holes to form the crossbars. Two drive wires are placed over the crossbar to allow for coincident current operation of the matrix. A sense wire is placed parallel to the drive wires but located beneath the superconducting sheet.

All of the memory elements are placed initially in the "zero" state, and then "write" currents of the opposite polarity insert a "one" (Figure 9.31b). In order to sense the state of a particular cell, the cross-

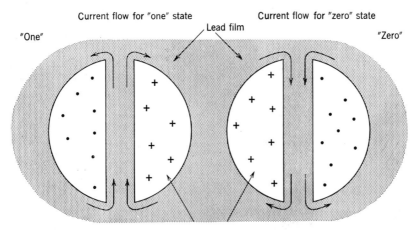

Figure 9.31b. Stable states of memory cell. (*Courtesy I.B.M. Jour. of Res. and Dev.*)

bar is driven into its normally conducting state (destructive read out). The sense wire, which had been magnetically shielded from the driven wires by the superconducting crossbar, will then have an induced voltage. The polarity is determined by the direction of the stored current in the memory cell. In addition, the shielding effect of the crossbar reduces the half-select noise pulses to zero. For the ferrite memory matrix the reduction of the noise pulses is obtained through careful selection of the ferrite cores.

Switching speeds of approximately 0.01 $\mu$sec have been reported in this type of an area with drive currents of approximately 150 ma.

### 9.6.9 Dielectric Memory Matrix (5, 16, 17)

Voltage-coincident memory matrices composed of single-crystal ferroelectric elements which are analogous to the current-coincident magnetic memory matrices have been constructed. A simple schematic diagram of such a matrix is shown in Figure 9.32a. If one of the ferroelectric crystals is at a remanent state of polarization, shown as point $a$ on the hysteresis loop in Figure 9.32b, the coincident "write" voltages applied as indicated change the state of polarization to point $b$.* There is a net change in polarization of $2\,P_R$, but no voltage appears across read-out resistor $R$ because of diode $D$. If the "read" voltages shown in

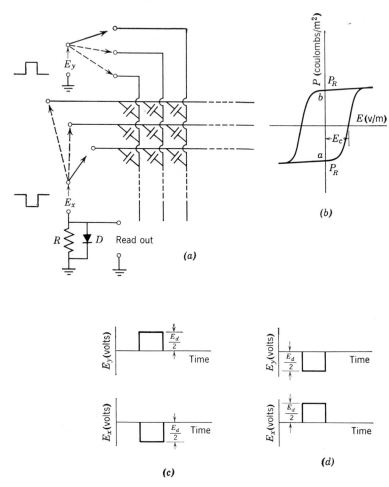

Figure 9.32. Ferroelectric memory matrix: ($a$) memory matrix; ($b$) ferroelectric hysteresis loop; ($c$) write "one" voltages; ($d$) read voltages.

Figure 9.32$d$ are applied to the terminals of the same storage cell, the polarization is returned to point $a$, and a voltage appears across $R$ indicating that a "one" has been stored. However, if the state of polarization was at point $a$, which corresponds to "zero" when the "read" voltages were applied, very little voltage would appear across $R$. The

* Switching data for barium titanate is given in Section 4.9 (Figure 4.28).

wave shapes of the voltages are the same as in the case of the magnetic memory matrix shown in Figure 9.23.

In a practical dielectric memory matrix there are problems in addition to those encountered in the magnetic matrix. First of all, the information cannot be read out by a single wire which threads the entire matrix. The schematic switch shown in Figure 9.32a must be bilateral so that the current through each switch can flow through the common resistor $R(5)$. Another read-out method is illustrated in Figure 9.33 (17). Here all the column drive leads thread a magnetic toroid on which there is a read-out winding. The current in a vertical drive lead which results from a change in polarization of one of the cells induces a voltage in the read-out winding. The diode in the output circuit eliminates the induced voltage during writing cycle.

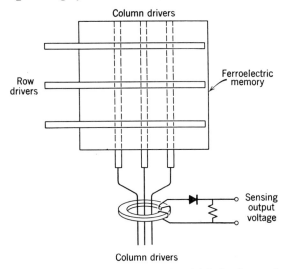

**Figure 9.33.** Dielectric memory matrix with inductive read out.

When applying the field $E_d$ to one memory cell at the intersection of a row and a column, the field $E_d/2$ is applied to every other element in the particular row and column. In addition to the noise problems similar to those discussed in the magnetic case, there is a problem peculiar to single-crystal barium titanate which is the ferroelectric currently used in these memory matrices. It has been pointed out (19, 20) that although barium titanate displays a square dynamic hystersis loop below its Curie temperature, applied voltages less than the coercive voltage will tend to depolarize a crystal.* In fact, in one particular

* This undesirable characteristic appears to have been eliminated in a new ferroelectric material called triglycine sulfate.

memory matrix (5) after one thousand half-voltage pulses the remanent charge was reduced approximately 50 per cent.

Advantages of this type of memory include ease of fabrication and high storage density. It is estimated that one square inch can accommodate 2500 bits. For a crystal only a few thousandths of an inch thick less than ten volts is required for the switching voltage. Also the current resulting from the polarization reversal of a cell is only a few milliamperes.

## 9.7 Transfluxor (21, 22)

Among the several applications of magnetic square-loop material that have been discussed the geometric configuration has been the same in every case. The toroidal form with an inner-to-outer diameter ratio close to unity has been preferred. With this dimensional ratio the magnetic field $H$ across the cross section differs by a small amount from the average field. However, certain desireable characteristics can be obtained by proper variations of the core geometry. A class of magnetic devices known as "transfluxors" has been devised in which the magnetic field varies considerably in magnitude across the core. One aim of this device is to develop a simple method for nondestructive read out of saturated cores. Though there are many applications of this principle, our discussion is limited to the basic mechanism underlying the simple transfluxor arrangement (21).

Figure 9.34 is a schematic of a two-holed ferrite core whose composition is similar to that used in other square-loop applications. The larger

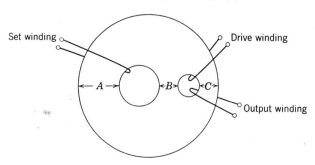

**Figure 9.34.** Two-holed transfluxor.

hole is offset from the center so that the cross-sectional area $A$ is at least equal to the sum of the areas $B$ and $C$. The ratio of the diameter of the larger hole to the outside diameter of the entire core is chosen small enough so that the field produced by a current in the set winding varies appreciably across the diameter of the core.

The over-all operation of the device can be described in a simplified form. A positive current pulse through the set winding is of sufficient magnitude to saturate legs $B$ and $C$. Leg $A$ may or may not be saturated, depending upon the width of leg $A$. Figure 9.35$a$ is a representation of the resultant magnetization in the core after the termination of the set current. If a current pulse is applied to the drive winding, the field

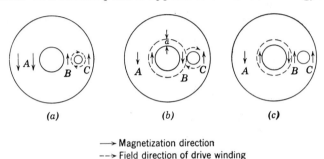

(a)     (b)     (c)

——→ Magnetization direction
--→ Field direction of drive winding

**Figure 9.35.** States of magnetization of the transfluxor: ($a$) blocked; ($b$) unblocked; ($c$) partially blocked.

produced tends to drive leg $B$ further into saturation and at the same time tends to decrease the magnetization in leg $C$. Under these conditions (with the magnitude of the drive current small) there is a very small change of magnetization around the small hole and therefore a very small signal in the output winding. This is known as the "blocked" condition of the core.

A negative current pulse is then applied to the set winding. The magnitude of this reverse current is just sufficient to reverse the magnetization in an annular ring of width $a$. The distribution of magnetization is then approximately that shown in Figure 9.35$b$. The application of a current pulse to the drive winding will reverse the magnetization in legs $B$ and $C$ without destroying the state of magnetization in leg $A$. The latter condition is true only for a current pulse of limited amplitude. With this reversal of magnetization we obtain a large signal at the output winding. This condition is known as the "unblocked" state of the core.

It should be noted that once a current pulse in the drive winding has reversed legs $B$ and $C$ succeeding pulses of the same polarity will produce no further output signal. In a sense the information stored in the core has been destroyed. However if an a-c signal is used as the read-out method, then a continuous output can be obtained in the "unblocked" state. Thus this configuration provides a gating action combined with a passive memory. In addition to the two states shown in Figures 9.35$a$ and 9.35$b$, we can obtain a series of intermediate states by making the reversal current sufficiently small. The distribution for this state is shown in Figure 9.35$c$.

### 9.7.1 Magnetization Distribution *

Although Figures 9.35$a$, $b$, $c$ represent the gross behavior of the core, the detailed distribution of magnetization is more complicated to ascertain. However, a qualitative study of this distribution should provide some insight into the operation and limitations of this type of device. As a guiding principle, we may state that after the removal of a pulse of current the magnetization will distribute itself so that the total energy of the system is a minimum. For simplicity let us consider only the contribution due to magnetic field energy. From the results of Chapter 1 we note that the field due to a distribution of dipoles is a result of the surface distribution of magnetization and the volume distribution ($\nabla \cdot \overline{\mathbf{M}}$). For the geometry involved there is probably only a negligibly small contribution from the latter term, since abrupt changes in $M$ are not to be expected. The magnitude of the surface magnetization that can remain is a function of the relative values of the coercive force of the material compared to the saturation magnetization. Since the magnitude of the coercive force for these materials is extremely small compared to $B_s$, the minimum energy considerations imply that the normal component of magnetization is probably essentially continuous across any boundary.

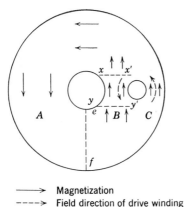

——→ Magnetization
- - -→ Field direction of drive winding

**Figure 9.36.** State of magnetization of blocked transfluxor.

Figure 9.36 is a more detailed diagram of the magnetization for the case discussed in Figure 9.35$a$. In the region around the small hole the magnetization is almost everywhere tangential to the surface. Furthermore, the magnetization per unit volume across a surface such as $e$–$f$ must be less than the value appearing in legs $B$ plus $C$. In other words, it is not possible to saturate all regions of this core simultaneously. The

* The arrows in Figures 9.36 to 9.38 are not to be given a quantitative interpretation.

arrangement shown in Figure 9.36 shows no fields due to surface magnetization.

We may ask why it is not possible to reverse the magnetization in leg $B$ when a drive current produces a field greater than $H_c$ in the directions shown by the dotted arrows (Figure 9.36)? If the magnetization did decrease in leg $B$, a very large field would be produced by the surface polarization at the imaginary surfaces $XX'$ and $YY'$ which would oppose the applied field. This condition could occur if the magnetization above and below $XX'$ and $YY'$ could be reoriented. However, this cannot be done without again creating additional surface polarization.

Why is it now possible to reverse the magnetization in legs $B$ and $C$ for the configuration shown in Figure 9.35$b$? The reason is that under these new conditions it is possible for the magnetization above and below the $XX'$ and $YY'$ surfaces (Figure 9.36) to change orientation without creating additional surface polarization. Figure 9.37$a$ is a more detailed schematic of Figure 9.35$b$. Figure 9.37$b$ is the approximate condition which exists in the core when legs $B$ and $C$ have been reversed in direction. The magnetization just above and below each leg has turned through approximately 180°. Under these conditions there results a minimum number of discontinuities in $M$. Furthermore, this

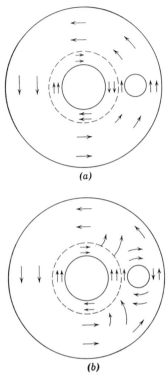

(a)

(b)

Figure 9.37. Unblocked transfluxor: (a) before application of drive current; (b) after application of drive current.

indicates that not only does $M$ undergo a change in each leg, but there is a concomitant reorientation elsewhere in the core. The degree to which this change extends throughout the core is a function of the geometry and driving field. The magnitude of those effects are somewhat difficult to ascertain. In general, the nonuniformity in driving field and $M$ would tend to yield poorer switching times as compared to the case of a more uniform toroid.

The intermediate case (Figure 9.35$c$) is somewhat more complicated. Figure 9.38$a$ is a detail of Figure 9.35$c$. In Figure 9.38$b$ is shown the possible rearrangement that takes place when the drive current is reversed. The outer portion of leg $C$ cannot change its magnetization.

In conclusion we see that each individual geometry and core must be studied carefully in order to determine at least qualitatively the effects that are obtained on switching time and signal-to-noise ratios. In general, the switching process is different in each volume of material.

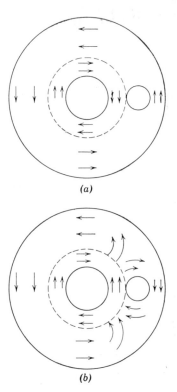

(a)

(b)

**Figure 9.38.** Partially blocked transfluxor: (*a*) before application of drive current; (*b*) after application of drive current.

## 9.8 Magnistor (23, 24)

Another illustration of a multihole core configuration is furnished in the element called a "magnistor." Figure 9.39 is a sketch of the basic construction. The complete core is constructed of two different types of magnetic material. The cross-hatched section consists of "soft-magnetic" material, i.e., its small signal permeability is a marked function of bias. The method of operation is quite straightforward. A current pulse is applied to the set winding so that both materials are brought to a point high on their respective magnetization curves. Upon removal of the pulse both cores relax to some equilibrium point so that there is a net magnetization in core 2. Partial saturation of core 2 represents one state, namely, low permeability. Hence the greater portion of the 15-mc generator signal appears across the load resistor (Figure 9.39). The two windings on core 2 are wound so that the "set" winding and the output windings are effectively decoupled as far as a-c signals are concerned.

The second state of core 2 is produced by a sufficiently large signal on the reset winding on core $A$. The winding polarities of core $A$ are such that the reset current tends to saturate both legs of core $A$ in opposing directions. This effectively introduces an air gap in series with the remainder of the magnetic structure. Hence core 2 returns to its demagnetized or high permeability condition, and the load voltage de-

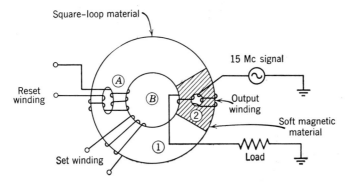

**Figure 9.39.** The magnistor. (Courtesy of Potter Instrument Co., Inc.)

creases from its previous value. A typical set of operation characteristics are shown in Figure 9.40.

As in the case of the transfluxor, the problem of the flux distribution
in the partially saturated state is comparatively difficult to obtain.

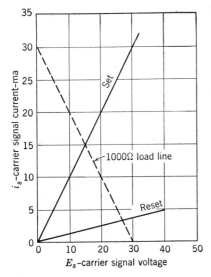

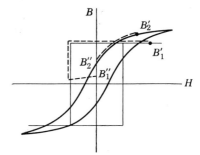

**Figure 9.40.** Typical operating characteristics of a Potter magnistor. (Courtesy of Potter Instrument Co., Inc.)

**Figure 9.41.** Magnetization characteristic of a magnistor.

Figure 9.41 is a plot of the hypothetical $B$-$H$ curves for the two core
materials. When the set current is applied the cores reach points such
as $B_2'$ and $B_1'$. The exact point attained is determined by the relative
cross-sectional areas, and the fraction of the total circumference appor-

tioned to each material. When the set current is removed the cores return to points such as $B_2''$ and $B_1''$. If there is an air gap between the two materials, the remanent points decrease still further. The reset current returns the system to the origin.

## 9.9   Use of Quadrature Fields (25)

Another configuration which has been tried for nondestructive read out of memory cores is illustrated in Figure 9.42a. A second core is placed in quadrature with the memory core. Small pulses of current in the read-out core produce a field at 90° to the remanent magnetization

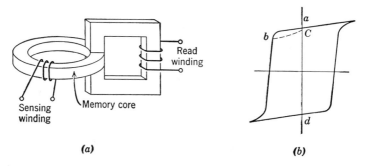

*(a)*                                      *(b)*

Figure 9.42.   Nondestructive read out.

in the memory core. This field tends to rotate the magnetization just under the pole faces. The resulting discontinuity of magnetization in the memory core produces a circumferential field which tends to reverse the magnetization in the memory core, i.e., the core is moved from point $a$ to point $b$ on the hysteresis loop (Figure 9.42b). This change in magnetization produces an output pulse (say positive) in the sensing winding. When the read-out current pulse is removed the core is returned to point $C$. This produces a negative output pulse in the sensing winding. Additional read-out current pulses produce successive positive and negative pulses of decreasing amplitude until the core reaches a reversible minor loop without destroying the information stored in the core. The magnitude of the sensing winding output pulses is primarily a function of the rate of rise of the current pulses in the quadrature core. It can be seen that if the memory core is originally in state $d$ the sequence of output pulses is a negative pulse followed by a positive pulse during read out.

A similar effect is obtained with the geometry shown in Figure 9.43.

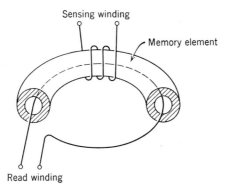

**Figure 9.43.** Cross-field nondestructive read out.

In this case the quadrature field acts over the entire toroid length. Thus the magnetization is rotated a small amount everywhere in the toroid.

## 9.10  Magnetic Shift Registers * (26, 27, 28)

One of the more widely used devices employing square-loop materials in digital-computer circuitry is the shift register. This is a device which stores binary information in a sequential manner. There are many variations in the circuit configurations which are used to accomplish this function. However, only two of the commonest types are discussed in this section.†

A two-core-per-binary-bit register is illustrated in Figure 9.44a together with the pulse sequence used to drive the register. The $A$ cores store the binary information in a manner similar to the memory matrix, i.e., the two remanent states represent the "one" and "zero" states. The $B$ cores serve as intermediate storage or delay elements as a particular bit advances along the register. If no information enters the register, all the cores are in the "zero" state. Hence, with winding polarities as indicated, the shift winding pulses merely force each core further into saturation along $a$–$b$ (Figure 9.44d). In the ideal case there would be very little voltage developed across the output winding $N_0$.

However, an input current pulse sets the first core in the "one" state. The output pulse which appears in the secondary winding $N_0$ is prevented

---

* The shift register is the basic element from which we can derive other logic circuits such as "and," "or," etc. (29, 30).

† Ferroelectric shift registers have also been constructed. However, the circuitry is much more complex due to the lack of a dielectric transformer (18).

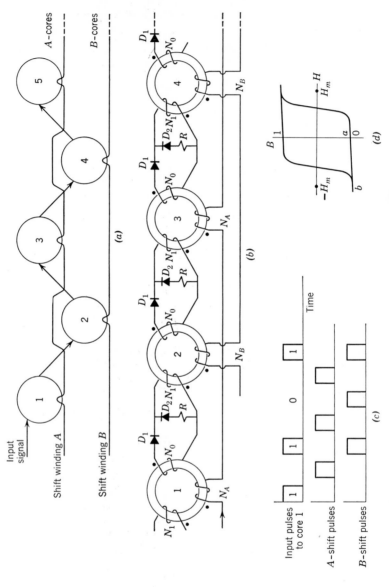

**Figure 9.44.** Two-core-per-bit shift register: (*a*) schematic diagram; (*b*) circuit diagram; (*c*) input and shift pulse sequence; (*d*) magnetization states of cores.

from reacting with core 2 by means of diode $D_1$. The following shift pulse $A$ resets core 1 to the "zero" state and sets core 2 to the "one" state, since the polarity of the output pulse is now reversed. This is followed by shift pulse $B$ which returns core 2 to the "zero" state and simultaneously sets core 3 to the "one" state. Thus a "one" has been shifted from core 1 to core 3. Diode $D_2$ prevents the voltage developed across $N_1$ at this time from reacting on core 1. An additional series resistor $R$ is sometimes added in order to prevent excessive loading due to the low forward impedance of $D_2$. It should be noted that another input pulse can be introduced into core 1 coincident with shift pulse $B$.

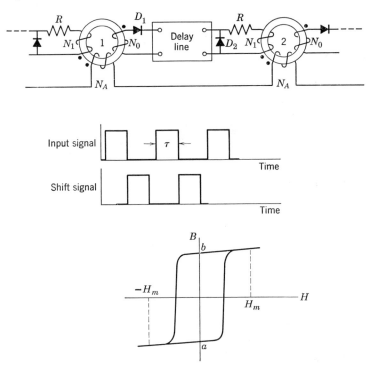

Figure 9.45.  Core plus delay-line shift register.

This system requires a two-phase clock and two cores per bit. A reduction in the number of elements can be made through the use of a delay network which replaces the $B$ cores, as shown in Figure 9.45. The maximum allowable time delay of the network is equal to the time interval between shift pulses; the minimum allowable time delay is equal to the width of the shift pulse. The operation is similar to that of the two-core per bit, but the storage function is accomplished by means of a delay line. The resistor $R$ performs the same function as before, but in addition it aids in the termination of the delay line. In practice this system is limited in its frequency of operation because of the difficulties of constructing a sufficiently compact delay line which has a minimum attenuation and is free from serious reflections and pulse distortion.

In both systems one of the serious limitations to very high speed operation (above 100 kc) is the noise voltage that is developed similar to that in the memory matrix. When a zero is stored in any core, current shift pulses with very short rise times produce a considerable output voltage across $N_o$. This pulse is of the proper polarity to partially set the succeeding core. As this noise pulse is transmitted down the register, it can build up and reach a magnitude comparable to a transmitted one. This noise pulse can be decreased by the following procedures:

1. Proper shaping of the leading edge of the shift pulse consistent with the desired switching time.

2. Decrease the number of output turns $N_1$ in order to decrease the distributed capacitance. This also increases the amount of current required.

3. Careful winding of the various coils to minimize the leakage flux.

4. Choice of cores with the flattest saturation region.

The other limiting feature at high frequencies is the core dissipation. In this regard the choice of core material is in favor of the thin metallic tapes rather than the ceramic ferrite. This is due in part to the greater surface to volume ratios that are attainable in the tape wound cores.

## 9.11    Magnetic Gating

The examples that were discussed in the previous sections were almost solely applicable to computer systems. The following sections, however, serve to illustrate the use of square-loop material in communications systems. This includes gating pulses for color TV, pulse-position modulation, and sync-clipping for TV.

### 9.11.1    Color TV Burst Gate

An example of a system which requires a controlled gate is found in the present color television receiver. In the present NTSC system of color television transmission the subcarrier (3.58 megacycles/sec) used to transmit the color information is suppressed and must be reintroduced at the receiver at the proper frequency and phase. Synchronizing information to accomplish this is transmitted during the flyback time in the form of eight or nine cycles of a 3.58 megacycles/sec signal called the "color burst." In the receiver this color burst is applied to a color-burst amplifier which drives a crystal whose output provides the required subcarrier to demodulate the color signal. The color-burst amplifier is normally biased off to prevent it from passing the video signal. A

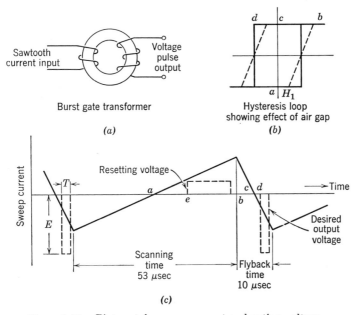

Figure 9.46. Picture-tube sweep current and gating voltage.

properly timed voltage of amplitude $E$ and time duration $T$ (see Figure 9.46) must be supplied to gate on the amplifier and allow passage of the color burst. This gating voltage can be obtained from the output of a transformer which has a core of square-loop material and which is driven by the sawtooth sweep current (Figure 9.46). The purpose of the core is to produce a large output pulse at a prescribed time during the short flyback time. A relatively small amplitude unwanted pulse is produced during the long trace time. The sweep current switches the core so that the zero crossings $a$ and $c$ correspond to the two remanent points on the major hysteresis loop. The two output pulses start at the times corresponding to the current values which produce $H_c$ (points $e$ and $d$). The time delay can be adjusted by the choice of core length and the number of primary turns since

$$H_c = \frac{N I_c}{l}$$

However, the more difficult problem is the nature of the output pulse during the flyback interval. As shown in Chapter 4, the rate of change of magnetization is roughly proportional to the difference between the driving $H$ and $H_c$. With a sawtooth current waveform this difference changes with time. Hence the desired width and pulse rise time is usually determined experimentally.

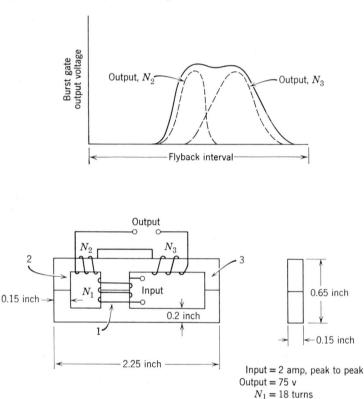

**Figure 9.47.** Burst gate transformer ($E$-frame configuration).

For color TV application the ferrite toroidal core produced too narrow a pulse. The output pulse can be broadened by introducing a small air gap in the toroid. This has the effect of shearing the observed hysteresis loop, as shown by the dotted line in Figure 9.46$b$. The excess field for reversing the magnetization is now less toward the end of the pulse; hence the final pulse width can be made approximately 4.5 $\mu$sec. However, due to the gradual curvature of the actual hysteresis loop the output pulse has a very poor trailing edge. The proper rise and fall times and adequate pulse width can be obtained by the use of two cores assembled in a single $E$-frame, as shown in Figure 9.47.

The sawtooth current drive is applied to the input winding $N_1$ on the center leg. When the flyback current reaches a value corresponding to $H_1$ (see Figure 9.46$b$) for leg 2 a voltage pulse as shown in Figure 9.47 is initiated across the winding $N_2$. Because the length of leg 3 is greater than leg 2 $I_{c3}$ is greater than $I_{c2}$, and the flux in leg 3 has not yet switched. At a later time, determined by the ratio of path lengths and slope of the flyback current, the field intensity in leg 3 reaches a value $H_1$ and a voltage appears across winding $N_3$. The composite output of $N_2$ plus $N_3$ is shown in Figure 9.47.

Two individual toroids would produce the same results. However, the $E$-frame construction is a better practical compromise. In order to maintain large enough fields in the outer two legs, it is necessary that the cross-sectional area of the middle leg be somewhat greater than the sum of the areas of the two outer legs. The decrease and nonuniformity in field is brought about by the rectangular geometry. In the experimental model it was found necessary to increase the cross-sectional area of the middle leg by about 25 per cent.

## 9.12   Pulse-Position Modulation

A variation of the circuit discussed in the Section 9.11 permits the construction of a simple pulse-position modulator. The general requirement of this type of modulator is that it vary the position of an otherwise periodic pulse in accordance with the amplitude variations of a modulating signal. One form of this modulator is shown in Figure 9.48$a$. The basic operation is similar to the burst gate delay element. A sawtooth current, which occurs at the sampling rate, drives the core into saturation in both directions. If an additional biasing current signal is added to the core, the time at which the output pulse begins can be varied in accordance with the bias. In the circuit shown in Figure 9.48$b$ two cores are used as a balancing system to decouple the sawtooth current from the modulating signal. The output pulse is taken from the secondary winding of one of the cores through a diode so that the reset pulses do not appear in the output. Several such modulators can be combined to form a multiplex communications system.

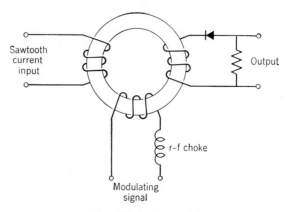

**Figure 9.48a.** Simplified pulse-position modulator.

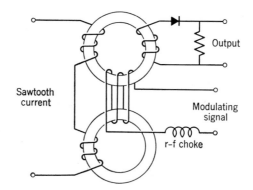

**Figure 9.48b.** Magnetic pulse-position modulator.

Typical operating data are shown below:

|  | Metallic Tape 4–79 Permalloy (1/8 mil) | Ferrite General Ceramic Type S-1 |
|---|---|---|
| (a) Pulse width | 0.5 μsec | 1.0 μsec |
| (b) Output voltage | 0.8 v/turn | 1.0 v/turn |
| (c) Modulation index | 25.0 μsec/amp | 25.0 μsec/amp |
| (d) Peak applied field | 4.0 oersteds | 2.0 oersteds |

## 9.13   Sync Clipper

Figure 9.49$a$ illustrates a transmitted composite monochrome TV signal. During the retrace time a horizontal synchronizing pulse is transmitted as an amplitude modulated signal (pedestal) at a level above the maximum allowed video signal. The sync pulse must be separated in the receiver by some form of amplitude discriminator. The square-loop core affords a method for this separation. The circuit in Figure 9.49$b$ illustrates the basic principle.

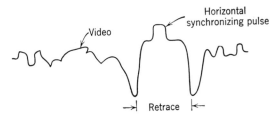

**Figure 9.49$a$.**   Transmitted television signal.

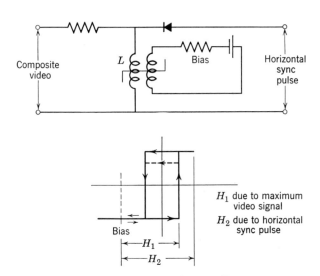

**Figure 9.49$b$.**   Magnetic sync clipper.

The bias (shown in Figure 9.49$b$) is adjusted so that the maximum video level cannot produce a field greater than $H_c$. In this case there is very little output across the core winding $L$. However, the sync pulse is of sufficient amplitude so that the magnetization of the core is partially reversed, thus developing an output voltage. The d-c bias then resets the core. The circuit should be adjusted so that the incoming sync pulse does not saturate the core because this would produce an output pulse of variable width.

The basic difficulty with this circuit is the comparatively low impedance that the core offers to the preceding vacuum tubes. With ferrite cores a typical value during magnetization may be 20 ohms. For a tape core this can be increased to about 300 ohms.

### 9.14   References

1. Horsch, J. R., "A Reliable Pulse Scaler of Arbitrary Order," *Proc. Nat. Electronics Conf.*, **11**, 1955, pp. 870–878
2. Van Nice, R. I., R. C. Lyman, "A Predetermined Scaler Utilizing Transistors and Magnetic Cores," *ibid.*
3. Rajchman, J. A., "Static Magnetic Matrix Memory and Switching Circuits," *R C A Rev.*, Vol. XIII, No. 2, June 1952, pp. 180.
4. ———, "Myriabit Magnetic Core Matrix Memory," *Proc. I.R.E.*, **41**, No. 11, October 1953, pp. 1407.
5. Pulvari, C. F., "Ferroelectrics and Their Memory Applications," *I.R.E. Trans. on Component Parts*, CP **3**, No. 1, March 1956, pp. 3–11.
6. Eckert, J. P., Jr., "Survey of Digital Computer Memory Systems," *Proc. I.R.E.*, **41**, No. 10, October 1953, pp. 1393.
7. Auerbach, I. L., "Digital Memory Systems," *Elec. Mfg.*, **53**, No. 4, October 1953, pp. 100.
8. Rajchman, J. A., "Ferrite Apetured Plate For Random Access Memory," *Proc. I.R.E.*, **45**, No. 3, March 1957, pp. 325–334.
9. Pohm, A. V., S. M. Rubens, "A Compact Coincident Current Memory," *Proc. Eastern Joint Computer Conference*, December 10–12, 1956, (published by AIEE).
10. Smith, D. O., "Magnetic Relaxation In Thin Films," *Proc. Conf. on Magnetism and Magnetic Materials (AIEE-I.R.E.)*, February 1957.
11. Bobeck, A. H., "A New Storage Element Suitable For Large-Sized Memory Arrays—The Twistor," *Bell System Tech. J.*, Vol. XXXVI, November 1957, pp. 1319–1340.
12. Brickwedde, F. G., "Cryogenics: Very-Low Temperature Physics and Engineering," *Recent Advances in Science*, Interscience Publishers, New York.
13. Kittel, C., *Introduction to Solid State Physics*, John Wiley and Sons, New York, 1956, Chapter 11.
14. Crowe, J. W., "Trapped-Flux Superconducting Memory," *IBM Journal of Res. and Dev.*, **1**, No. 4, October 1957, pp. 295–303.
15. Garwin, R. L., "An Analysis of the Operation of a Persistent-Supercurrent Memory Cell," *IBM Jour. of Res. and Dev.*, **1**, No. 4, October 1957, pp. 304–308.
16. Anderson, J. R., "Ferroelectric Storage Elements for Digital Computers and Switching Systems," *Elec. Eng.*, **71**, October 1952, p. 916.
17. Lemme, D. H., "A Ferroelectric Amplifier and Memory Circuit as Duals of Magnetic Devices," M.S. thesis, MIT, Dept. of Eng., 1955.
18. Anderson, J. R., "A New Type of Ferroelectric Shift Register," *I.R.E. Trans. on Electronic Computers*, EC-5, No. 4, December 1956, pp. 184–191.

19. Merz, W. J., "Domain Formation and Domain Wall Motion in Ferroelectric BaTiO₃ Single Crystals," *Phys. Rev.*, **95**, August 1, 1954, p. 690.
20. Wieder, H. H., "Activation Field and Coercivity of Ferroelectric BaTiO₃, *J. Appl. Phy.*, **27**, March 1957, pp. 367–369.
21. Rajchman, J. A., A. W. Lo, "Transfluxor," *Proc. I.R.E.*, **44**, No. 3, March 1956, p. 320.
22. Abbott, H. W., J. J. Suran, "Multihole Ferrite Core Configurations and Applications," *Proc. I.R.E.*, **45**, No. 8, August 1957, pp. 1081–1093.
23. Snyder, R. L., "An Ideal Component for Control Systems," *Research & Engineering*, July–August 1955, p. 33.
24. ———, "Magnistor Circuits," *Electronic Design*, August 1955, p. 24.
25. Buck, D. A., W. I. Frank, "Nondestructive Sensing of Magnetic Cores," *Trans. AIEE*, Communications and Electronics, June 1954, pp. 822–830.
26. Wang, A., W. D. Woo, "Static Magnetic Storage in Delay Lines," *J. Appl. Phy.*, **21**, No. 1, January 1950, pp. 49–54.
27. Sands, E. A., "An Analysis of Magnetic Shift Register Operation," *Proc. I.R.E.*, **41**, No. 8, August 1953, pp. 993–999.
28. Loev, D., et al., "Magnetic Core Circuits for Digital Data-Processing Systems," *Proc. I.R.E.*, **44**, No. 2, February 1956, pp. 154–162.
29. Lincoln, A. J., "Ferromagnetic Core Logical Circuitry and Its Application to Digital Computers," Memorandum Report No. 911, August 1955, Ballistic Research Lab, Aberdeen Proving Ground, Md., available at U.S. Department of Commerce, OTS.
30. Evans, W. G., et al., "Magnetic Logic Circuits for Industrial Control Systems," *Trans. AIEE*, Applications and Industry, July 1956, pp. 166–171.
31. Buck, D. A., "The Cryotron—A Superconductive Computer Component," *Proc. I.R.E.*, **44**, No. 4, April 1956, pp. 482–494.
32. Karnaugh, M., "Pulse-Switching Circuits Using Magnetic Cores," *Proc. I.R.E.*, **43**, No. 5, May 1955.
33. Newhouse, V. L., "The Utilization of Domain Wall Viscosity in Data-Handling Devices," *Proc. I.R.E.*, **45**, No. 11, November 1957, pp. 1484–1492.
34. Rajchman, J. A., "A Survey of Magnetic and other Solid-State Devices for the Manipulation of Information," *I.R.E. Trans. on Circuit Theory*, CT-4, No. 3, September 1957, pp. 210–225.
35. Arrott, William, "Magnetic Materials Push Back Design Stops," *Elec. Mfg.*, **59**, No. 1, January 1957.
36. Richards, R. K., *Digital Computer Components and Circuits*, D. Van Nostrand Company Inc., Princeton, N. J. (includes bibliography of periodical articles).

# Chapter ten

# Magnetic Recording

## 10.0 Introduction

The storage of information in digital form by utilizing square-loop
magnetic or dielectric material is discussed in Chapter 9. Each binary
bit is usually stored in a discrete magnetic core or capacitor. The
ability to store analogue as well as digital data, however, is made possible
by the use of a continuous nonlinear dielectric or magnetic media.*
Our particular interest in this problem is to observe in some detail the
magnetization or polarization process which takes place as information
is recorded or played back. Magnetic or dielectric recording thus affords
another illustration of the use of the hysteretic nature of certain materials.

Of the two methods, magnetic recording has been developed to a
highly refined system. The analogous process of dielectric recording
has not to date received the same attention. The difficulty centers
about the problem of maintaining an external electric field for considerable periods of time in the presence of ionized media. Hence the
major portion of the chapter is concerned with the magnetic recording
process.

In its broadest sense the term magnetic recording can be applied to
any recording technique in which some phase of magnetics is intimately

---

* The use of a continuous media usually suggests that the information storage
will not be of the random access type discussed in Chapter 9.

**404**

associated with either the record or playback process. By way of example the following recording systems can be cited:

1. Conventional magnetic recording system in which a distribution of magnetization is produced in a magnetizable medium by a recording head and is played back by sensing the flux distribution around the recorded tape.

2. Ferrography (19), in which magnetic powder is attracted to the magnetic image on the master, much as the ink adheres to a half-tone plate in conventional printing. A permanent copy is then "printed" by picking up the powder image on a tacky paper laid over the master. The recorded information is thus read optically.

3. Physical recording, in which a variation in physical distribution of magnetic or conducting material is produced on a surface by machining or other techniques, while playback is accomplished by sensing the change in magnetic reluctance or permeability as the distribution is moved in front of the playback head. The conventional magnetic recording system has received most of the attention, and it is with this recording method that the present-day success of magnetic recording has been achieved. It is well to remember the other systems when unconventional applications are contemplated. Because of its position in the field the conventional magnetic recording system is discussed at some length.

## 10.1   Record Process.   Magnetic History

The basic components of the recording system are illustrated in Figure 10.1. Information is supplied to the magnetic medium via the record

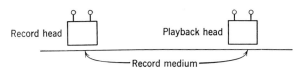

Figure 10.1.   Recording system.

head, and the magnetic state of the medium is read out by means of the playback head. Though the medium is shown as moving with a velocity while the heads are stationary, there are many systems in which both the head and medium are in motion.

The purpose of the record head is to produce a highly localized magnetic field with a controllable intensity. The need for a highly localized field is evident when we consider that it is desired to alter the state of magnetization in a very small region of the medium if a high density of information is to be achieved. As a first step in the record process it is necessary to know the time-varying field to which an element of tape is exposed. Although many physical shapes for the field-defining structure have been used, they fall into two general classes: gap type and strip type (Figure 10.2).

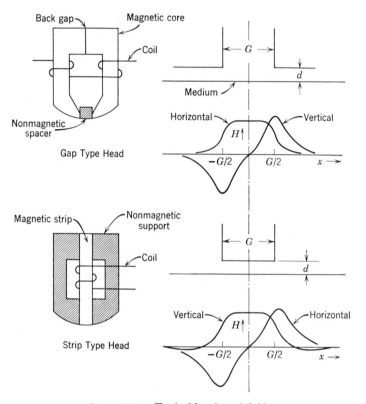

**Figure 10.2.** Typical heads and fields.

The generalized history of an element of the magnetic medium can be expressed in functional form in the following manner. If the head is energized with a constant current, then an element of tape at a distance $x$ from the head will experience field

$$f = h(x) \tag{10.1}$$

which depends on the head geometry.

If a time-varying current (produced by the bias and information signals) is used, the field at a distance $x$ is

$$f = h(x)g(t) \qquad (10.2)$$

where $g(t)$ is the modulating function.

If, in addition, the recording medium moves with a velocity $v$ with respect to the head, then

$$f(t) = h(vt)g(t) \qquad (10.3)$$

The complete time history of a magnetic element is thus described by equation 10.3. For example, if the head produced an infinitely narrow field distribution, then $h(x)$ would be an impulse function,

$$\delta(x) = 0 \qquad x \neq 0 \qquad (10.4)$$

$$\delta(0) = C \qquad x = 0$$

Hence

$$f(0) = Cg(0) \qquad (10.5)$$

which indicates that a distribution of the impulse type samples the modulating function at successive intervals and applies these samples in turn to successive elements of tape.

Practical head configurations, as shown in Figure 10.2, however, produce more diffuse field distributions than the idealistic "spike" described above. The history to which the tape is now exposed becomes exceedingly complex. In the following sections the problem of how this complex history combines with the nonlinear magnetic characteristic of the tape to produce a linear relationship between the recorded information and the input data is discussed in greater detail.

## 10.2   Erase Process

It is important to note that the recording must start with the erase process, i.e., the process of obliterating old recordings and preparing the magnetic medium for new information. Erasure is normally accomplished in three ways: a-c erase, d-c erase to maximum remanent condition, and d-c erase to neutral condition.

### 10.2.1   A-c Erase

The a-c erase technique (also called supersonic and high-frequency erase) is most commonly used in audio recorders. The magnetic history corresponding to a-c erase is shown in Figure 10.3$a$, where $H_s$ is the field required to saturate the medium. The modulation in amplitude is a consequence of the head field distribution and the motion of the medium past the head. The portion of the history preceding the last cycle to exceed the saturating field can be ignored because the medium has been carried into saturation. The active portion is the trailing portion which closely resembles a damped sinusoidal wave. The $B$-$H$

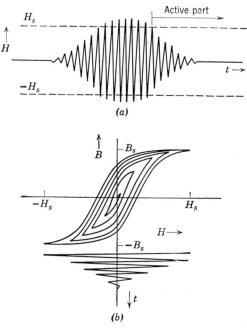

**Figure 10.3.** ($a$) Erase history; ($b$) $B$-$H$ history for active part.

history due to this active portion is shown in Figure 10.3$b$. Experiments indicate that if the ratio of succeeding peaks is large enough (a ratio of 0.95 for some media) the medium will be left in a neutral (randomly magnetized) state. If, however, the field decays more rapidly than some critical value, the medium will be left in a state which is not necessarily neutral. The actual magnitude and polarity of the remanent value, if not zero, will depend upon the phase and amplitude of the high-frequency field at the time it has a peak amplitude for a given element of medium. Thus it can be seen that if the erasing procedure is to be effective the peak value of the field must exceed the saturation value and the decay of the field must be gradual. The significant result of a-c erasure is a neutral magnetic medium. This is the lowest noise condition of the medium. For this reason a-c erase results in the best signal-to-noise ratio for low-level signals and is universally used for high-quality recorders. Although a-c erasure is usually accomplished by a head excited with the high-frequency current, it can also be accomplished by a series of alternating polarity permanent magnets (21) properly oriented and spaced to produce a decaying alternating polarity field through which the medium passes.

### 10.2.2 D-c Erase

D-c erase can be accomplished with a permanent magnet or an electromagnet. The permanent magnet is simple, but the magnitude of the field is more easily controlled with an electromagnet. Although d-c erase can be adjusted to leave the medium in any remanent condition, the two most important are maximum remanence and zero remanence. The method of accomplishing a neutral erase with a permanent magnet can be visualized with reference to Figure 10.4a. When the medium

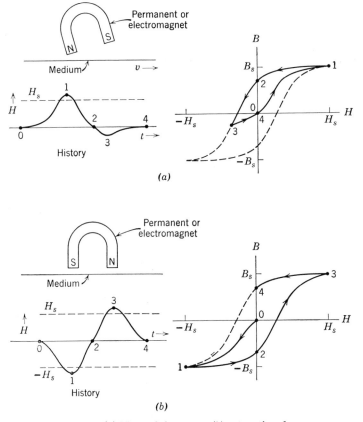

Figure 10.4. (a) Neutral d-c erase; (b) saturation d-c erase.

passes the first pole of the erase magnet it is saturated and left in the maximum remanent condition. The field due to the second pole of the magnet is lower in strength so that the medium is driven from point 2 to point 3 in Figure 10.4a. The value of the field at point 3 is adjusted so that when the field is removed the final remanent value (point 4) is zero. Adjustment of the field at point 3 is accomplished by orientation and/or by shaping of the pole pieces. It is a fairly critical adjustment, but when properly done it results in an erased noise level in the medium which is close to that attained with a-c erase.

If the field strength of the second pole to which the medium is exposed is reduced or if the strength of the second pole is at least as great as the first pole (Figure 10.4b), the final remanent flux density will closely approach the maximum remanent value for the medium. This method is commonly called saturation erase. It differs from the preceding case only in the degree to which the second pole influences the result. It should be pointed out here that the picture just presented is strictly true only if the poles are very far apart so that the magnitude of the field between them can approach zero. Actually, there is considerable rotation of the direction of magnetization in the medium while it passes by the magnet. Strictly speaking, rotational hysteresis must therefore be considered. However, the results in most cases conform to the simple picture.

## 10.3   Recording Process

Starting from the two alternative erased states, it is the function of the recording process to produce a distribution of magnetization in the medium such that the magnetic flux through a playback head scanning the recorded medium shall be proportional to the input information signal. This is usually taken to mean that the remanent distribution of magnetization along the medium shall have the same functional form as the input function of time; a constant scanning velocity is assumed in this case. The nominal direction of magnetization may be longitudinal (parallel to the direction of motion), perpendicular (perpendicular to the medium surface and the direction of motion), or transverse (parallel to the medium surface and perpendicular to the direction of motion).

If the information signal is applied to a record head with an infinitely short gap, the temporal history results in a pulse being applied to each element of medium as it passes the head, with the amplitude of the pulse being uniquely determined by the amplitude of the information

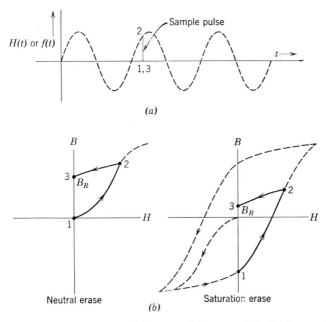

*(a)*

*(b)*

**Figure 10.5.** Short gap histories: (a) temporal history of single element; (b) *B-H* history of a single element.

signal at the time the element is under the head (Figure 10.5a). In Figure 10.5b is shown the *B-H* history of an element of medium corresponding to the above temporal history for both neutral and saturation erase. The final remanent value $B_R$ of the element is indicated by point 3. A transfer characteristic can be obtained by plotting $B_R$ versus $H$,

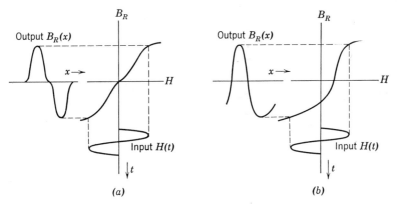

*(a)*            *(b)*

**Figure 10.6.** Transfer characteristic. Short gap with no bias: (a) neutral erase; (b) saturation erase.

as shown in Figure 10.6. For sinusoidal information signals the distortion would be as shown in the output signals. Neutral erase results in odd harmonic distortion, and saturation erase results in even harmonic distortion.

### 10.3.1 Linearization

An examination of the initial magnetization curve and the hysteresis loop indicates that there are straight regions of steep slope of which it should be possible to take advantage by combining some proper signal with the information signal. Such additions, called bias, may commonly be a constant d-c field, unidirectional or bidirectional pulses, or an a-c field.

All of the bias systems accomplish the linearization of the recording by increasing the sensitivity to small recording fields. In many cases there will be a value of bias field for maximum sensitivity and a different value, usually higher, for minimum amplitude variation in signal. In many cases the remanent magnetization in an element of magnetic medium will be found to be simply related to the peak field that the element experiences, as long as no reversal of field occurs during the subsequent history. Although not always accurate, this rule can facilitate a simple description of some recording processes by eliminating the necessity for considering the rest of the history.

The details of how the various bias signals produce their linearizing action are not completely known. The process appears somewhat similar to a "shaking" process in a mechanical system in which the effects of static friction can be reduced by vibration in order to allow other forces (normally too small to overcome static friction) to attain an equilibrium condition. The bias field magnitude is made large enough to overcome most of the potential barriers in the medium and to make possible the equilibrium between the applied information signal field and other internal forces which would not otherwise be able to overcome the barriers. The result is an increased sensitivity to low applied fields which will improve the linearity of the magnetization process. That the aggregate magnetic state of an ensemble of magnetic particles can be made proportional to a small component of an applied magnetic field is evidence that nature is not always un-cooperative. The magnitudes of the bias field necessary are always of the order of the coercive field for the medium.

### 10.3.2   D-c Bias

Referring to Figure 10.6, it can be seen that in each case two obvious things can be done to make the output a linear replica of the input. The peak-to-peak information signal swings can be reduced and a constant d-c field can be added to the signal (2, 23). This added d-c field field or bias corresponds to points in the middle of a straight portion of the transfer characteristic. Qualitatively the temporal and $B$-$H$ histories of an element of medium using d-c bias are the same as in Figure 10.5, but the resulting values of applied $H$ are restricted to one polarity. In Figure 10.7 is shown the linearization which results from the use of

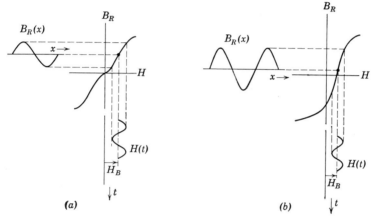

**Figure 10.7.** Linear transfer characteristic. Short gap with d-c bias: ($a$) neutral erase; ($b$) saturation erase.

d-c bias. The use of a saturation erase with d-c bias results in a greater dynamic range than does neutral erase.

### 10.3.3   Pulse Bias

The above discussion also applies to pulse bias recording during the "on" time of the pulse. The transfer characteristic for the pulse bias case is shown in Figure 10.8. The actual input time function is a series of samples which transfer over to a series of magnetized spots on the medium. For saturation erase the zero reference of the recording is the maximum negative remanence value. The playback signal from such a recording consists of the modulation on the pulses. The pulses themselves are not resolved. This played back modulation is a linear replica of the information signal as modified by the characteristic of

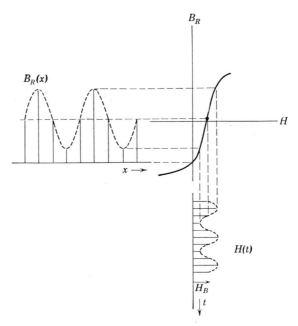

**Figure 10.8.** Pulse bias transfer characteristic. Short gap head, saturation erase.

the playback system. The sample rate must be at least twice the highest information frequency to be recorded. To minimize playback filter problems a higher sample rate is desirable.

### 10.3.4 Long Gap Effects with D-c or Pulse Bias

If the head field distribution has a width greather than zero, i.e., if the head gap has a length greater than zero, further distortion is possible. If the information signal change is negligible during the time it takes an element of medium to pass the gap, the foregoing discussion still applies. If, however, the information function changes significantly while the element passes the gap there will be distortion. This situation will prevail if the head gap (hence the head field) is comparable in extent to the recorded wavelength. The recorded wavelength is dependent upon the recorded frequency $f$ and the speed of the medium $v$. It is defined by $\lambda = v/f$. In this case the magnetization of the element is determined by the peak field it experiences while under the head.

The distortion caused by a record head field distribution with dimensions which are comparable to the recorded wavelength of the in-

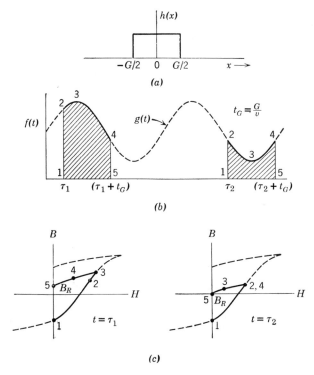

**Figure 10.9.** Rectangular distribution with d-c bias: (a) rectangular head field distribution; (b) temporal histories for elements at times $\tau_1$, $\tau_2$; (c) B-H history of an element.

formation signal can be visualized for the d-c bias case by considering an idealized rectangular head-field distribution (Figure 10.9a). As the element of medium passes the head, the total time-varying function (information plus bias) is gated on, and the temporal histories shown in Figure 10.9a result. The significant feature of the corresponding B-H histories is that the remanent magnetization is determined by the peak field to which the element of medium is exposed. The peak field rule applies very accurately to this recording method.

One way to visualize the distortion produced by the long gap head is to consider that the input $f(t)$ is distorted into an effective input function $F(t)$. The function $F(t)$ is a plot of the peak field that each element of medium experiences when scanned by a head with a gap length $G$. With the rectangular head distribution, the function $F(t)$ is easily constructed by determining for any $t$ the peak value of $f(t)$ in the interval $\tau_1 < t < (\tau_1 + t_G)$ where $t_G = G/v$. An example of this process is

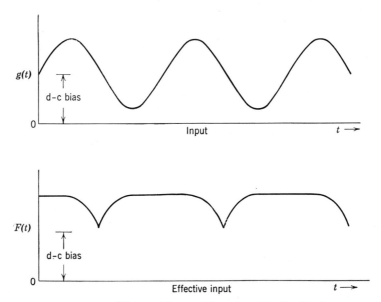

**Figure 10.10.** Distorted input with rectangular distribution.

shown in Figure 10.10. The extended field distribution cannot successfully reproduce the shape of the function, and there is a time inde-
terminacy.

The same procedure will yield the effective input function $F(t)$ for
the pulse bias case, as shown in Figures 10.11 and 10.12. It can be seen
that the effective sample length (Figure 10.12) is increased and can
even result in overlapping of samples. As the number of samples is
increased, the results approach the d-c bias case in the limit.

Once the effective input function $F(t)$ has been determined, the corresponding distribution of magnetization in the medium can be obtained by using the short-gap transfer characteristic as in Figure 10.7
and 10.8. If the operating range is over the linear portion of the transfer
characteristic, there will be no further distortion and the distribution
will have the same functional form as $F(t)$.

More realistic head-field distributions extend beyond the edges of the
gap. They may either have a single gaussianlike hump or be saddle
shaped and may be skewed with respect to the center line of the gap.
In all cases the temporal history of an element of medium is given by
equation 10.3, and the peak field rule carefully applied will give the
effective input function $F(t)$. Examples of typical distortions that
might result from realistic distributions are shown in Figure 10.13. It
is characteristic of these unidirectional bias systems that the maxima

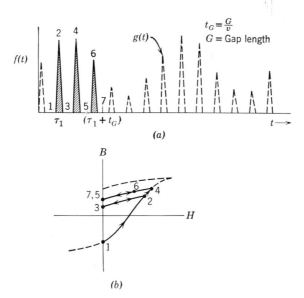

Figure 10.11. Rectangular distribution with pulse bias: (a) temporal history at $t = \tau_1$; (b) B-H history at $t = \tau_1$.

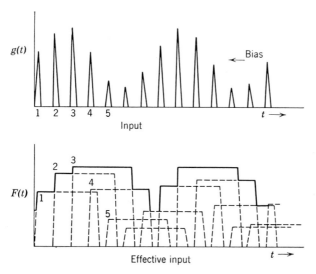

Figure 10.12. Rectangular distribution with pulse bias.

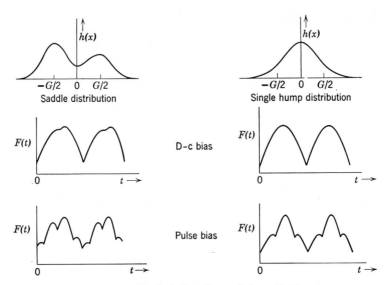

**Figure 10.13.** Typical distortions of sinusoidal inputs.

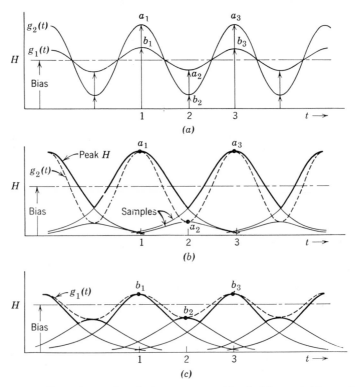

**Figure 10.14.** Dependence of resolution upon record level: (*a*) sampled input signals; (*b*) loss of *H*-sample at high level; (*c*) proper *H*-sample at low level.

are flattened and the minima are made sharper. Portions of the function $F(t)$ have taken on the shape of portions of the head field distribution, which is particularly true of the pulse bias case.

A further consequence of realistic head distributions is the dependence of distortion and resolution upon the record level. This effect is best illustrated by the pulse bias system.

In Figure 10.14 are shown two sampled signals $g_1$ and $g_2$ to be recorded by a head with a single hump distribution. The two signals are of the same frequency but have different amplitudes. It can be seen in Figure 10.14b that the effect of the second sample is lost for the high amplitude signal. Any presence of that frequency in the recording is due to the shape of the head field, not to a proper sampling. In Figure 10.14c it can be seen that at reduced amplitude the proper sample levels are present at the sample points.

### 10.3.5  A-c Bias (3, 7, 8, 29, 40)

When the medium is left in a neutral condition by the erase process a-c bias is commonly used. Of the various bias methods, a-c bias is most aptly described as a "shaking process." By its use the transfer characteristic is made to depend upon the essentially straight and parallel portion of the major hysteresis loop of the record medium. The bias signal $f_B(t)$ which is added to the information signal $f_s(t)$ is of such an amplitude as to produce a peak field of the order of the coercive field for the medium. In Figure 10.15a are shown the temporal and $B$-$H$ histories with no signal field and a single humped head-field distribution.

If the bias frequency is high enough relative to the record head resolution, an element of medium will be returned to the neutral state after passing the head. If this condition is satisfied, the bias field will make no permanent contribution to the remanent magnetization. It can be shown experimentally that if the decay is more rapid there can be a remanent condition other than zero due to the bias signal alone.

If the information signal has a constant value $f_s(t)$, as indicated in Figure 10.15b, the $B$-$H$ history will describe a series of minor loops offset from the origin. If it is assumed for the moment that the signal field can be made constant as the bias field decays, the offset will be the information signal field, and the bias field will decay to zero around point $b$. If the information signal is now reduced to zero, the final state of the medium will be the remanent point $c$. The linear nature of the process is reasonable when it is considered that the minor loop traversed by the bias field normally cannot exceed the confines of the major hysteresis loop; hence it must travel up and down the parallel sides of the loop when the information field is applied. The average of the decaying minor loop will travel along a straight line through the origin (Figure 10.15$b$). Since the record head field is nonzero in extent, the information signal $f_s(t)$ does change during the passage of the element of medium past the head. The effect can be visualized by considering that the point $b$ in Figure 10.15$b$ shifts in a manner determined

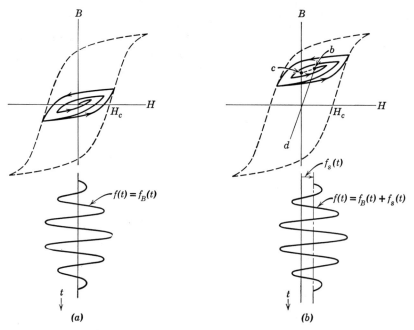

**Figure 10.15.** $B$-$H$ history, a-c bias: ($a$) bias only; ($b$) information and bias.

by a temporal history such as that shown in Figure 10.9 or 10.11. The decaying of bias and information field together leads to a reduction in remanent magnetization, commonly called "record demagnetization" (31, 40), but the linear aspects of the process are preserved.

If the bias frequency is not sufficiently high to result in a neutral medium, it may be recorded. This does not destroy the linearizing action relative to the information signal, but it may increase the noise level. Usually the playback system will filter out the recorded bias signal.

The record process with a-c bias is similar to the use of a nonlinear impedance as a modulating device in circuit theory. The straightforward application of the usual analysis techniques is difficult because of the presence of hysteresis and the lack of an analytic representation for the magnetic medium. The bias and information signals are added and impressed on the magnetic medium where the modulation takes place. The recorded spectrum would be expected to consist of the information signal and its harmonics and the bias signal with side bands. If the bias frequency is high enough, neither it nor its side bands will be played back. As in the case of a push-pull circuit, the symmetry dictates that the even harmonics of the information signal will be canceled out. This leaves only the odd harmonics to produce distortion. The bias and information signal levels can be chosen to minimize odd harmonic distortion. The transfer characteristic with a-c bias is shown

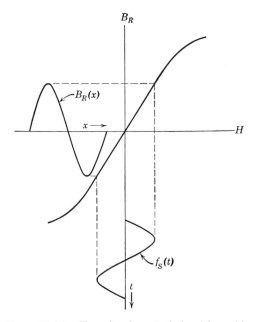

**Figure 10.16.** Transfer characteristic with a-c bias.

in Figure 10.16. It will be noted that the information input signal and its replica have a zero average value, and the manner of overload is the same for positive and negative swings.

### 10.3.6 Optimum Bias Considerations (40)

The requirement that the bias make no contribution to the playback signal determines the lower limit for the bias frequency. If the gap is short, the bias frequency must be increased, if the cycle-to-cycle decay is to be made small enough. Since the gap length also determines the highest signal frequency resolved, the bias frequency can be, and usually is, expressed in terms of the highest signal frequency to be recorded. A bias frequency which is five times the highest signal frequency is usually quite satisfactory, and as low as three times is satisfactory in many cases. A sharply defined gap which is exploited to the limit will require higher bias frequencies than a gap of the same nominal length which has rounded edges. The degradation increases more or less gradually as the bias field decrement is increased, so that the lowest bias frequency will depend upon the degradation which can be tolerated.

Some typical bias curves are shown in Figure 10.17. (Note that for the a-c and pulse bias cases the peak swing from zero is plotted.) The curves for the various bias systems all exhibit a fairly rapid increase in output for bias values less than optimum and a somewhat more gradual change in output above the optimum. The curves for the three bias systems are very similar in shape, and for many applications the optimum bias values will be very nearly the same. The particular data shown in Figure 10.17 were chosen to show the result of operating at frequencies high enough to cause deviation from ideal conditions. The maximum of the curves in Figure 10.17*b* occurs at higher values than in 10.17*a* and 10.17*c* because the increased losses and reduced permeability of the head core at 2 mc decreases the effectiveness of the applied bias excitation. The maximum corresponds to the bias for greatest record sensitivity, but in general a somewhat higher value will result in a more steady signal. In the d-c and pulse bias systems there will be a reduction in output for bias levels greater than optimum, accompanied by an increase in record harmonic distortion. When a-c bias is used there will be a reduction in output for high bias values but very little increase in distortion. The increase in distortion for over-bias in the d-c and pulse bias cases is due to a shift in operating point, so that signals above a certain value will tend to saturate in one direction; in the case of a-c bias the origin remains the operating point, hence no even harmonic distortion. The reduction in output for the over-biased condition is due to increased record demagnetization. If the signal field component level remains unchanged while the bias is increased above optimum, it means that the signal field will have decayed (as required by the history) to a lower than normal value before the bias field has decayed to a value which will not overcome the potential barriers. This applies to all bias methods.

It is sometimes expedient to use a-c bias with d-c erase. If the d-c erase has resulted in a neutral medium, there will be little difference, except perhaps a slight increase in noise. If the d-c erase has resulted in a saturated medium, the noise will be higher, and second harmonic distortion will be present.

An interesting consequence of the wavelength dependence of the depth of magnetization occurs when optimization of bias levels is attempted.* It is found that the optimum bias level for short wavelengths

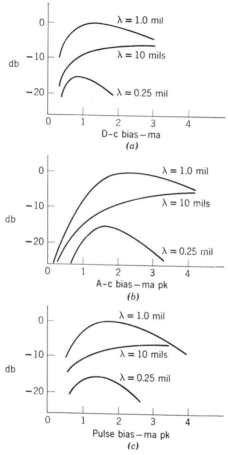

Figure 10.17. Typical bias curves: (a) d-c bias, $G = 0.1$ mil, velocity $= 100$ in./sec; (b) a-c bias, $G = 0.1$ mil, velocity $= 100$ in./sec, 2 mc bias; (c) $G = 0.1$ mil, velocity $= 100$ in./sec, bias pulse rate $= 400$ kps, bias pulse width $= 0.6$ μsec.

is less than the optimum level for long wavelengths. Because the bias field, like the record field, varies through the medium the optimum bias current in the head must be such as to produce the best average result for the active layers of the medium. Since the active layers of the medium for short recorded wavelengths are near the surface, it follows

* See Section 10.3.9.

that the bias requirement will be less than for the long recorded wavelengths where the complete tape thickness is active. These effects can be minimized by head designs which minimize the field variation through the medium thickness.

### 10.3.7 Effect of Record Head Spacing

The effect of spacing between the record head and the medium is normally neglected in all but computer drum applications. It is usually assumed that the spacing does not vary and that the head can be

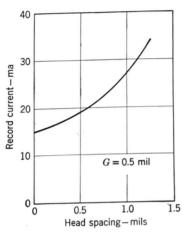

Figure 10.18. Record current required with spaced heads (output constant).

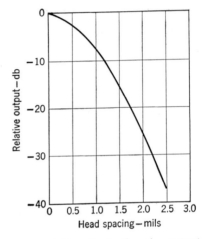

Figure 10.19. Reduction in output with spaced record head. Record and bias levels fixed at optimum for zero spacing. Playback head spacing fixed, $G = 0.5$ mil.

driven hard enough to overcome the loss in field intensity due to the spacing. Three effects of record head spacing will be considered: loss of resolution, change in bias requirements, and change in signal current requirements.

The effect of record head spacing upon resolution is apparent from plots of field-strength distribution around the head. High spatial gradients of field strength are necessary for high resolution. As the spacing increases, the spatial gradients become less, hence the resolution capabilities are reduced. Because of the higher drive necessary when spaced the record head may become saturated. If this occurs, a more serious loss in resolution results. The gap edge will saturate first and become magnetically equivalent to a head with rounded gap edges.

Formulas for calculating the increase in record-current and bias requirements with increasing head-to-medium spacing are not at present available. If the head in the region of the gap is likened to a simple dipole, the field should vary as the inverse first power for close spacings and the inverse third power for large spacings. Figure 10.18 shows a typical curve of required bias and record current for constant output as the spacing is varied. This curve is approximately the same for different recorded wavelengths. When the record and bias levels are held constant there is a change in output and linearity with varying head-to-medium spacing. A typical curve is shown in Figure 10.19. The effect of increased spacing upon linearity is due primarily to changed bias requirements which result from the spacing change. The reduction in output is due both to changed bias requirements and the lower intensity signal field affecting the medium.

## 10.3.8  Head Saturation

Except for modulator type playback heads, the flux densities in playback heads are much lower than saturation. Record heads may often operate at flux density levels approaching saturation; this is particularly true of spaced record heads with their higher drive requirements. Usually the saturation occurs at the pole tips around the gap because there the cross section is a minimum. As a result, head saturation has a direct effect on performance; it tends to increase the effective gap length and decrease resolution. The record level at which saturation occurs can be detected by a series of impedance measurements at various levels of drive and can also be detected from input-output data on the actual recording system if the characteristics of the medium and playback head are known from previous data.

## 10.3.9  Demagnetization Effects

The magnetization in the medium is subject to the demagnetizing influence of the surface poles associated with it. To see what is involved consider the idealized case in which an element of the medium is exposed to some magnetic history ultimately ending in a zero applied field without movement of the head relative to the medium. At the end of the history the medium will be in some remanent state, and it will stay in this state indefinitely as long as the head structure is not moved. If the head is moved (contact between head and medium is assumed), the surface poles which had been partially neutralized by the high permeability pole faces of the head will now influence and change the remanent distribution in the medium. The result is a decrease in the magnitude of the remanent flux which is severer the shorter the length of the magnetized element. In most actual recording systems these idealized conditions do not prevail; an element of medium emerges from the influence of the head having experienced the combined effects of history and demagnetization. Various persons have attempted calculation of the self-demagnetization, but except for wire very few results are available, and there is evidence to indicate that it is not too important for wavelengths longer than 0.5 mil. In general, the self-demagnetization associated with a magnet is greater for short stubby magnets. High coercive force decreases self-demagnetization, whereas high remanence increases self-demagnetization. From these general considerations we would expect short recorded wavelengths to be more susceptible to self-demagnetization when longitudinal magnetization is used and less susceptible when perpendicular magnetization is used.

One result of demagnetization is the confining of short wavelength signals to the surface of the medium. The field produced by a record head falls off with the distance from the head, as discussed elsewhere. In the absence of demagnetization effects such a varying field would cause the magnetization to decrease in the layers of medium farther from the head. This variation, however, would be the same for all recorded wavelengths. In actuality, each layer of the medium applies a demagnetizing field to all other layers of the medium. The demagnetizing field produced by the surface layer of the medium will be the greatest, since it has the greatest remanent magnetization; conversely, the demagnetizing field due to the layers remote from the head will be the least because they have a smaller magnetization. The demagnetizing fields will be greatest for short recorded wavelengths. Consider two layers of the medium, one remote from the head and one close to the head. When the field is applied by the record head the near layer will have a magnetization $B_1$ and the remote layer will have a magnetization $B_2$. If the recorded wavelength is long enough, the demagnetizing field will be very small and the two layers will remain substantially at $B_1$ and $B_2$ (Figure 10.20a) after the removal of the recording field. The ratio of $B_1$ to $B_2$ will be substantially the same as the ratio of the fields to which the layers were exposed. If, however, the wavelengths are short enough to produce strong demagnetizing fields, two effects can take place. The first effect will be a reduction of magnetization due to the self-demagnetizing field of each element on itself. As a result, the magnetization will fall to $B_1'$ and $B_2'$ along appropriate hysteresis loops (Figure 10.20b). The second effect will be a further reduction in magnetization due to the demagnetizing field pro-

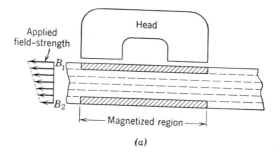

(a)

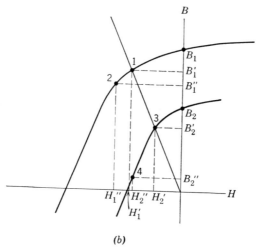

(b)

Figure 10.20. Demagnetization with nonuniform applied field: (a) magnetized elements; (b) demagnetization curves.

duced by the other layer of the medium. As stated earlier, the remote layer will experience the greatest applied demagnetizing field. As a result of the applied demagnetizing fields, the magnetization in each layer will reach points $B_1''$ and $B_2''$, respectively (Figure 10.20b). It is evident that

$$\frac{B_2''}{B_1''} < \frac{B_2'}{B_1'} \quad \text{if} \quad \frac{B_2' - B_2''}{B_1' - B_1''} > \frac{B_2'}{B_1'} \tag{10.6}$$

and

$$\frac{B_2'}{B_1'} < \frac{B_2}{B_1} \quad \text{if} \quad \frac{B_2 - B_2'}{B_1 - B_1'} > \frac{B_2}{B_1} \tag{10.7}$$

The inequalities of equation (10.6) are satisfied for most materials; in fact, usually $(B_2' - B_2'')/(B_1' - B_1'') > 1$. The inequalities of equation (10.7) are also satisfied for most materials, although perhaps not with so great a margin. It follows that for short wavelengths

$$\frac{B_2''}{B_1''} < \frac{B_2}{B_1}$$

Thus, for short wavelengths the effect will be to cause the final medium magnetization to fall off even more rapidly than the original head field for layers below the surface. This will cause short wavelengths to have their magnetization relatively more confined to the surface layer of the medium. This is summed up, somewhat inaccurately, by saying that short wavelengths are on the surface, whereas long wavelengths penetrate the thickness of the recording medium.

### 10.3.10  Aging Effects in a Magnetic Record

Unless it is exposed to excessive magnetic fields or temperatures, a recording made on a conventional recording medium is essentially unchanged by inactive storage. However, there is a reduction in the output from a particular recording with each playback. The reduction on the first playback is the severest, and the ultimate loss may be 6 db or greater. The output level for repeated playbacks tends to approach some final level asymptotically. Usually the drop is less than 6 db, and an essentially constant output is reached after five to ten playbacks. (This effect is quite similar to the aging of permanent magnets when the keeper is removed and replaced.) Although aging is noted with only the head core structure passing over the medium, it is found that the effects are modified when a conventional wound head structure is used.

### 10.3.11  Print Effect

The magnetization of a section of magnetized tape (or wire) which is stored on a roll tends to affect the magnetization of adjacent sections of tape. This tendency to introduce spurious signals on adjacent tape layers is known as the "print effect."

Investigations (17, 20, 22, 28, 37) have shown that this effect is a function of the recorded wavelength, the temperature, the distance between layers of tape, the time of contact of the tapes, the time elapsed since the ending of contact, and the magnitude of the recorded magnetization of the tape. The print effect is an example of small signal recording without bias.

The field at a distance $y$ from the tape of thickness $a$, for $\pi a/\lambda \ll 1$ is directly proportional to (37)

$$H(y, a, \lambda) = \frac{\pi a}{\lambda} e^{-2\pi y/\lambda} \tag{10.8}$$

where $\lambda$ is the recorded wavelength. But the printed flux is directly proportional to the recorded flux, so as the wavelength decreases the printed flux first increases as $1/\lambda$ and then decreases as the exponential term becomes dominant. The maximum field is obtained for $\lambda = 2\pi y$. The printed flux is also directly proportional to the storage temperature of the tape roll and the logarithm of the contact time and inversely proportional to the logarithm of the time elapsed since contact ended.

It is also important to keep the stored tape away from a strong magnetic field because the field will act as a bias field and thus increase the print effect or even cause partial erasure of the recorded magnetization.

## 10.4   Heat as a Linearizing Agent

To use heat as the linearizing agent the sample is exposed to the magnetizing field and the temperature is raised to an optimum value and then lowered to normal. The remanent flux produced by this process will be a linear function of the applied magnetic field. As with other bias methods, the applied field must not approach saturation. The temperature must exceed some minimum value, if satisfactory linearization is to be accomplished, but may be higher than this minimum without detrimental effect if the magnetizing field is maintained until the temperature has dropped to normal.

## 10.5   Specific Recording Media (23, 50)

The medium actually used in magnetic recording can be classified as metallic or nonmetallic. It is also possible to classify the various media by their geometry: wire, tape, rigid. Further breakdowns are possible in terms of constituents and manufacturing techniques. Magnetically speaking, the coercive force $(H_c)$ and the maximum remanent flux $(B_r)$ are the most significant properties.

### 10.5.1 Metallic Media

The first magnetic material used was carbon steel wire, as in Valdemar Poulsen's (1) first recorder. Other materials which have been considered or used are tungsten steel, Vicalloy, 420 type stainless steel, 18-8 type stainless steel, and cunife. Some of the properties are listed in Table 10.1. The magnetic properties of all of the metallic media

## Table 10.1

### Metallic Recording Media

| Medium | Composition | $H_c$ (oersteds) | $B_r$ (gauss) |
|---|---|---|---|
| Carbon steel wire | | 40 | 10,000 |
| 420 stainless | 12–14 per cent Cr | 60 | 7,000 |
| 18-8 stainless | 18 per cent Cr, 8 per cent Ni | 200 | 3,000 |
| Tungsten steel wire | | 30 | 12,000 |
| Vicalloy | 52 Cu, 11 Va, 37 Fe | 200 | 11,500 |
| Cunife | 60 Cu, 20 Ni, 20 Fe | 500 | 5,500 |
| Nickel-cobalt plate | 80 Co, 20 Ni | 250 | 10,000 |

are obtained only by proper cold work and heat-treating. Carbon steel wire was still in the magnetic recording picture until the introduction of stainless steel recording wire in the early 1940's. A typical remanent flux curve for carbon steel wire is shown in Figure 10.21. The

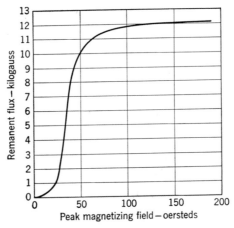

**Figure 10.21.** Remanent flux, carbon steel wire. (Courtesy Armour Research Foundation (47).)

relatively high $B_{rm}$ of the carbon steel wire yields the large playback voltage which is desirable; however, the low coercive force and high remanence combine to produce layer-to-layer printing and poor short wavelength resolution.

It was coincident with the introduction of stainless steel recording wire that magnetic recording became more than a novelty or a specialized scientific tool. Stainless steel wire Figure 10.22 is 3.6 mils in diameter,

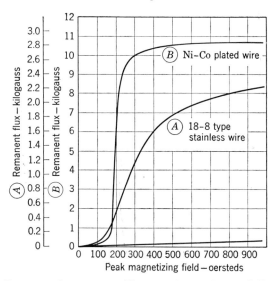

Figure 10.22. Remanent flux, curves. (Courtesy Armour Research Foundation (47).)

and although it has low remanence, hence low output, its higher coercive force resulted in improved resolution, and wavelengths as short as 2 mils were recorded.

Another type of wire (23) is made by plating a nickel-cobalt alloy on a brass wire (Figure 10.22). It is not cold-worked or heat-treated but does give evidence of large mechanical strains. This wire is not much used at the present time. The diameter of the plated wire is somewhat greater than the standard stainless steel wire; hence it is not always interchangeable.

Metallic magnetic recording media of the materials mentioned have also been used in tape form. As such, the magnetic properties are the same as in the wire form. Nickel-cobalt plated tape has been used in computers. Stainless steel tape up to 6 inches wide has been used in special recorders in which it had to withstand rough treatment. Stainless steel requires severe cold-working to develop the magnetic properties. For tapes this is accomplished by rolling, which is not so satisfactory as drawing wire. The stainless steel tapes are 1.5 to 3 mils thick and are fairly stiff. Because of the stiffness metallic tapes do not conform well to record and playback heads and tend to have a higher noise level than nonmetallic tapes.

Metallic recording media have found considerable use in a rigid form, such as a drum or disk. Nickel-cobalt plating is the commonest, although some work has been done with tape or cunife wire wound around a drum. Metallic drums have excellent wearing properties when used with metallic contact heads.

### 10.5.2  Nonmetallic Media

Nonmetallic magnetic recording media normally use iron oxide powder in some form held in a nonmetallic binder. The commonest materials are $\gamma Fe_2O_3$ (red) and $Fe_3O_4$ (black) in small particles 1 $\mu$ or less in size. The red oxide is used almost exclusively now. Other magnetic powder can be used and investigation is still continuing to devise better materials. The particles which are needlelike in shape, may be oriented by a magnetic field during the coating process. At the present state of the magnetic recording art the nonmetallic media, particularly tapes, are by far the commonest. The pigment in most commercially available tapes does not exceed 40 per cent of the volume of the coating. Some common binders are cellulose acetate, cellulose nitrate, epoxy resins, and the vinyl compounds, although many others can be used. The coercivity of the magnetic powder may vary from 100 to 500 oersteds, although most commercially available coatings are in the 200–300 oersted range. The coercivity is an intrinsic property of the particles, and the remanence is a function of the particular dispersion, i.e., the density of powder in the binder and the manufacturing techniques. Typical values of remanence are 600 and 1200 gauss, although they may vary from 300 to 1500 gauss (Figure 10.23). Obvious mechanical difficulties exist when the percentage of powder is made too great, particularly in tapes.

The commonest form for nonmetallic media is tape in which a suspension of the powder in the binder is coated on a flexible backing for strength. Acetate film backings are commonly used, but mylar film backings are finding increased use. The mylar has the advantage of being dimensionally quite stable with changes in temperature or humidity. It has a higher resistance to breaking than acetate, but it does distort severely under high stress. Tapes of the coated type are now available in a number of thicknesses and coatings. Acetate backings from 0.8 to 1.5 mils are used, and mylar backings range from 0.5

to 1.5 mil. The thickness of the coatings varies from 0.3 mil to 0.7 mil. Over-all tape thickness of the commonest standard tape is 2.2 mils. Tapes are made in large widths and slit to the desired widths (commonly $\frac{1}{4}$ and $\frac{1}{2}$ inch).

Nonmetallic tapes can also be made in the form of a uniform dispersion of the magnetic powder throughout the volume of the tape. This tape has no backing, and in order to maintain a usable strength the density of particles must be less than in the coated tapes. Because of the lower

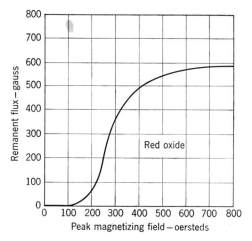

Figure 10.23. Remanent flux, tape. (Courtesy Minnesota Mining and Manufacturing Co. (50))

density the $B_r$ is lower, but since the total thickness is active the long wavelength output does not suffer greatly. These tapes are not much used.

Nonmetallic tapes, particularly of the thinner varieties, are very flexible and have the ability to conform very well to the heads; this is important at short wavelengths. At present the coated type tapes have the best short wavelength characteristics (high-frequency response) of any medium. In good equipment saturated signal-to-noise ratios of 60 db are possible over an eight-to-ten octave range. In normal use, and with some care in storage, excellent tape life can be realized.

These powders can also be coated on rigid backings by spraying or dipping. The tape manufacturers make paintlike suspensions, and magnetic drum recorders are commonly made by spraying on an aluminum drum surface. Care must be taken in this process to get a uniform coating, free from crazing or other defects. For contact-head use the life of these coatings does not compare with the metallic surfaces.

## 10.6    Playback Process

### 10.6.1    Reciprocity

Magnetic record-playback systems are used for many applications in frequency ranges from a few cycles per second to a number of megacycles per second. For a given application a certain bandwidth must be reproduced from the magnetic media, so it is necessary to know the frequency response of the playback system, which is determined primarily by the resolution of the playback head. To calculate this resolution for a given head geometry we must solve a rather complex field

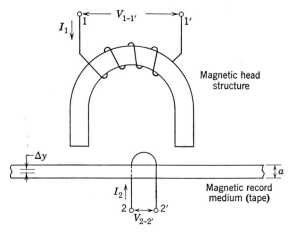

**Figure 10.24.** Schematic representation of a magnetic playback system.

problem. Wallace (32) approaches the problem from this point of view for one idealized head geometry. It appears that a more useful approach is to determine the field distribution the head would produce as a record head and then apply the reciprocity theorem (37) for four terminal networks to determine how the playback head would react to this field. The word reciprocity implies that the entire system under consideration is operating in its linear region. Although the recording process is highly nonlinear, the playback process is probably linear in its operation, so that the application of the reciprocity theorem to the latter is valid. The first assumption which must be made is that the permeability of the tape is unity, although some tapes may have values from two to five. It appears that the effect of the higher permeabilities is to deteriorate the short wavelength response of the system. The second assumption is that the permeability of the head core is very large. In practice, it is usually at least a hundred.

A general representation of a magnetic playback system is shown in Figure 10.24. In the actual process a previously magnetized tape travels at a fixed velocity near a magnetic structure, and it is desired to know what voltage appears at terminals 1–1' for a given magnetization on the tape. In order to convert this system to a four-terminal network, assume that the magnetization on the tape is replaced by a small equivalent current loop 2–2' properly oriented about the tape position to produce the same external field.

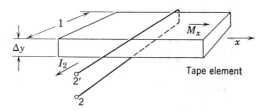

**Figure 10.25.** Equivalence of a current loop and magnetization on the tape.

If one considers terminals 2–2' open, this is equivalent to the removal of the tape. A current $I_1$ in the magnetic head now considered as a record head produces a magnetic field at point 2. The open circuit voltage at terminals 2–2' is $V_{2-2'} = I_1 Z_{12}$, where $Z_{12}$ is the transfer impedance between terminals one and two.

Next let terminals 1–1' be open and put a current through 2–2'. This is equivalent to running a properly magnetized tape through the system. Then

$$V_{1-1'} = I_2 Z_{21}$$

By using the reciprocity relationship ($Z_{12} = Z_{21}$), this becomes

$$\frac{V_{2-2'}}{I_1} = \frac{V_{1-1'}}{I_2} \tag{10.9}$$

where $V_{2-2'}$ is the voltage produced by the flux through coil 2 due to the field produced by the head. If the tape is oriented in the $x$-direction, as shown in Figure 10.25, and is of unit width, then the voltage $V_{2-2'}$ at a differential element of tape is

$$V_{2-2'} = j\omega \, \Delta\phi_{2-2'} = -j\omega\mu_0 \frac{\partial A}{\partial x} \Delta y \tag{10.10}$$

where $A$ is the scalar magnetic potential produced at point 2 by the head and

$$-\frac{\partial A}{\partial x} = H_x \tag{10.11}$$

The magnetization in the tape can also be written in terms of the current $I_2$. Since the coil has been oriented, as shown in Figure 10.25, the magnetization must be parallel to the $x$-axis. The equivalent dipole produced by $I_2$ is $\mu_0 I_2 \Delta y$. The equivalent dipole produced by the volume magnetization $M_x$ is $M_x \Delta y \Delta x$. Hence

$$I_2 = \frac{M_x}{\mu_0} \Delta x \tag{10.12}$$

The open circuit voltage is

$$V_{1-1'} = j\omega \, \Delta\phi_{1-1'} \tag{10.13}$$

where $\phi_{1-1'}$ is the flux produced by the magnetized tape. Hence from equations 10.9 through 10.13, in the limit

$$\phi_1 = -\frac{1}{I_1} \int_0^a dy \int_{-\infty}^{+\infty} \frac{\partial A}{\partial x} M_x \, dx \tag{10.14}$$

where the magnetized tape of thickness $a$ extends from minus infinity to plus infinity.

The interpretation of equation 10.14 gives an interesting picture of the playback mechanism. The results indicate that if the tape is magnetized only in the $x$-direction then it is just the $x$-component of the field produced by the head that "senses" the tape magnetization over the entire length of tape. If the tape is recorded with a $y$-component of magnetization, then an additional term will be added which will contain the product of $M_y$ and $\dfrac{\partial A}{\partial y}$ (the $y$-component of the head field).

In order to determine the playback response as a function of recorded wavelength, it is necessary merely to assume a distribution of magnetization $M_x = M \cos \dfrac{2\pi}{\lambda} (x - vt)$. If the head under consideration is symmetric about the $y$-axis, then the only portion of $M_x$ needed in the integration is $M_x = M \cos \dfrac{2\pi x}{\lambda} \cos \dfrac{2\pi vt}{\lambda}$.

### 10.6.2  Typical Head Responses (12, 26, 32, 37, 41, 42)

As an example of the application of the previous theory, consider configuration I (37), a head which is symmetrical with respect to both the $x$- and $y$-axes and which extends to infinity in both directions (Figure 10.26). Consider a tape of thickness $a$ and unit width to pass through

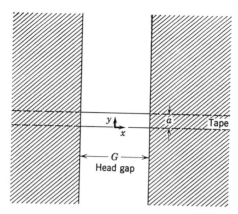

**Figure 10.26.** Head with infinite dimensions. (Westmijze, 1953.)

the head material parallel to the $x$-axis. The distribution of magnetization in the tape is assumed to be

$$M_x = M \cos \frac{2\pi x}{\lambda} \cos \frac{2\pi v t}{\lambda} \tag{10.15}$$

$$M_y = M_z = 0$$

The potential distribution for this type of head is simply

$$A = \frac{Ix}{G} \tag{10.16}$$

Substitution of equations 10.15 and 10.16 into 10.14 yields

$$\phi = Ma \left( \frac{\sin (\pi G/\lambda)}{\pi G/\lambda} \right) \cos \frac{2\pi v t}{\lambda} \tag{10.17}$$

The factor in parentheses is the gap loss factor which indicates that the flux $\phi$ will be zero for $G/\lambda = n$ where $n$ is an integer.

Some of the other head configurations for which the response has been calculated by Westmijze and others are tabulated in Table 10.2.

Configuration II (37) is a head formed by two thin sheets in the $y = 0$ plane which extend to infinity. The head is symmetrical with respect to the $y$- and $z$-axes. The tape travels parallel to the sheets in the $x$-direction (Figure 10.27).

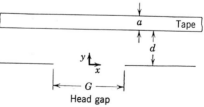

**Figure 10.27.** Thin sheet head. (Westmijze, 1953.)

## Table 10.2

### Response Functions for Playback Heads

| Head Configuration | Response $\left(\phi = \phi' \cos \dfrac{2\pi vt}{\lambda}\right)$ |
|---|---|

I. Infinite head,
Figure 10.26
(both sides of tape)

$$\phi' = Ma\left(\frac{\sin(\pi G/\lambda)}{\pi G/\lambda}\right)$$

II. Thin sheet head,
Figure 10.27
(one side of tape)

$$\phi' = Ma\left(\frac{1 - e^{-2\pi a/\lambda}}{(2\pi a/\lambda)}\right)(e^{-2\pi d/\lambda})J_0\left(\frac{\pi G}{\lambda}\right)$$

where $J_0\left(\dfrac{\pi G}{\lambda}\right)$ is the zero-order Bessel function

III. Semi-infinite head,
Figure 10.28
(one side of tape)

$$\phi' = Ma\left(\frac{1 - e^{-2\pi a/\lambda}}{(2\pi a/\lambda)}\right)(e^{-2\pi d/\lambda})S\left(\frac{\pi G}{\lambda}\right)$$

where $S\left(\dfrac{\pi G}{\lambda}\right) \approx \dfrac{3^{1\!/6}\Gamma(\frac{2}{3})}{\pi^{1\!/3}}\dfrac{\sin[(\pi G/\lambda) + \pi/G]}{(2\pi G/\lambda)^{2\!/3}}$

IV. Double head,
Figure 10.29
(both sides of tape)

$$\phi' = a\left(\frac{e^{-2\pi d/\lambda}(1 - e^{-2\pi a/\lambda}) - e^{2\pi d/\lambda}(1 - e^{2\pi a/\lambda})}{4\pi a/\lambda}\right)S$$

where $S' = \displaystyle\int_{-\infty}^{+\infty} \frac{\partial A}{\partial x}M_x\,dx$

integrated along the $x$-axis

Configuration III (37) is a semi-infinite head which begins to approach a practical head in form. It consists of two permeable blocks separated

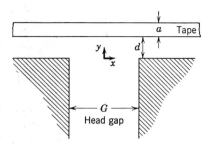

**Figure 10.28.** Head with semi-infinite gap. (Westmijze, 1953.)

by the gap $G$ and extending to infinity in the $(-y\text{-})$, $x$-, and $z$-directions. It is on only one side of the tape (Figure 10.28).

Configuration IV consists of two generalized heads with semi-infinite dimensions, one on each side of the tape. The configuration has $y$-axis symmetry (Figure 10.29).

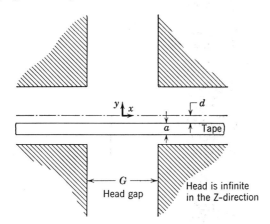

**Figure 10.29.** Double head.

An examination of Table 10.2 shows that in each case the gap loss factors have zeros at approximately those recorded wavelengths given by $\lambda = G/n$ where $n$ is an integer; this, however, is strictly true only for Configuration I.

The factor $(1 - e^{-2\pi a/\lambda})/(2\pi a/\lambda)$ is called the thickness loss factor (32, 37). For very thin tapes this factor is unity. Strictly speaking, this factor denotes a gain in long wavelength output with increasing tape thickness rather than a loss in short wavelength output.

The factor $e^{-2\pi d/\lambda}$ is the spacing loss factor. As would be expected, head-to-tape spacing results in a loss of short wavelength output.

The significant feature of these loss factors for head configurations I, II, and III is that they are independent. The independence of the gap loss factor for an actual head is demonstrated in Figure 10.30. For this data a conventional head was used which had a nominal gap spacer of 0.005 inch; the tape speed was 2.3 inches per second. For the different head-to-tape spacings of 0, 1.0, and 2.0 mils it will be noted that within the accuracy of the data no shifts in zeros are noted.

In configuration IV the gap loss factor is separable but the thickness and tape position factors are not. It will be noted that the thickness and tape position terms consist of the sum of two terms, each of which has the form of the thickness and spacing factors of the other configurations. This form of the result emphasizes the fact that the total flux is due to the contribution from the two heads.

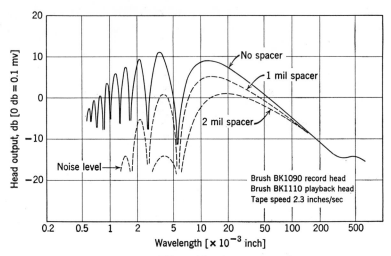

**Figure 10.30.** Effect of head-to-tape spacing.

These special cases can be generalized as follows. A head on only one side of the tape is necessary for separation of spacing and tape thickness factors, whereas $y$-axis symmetry is necessary for separation of the gap loss factor.

The response of configuration III to longitudinal magnetization is equal to the response to perpendicular magnetization, except for a 90° phase shift which is independent of frequency. Referring to Figure 10.31, assume a sinusoidal distribution of flux on the tape. For lon-

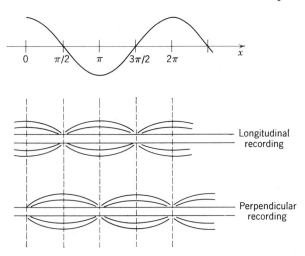

**Figure 10.31.** Lines of flux external to a magnetized tape.

gitudinal recording the surface flux density is zero at $x = 0$ and $x = \pi$ and a maximum at $x = \pi/2$ and $x = 3\pi/2$. For perpendicular recording the surface flux density is a maximum at $x = 0$ and $x = \pi$ and zero at $x = \pi/2$ and $x = 3\pi/2$. Therefore, at a point external to the tape these two cases are identical, except for a 90° phase shift.

### 10.6.3 Rate of Change Playback (12, 15, 26, 37)

In the method of playback most commonly used, the voltage induced in the output winding is proportional to the rate of change of flux through the head. This results in an increase in the output voltage of 6 db per octave. Since this increase is superimposed on the output curve already discussed, the high-frequency response is improved. Figure 10.30 shows the type of response curve obtainable in a rate of change playback system. In order to obtain a flat response from the playback amplifier, both high- and low-frequency compensation are needed.

### 10.6.4 Proportional Playback (36, 39, 43)

In a proportional playback system the voltage induced in the output winding is proportional to the recorded flux in the tape rather than its rate of change. Thus in the low-frequency or long wavelength region the response is reasonably flat to wavelengths approaching the physical length of the head. Hence no low-frequency equalization is usually needed. In the high-frequency or short wavelength region the response is poorer than in rate-of-change playback, since the same losses are present without the 6 db per octave rise with frequency.

At very long wavelengths the response is limited by the finite length of the head. The head field distribution inserted into equation 10.14 contained a contribution which was largely due to the gap. No other parts of the head field were introduced because of the assumption of an infinite head length. If a head field component is added as a result of the finite head length, peaks and valleys will be found in the long wavelength portion of the response curve (Figure 10.30). In order to minimize the head field due to the head length, the playback head is swept back away from the tape. For wavelengths longer than the head length the response decreases at the rate of 12 db/octave or greater.

## 10.7   Transient Response of the Head by Flux Plotting

For those head configurations in which the analytic calculation of the field produced by the head becomes prohibitive the use of flux plotting techniques can yield useful information.  Moreover, in order to simplify the calculation it is more practical to assume a pulse of magnetization rather than a sinusoidal distribution.

Figure 10.32 shows a typical head and tape configuration.  The tape has a longitudinally magnetized signal recorded in the form of a pulse.

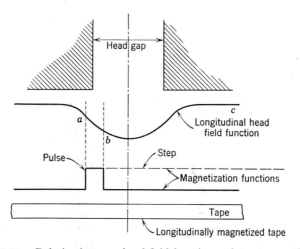

**Figure 10.32.**  Relation between head field function and tape magnetization.

Below the head is shown a plot of the longitudinal component of the field produced by the head.

According to equation 10.14, the total flux in the head for the particular position of the pulse is found by multiplying the value of the magnetization by the field at the same point and integrating over the extent of the pulse.  For example, for the position of the pulse which is shown the instantaneous value of the flux in the head is proportional to the area under the field plot from $a$ to $b$.  The complete response can then be obtained by moving the pulse along the tape and calculating the area of the proper segment.  Since the response to the leading edge of the sharply rising pulse is the same as that of the trailing edge, it is just as useful and perhaps more convenient to consider a unit step function.  In this case the instantaneous flux would be the total area under the flux plot curve from $a$ to $c$.  A series of integrations could then be made with a planimeter to ascertain quickly the amount of distortion produced by the head. This method determines what may be called the transient response of the head.

## 10.7.1   Flux Plotting (14, 16)

The remaining problem is that of obtaining a satisfactory field plot. The field distribution around a head is three-dimensional and as such would pose a difficult problem. By making the width of the head large compared to the gap length the side fringing can be neglected, except for possible cross-talk among several adjacent heads. The field distribution in this case can be considered two-dimensional, so that the previous discussion applies. Some graphical methods, although applicable to all geometries, are very laborious. Direct measurement of the magnetic field intensity by the use of suitable probes has been accomplished with both standard heads and scaled-up models. Analogue field plotting by measuring the voltage distribution in a current-carrying sheet using suitable electrode geometries appears to be the most practical, although the labor is still considerable.

Direct measurement of the field around an actual head has been accomplished with a single conductor which can be moved by micrometer adjustments (31). A commoner direct field measurement technique utilizes a large model of a head which permits the use of a more sensitive but larger probe.

Analogue field plotting has been carried out extensively with electrolytic tanks or resistance paper. Conducting models of the head pole pieces are immersed in the conducting electrolyte of the tank. By keeping the pole pieces at electrical potentials which are the analogues of the magnetic potentials of the head pole pieces currents are produced in the electrolyte which have a flow pattern analogous to the magnetic flux pattern around the head. The spatial distribution of electrical field in the tank is the same as the corresponding magnetic field distribution and is obtained by direct measurement of the electrical field in the electrolyte or by calculation from the measured potential distribution.

The use of the resistance paper rather than electrolytic tanks affords great convenience in that the head structure may be painted on the paper with silver paint. A field plot may be made with a single probe and high impedance voltmeter. The potential is then determined from point to point along a line which represents the position of the tape. The potential difference between two adjacent points divided by the separation is a measure of the field intensity.

The size and placement of the electrodes on the paper must be chosen to conform to the boundary conditions dictated by the head. Advantage should be taken of all axes of symmetry which may be converted to equipotential lines. In addition, the edge of the resistance paper may be used as a line along which the normal component of current flow is known to be zero. In order to be effective, the field plot must be extended far enough so that the field essentially approaches zero compared to the field strength at the maximum points. Probably a 20-to-1 decrease in field strength is sufficient.

As an example of the use of flux plotting techniques, the method was applied to a conventional gap-type head configuration to determine the effect of rounding of the gap edges. In Figure 10.33 are shown the

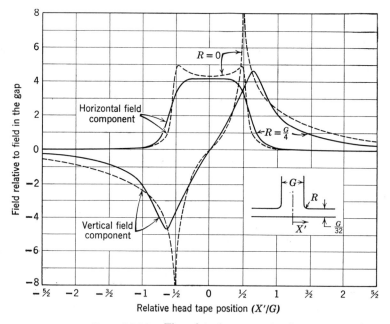

**Figure 10.33.** Flux plot of gap-type head.

horizontal and vertical field components for a gap-type head with square and rounded corners. The dimensions are relative to the gap width, and the flux amplitude is given relative to the value deep in the gap. If a step function of longitudinal magnetization is assumed at a spacing of $G/32$ from the head such that

$$M_x = 0 \quad \text{for} \quad x \leqq 0$$

$$M_x = 1 \quad \text{for} \quad x > 0$$

$$\int_{-\infty}^{+\infty} \frac{\partial A}{\partial x} M_x \, dx = \int_{x'}^{+\infty} \frac{\partial A}{\partial x} \, dx$$

then the flux through the head can be determined for any position of the tape by integrating the area under the horizontal flux plot curve from $x = x'$ to $\infty$. The step function response for this head with a given radius at the corner is shown in Figure 10.34. Also shown is the corresponding response curve for a step function of perpendicular magnetization in the tape.

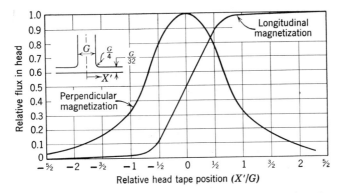

Figure 10.34. Transient response of gap-type head to a step function of tape magnetization.

From the flux plots it can be seen that the increased radius of the corners degrades the short wavelength response. This head has a perfect low-frequency response to direct current, since the head represented by the flux plots has infinite dimensions. A practical gap-type head would have no response at direct current, where by direct current is meant a recording of infinite wavelength.

It can be seen that the impulse or step-function response method of evaluation of the performance of a head is relatively quick and describes rather completely the performance of the head. In many respects it is a more useful type of representation than the frequency and phase characteristics which may be obtained from it by numerical methods.

## 10.8   Head Construction (38)

Typical head materials are either the laminated metallic variety or ferrites, both of which possess high permeability. Although both materials can be formed to have short, well-defined gaps, it is found that the laminated material (e.g., mumetal) maintains a uniform gap when it wears down. Ferrite heads, on the other hand, erode at the gap edges, so that the effective gap length increases even at low tape speeds (44).

## 10.8.1 Record Heads

A recording head must compromise resolution, core saturation and losses, and drive. In a gap type recording head the recording is made by the leakage flux at the gap. If close contact is maintained between the tape and the head, then the record head resolution is determined by the sharpness of the sharpest gap edge rather than the gap length. At larger head-to-tape spacings it is the gap length itself which controls the resolution. It is desired to make the leakage flux a maximum by

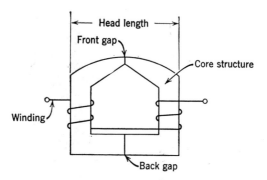

**Figure 10.35.** Conventional record-playback head.

means of a larger front gap length (Figure 10.35). However, the maximum length is limited by the available driving current and the desired resolution.

## 10.8.2 Rate-of-change Playback Head

A conventional playback head is shown in Figure 10.35. One important feature is the relative construction of the back gap to the front gap. In order that the tape may produce the maximum flux inside the head, the ratio of the front gap reluctance to the reluctance of the path through the core and back gap must be as large as possible. This accounts for the usually smaller cross-sectional area of the front gap.

For the playback of short wavelengths the front gap must, of course, be short compared to the shortest recorded wavelength. The effective gap length is determined by the sharpness of the gap corners. If the gap edges are rounded or if the gap length is not constant across the track width, the response curve will not exhibit the sharp nulls shown in Figure 10.30. The peaks and nulls will begin to merge, and the response will show a gradual trailing off at the shorter wavelengths.

The long wavelength response of a head falls off for wavelengths greater than the length of the head (37, 39). Auxiliary projections can be added to a head to increase its long wavelength response. Other techniques are also possible. Perpendicular recording is capable of going to much longer wavelengths but usually at the expense of short wavelength response. Another technique is to skew the gap at an angle of approximately 45° to the direction of tape travel.

### 10.8.3   Proportional Playback Heads (36, 39, 43)

One type of proportional playback head is the magnetic modulator head. In this type of head the signal flux controls a locally supplied excitation flux. These heads can be divided into two categories: those with signal flux parallel to the exciting flux and those with the signal flux perpendicular to the exciting flux. In all cases there is no exciting signal coupled to the output winding, except in the presence of signal flux. This decoupling is inherent in the perpendicular case and is accomplished by a balanced bridge arrangement in the parallel case. Although there is a number of variations of this head, a basic design for the parallel case is presented schematically in Figure 10.36. The front gap is shown at the top of the figure. Coils $C$ and $D$ are the signal windings and are connected series

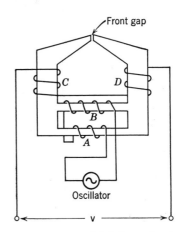

Figure 10.36.   Modulator head, parallel type.

aiding. Coils $A$ and $B$ are connected to a high-frequency oscillator in opposition, so that the flux produced cancels in the signal winding for a magnetically balanced structure. The cross section of the legs on which coils $A$ and $B$ are wound is small enough so that the oscillator signal is large enough to saturate the legs. The presence of signal flux in the head drives one of the legs out of saturation, unbalancing the magnetic structure and causing a voltage to be induced in the signal winding. This voltage, as with all modulator heads, is of the suppressed carrier form having a carrier frequency of twice the oscillator frequency. As the signal flux changes with time, this change appears as amplitude modulation of the carrier. The head is often purposely unbalanced, so that a carrier is always present to aid in demodulating the signal.

Other variations of a modulator head are shown in Figures 10.37 and 10.38. In these designs a single oscillator winding is used in such a way that the flux produced is perpendicular to the signal flux.

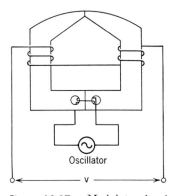

**Figure 10.37.** Modulator head, perpendicular type A.

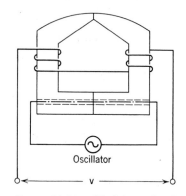

**Figure 10.38.** Modulator head, perpendicular type B.

A second type of proportional playback head is the electron beam head. One design is shown in Figure 10.39. It consists of an electron gun, two magnetic pole pieces, two collector plates, and an external magnetic core structure with a front gap to pick up the flux from the

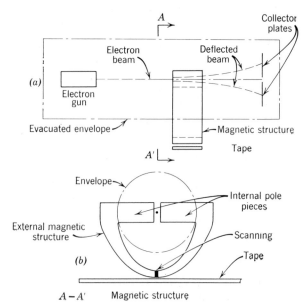

**Figure 10.39.** Schematic diagram of electron beam head: (a) side view, (b) section A-A'.

tape. With no flux in the front gap, the electron beam splits equally between the two collector plates. With magnetic flux in the core, the beam is deflected so that more electron current is picked up by one plate than the other, thus giving an unbalanced output from the tube.

A second design of an electron beam head which has an increased sensitivity is shown in Figure 10.40 (47). The electron beam is reflected

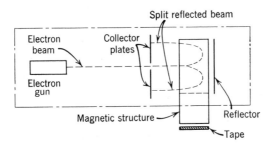

**Figure 10.40.** Reflexed electron beam head.

by the reflector plate and returns to the collector plates. The division of current between the plates depends upon the magnetic field. The electron beam is deflected when its velocity is nearly zero rather than a maximum; thus a smaller magnetic field is required for the same deflection.

The major difference between the electron beam head and the modulator head is that there is no high-frequency field present. Hence the core structure can be designed for the highest signal frequency instead of the oscillator frequency. Thicker laminations could be used and thereby simplify head fabrication.

## 10.9   Dielectric Recording

Dielectric recording, in the same sense as magnetic recording, refers to any recording process which makes use of the properties of dielectric materials. Conceptually, dielectric recording systems using ferroelectric materials, which are the dual of the magnetic recording system described earlier, are possible. In addition, other systems, using either ferroelectric or nonferroelectric materials, are possible because of the existence of isolated electric charges. Except in the case of storage tube and xerography, dielectric recording has not had a very great technological development.

### 10.9.1  Record Process.  Induction

Dielectric recording by induction (52) refers to a process in which the information is stored as a distribution of electric polarization in the volume of record medium.  Most of the experience with induction dielectric recording has been with nonferroelectric media.  The recorded polarization appears to be proportional to the applied field, but the record process takes as much as several seconds to reach a stable maximum value.  The recorded signal is not permanent and decays to one half value in a few seconds.  It appears that the process does not utilize the hysteresis effects to advantage.  The observed resolutions have been at least an order of magnitude poorer than that attainable with magnetic recording.

A recent patent of W. P. Mason (54) indicates a possible fruitful direction.  In this case a ferroelectric (barium titanate) was used as the medium, and recordings of excellent resolution and permanency were reported.  This approach appears closer to standard magnetic recording techniques and does make use of the hysteresis of the barium titanate.  Playback is accomplished by using a carrier and determining the capacitance or dielectric constant of the region directly under the probe which is in intimate contact with the medium.  The dielectric constant depends upon the recorded state of the medium.

### 10.9.2  Coronal Spraying

Dielectric recording by coronal spraying (52) refers to a process in which charged particles are applied to the surface of a dielectric medium with a distribution representative of the information to be recorded.  This process is possible in dielectric recording because of the existence of isolated electrical charges.  It has no analogy in magnetic recording and requires higher potentials than the nonferroelectric recording by induction if the ions must be produced by the recording potential.  The recording amplitude increases linearly with record head potential over a usefully wide range, but there is a minimum below which no "spraying" takes place.  The actual recording takes place in a time as short as a microsecond, and the lifetime of a signal may be as long as minutes or shorter than a second, depending upon the medium and the recorded wavelength.  The resolution is slightly better than induction recording and is probably limited by the resolution of the heads used.

Work has been carried out at the Marine Physical Laboratory of the University of California (53) on the investigation of the sprayed charge dielectric recording technique with nonferroelectrics. The theoretical response of a circular probe was derived and experimental results were reported. In this system the electric charges are obtained from a r-f arc or from a point-to-plane r-f corona discharge. Storage times of 1 to 100 hours were attained. A frequency response of 1 cycle to 5 kc at a surface velocity of 330 in/sec with a dynamic range of 50 db was reported.

### 10.9.3  Electro Optical Recording

Electro-optical dielectric recording (52) refers to the production of a distribution of charge on the surface of a medium by the use of electro-optical phenomena, such as the photoconductive effect in selenium. The surface upon which the recording is to be made (selenium, phosphor, or other photoconductive film) is first uniformly charged with charges of one polarity in the dark. The information to be recorded is then applied in the form of a modulated light beam which is focused to a very small spot or line. The application of light to a spot on the film increases the photoconductivity permitting the charge to leak off in that area. Since the photoconductivity is a function of light exposure time and intensity, a controlled distribution of charge results on the surface of the medium. There is reciprocity between light intensity and time of exposure. By using a very high-intensity light source exposure times can be as low as a microsecond. Selenium surfaces appear to have shorter time constants than phosphor surfaces. Resolution of sinusoidal wavelengths as short as 4 mils have been accomplished, and signal-to-noise ratios of 15 to 20 db for wavelengths greater than 0.1 inch have been observed. The resolution on record is determined by the size of the scanning light spot and the characteristics of the photo-conductive film; at present selenium appears to be the best. The recording is not permanent, but it has a considerably longer life than the other methods; half lives of 220 and 90 minutes have been noted for selenium and phosphor, respectively.

### 10.9.4  Recording Media

The media used for induction or for coronal spraying dielectric record-ing have for the most part been nonferroelectric and include the follow-ing (52):

Polyvinyl chloride tape
Polyvinyl chloride tape impregnated with barium titanate
Polyethylene tape

Polyethylene tape containing barium titanate
Polyethylene tape containg gamma $Fe_2O_3$
Polystyrene tape
Teflon tape
Cellophane tape
Masking tape
Plastic electrical tape
Black friction tape
Electrician rubber tape
Ceresin wax impregnated tape
Carnuba wax impregnated tape
Paraffin wax impregnated tape

The polyvinyl chloride tape is the most successful of this group. A very high surface resistivity is one of the more important requirements of a dielectric recording medium. The use of ferroelectric barium titanate has been described in Mason's patent (54).

For electro-optical recording two of the media considered have been vitreous selenium evaporated on a thin film and metal and phosphor coated on a conducting backing. The selenium surface has been more successful, being about 6000 times as light sensitive as the phosphor tested. Also, the resolution of the selenium surface is about three times better. The selenium is better for storage up to 6 hours, and for longer times phosphor is better.

## 10.10  Playback Processes.  Xerography

A dielectric recording can be made visible by dusting it with a suitable dielectric powder, usually black. This technique is well developed in a reproduction process called xerography. In this process electro-optical dielectric recording is used, and the charged photoconductive surface is exposed like a photographic plate. The exposed plate is then dusted with powder, and the print is made by laying a special tacky paper over the plate so that it will pick up the powder image from the plate.

### 10.10.1  Storage Tubes

An optical image stored on the photosensitive surface of a storage tube can be scanned by the electron beam in the tube, and the image will be converted to electrical signals as the surface is discharged by the beam. This technique is used in television camera tubes and in data storage systems in which, in many cases, the recording is done also by an electron beam from the opposite side of the storage surface. In general, such playback (or read out) is destructive.

### 10.10.2 Probes

The charge distribution of a recorded medium can be played back nondestructively by using a scanning probe or head. The same general types of probe can be used for record or playback. The probes fall into two categories: the strip type which may be shielded or unshielded and

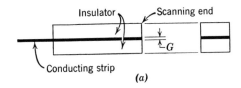

(a)

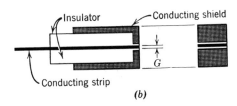

(b)

Figure 10.41. Strip-type heads: (a) unshielded probe; (b) shielded probe.

the gap type. The unshielded probe (Figure 10.41a) is simply a conducting strip supported in an insulating body. The resolution is determined by the field distribution around the scanning end of the probe, and for close spacing between the probe and recording it is approximately equal to the strip length $G$; the analogy between the strip length and the gap length for magnetic recording is evident. Although a flat strip is shown, it could have any useful cross section.

A shielded probe (Figure 10.41b) is closely related to a two-plate condenser having a guard ring for each plate to reduce edge effects. The strip element is more or less surrounded by a conducting surface which is not electrically connected to it. The shield and strip need not be at the same physical level. As a record head, the shield is kept at a potential near the strip potential, just as in the case of the condenser guard ring. The effect is to restrict the spreading of the field due to the strip. As a playback head, the shield is usually at ground potential; as a record head, it is near the strip potential. A shielded probe has better resolution than an unshielded probe.

The ball type head of Figure 10.42 is an example of heads in which the scanning element is in direct contact with the medium (54). The

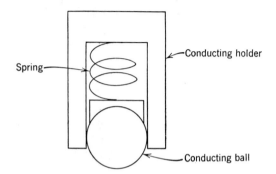

Spring

Conducting holder

Conducting ball

**Figure 10.42.** Ball-type head.

rolling ball reduces friction. This type of head was used by Mason in his dielectric recording system discussed earlier.

## 10.11   References

1. Poulsen, Valdemar, (the original patent), U.S. Patent No. 661,619, November 13, 1900.
2. Pederson, P. O., V. Poulsen, U.S. Patent No. 873,083, December 10, 1907 (d-c bias).
3. Carlson, W. L., G. W. Carpenter, U.S. Patent No. 1640881, August 30, 1927 (a-c bias).
4. Camras, M., "Magnetic Recording on Steel Wire," M.S. Degree, Illinois Institute of Technology, 1942.
5. Hickman, C. N., "Sound Recording on Magnetic Tape," *Bell System Tech. J.*, April 1937, pp. 165–177.
6. Lubeck, H. V., "Magnetic Recording on Films with Ring Heads," *Akust. Z.*, November 1937, pp. 273–295.
7. Toomim, H., D. Wildfeuer, "The Mechanism of Supersonic Frequencies as Applied to Magnetic Recording," *Proc. I.R.E.*, November 1944, pp. 664–668.
8. Holmes, L. C., D. L. Clark, "Supersonic Bias for Magnetic Recording," *Electronics*, July 1945, pp. 126–136.
9. Camras, M., "Theoretical Response from a Magnetic Wire Record," *Proc. I.R.E.*, August 1946, pp. 587–602.
10. ————, "Magnetic Sound for Motion Pictures," *J. Soc. Motion Picture Engrs.*, January 1947, pp. 14–28.
11. Howell, H. A., "Magnetic Sound Recording on Coated Paper Tape," *J. Soc. Motion Picture Engrs.*, January 1947, pp. 36–49.

12. Kornei, O., "Frequency Response of Magnetic Recording," *Electronics*, August 1947, pp. 124–128.
13. Wetzel, W. W., "Review of the Present Status of Magnetic Recording Theory," *Audio Engng.*, November 1947, pp. 14–17, December 1947, pp. 12–16, 37, January 1948, pp. 26–30, 46–47.
14. Clark, D. L., L. L. Merrill, "Field Measurements on Magnetic Recording Heads," *Proc. I.R.E.*, December 1947, pp. 1575–1579.
15. Boyers, J. S., "Factors Affecting Frequency Response and Distortion in Magnetic Recording," *Audio Engng.*, May 1948, pp. 18–19, 46–47.
16. Begun, S. J., "Magnetic Field Distribution of a Ring Recording Head," *Audio Engng.*, December 1948, pp. 11–13, 39.
17. Vinzelberg, B., "The Printing Effect in Tapes of Magnetophone Films," *Funk U. Ton*, December 1948, pp. 633–639.
18. Cooter, I. L., "Magnetic Fields Surrounding Recording Wires," *Elec. Eng.*, March 1949, p. 433.
19. Herr, R., "Making Magnetic Recordings Visible," *Audio Engng.*, April 1949, p. 23.
20. Johnson, S. W., "Factors Affecting Spurious Printing in Magnetic Tapes," *J. Soc. Motion Picture Engrs.*, June 1949, pp. 619–628.
21. Herr, R., "Magnetic Tape Erasure by Permanent Magnets," *Audio Engng.*, August 1949, pp. 14–16, 29–30.
22. Camras, M., R. Herr, "Duplicating Magnetic Tape by Contact Printing," *Electronics*, December 1949, pp. 78–83.
23. Begun, S. J., "Magnetic Recording," Murray Hill Books, Inc., New York, 1949.
24. Frayne, J. G., H. Wolfe, "Elements of Sound Recording," J. Wiley and Sons, New York, 1949.
25. Guckenburg, W., "Relations Between Ring Head and Magnetic Tape in Reproduction," *Funk U. Ton*, January 1950, pp. 24–33.
26. Axon, P. E., "Overall Frequency Characteristic in Magnetic Recording, *B.B.C. Quart.*, Spring 1950, pp. 1–8.
27. ———, "Overall Frequency Characteristic in Magnetic Recording," *B.B.C. Quart.*, Spring 1950, pp. 46–53.
28. Daniel, E. D., P. E. Axon, "Accidental Printing in Magnetic Recording," *B.B.C. Quart.*, Winter 1950–1951, pp. 241–256.
29. Zenner, R. E., "Magnetic Recording with A.C. Bias," *Proc. I.R.E.*, February 1951, pp. 141–146.
30. Rettinger, M., "A.C. Magnetic Erase Heads," *J. Soc. Motion Picture Television Engrs.*, April 1951, pp. 407–410.
31. Muckenhirn, O. W., "Recording Demagnetization in Magnetic Tape Recording," *Proc. I.R.E.*, August 1951, pp. 891–897.
32. Wallace, R. L., Jr., "The Reproduction of Magnetically Recorded Signals," *Bell System Tech. J.*, October 1951, pp. 1145–1173.
33. Daniels, H. L., "Boundary Displacement Magnetic Recording," *Electronics*, April 1952, pp. 116–120.
34. Schmidbauer, O., "The Field of the Harmonically Magnetized Tape," *Frequenz*, October 1952, pp. 281–290, November 1952, pp. 319–324.
35. Bick, J. D., "Methods for Measuring Surface Induction of Magnetic Tape," *J. Audio Engng. Soc.*, January 1953, pp. 4–9.
36. Wiegand, D. W., "A Flux-Sensitive Head for Magnetic Recording Playback," (abstract) *I.R.E.*, Convention Record, Part 3-*Audio*, March 1953, p. 43.

37. Westmijze, W. K., "Studies on Magnetic Recording," Philips Research Repts., April 1953, pp. 148–157, June 1953, pp. 161–183, August 1953, pp. 245–269, October 1953, pp. 343–366.
38. Kornei, O., "Structure and Performance of Magnetic Transducer Heads," *J. Audio Engng. Soc.*, July 1953, pp. 225–231.
39. Skellett, A. M., L. E. Leveridge, J. W. Gratian, "Electron Beam Head for Magnetic Tape Playback," *Electronics*, October 1953, pp. 168–171.
40. Axon, P. E., "An Investigation into the Mechanism of Magnetic-Tape Recording," *IEE*, Volume 99, May 1952, pp. 109–126.
41. Daniel, E. D., P. E. Axon, "The Reproduction of Signals Recorded on Magnetic Tape," *IEE*, Volume 100, May 1953, pp. 157–167.
42. Daniel, E. D., "The Influence of Some Head and Tape Constants on the Signal Recorded on a Magnetic Tape," *IEE*, Volume 100, May 1953, pp. 168–175.
43. Kornei, O., "Survey of Flux Responsive Reproducing Heads," *J. Audio Engng. Soc.*, July 1954.
44. Chynoweth, W. R., "Ferrite Heads for Recording in the Megacycle Range, *Tele-Tech.*, August 1955.
45. Kornei, O., "A Magnetic Head for the Megacycle Range," *I.R.E.* Convention Record, 1956.
46. Howling, D. H., "Noise in Magnetic Recording Tapes" *J. Acoust. Soc. Am.*, 1956, pp. 977–987.
47. "Magnetic Recorder Licensee Service Bulletins," Armour Research Foundation of Illinois Institute of Technology, Chicago.
48. "Bibliography of Magnetic Recording," Magnetic Recorder Licensee Service, Bull. No. 64, Armour Research Foundation of Illinois Institute of Technology, Chicago, Period 1888–1950.
49. "Bibliography of Magnetic Recording 1900–1953," Sound Talk Bull. No. 29, Minnesota Mining and Manufacturing Company, August 1954.
50. "Sound Talk Bulletins." Minnesota Mining and Manufacturing Company, St. Paul, Minnesota.
51. "Proceedings of Magnetic Recording Technical Meeting," Armour Research Foundation of Illinois Institute of Technology, Bull. No. 94, October 1956.
52. "Final Engineering Report on Dielectric Recording," Engineering Research Associates, Contract AF33(038)-10965, 1950–1953.
53. Anderson, V. C., "A Recording-Reproducing System Using a Dielectric Storage Medium," University of California Marine Physical Laboratory, Contract NObsr-43356, 1955.
54. Mason, W. P., et al., Patent No. 2,775,650, "Ferroelectric Recording and Reproduction of Speech."
55. Daniel, E. D., P. E. Axon, "A Survey of Factors Limiting the Performance of Magnetic Recording Systems," *J. Audio Engng. Soc.*, January 1957, pp. 42–52.

# Chapter eleven

# Magnetic and Dielectric Measurements

## 11.0 Introduction

The careful measurement of the various material parameters which affect device behavior is of considerable importance. However, a detailed consideration of the various procedures which may be used are not carried out in this book. The excellent literature available in this area contains the necessary details. In general, there is presented in broad outline the methods of measurement of various parameters and the problems encountered. The parameters of interest are the small signal permeability, dielectric constant, the non-linear or large signal characteristics, the electro-mechanical constants, and the microwave properties. In particular, the electromechanical properties are discussed in some detail in order to present a unified treatment of the electro-strictive and magnetostrictive measurements.

## 11.1 Small Signal Permeability

Whenever it is feasible, intrinsic permeability measurements are made on toroidal samples of the magnetic material in question. One area in which toroidal measurements may not be too meaningful occurs in the use of magnetic devices utilizing ferrite rods. Although we use the same initial ingredients in the preparation of a ferrite, it will be found that extruded rod samples have different characteristics than those of pressed toroids. In such cases measurements can be made on toroids cut from the rod specimen. Our discussion is concerned primarily with toroidal cores.

The particular method we employ depends on the frequency range of interest. For the low frequency range of several kc to about 5 mc it is usually sufficient to wind the toroid with a uniform single-layer winding. By means of standard bridges or Q-meters we measure the inductance and Q of the toroid. The permeability is then calculated from the toroidal inductance formula

$$L = \frac{\mu \mu_0 A N^2}{l} \tag{11.1}$$

Several precautions, however, are necessary.

1. For very low frequencies, particularly below 1 kc, it is necessary to use a sufficient number of turns so that operation will take place over the linear region, i.e., to keep the flux density excursion low. The signal voltage should be decreased to the point at which no apparent inductance change takes place.

2. At higher frequencies it becomes more difficult to separate out the losses due to the copper. In many cases it is even insufficient to use the same number of turns on a nonmagnetic form of the same dimensions as an independent measurement of copper losses. This is due to the fact that the presence of the ferrite alters the field distribution within the wire. Not only is the high permeability a factor, but the high dielectric constant of certain ferrites will affect the turn-to-turn capacitance.

3. For the lower permeability ferrites it has been found that the calculated $u$ varies with the number of turns. In other words, the leakage inductance becomes an appreciable portion of the total inductance in this case. The core size should be chosen for a given frequency so that a winding as uniform as possible may be placed on the core.

4. The value of $l$ in equation 11.1 is the average path length around the toroid (1). This is usually taken to be $2\pi(r_1 + r_2)/2$, where $r_1$ and $r_2$ are the inner and outer radii. However, this is a valid approximation for only a certain range of ratios of $r_2/r_1$. For a uniformly wound core the value of $H$ at a distance $r$ from the center is

$$H = \frac{NI}{2\pi r} \tag{11.2}$$

The average value of $H$ across the cross section is

$$H_{av} = \frac{NI}{2\pi} \frac{1}{r_2 - r_1} \ln r_2/r_1 \qquad (11.3)$$

This can be expanded in the following power series

$$H_{av} = \frac{NI}{2\pi} \frac{2/r_1}{(r_2/r_1) - 1} \left( \frac{r_2/r_1 - 1}{r_2/r_1 + 1} + \frac{1}{3} \frac{(r_2/r_1 - 1)^3}{(r_2/r_1 + 1)^3} \cdots \right) \qquad (11.4)$$

For $r_2/r_1 \sim 1$ this reduces to

$$H_{av} = \frac{NI}{\pi(r_2 + r_1)} \qquad (11.5)$$

the average radius is derived. The fractional error made in neglecting the cubic term is

$$\frac{\Delta H_{av}}{H_{av}} = \frac{1}{3} \left( \frac{r_2/r_1 - 1}{r_2/r_1 + 1} \right)^2 \qquad (11.6)$$

Hence the error is less than 1 per cent for $r_2/r_1$ less than 1.5.

Aside from the geometrical factor, the greatest difficulties are encountered in adequately correcting for the winding losses. This can be obviated through the use of a co-axial method in which a single conductor threads the core. For the frequency range of 0.05 mc to 50 mc a commercial r-f permeameter sketched in Figure 11.1 is available (2–5). This system is essentially a transformer with a single-turn

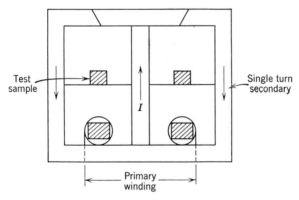

**Figure 11.1.** Schematic of $RF$ permeameter.

secondary formed by the outside cylindrical housing and the center conductor. The primary is a toroidal winding on a metallic tape core or a ferrite core, depending on the frequency range. The test core is placed inside the cavity and situated symmetrically with respect to the center rod. Hence the primary current induces a secondary current which flows through the cylindrical walls and back through the center rod. The secondary currents produce a circular magnetic field around the test core, whose presence is detected by an impedance change in the primary.

The actual measurements are made at the primary by means of a $Q$-meter. By resonating the calibrated cavity with and without the test sample it is possible to calculate accurately the small signal permeability and the $Q$ of the ferrite core.

A variation of the coaxial technique allows the range of measurement to be extended to 10,000 mc. A thin toroidal sample of ferrite is placed at the shorted end of a coaxial transmission line, i.e., in a region of high magnetic field. In the frequency range of 10 to 1500 mc it is possible to obtain the permeability of the ferrite through a measurement of the input impedance of the line. General commercial bridges are available which cover this frequency and thus greatly simplify the measurements problem. Typical bridges are (1) General Radio Type 1601A (10 to 165 mc) which measures the equivalent series impedance, (2) Boonton RX Bridge Type 250A (0.5 to 250 mc) which measures the input admittance, (3) General Radio Type 1602 UHF admittance bridge (41 to 1500 mc).

Above this frequency range more accurate data can be obtained by measurements of the standing wave ratio on a slotted line. This data, combined with the shift in the voltage minimum due to the ferrite, permits a calculation of the real and imaginary parts of the scalar permeability (6–9, 20).

## 11.2 The Measurement of the Microwave Permeability Tensor of Ferrites (10, 11)

It has been shown in Chapter 7 that a ferrite of infinite extent magnetized in the direction of propagation of an electromagnetic wave can be considered to have two scalar permeabilities, each associated with one of the two senses of circular polarization into which the wave may be decomposed. These permeabilities are $u \pm \kappa = (u' \pm \kappa') - j(u'' \pm \kappa'')$ where the permeability tensor is given by

$$\mu_T = \mu_0 \begin{bmatrix} \mu & -j\kappa & 0 \\ +j\kappa & \mu & 0 \\ 0 & 0 & 1 \end{bmatrix} \tag{11.7}$$

and where $u = u' - ju''$
$\kappa = \kappa' - j\kappa''$

Hence there are four individual quantities to be measured, and it is evident that the real parts will be associated with frequency or phase characteristics and the imaginary parts with attenuation.

One of the more usual techniques utilizes a small ferrite specimen (either disk or sphere) placed next to the end wall in a circular cylindrical cavity excited in a $TE_{11n}$ mode. Any of these modes is similar to the $TE_{11}$ mode in a circular waveguide and, as in the latter, is "degenerate." By this we mean that an independent mode which has the same phase constant as the first simultaneously exists. In this particular case the second mode is just the first rotated through $90°$. If an external magnetic field is applied along the axis of the cylinder and the cavity is excited in one of the linear modes, the precessing electrons will couple some of the energy of this mode to the orthogonal mode and thus excite it. It is easier to describe the situation in terms of the circularly polarized modes previously mentioned rather than with reference to these linearly polarized modes. Under ordinary circumstances (no ferrite present) these modes are also degenerate. We may regard the exciting linear mode as being composed of the two counterrotating circular components. Since each of these components "sees" a different effective (complex) permeability of the ferrite, the degeneracy of the modes disappears and each has its own resonant frequency and cavity $Q$. Experimentally, this means that if we observe (an on oscilloscope) the cavity response to a frequency-swept signal before and after the application of an external field a significant change will take place. The familiar bell-shaped curve, typical of a resonant circuit, splits in two as the applied field increases from zero. As the field increases further, the distance between peaks widens as one peak moves in the direction of increasing frequency and the other remains stationary. Quantitatively,

$$\Delta f_{\pm} = f_0 A v(\mu' \pm \kappa' - 1) \tag{11.8}$$

$$\Delta\left(\frac{1}{2Q_{\pm}}\right) = Av(\mu'' \pm \kappa'' - 1) \tag{11.9}$$

where $\Delta f_{\pm}$ are the shifts in resonant frequencies from the empty cavity value,

$\Delta\left(\dfrac{1}{Q_{\pm}}\right)$ are proportional to the powers absorbed in the ferrite by the two modes,

$A$ is a factor depending upon the mode and cavity dimensions

$v$ is the ferrite volume.

In practice, the separating out of the two contributions to the observed cavity response poses certain difficulties. For small fields the overlap might prevent accurate measurement of the $Q$'s and actually cause a small error in the frequency separation. Hence an evident improvement would consist in exciting the cavity in only one of the circularly polarized modes at a time. This can be done in a variety of ways, and this technique is now invariably used. We can now observe the cavity's response to each mode separately and unambiguously obtain the required parameters.

There are a number of practical considerations which must be considered if accurate results are desired. First, we see from the above expressions that the deviations are proportional to the ferrite volume, so that we might be tempted to use rather large specimens in order to enhance the observed effects. However, since the derivation of the quantitative results is based on a perturbation treatment, we must restrict ourselves to small spheres. Even so, there is a size effect, and if spheres larger than about 0.5 mm in diameter are used the results must be extrapolated to zero radius.

Second, a wall-proximity effect manifests itself, due partly to the "image" of the sphere in the end wall. This effect is considerably reduced by moving the sphere a diameter or two away from the end wall. (The ferrite was placed there in order to place it in a region of maximum r-f magnetic field and minimum r-f electric field.)

Third, although by this technique we can obtain the basic ferrite microwave parameters, the method is valid for extremely small specimens, and it has been shown that there can be variations not only from batch to batch of ostensibly the same material but also between samples taken from the same rod. Hence it would be desirable to be able to measure the tensor components for samples of a size more nearly equal to those found in actual devices. This has been done recently (12) by using $1 \times 0.090$ inch diameter rods in a circular waveguide. Applying formulas developed by Berk for the propagation constant for small diameter rods, the actual phase shift and attenuation of the two circularly polarized components have been measured as a function of applied magnetic field. The tensor components so deduced are in good agreement with the average results of other workers' cavity measurements. The cavity technique does have the advantage that the complex dielectric constant of the ferrite can be readily obtained by moving the specimen from region of maximum r-f magnetic field to a region of maximum r-f electric field.

## 11.3   Methods of Measurement of Dielectric Constant

An excellent description by Field (13) details the methods in practical use for the measurement of complex permittivity of linear dielectrics in the frequency range from direct current to 100 megacycles. Using lumped-constant concepts, the two components of the complex permittivity are computed from measurements of auxiliary quantities which depend on the frequency range involved. Field (13) describes the use of current-time curves for frequencies from 0 to 10 cps, impedance bridges for frequencies from 10 to $10^7$ cps, and $Q$-meters for frequencies from $10^5$ to $2 \times 10^8$ cps. The preparation of samples, electroding, corrections for edge-effects, and the circuitry required are considered in detail.

For frequencies above several hundred megacycles distributed constant methods become necessary as it becomes increasingly impossible to achieve lumped circuit performance with practicable apparatus. Detailed descriptions of the methods and apparatus in use have been shown by Westphal (14). In particular, he describes the use of transmission lines, waveguides, and cavities to extend the frequency range of measurement to the centimeter range.

## 11.4   Piezoelectric Measurements (19, 21)

### Static Measurements

The simplest and historically first method of determining piezoelectric constants consists of measuring the potential difference appearing between suitable electrodes attached to piezoelectric crystals (or polarized ceramics) which are subjected to mechanical loading. Conversely, with highly refined optical means it is possible to measure deformations of a piezoelectric crystal when it is subjected to an applied d-c electric field. These measurements may be deduced from the relations (given in Chapter 3) for the simple one dimensional case.

$$D_3 = \epsilon_{33}{}^T E_3 + d_{33} T_3 \qquad (11.10)$$

$$S_3 = d_{33} E_3 + s_3{}^E T_3 \qquad (11.11)$$

where the variables represent small variations about a bias value. In Figure 11.2$a$ the piezoelectric material, polarized in the 3-direction, is subjected to an applied stress $T$. The electrodes are connected to an electrometer which may be assumed to have a negligible loading effect.

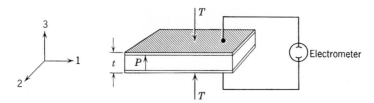

Figure 11.2$a$.   Static measurement of piezoelectric constant $g_{33}$.

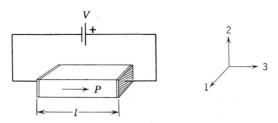

Figure 11.2$b$.   Static measurement of piezoelectric constant $d_{33}$.

Since there is no change in the free charge, $D_3 = 0$. Hence from equation 11.10 the magnitude of the internal field becomes

$$E_3 = \frac{d_{33}}{\epsilon_{33}^T} T_3 = g_{33} T_3 \tag{11.12}$$

If this field is assumed to be uniform through the thickness $l$, a potential difference $V$ appears across the electrodes of magnitude

$$|V| = \frac{|E_3|}{l} \tag{11.13}$$

Thus the piezoelectric coefficient $g_{33}$ can be computed as

$$g_{33} = \frac{|V|l}{T_3} \tag{11.14}$$

If as shown in Figure 11.2$b$ the piezoelectric material is subjected to an applied electric field and permitted to deform without external mechanical constraints, then $T_3$ is zero and the strain is

$$s_3 = d_{33} E_3 \tag{11.15}$$

$E_3 = V/l$ if a uniform internal field is assumed.   Thus

$$d_{33} = \frac{s_3 l}{V} \tag{11.16}$$

Measurement of the exceedingly small strains produced in this manner is quite difficult. However, since the $g_{33}$ and $d_{33}$ coefficients are related $(d_{33} = g_{33}/\epsilon_{33}^T)$, it is only necessary to determine $\epsilon_{33}^T$ and $g_{33}$ by the previous method. The dielectric constant is simply determined by a measurement of the low-frequency capacitance with zero applied stress. At low frequencies (low compared to the first possible resonant mode of vibration)

$$C = \frac{\epsilon_{33}^T A}{l} \qquad (11.17)$$

Other piezoelectric constants may be determined in a similar manner. For example, $g_{31}$ is found by applying stresses in the 1-direction and measuring the potential difference appearing between electrodes perpendicular to the 3-direction, with the polarization $P$ oriented in the 3-direction.

## 11.5 Dynamic Piezoelectric Measurements. Side-Plated Resonator

Let us examine the input impedance of a side-plated long thin bar resonator driven electrically with both ends mechanically free. Figure 11.3$a$ is the general equivalent circuit developed in Section 3.7, with the additional assumption that the clamped input impedance is lossless and reduces to the clamped capacitance $C_0$. In the region of the fundamental resonance $(L = \lambda/2)$ the circuit approximates the lumped constant circuit shown in Figure 11.3$b$. $R_m$, $C_m$, $L_m$ represent mechanical resistance, compliance, and mass, respectively. $R_1$, $C_1$, $L_1$ represent these same quantities referred to the electrical input.

The behavior of the network can be observed graphically by means of an admittance plot in the complex $(G + jB)$ plane. The admittance of the series $R_1$, $L_1$, $C_1$ branch describes a curve closely approximating a circle; whereas the lossless clamped capacitance branch has a susceptance whose locus is the $jB$-axis. In most cases it may be assumed that over a small frequency range in the neighborhood of mechanical resonance the susceptance of $C_0$ does not vary appreciably but the locus of the mechanical branch sweeps through a full circle. The combined admittance locus is shown in Figure 11.4. Actual measurements yield a locus which does not depart very much from the circle diagram.

$f_0$ is the frequency at which the series $R_1$-$L_1$-$C_1$ branch is resonant (mechanical resonance), $G_0$ is the conductance at this frequency, and $jB_0$ represents the susceptance of the clamped capacitance $C_0$. The

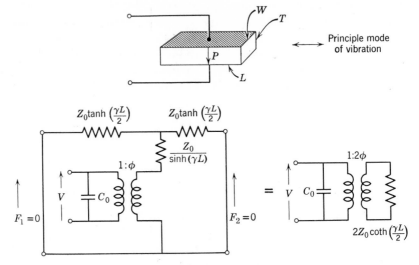

Figure 11.3$a$.  Equivalent circuits—side-plated resonator.

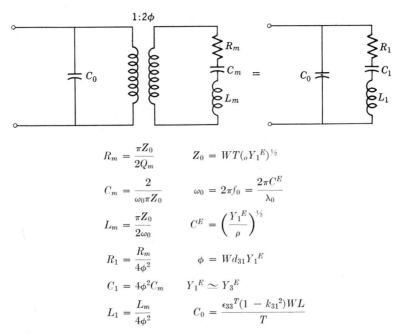

$$R_m = \frac{\pi Z_0}{2Q_m} \qquad Z_0 = WT(_0 Y_1{}^E)^{1/2}$$

$$C_m = \frac{2}{\omega_0 \pi Z_0} \qquad \omega_0 = 2\pi f_0 = \frac{2\pi C^E}{\lambda_0}$$

$$L_m = \frac{\pi Z_0}{2\omega_0} \qquad C^E = \left(\frac{Y_1{}^E}{\rho}\right)^{1/2}$$

$$R_1 = \frac{R_m}{4\phi^2} \qquad \phi = W d_{31} Y_1{}^E$$

$$C_1 = 4\phi^2 C_m \qquad Y_1{}^E \simeq Y_3{}^E$$

$$L_1 = \frac{L_m}{4\phi^2} \qquad C_0 = \frac{\epsilon_{33}{}^T (1 - k_{31}{}^2) WL}{T}$$

Figure 11.3$b$.  Lumped constant equivalent circuit—side-plated resonator.

points $f_1$, $f_2$ represent the half-power frequencies of the series $R_1$-$L_1$-$C_1$ circuit and occur when the mechanical conductance is one half the maximum $G_0$. The corresponding susceptances are $+jB_1$ and $-jB_2$. The points labeled $f_m$, $f_n$ represent maximum and minimum input admittances, respectively.

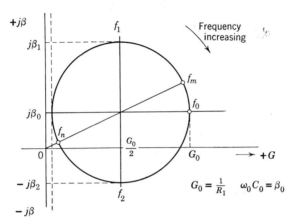

Figure 11.4. Admittance locus—electromechanical resonator.

The required material constants may be obtained by determining several of the key points on the admittance locus. It usually suffices to obtain $f_0$, $f_1$, $f_2$, $G_0$, and $B_0$. In terms of the simplified equivalent circuit (Figure 11.3$b$)

$$R_1 = 1/G_0 \tag{11.18}$$

$$\omega_0 C_0 = B_0 \tag{11.19}$$

$$Q_m = \frac{f_0}{f_1 - f_2} \tag{11.20}$$

A very useful instrument for the measurement of piezoelectric parameters is the Wayne-Kerr bridge which measures an admittance in terms of the equivalent shunt $R$ and $C$. Of course, a straightforward method would be to measure values of $R$ and $C$ for a large number of discrete frequencies covering the band from below to above mechanical resonance. This entails considerable labor and requires one to two hours of careful measurement time.

A much more rapid method consists of first measuring the input capacitance at very low frequencies (below resonance) and assuming that this value is a first approximation to the damped capacitance $C_0$. (It will be in error by the factor $(1 - k^2)$.) The susceptance arm of the bridge is preset to this value, and the bridge is balanced by varying the resistance arm with an applied frequency close to mechanical resonance. A number of successive balances are made for small variations of applied frequency until the minimum value of measured $R$ is obtained. Small corrections to the preset value of the susceptance arm are then tried, again balancing for minimum $R$. The final balance thus yields values for $C_0$, $R_1$, $f_0$. The resistive arm is now preset to a value $2R_1$, and the bridge is rebalanced by varying both the susceptive arm and frequency. Two such balances corresponding to the half-power points $f_2$ and $f_1$, with capacitances (or inductances) corresponding to the susceptances $B_2$ and $B_1$ (see Figure 11.4), can be obtained. Although the values of $B_2$ and $B_1$ are not needed for computing the necessary constants, they may provide a valuable cross-check on the accuracy of measurement. From Figure 11.4 it may be noted that $B_2 + B_1 = 2B_0$ where the quantities are treated algebraically. ($B_2$ may be negative.) The material constants can then be computed from the measured values of $R_1$, $C_0$, $f_0$, $f_1$, $f_2$.

By use of the tabled formulas in Figure 11.3$b$ it can be shown that

$$R_1 = \frac{\pi Z_0}{8Q_m\phi^2} \tag{11.21}$$

Substituting for $Z_0$ and $\phi$, $R_1$ becomes

$$R_1 = \frac{\pi^2}{8Q_m\omega_0 C_0}\left(\frac{1 - k_{31}^2}{k_{31}^2}\right) \tag{11.22}$$

Hence

$$k_{31}^2 = \frac{1}{1 + (8Q_m\omega_0 C_0 R_1/\pi^2)} \tag{11.23}$$

The dielectric constant $\epsilon_{33}^T$ may be computed from the equation for $C_0$.

$$\epsilon_{33}^T = \frac{C_0}{1 - k_{31}^2}\frac{T}{WL} \tag{11.24}$$

The piezoelectric coefficients $d_{31}$ and $g_{31}$ may then be computed from

$$d_{31}^2 = \frac{\epsilon_{33}^T k_{31}^2}{Y_3^E} \tag{11.25}$$

$$g_{31} = d_{31}/\epsilon_{33}^T \tag{11.26}$$

where $Y_3^E = 4L^2 f_0^2 \rho$.

### 11.5.1 End-Plated Resonator

The equivalent circuit for the free-free end-plated bar is shown in Figure 11.5, where the electrical losses have been neglected. The formulas for each parameter are the same as those given in equations 11.10 to 11.15 with the following modifications:

$$Z_0 = WT(\rho Y_3^D)^{1/2} \qquad C_0 = \epsilon_{33}^T(1 - k_{33}^2)\frac{WT}{L}$$

$$\omega_0 = \frac{2\pi C^D}{\lambda_0} \qquad C_1' = \frac{C_0 C_1}{C_0 - C_1}$$

$$C^D = \left(\frac{Y_3^D}{\rho}\right)^{1/2} \qquad Y_3^D = \frac{Y_3^E}{1 - k_{33}^2} \qquad (11.27)$$

$$\psi = \frac{k_{33}^2}{g_{33}}\frac{WT}{L} \qquad R_1 = R_m/4\psi^2$$

$$C_1 = 4\psi^2 C_m$$

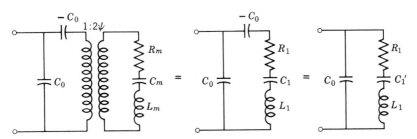

Figure 11.5. Lumped constant equivalent circuits—end-plated resonator.

If we define the mechanical angular resonant frequency and mechanical $Q_m$ by

$$\omega_0^2 = 1/L_1 C_1 \qquad (11.28)$$

$$Q_m = 1/\omega_0 C_1 R_1 \qquad (11.29)$$

it can be seen that due to the effect of the $-C_0$ term on the series $R_1$, $L_1$, $C_1$ branch there will be measured a resonant angular frequency $\omega_0'$

and mechanical $Q_m'$ which differ from those given by equations 11.24 and 11.25. Thus

$$(\omega_0')^2 = 1/L_1 C_1' \tag{11.30}$$

$$Q_m' = 1/\omega_0' C_1' \tag{11.31}$$

It can be shown that the frequency $\omega_0'$ is related to $\omega_0$ approximately by

$$\omega_0 \simeq \omega_0' \left( \frac{\pi^2 - 4k_{33}^2}{\pi^2 - 8k_{33}^2} \right) \tag{11.32}$$

If we proceed as before to obtain the necessary expression to permit the computation of $k_{33}^2$ from the values of $R_1$, $Q_m$, $\omega_0$, and $C_0$ by use of equations 11.27, 11.28, 11.29, then

$$k_{33}^2 = \frac{\pi^2}{8\omega_0 C_0 R_1 Q_m} \tag{11.33}$$

where $\omega_0$ and $Q_m$ are *calculated* on the basis of resonance between the mechanical quantities $L_1$, $C_1$. To correct for the measured quantities $\omega_0'$, $Q_m'$, let $k_{33}'$ be computed from the measured values

$$(k_{33}')^2 = \frac{\pi^2}{8\omega_0' C_0 R_1 Q_m'} \tag{11.34}$$

Then

$$\frac{k_{33}^2}{k_{33}'^2} = \frac{\omega_0' Q_m'}{\omega_0 Q_m} \tag{11.35}$$

Introducing equations 11.29, 11.31, and 11.29 into 11.35

$$\frac{k_{33}^2}{k_{33}'^2} = 1 - C_1/C_0 \tag{11.36}$$

From equation 11.27 and auxiliary equations it may be shown that

$$\frac{C_1}{C_0} = \frac{8}{\pi^2} k_{33}^2 \tag{11.37}$$

Hence

$$k_{33}^2 = \frac{(k_{33}')^2}{1 + 8(k'_{33})^2/\pi^2} \tag{11.38}$$

The calculation of $Y_3^E$ differs slightly from the previous case. Utilizing the definitions given above,

$$Y_3^E = 4L^2 \rho f_0^2 (1 - k_{33}^2) \tag{11.39}$$

However from equation 11.28

$$f' \cong f_0' \left( \frac{\pi^2 - 4k_{33}^2}{\pi^2 - 8k_{33}^2} \right) \tag{11.40}$$

Therefore,

$$Y_3^E = 4L^2 \rho (f_0')^2 (1 - k_{33}^2) \left( \frac{\pi^2 - 4k_{33}^2}{\pi^2 - 8k_{33}^2} \right) \tag{11.41}$$

where correction has been made for the measured value of frequency $f_0'$ rather than $f_0$.

Again $d_{33}$ and $g_{33}$ may be computed from

$$d_{33}^2 = \frac{\epsilon_{33}^T k_{33}^2}{Y_3^E} \tag{11.42}$$

$$g_{33} = \frac{d_{33}}{\epsilon_{33}^T} \tag{11.43}$$

### 11.5.2 Disk Resonator. Determination of Piezoelectric Properties Using Impedance Bridge

It is often very convenient to prepare disk samples of ferroelectric ceramic materials for determination of piezoelectric properties rather than bars. By referring to Figure 11.6 and comparing it with the side-plated long thin bar resonator of Figure 11.2 it is seen that the effective mode of piezoelectric excitation is similar, via the $d_{31}$ coefficient, but that mechanical vibration in the disk is modified by the constraints imposed by the circular geometry.

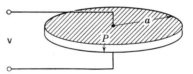

Figure 11.6. Disk resonator.

Mason (15) has developed expressions for the electrical input admittance for a resonating piezoelectric disk and indicates a very useful method for determining the radial electromechanical coupling coefficient $k_\rho$ from maximum-minimum impedance measurements. This is discussed in later paragraphs. A more accurate determination using the admittance bridge method already described (Figure 11.5) can be made by extending Mason's formulation.

Substituting in Mason's expression for the admittance of a piezoelectric vibrating disk in terms of the present nomenclature,

$$Y = j\omega C_0 \left[ 1 + \frac{k_\rho^2}{1 - k_\rho^2} \left( \frac{(1 + \sigma)J_1(\omega a/C)}{(\omega a/C)J_0(\omega a/C) - (1 - \sigma)J_1(\omega a/C)} \right) \right] \tag{11.44}$$

where $C_0$ is the clamped capacitance,

$k_\rho$ is the radial electromechanical coupling coefficient,

$\sigma$ is Poisson's Ratio,

$C$ is velocity of propagation,

$J_0, J_1$ are Bessel functions,

$a$ is the radius of the disk.

Mason also shows the following relations:

$$C_0 = \frac{\epsilon_{33}{}^{RC} A}{t} \tag{11.45}$$

where $\epsilon_{33}{}^{RC}$ is the radially clamped permittivity.

$$\epsilon_{33}{}^{RC} = \epsilon_{33}{}^{T}(1 - k_\rho{}^2) \tag{11.46}$$

$$k_\rho{}^2 = k_{31}{}^2 \left(\frac{2}{1 - \sigma}\right) \tag{11.47}$$

$$C_0 = \left(\frac{Y_1{}^E}{(1 - \sigma^2)\rho}\right)^{1/2} \tag{11.48}$$

$$\omega_0 = \frac{2.03}{a} \left(\frac{Y_1{}^E}{(1 - \sigma^2)\rho}\right)^{1/2} \tag{11.49}$$

Now mechanical resonance occurs when the denominator of the right-hand expression in the parentheses of equation 11.44 is zero. Thus

$$\frac{\omega_0 a}{C} J_0\left(\frac{\omega_0 a}{C}\right) - (1 - \sigma)J_1\left(\frac{\omega_0 a}{C}\right) = 0 \tag{11.50}$$

For $\sigma$ assumed to be 0.3 the first root which satisfies 11.50 is

$$N_1 = \frac{\omega_0 a}{C} = 2.05 \tag{11.51}$$

From equations 11.50 and 11.51

$$N_1 J_0(N_1) = (1 - \sigma)J_1(N_1) \tag{11.52}$$

The whole right-hand expression within the bracket of equation 11.40 represents the mechanical behavior referred to the electrical circuit as a function of angular frequency $\omega$. We wish to examine the effects in the neighborhood of resonance. Define the fractional deviation $r$:

$$r = \frac{f_1 - f_0}{f_0} = \frac{\Delta f}{f_0} = \frac{\omega - \omega_0}{\omega_0} \tag{11.53}$$

If (as shown by Mason) $J_0(\omega a/C)$ and $J_1(\omega a/C)$ are expanded in a Taylor series about $\omega_0$, neglecting higher powers of $\Delta f$,

$$J_0(\omega a/C) = J_0(N_1) - \frac{2\pi a}{C} J_1(N_1) \, \Delta f + \cdots \qquad (11.54)$$

$$J_1(\omega a/C) = J_1(N_1) + \frac{2\pi a}{C}\left(J_0(N_1) - \frac{J_1(N_1)}{N_1}\right) \Delta f + \cdots \qquad (11.55)$$

Noting from equation 11.51,

$$\frac{2\pi a}{C} = \frac{2\pi f_0 a}{C} \cdot \frac{1}{f_0} = \frac{N_1}{f_0} \qquad (11.56)$$

and from 11.45

$$\omega = \omega_0(1 + r) \qquad (11.57)$$

and substituting equations 11.54, 11.55, 11.56, 11.57, 11.52 into 11.44

$$Y = j\omega_0(1 + r)C_0\left(1 + \frac{k_\rho^2}{1 - k_\rho^2} \times \frac{2(1 + \sigma)}{N_1^2 - \sigma^2 - 1} \times \frac{1 - r\sigma}{2r}\right) \qquad (11.58)$$

Let us compare this expression with that obtained for the simplified lumped constant equivalent circuit of Figure 11.7.

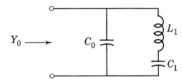

$$Y = j\omega C_0 + j\left(\frac{\omega C_1}{1 - \omega^2 L_1 C_1}\right) \qquad (11.59)$$

Figure 11.7. Lumped constant equivalent circuit—lossless case.

But from equation 11.53 $\omega = \omega_0(1 + r)$ and

$$\omega_0^2 = 1/L_1 C_1 \qquad (11.60)$$

Introducing equations 11.53 and 11.60 into 11.59 and neglecting higher powers of $r$,

$$Y = j\omega_0 C_0(1 + r)\left(1 - \frac{C_1}{C_0}\frac{1}{2r}\right) \qquad (11.61)$$

Comparison of expressions 11.58 and 11.61 lead to the following equivalence for small deviations. It is assumed that since $\sigma \cong 0.3$ the quantity $\sigma r$ is negligible compared to unity and thus

$$\frac{1 - \sigma r}{2r} \cong \frac{1}{2r} \qquad (11.62)$$

$$\frac{C_1}{C_0} = \frac{k_\rho^2}{1 - k_\rho^2} \times \frac{2(1 + \sigma)}{N_1^2 - \sigma^2 - 1} \qquad (11.63)$$

Solving for $k_\rho^2$ from equation 11.63,

$$k_\rho^2 = \frac{1}{1 + \dfrac{2(1 + \sigma)}{N_1^2 - \sigma^2 - 1} \times \dfrac{C_0}{C_1}} \qquad (11.64)$$

Introducing the mechanical loss $R_1$ as shown in Figure 11.8, and since
$Q_m = \dfrac{1}{\omega_0 C_1 R_1}$

$$k_\rho^2 = \frac{1}{1 + [2(1 + \sigma)/N_1^2 - \sigma^2 - 1]\omega_0 C_0 R_1 Q_m} \qquad (11.65)$$

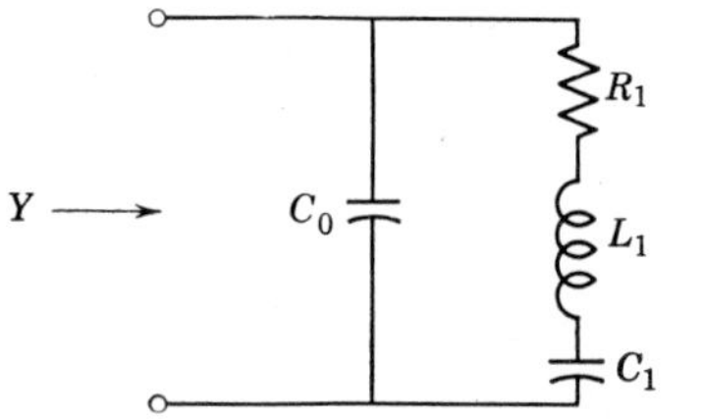

**Figure 11.8.** Lumped constant equivalent circuit with mechanical loss.

We may now proceed as in the preceding case for the side-plated bar to measure $C_0$, $\omega_0$, $R_1$, and $Q_m$ and determine $k_\rho^2$ from equation 11.65. A comparison of 11.65 and the corresponding expression 11.23 is instructive:

Assuming $\sigma = 0.3$, $N_1 = 2.05$,

$$k_{31}^2 = \frac{1}{1 + 0.811\omega_0 C_0 R_1 Q_m} \qquad (11.66)$$

$$k_\rho^2 = \frac{1}{1 + 0.835\omega_0 C_0 R_1 Q_m} \qquad (11.67)$$

and thus the circular geometry has a moderate effect on the vibration as compared with the bar geometry.

From the foregoing calculation and measurements the permittivities $\epsilon_{33}^{RC}$ and $\epsilon_{33}^T$ may be calculated by use of equations 11.45 and 11.46. $k_{31}^2$ may be determined from equation 11.47, and proceeding as already outlined values of $Y_1^E$, $d_{31}$, $g_{31}$ may be determined.

### 11.5.3 Determination of Electromechanical Coupling by Maximum and Minimum Impedance Methods

A method for calculating electromechanical coupling coefficients from simple measurements of the resonant and antiresonant frequencies of a piezoelectric resonator is described by Mason (15). The method consists of accurately measuring the frequencies $f_m$ and $f_n$ of Figure 11.3, i.e., the frequencies for which the input impedance is minimum and maximum, respectively, and assuming that these frequencies correspond to the resonant frequency $f_0$ of the series $R_1$, $L_1$, $C_1$ branch and the antiresonant frequency $f_a$ of the two branches. Mason has shown that for the long thin bar

$$k^2 = \frac{\pi^2}{4} \frac{\Delta f}{f_0} \left[ 1 + \left( \frac{4 - \pi^2}{4} \right) \frac{\Delta f}{f_0} + \left( \frac{\pi^2 - 4}{4} \right) \frac{\pi^2}{4} \left( \frac{\Delta f}{f_0} \right)^2 \cdots \right] \quad (11.68)$$

where $\Delta f = f_a - f_0$, and for the side-plated disk vibrating in a radial direction with the electrical field and polarization applied in the thickness direction

$$k_p^2 = \frac{\Delta f}{f_0} \left( \frac{N_1^2 - (1 - \sigma^2)}{1 + \sigma} \cdots \right) \quad (11.69)$$

where $R_1$ for barium titanate is given as 2.03 for a value of Poisson's ratio $\sigma = 0.27$. A typical measuring arrangement is shown in Figure 11.9.

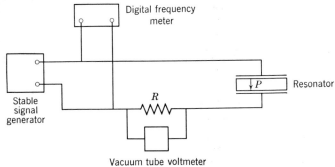

**Figure 11.9.** "Max-min" measurement of piezoelectric resonator.

The bar is excited by a signal generator in series with a small resistance $R$. Maximum and minimum voltmeter readings, as the frequency is varied around resonance, will indicate passage through the minimum and maximum input impedances of the resonator. These frequencies can be obtained directly from a suitably calibrated signal generator or preferably with the aid of a digital frequency counter. The resistance $R$ should be made small compared to the effective mechanical resistance $R_1$ of the resonator, but yet not so small that the minimum voltmeter reading is obscured by extraneous electrical noise, including second and higher harmonic distortion components usually present in available generators. The internal generator impedance must also be quite small so that it may approximate a constant-voltage source. A considerable shift in measured frequency for minimum impedance can result if these precautions are not taken.

This quick operational method can be used for the mass testing of identical resonators but may not be sufficiently accurate for materials with low values of the product $k^2 Q_m$. As can be seen from the admittance plot of Figure 11.4, the frequencies for maximum admittance $f_m$ and resonant frequency $f_0$ do not coincide. It can be seen also that if the diameter of the circle $G_0$ is very large compared to the displacement $jB_0$ of the diameter from the zero $jB$ axis, the two frequencies will tend to coincide. Thus for small error the ratio $G_0/B_0$ should be very large. Let us examine this ratio in terms of more fundamental terms. From equation 11.27,

$$ G_0 = \frac{1}{R_1} \qquad B_0 = \omega_0 C_0 \qquad \frac{C_1}{C_0} = \frac{8}{\pi^2} k_{33}{}^2 \qquad Q_m = \frac{1}{\omega_0 C_1 R_1} \qquad (11.70) $$

Thus $G_0/B_0 = (8/\pi^2)k_{33}{}^2 Q_m$ for the end-plated bar. For quartz $k_{33}{}^2 Q_m$ may range approximately 50 to 3000, depending on mounting. For a barium-titanate ceramic this quantity may range from 10 to 200. Thus considerable error may be introduced for the poorer ceramic. The same considerations obtain for the transverse-plated long bar. However, in this case the quantity $k_{31}{}^2 Q_m$ is two to three times smaller than the corresponding $k_{33}{}^2 Q_m$ quantity, and thus the error may be considerably larger.

### 11.5.4  Sources of Error in Impedance Bridge Measurements

It was assumed in Section 11.5 that the lossless clamped susceptance $j\omega C_0$ could represent the input damped admittance $Y_0$. If the input electrical loss were appreciable and $Y_0 = G_0 + jB_0$, the admittance plot of Figure 11.4 would become as shown in Figure 11.10, still assuming the $Y_0$ remained approximately constant over the small frequency range between the half-power points $f_1$ and $f_2$. It is seen that the half circle is merely translated along the $G$-axis, a distance equal to the input electrical conductance $G_e$.

The resonant frequency $f_0$ and half-power frequencies $f_1$ and $f_2$ will remain essentially unchanged, and thus the calculated value of $Q_m$ from these values is accurate. The measured value of $G_0'$, the maximum conductance, however, must be corrected. A low-frequency measurement of the resonator on a capacity bridge can be used to determine $G_e$, the frequency far enough removed from the first resonant mode, so that the mechanical circuit can be neglected in the equivalent electrical representation. Then

$$R_1 = \frac{1}{G_0} = \frac{1}{G_0' - G_e} \quad (11.71)$$

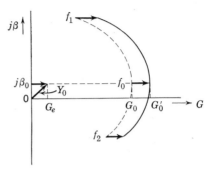

Figure 11.10. Admittance plot including electrical loss.

If it may not be assumed that $Y_0$ remains constant over the frequency range $f_1 - f_2$ and $G_e$ is appreciable, then the simple correction given is insufficient. As shown in a subsequent paragraph, the criterion for this assumption, to be true, is that $k^2Q_m$ be high, which would imply that diameter $G_0$ of the circle would be quite large compared to the displacement $Y_0$. A value of $k^2Q_m$ of 100 would result in an error of approximately 2 per cent for a resonator with an electrical loss factor as high as unity ($|B_0| = |G_e|$). For extreme cases when $k^2Q_m$ is low and the electrical loss factor is very high note the analysis given by Martin (16).

### 11.5.5 Typical Bridge-Measuring Equipment

It has been found expedient in laboratory work to be able to make bridge measurements over a rather wide frequency range. Also, the wide range of values of dielectric constant, coupling coefficient, and mechanical $Q_m$ for different ferroelectric materials and for different geometrical configurations requires a bridge with a range of balance over a wide admittance range. A Wayne-Kerr bridge with input drive transformer capable of being balanced at any frequency from 15 kc to 5 mc by separate front-mounted controls serves admirably for the purpose. For repetitive testing of samples with reasonably similar geometry and characteristics any good impedance or admittance bridge may be used. A typical arrangement of apparatus is shown in Figure 11.11.

The preamplifier is designed to provide moderate gain (5 db) at low noise level to raise the operating level of the output balance signal. The low pass filter made of plug-in units may consist of one constant $k$-section and two $m$-derived half sections. This will tend to eliminate harmonics generated by the signal generator or sample. The high-pass filter (2 $R$-$C$ sections), with a transition frequency of 1 kc, attenuates 60 cps pickup by 60 db, 120 cps pickup by 40 db, and higher harmonics to a lessor degree. A Lissajous figure is formed on the oscilloscope for

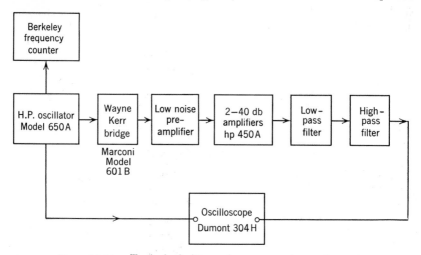

**Figure 11.11.** Typical admittance locus measuring equipment.

an unbalanced condition. At balance this figure degenerates into a horizontal line. With some practice, the use of the oscilloscope representation permits quite rapid balancing of both the $C$ and $R$ branches of the bridge. A communication-type receiver covering the 15 kc to 5 mc frequency range would probably yield better noise rejection in a narrow tunable frequency band, but it is cumbersome to use for this application, since it would require tracking as the generator frequency is varied to obtain the required critical frequency points on the admittance circle.

A few general criteria for the equipment used can be stated.

1. A low-drift signal generator with minimum harmonic content is necessary.

2. Amplifiers and oscilloscope should have wide bandwidth; in practice, about 15 kc to 1 mc is satisfactory.

3. Shielding of the filters and good coaxial cabling, as well as low noise amplifiers are required.

4. A digital frequency counter has been found indispensable. Since $Q_m$'s of the order of 1000 are frequently measured, the usual calibration

of even the best signal generators is insufficient, and slight frequency drift will cause large errors.

5. Care in mounting samples with high $Q_m$ is essential. For many ceramic ferroelectrics the use of styrofoam (foamed polystyrene) as a base on which the sample can be placed seems adequate, provided the edges of the sample are completely free to vibrate.

## 11.6  Magnetostrictive Measurements

The electromechanical properties of magnetic materials, in particular the ferrites, can be determined in a manner similar to that described for the titanates. The most convenient geometry for these measurements is the toroid, since in other structures, such as bars, the magnetic field pattern is not well defined. As a result, the measured parameters would then be effective values rather than the actual material constants.

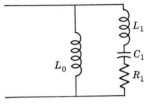

Figure 11.12. Equivalent circuit of magnetostrictive toroid.

The equivalent circuit for the magnetostrictive toroid biased at some remanent value is shown in Figure 11.12. The parameters have the following values:

$$L_0 = \frac{\mu^s A N^2}{2\pi r} \tag{11.72}$$

$$L_1 = \frac{L_0}{k_m{}^2} \qquad k_m{}^2 = \frac{\omega_0 L_0}{Q_m R_1} \tag{11.73}$$

$$Q_m = \frac{\omega_0 L_1}{R_1} \tag{11.74}$$

$$\omega_0 = \frac{1}{\sqrt{L_1 C_1}} = \frac{1}{r}\sqrt{\frac{Y^B}{\rho}} \tag{11.75}$$

where $\mu^s$ = permeability measured at constant strain far below resonance,

   = $\mu^T(1 - k^2)$ when $u^T$ is measured at constant external stress, usually $T = 0$,

$A$ = cross-sectional area of toroid,

$r$ = average radius (these formulas are valid for ratios of inner to ratios of radii close to one),

$k_m$ = magnetostrictive electromechanical coupling coefficient,

$\omega_0$ = mechanical resonant frequency,

$E^B$ = Young's modulus measured at the remanent flux density $B$,

$\rho$ = density of ferrite.

The circle diagram method or the maximum-minimum impedance method subject to the same assumptions previously described in Section 11.5.4 is completely applicable for the determination of the various parameters. The only difference occurs in equation 11.73. The ratio of $L_1/L_0$ is similar to the ratio $C_1/C_0$ (equation 11.70), except for the factor $8/\pi^2$. This additional correction in the piezoelectric case is due to the fact that the strain distribution is sinusoidal for the vibrating bar, whereas it is constant along the circumference for the toroid.

## 11.7   Dynamic Hysteresis Loop (17)

In many of the applications discussed in the preceding chapters it was necessary to know the shape of the hysteresis loop (magnetic or dielectric) under various driving conditions. One method of presenting this information is on a hysteresigraph, which displays the driving field ($E$ or $H$) on the horizontal axis of an oscilloscope and the resulting flux density ($D$ or $B$) on the vertical axis. Aside from the problem of producing the proper driving voltage or current, the main difficulty is the accommodation of the very large bandwidth requirements due to the nonlinearity of the test material. One estimate places the bandwidth at 100 times the fundamental driving frequency. The following discussion presents some of the problems encountered in the design and construction of a 1-mc hysteresigraph for magnetic core testing. The same system can also be used for the testing of nonlinear dielectrics.

A schematic of the system is shown in Figure 11.13. A toroidal sample whose ID to OD ratio was chosen as indicated in Section 11.1 was used as the test core. The value of $H$ was determined by measuring

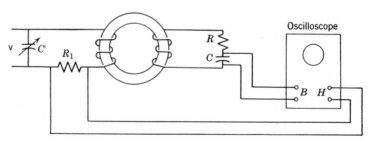

Figure 11.13.   Schematic of hysteresis loop apparatus.

the voltage across a small resistor in series with the drive winding. The value of $B$ was determined by the voltage across the capacitor of an $R$-$C$ integrator placed on the output of a secondary winding on the core.

### Driver Requirements

For the testing of magnetic materials for high-power applications at high frequencies it is usually desirable to maintain a sinusoidal flux through the core. This requires a low driver impedance plus $H$ resistor compared to that of the test core. In many cases, particularly in the higher frequency range, the core dimensions are kept very small. This is necessary in order to keep the peak currents required for saturation down to a reasonable value and also to keep the dissipated power in the core small. The core impedance under these conditions can be less than 1 ohm. Hence a driver with 20- to 100-watt capacity is not unusual. In certain cases there is some improvement in the wave shape by means of a feedback signal from the secondary winding to an appropriate point in the driver circuit.

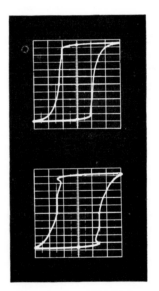

If the condition that the flux remain sinusoidal is relaxed somewhat, especially during the time interval as the core is driven into saturation, the peak current supplied by the drivers may be decreased. This can be accomplished by means of an adjustable capacitor shown as $C'$ in Figure 11.13. When $C'$ has the proper value it will charge while the core is driven up the loop. At the time that the core suddenly saturates the capacitor will discharge through the core. Thus $C'$ provides the necessary peak currents. Improper adjustment of $C'$ may produce "ferroresonance" and subharmonic oscillation.*

Figure 11.14. Effect of inductance of $H$-resistor.

### H-Resistor

The value of $R_H$ must be smaller than the core impedance in order to maintain sinusoidal flux in the core. This raises two problems. One, additional amplifier gain is needed in the $H$-channel. Two, extreme care must be taken to ensure that the resistor is noninductive. Since the rate of change of current is very high as the core abruptly saturates, the inductive effect of the H-resistor will produce spurious $B$-$H$ characteristics, as shown in Figure 11.14.

* Section 8.12.

### Integrator *

The $R$-$C$ time constant is chosen so that $1/\omega_f C \ll R$ where $\omega_f$ is the lowest frequency component of interest. Furthermore, $R$ must be much larger than the secondary winding impedance in order to minimize the loading effect of the secondary current. Considerable improvement can be obtained in the integrator operation by the use of active integration networks.

### Primary and Secondary Windings

The ideal winding geometry requires that the drive winding be wound uniformly about the core in order to obtain a uniform $H$-field, whereas the $B$-winding can be placed arbitrarily. However, the primary-to-secondary capacitance introduces sufficient phase-shift problems so as to require a considerable amount of compromise. Figure 11.15 indicates the distortions which can occur under various winding conditions. Two separated windings gave the most nearly reproducible results. One solution to this problem is to construct a single-turn transformer similar to that of the r-f permeameter (Section 11.2). A third core is inserted within the cavity and performs the function of a current transformer to measure the drive current in the vertical leg.

### Amplifiers

The essential requirement is that both the vertical and horizontal amplifiers, together with the associated attenuators and cabling, be very carefully matched with respect to relative phase shift over the entire bandwidth. It has been estimated that the required bandwidth of the system is approximately 50 to 100 times the fundamental frequency; especially where it is desirable to portray the loops far out into saturation. In addition, relatively high gain is required, particularly for the $B$-channel where the output voltages across the integrating capacitor is very small. A successful 1-mc system has been constructed with distributed delay line amplifiers having a bandwidth of 200 mc. A block diagram of this system is shown in Figure 11.16.

The amplifiers in this particular system were Spencer Kennedy Laboratory wide-band (200 mc) distributed amplifiers. The 202C model provides 20-db gain; while the 200B model provides 10 db. Both amplifiers are operated class A. The 2146 amplifier is a class B power amplifier.

---

* For nonlinear dielectrics the integrator is merely a large series capacitor. In this case $D = CV/A$, where $C$ is the value of the capacitor, $A$ is the surface area of the test sample, and $V$ the voltage across the integrator.

Since the $B$ voltage was usually the smaller of the two signals, three 202C amplifiers in cascade were needed. This required the introduction of a wide-band delay cable in the $H$-channel in order to compensate for the increased delay of the amplifiers in the $B$-channel. The 200B amplifier provided a 180° phase inversion for the push-pull amplifiers.

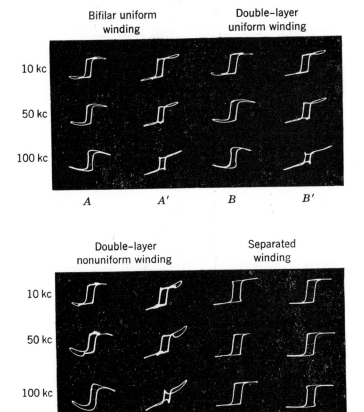

Figure 11.15. Effect of coupling capacity on hysteresis loops. Primed oscillograms were made on the same sample by reversing the polarity of one of the windings.

The 10-db loss pad compensated for the 10-db gain of the 200B amplifier. A special high sensitivity DuMont oscilloscope was used to obtain sufficient deflection.

The testing of square loop materials at high frequencies places the most stringent requirements on the amplifier. However, for digital applications in which constant-current or constant-voltage pulses are

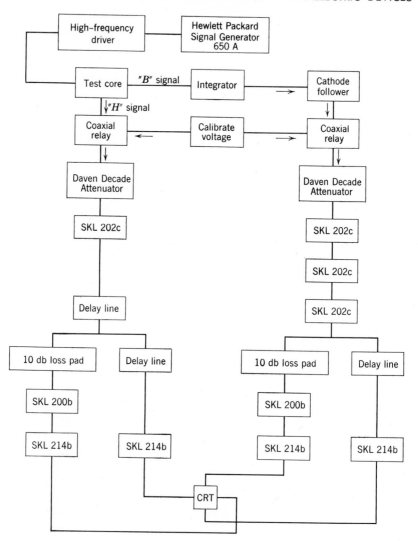

**Figure 11.16.** Block diagram of high-frequency hysteresigraph.

applied the hysteresigraph is usually not the most fruitful tool. In these cases direct observation of the output voltage or integrated output voltage on a linear time base gives the most useful information. The testing of square-loop cores for computer memory applications, in particular, has become very exacting. However, the methods for the determination of squareness ratio, switching time, etc., have not as yet been standardized, hence are not discussed here.

## 11.8 Fabrication of Ceramic Electromechanical Devices. Introduction

In preceding chapters a number of devices fabricated from special ceramic materials have been described. In some cases performance has depended on electrical and magnetic properties and geometry; in other cases mechanical (or acoustical) and electromechanical properties are of primary importance. In practice, optimum performance with a given material can be realized only by giving careful attention to details of fabrication and processing. The following sections include a description of some techniques now used for the mechanical shaping, mounting, bonding, and electroding of ceramic materials and the subsequent electrical processing. A qualitative description is given of the problems associated with the effects that processing and aging have on the electromechanical properties.

## 11.9 Shaping the Ceramic

Electromechanical ceramics are usually dense, brittle, and hard. Because of this ordinary metal fabrication methods cannot be used. However, shaping by abrasive cutting, grinding, lapping, and ultrasonic drilling is not difficult if proper care is taken. Cutting can be accomplished by using abrasive wheels of aluminum oxide, silicon carbide, or diamond. The latter is probably the best to use. A typical diamond wheel for cutting ceramics has a grit size of 50, a grit concentration of 150, and is used at 4000 to 6000 surface feet per minute with a cutting rate of 2 to 4 square inches per minute. Water is used as a coolant. The specimen can be held firmly by temporarily bonding the ceramic to a glass plate with a compound such as G.E. No. 7036 adhesive stick * or Dennison No. 9335.† These adhesives afford an easy method for bonding and removing, and they can be used with irregular shapes and nonstandardized specimen dimensions. The glass plate is securely held by a viselike jig. The cutting wheel is set to cut completely through the ceramic and into the glass plate.

If a flat and polished surface is desired the lapping techniques common to the optical industry can be used (22, 23, 24). Alumina and silicon carbide are good abrasives. In polishing a surface for X-ray observa-

* Special Chemical Products Works, General Electric Lamp Division, Cleveland, Ohio.
† Dennison Manufacturing Company, Framingham, Massachusetts.

tion care should be exercised, since the polishing process can affect the electrical orientation of the crystal or crystallites in a surface layer. This effect has been observed in ferroelectric barium titanate (25).

## 11.10   Use of Adhesives.   General Considerations

Many electromechanical devices are composed of several individual parts. For these bonding is required between ceramic and metal, rubber, or other pieces of ceramic. In addition to the usual bond properties which must be considered, such as brittleness, strength, thermal expansion, and water absorption, the acoustical and electrical properties are important, i.e., density, modulus of elasticity, mechanical $Q$, breakdown voltage, and dielectric constant. To be meaningful these properties should be determined under the conditions which the bond is to experience in the device, for wide variations in parameters are possible. For example, the specific acoustic impedance of rubber may vary 50 to 1 as the geometry and/or frequency is varied (26,27).

### 11.10.1   Adhesion

A bond between two materials is brought about by two phenomena, mechanical and specific adhesion. Mechanical adhesion consists of the wedging and interlocking of the adhesive in surface irregularities, cavities, or pores of mating surfaces. Specific adhesion depends on three types of chemical-physical bonds: polar bonds, covalent bonds, and bonds resulting from Van der Waals' forces. According to modern views, specific adhesion is the most important type even with porous adherends.

When the interfacial forces between the adhesive and the adherend are greater or equal to the cohesive forces of the adhesive wetting will occur. Wetting is a visible sign of specific adhesion and is a necessary but not sufficient condition for bonding. Before complete wetting can occur the surface of the adherend must be clean. Therefore, surface preparation is of fundamental importance. Most surfaces are contaminated with moisture, oxide layers, oils, greases, adsorbed gases, etc., which must be removed. This may dictate chemical cleaning or perhaps only rubbing the surface with an abrasive. Roughening the surface with abrasives is an aid to adhesion primarily because the surface 'is both cleaned and increased in effective area, thereby aiding specific adhesion.

### 11.10.2 Epoxy Resins

Generally speaking, most adhesives are organic materials. An organic adhesive which has many desirable characteristics is the thermosetting ethoxyline or epoxy resin. This resin has good adhesion with a wide variety of materials, including ceramic, metal, and cyclized rubber.* It gives off very little volatile material in the curing process so that shrinkage is minimized. It is chemically inert to common solvents, acids, and alkalies.

There is a whole family of these epoxies. To the resin base of the epoxy, fillers, plasticizers, or other agents are added to change such properties as shrinkage during the curing process, thermal expansion, and curing time (28, 29).

In most epoxy adhesives it is necessary to mix two compounds, the base material and a hardener, before the adhesive is ready for use. Some of these adhesives require baking at an elevated temperature, whereas others cure at room temperature. An example of the first type is Hysol † 2515B and, the latter, Hysol 6020. Ten parts by weight of the 6020 is mixed with one part of Houghton's hardener "C." This mixture will harden at room temperature after several hours. If the temperature of the mixture is permitted to rise as a result of the exothermic reaction, hardening will occur in a shorter time. To 100 parts by weight of Hysol 2515B 30 parts of hardener "E" are added to obtain a mixture that will cure in 10 minutes at 200° C or in 14 hours at 130° C.

Properties typical of an epoxy are the following:

1. Thermal coefficient of linear expansion, $90 \times 10^{-6}$ to $25 \times 10^{-6}/°$ C
2. Dielectric strength,‡ 400 to 500 v/mil
3. Dielectric constant, 3 to 5 at room temperature
4. Specific gravity, 1.1 to 2.0
5. Modulus of elasticity, $0.3 \times 10^6$ to $2.6 \times 10^6$ psi
6. Tensile strength, 5000 to 12,000 psi
7. Compressive strength, 6000 to 18,000 psi
8. Mechanical $Q$ (at low frequencies), approximately 50.

* The cyclizing process involves the etching of the rubber surface with concentrated sulfuric acid for a period of two minutes or more.

† Houghton Laboratories, Inc., Olean, New York.

‡ Epoxies can be made to conduct by adding a conducting material to the resin (30).

### 11.10.3 Glass Bonds

Adhesives having a glass base have been made and used to good advantage with ceramics. Since the mechanical $Q$ of glass ranges from 1000 to 2000, adhesives which use glass as a base can be expected to have high $Q$'s. Adhesion between the glass and metals and ceramics is high. Some glass adhesives can be made into good conductors by adding a silver powder to a slurry of glass and organic binder. Bonds can be formed by applying the slurry to ceramic or metal, drying in air or a low-temperature oven to remove the volatile material, joining the pieces under pressure, and then firing in an oven. After firing the bond is silvery in appearance. Dupont No. 6020 silver is an adhesive, which can also be used as an electrode material.

## 11.11    Electrodes, Coils, and Mechanical Supports. General Considerations

As is true with the usual dielectric and magnetic devices, piezoelectric and magnetostrictive devices must be provided either with electrodes or with driving coils. Techniques used for the commoner magnetic and dielectric devices can, in general, be applied to electromechanical devices. However, since mechanical motion is inherent in electromechanical devices, the motion should not be impaired by the mounting, particularly if the device depends upon the resonance phenomenon for proper operation. An analogous situation arises when using high permeability ceramics for nonelectromechanical applications. These materials are magnetostrictive to varying degrees, even though this property is not used directly. When these materials are embedded in a potting compound a low shrinkage compound should be used. Otherwise, the strain induced in the ceramic as a result of this shrinkage may decrease or increase the permeability from the unstrained value.

### 11.11.1   Electrodes

Electrodes are a fundamental and integral part of any dielectric device. In special cases they are also used in magnetic devices. Electrodes should be low in electrical resistance, adhere well to the ceramic, facilitate electrical connection to the external circuit, and should not be lossy acoustically. Since there is no method of providing an electrode which will have all these desirable qualities, in practice a compromise must be made. Much work has been done in investigating electrode properties, but more work is needed. The role of the electrode when used on quartz crystals has been studied extensively (40).

Electrodes may be applied in many ways; for example, vapor deposition, sputtering, electroplating to a base metal, silk screening, "soldering" (39) directly to ceramic, and brushing on a metallic paste. Air-dry and fired-on silver paste electrodes are used extensively, the former for temporary electrodes and the latter generally for permanent electrodes. These "permanent" electrodes can be removed with dilute nitric acid if desired. A typical paste is Dupont No. 4817, which can be applied with a clean red sable brush and allowed to set at room temperature. (This process may be accelerated by use of an infrared heating lamp.) Dupont No. 6020 silver paste is applied at room temperature and is fired in an oven at 400–450° C for 10 minutes. Several coats can be applied and dryed with an infrared lamp before firing, if desired. As cited above, this mixture has glass as a base and is useful as an adhesive.

We usually consider an electrode a thin, homogeneous, highly conductive material, with a sharp boundary at the ceramic-electrode interface. If the electrode is the fired-on type, there may be a layer of material which is in reality a low-conductivity glass and which lies between the high conductivity material and the ceramic. Among other things, this results in a decrease in the apparent dielectric constant of the ceramic (39). The variation of resistance with voltage of this "sandwich" electrode has been investigated for several types of electrode (31). Also, it has been observed that compared to fired-on metal paste electrodes vapor deposition of noble metal electrodes on single crystal barium titanate results in a decrease in loss per cycle, as attested by a measured decrease in area of the hysteresis loop (32). There is evidence that electrode resistance is a function of time as well as thickness, voltage, and the metal used.

When silver electrodes are used the possibility of silver migration must be considered. In the presence of an electric field and in a humid atmosphere silver ions will migrate into and eventually through certain insulating materials (33, 34, 35). The resulting effects on the electrical properties of the ceramic may be quite serious.

Another phenomenon which occurs in ferroelectrics having titanate as a major constitutent is that of a decrease in d-c resistivity with time. This effect likewise requires the presence of water and an electric field. The resistivity changes as a result of an electroreduction process involving a film of water which transforms the ceramic from an insulator to an $n$ type semiconductor. This reduction begins at the surface and works inward until the thickness of the remaining ceramic has been reduced to a point at which it can no longer withstand the electric gradient and electrical breakdown results. The reaction is reversible before breakdown occurs because it is due to electrolysis of absorbed water and the evolution of oxygen. Firing in an oxidizing atmosphere replaces the oxygen and drives off the water (36, 37).

### 11.11.2 Mounting

In general, resonant devices should be mounted at displacement nodes. If points other than nodes are used, the mechanical impedance and mechanical $Q$ * of the mount must be considered (38). There are many useful modes of vibration which have no nodal lines but rather only nodal points.† Some configurations do not even have nodal points, and other mounting means must be used. For example, consider a toroid made of magnetostrictive ferrite vibrating in the fundamental radial mode without a node, i.e., the inner and outer radii move in the same direction and in time phase. If the core is mounted in a channel, as

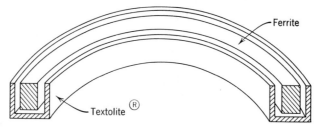

® General Electric Co.

**Figure 11.17.** Mounting of magnetostrictive core.

shown in Figure 11.17, it is free to vibrate. The core may be supported on loops of nylon thread at a few points around the channel. The coil of wire is wound around the channel. With this method mechanical $Q$'s of several thousand can be achieved. With the wire wound directly on the core, the $Q$ may be reduced to as low a value as 200.

Small piezoelectric devices can be mounted by soldering to the electrode or by the use of pressure devices (38). Larger pieces can be

* Strictly speaking, the term "mechanical impedance" includes the effect of loss which is intrinsic in the term "mechanical $Q$." Since mechanical impedance is often used in a lossless sense, both terms are used here to emphasize the importance of losses.

† Reference 65 has a description and drawing which show the mounting of a magnetostrictive device with consideration given to various modes of vibration.

mounted by drilling a hole in the ceramic. For some applications it is desirable to fix one end of the vibrator firmly, and for some vibrational modes this can be done by using a suitable adhesive. One method of nonnodal mounting makes use of a rigid foamed polymer.* In this method the vibrator is supported by a foam block which encompasses a section of the vibrator. Before assembling the unit a hole in the foam block is made slightly smaller than the cross section of the bar. When assembled the pressure between the foam and ceramic is usually sufficient to hold the vibrator. A small amount of adhesive (such as G.E. Glyptal) can be used to form a bond between the ceramic vibrator and foam to give a more secure assembly.

A mechanical connection to an electrode may serve as an electrical connection as well. However, it is often necessary to make an electrical connection at a point of large motion. Again this means that mechanical impedance and $Q$ of the connecting device must be taken into account. One method of making an electrical connection to such a point is to solder a small wire to the electrode. The mass of the wire and solder joint should be small, and the wire should be flexible. The soldering should be done quickly when thin ceramics are used to prevent fracture of the specimen. The composition of the solder depends upon the electrode composition. Since the electrode is thin, it may go completely into solution with the solder and disappear. When silver electrodes are used the solder should contain at least 1 per cent silver (a suitable composition is 78 per cent lead, $20\frac{1}{2}$ per cent tin, and $1\frac{1}{2}$ per cent silver).

## 11.12  Polarization and Magnetization

The technique for applying a bias depends very strongly on the type and geometry of the specific material. For example, since the coercive force of most magnetostrictive ferrites is usually of the order of two or three oersteds, those geometries which contain large air gaps (e.g., rods) will require a constant biasing current or an external magnet. Toroidal structures, on the other hand, can be biased by applying a circumferential field and then slowly decreasing the field so that operation takes place at a remanent point. The temperature stability, coupling coefficient, and, partly, the mechanical $Q$ are functions of the biasing magnetization (79).

In the piezoelectric ceramic case the polarization procedure is somewhat more involved, due to its comparatively high coercive field, and

_____
* Such as the Dow Chemical Company's Styrofoam.

the procedure may vary from one material to another. It is important to obtain the proper polarization in order to realize the optimum electro-mechanical coupling. Furthermore, with poor polarization spurious vibration modes may result (41, 42). Variation in the degree of polariza-tion will also casue variation in "mechanical" properties such as Young's modulus, but these variations will be small (43, 44, 45).

### 11.12.1 Polarization of Barium Titanate Ceramics

Two methods of polarizing are commonly used. In the preferred method the ceramic is placed in an oil bath, the oil is heated to a tem-perature above the Curie temperature, say 130° C, and an electric field is applied to the sample while the oil is permitted to cool. When the temperature has decreased to approximately 30° C the piece is properly polarized. The field used for this "hot" polarizing process may be as low as 10 v/mil (40,000 v/m), but 20 v/mil is probably a better value; this depends somewhat upon the material composition. The upper voltage limit is the breakdown voltage which, of course, depends on the composition, impurities, and homogeneity. A-c fields applied to the ceramic have been used as a means of heating (49).

The second procedure for barium titanate is merely to apply the voltage at room temperature for an hour or more. The field often used is 40 v/mil, but higher fields may be used to effect slight increases in polarization (49, 50, 51, 52, 53). The affect that the magnitude of the polarizing field and the length of time that the field is applied have upon the coupling coefficient is shown in Figure 11.18.

Polarization in barium titanate can be temporarily increased by apply-ing pressure normal to the direction of polarization. After the pressure is removed the polarization will gradually decrease to the normal value (46, 54).

It may be desirable to use an applied static bias field instead of a permanent polarization while the device is operating. If the device is to be used with large signals, both permanent polarization and applied bias fields may be used. This will decrease the hysteresis loss and help prevent depolarization (52, 55, 56, 57). Depolarization will occur when a polarized specimen is heated to a temperature above the Curie point. It will likewise result from the application of a high compressive stress along the axis of polarization (58) and, of course, from a sufficiently strong electric field opposing the direction of the remanent field. It has also been observed that a very weak electric field opposing the direc-tion of the remanent field over a long period of time can result in de-polarization. A d-c field of 1 v/mil applied at room temperature is suf-

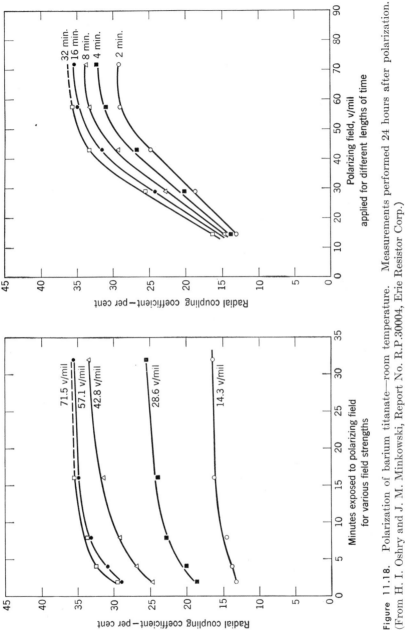

**Figure 11.18.** Polarization of barium titanate—room temperature. Measurements performed 24 hours after polarization. (From H. I. Oshry and J. M. Minkowski, Report No. R.P.30004, Erie Resistor Corp.)

ficient to depolarize barium titanate over a period of a few months. This is an important practical consideration in the application of piezo-electric devices.

In addition to the tailored polarization of piezoelectric ceramics, there is evidence of surface polarization which may be a consideration when very thin pieces are used. Surface effects have been studied in single crystals (59, 53).

### 11.12.2  Polarization of Other Ferroelectrics

Polarizing ferroelectric ceramics other than barium titanate may require varied techniques. In lead metaniobate, for example, the resistivity decreases rapidly as temperature is increased above 250° C (60). Polarizing at the Curie temperature 570° C is not possible at present, but this material can be polarized at 80 v/mil at 250° C (61). In a particular lead zirconate-lead titanate solid solution, 90 v/mil are not sufficient to polarize at room temperature, but by increasing the voltage to 120 v/mil strong polarization results. Certain bodies composed of these lead zirconate-lead titanate solutions are polarized at 175 v/mil (62, 63, 64, 76).

## 11.13  Aging of Ceramics.   General Consideration

The term "aging" refers to the fact that various material parameters change in value as a function of time. Little is known about the aging characteristics of magnetostrictive ceramics. Aging is known in magnetostrictive metals. Here the artificial aging treatment depends upon the mode of vibration that is to be used (65).

Aging in ferroelectric ceramics has been studied in great detail (48, 66, 67, 68). It has been generally observed that the dielectric constant for polarized and unpolarized material varies as a logarithmic function of time. The same characteristic appears to be true for the other material parameters. Although most of the experimental work has been carried out with barium titanate, there has been some work reported on the aging characteristics of the coupling coefficient of lead zirconate-lead titanate solutions (48, 67).

### 11.13.1  Aging of Barium Titanate

Aging of barium titanate has been and is being studied extensively. Mason has proposed a mechanism to account for the aging of both polarized and unpolarized ceramics (46). The change of all parameters is attributed to a reduction of net polarization in the individual grains of the ceramic. Experiments and calculations have been made to verify this (46, 69). According to Mason the polarization reduction in the grains is caused by the movement of domain walls (70, 71, 72, 73, 74).

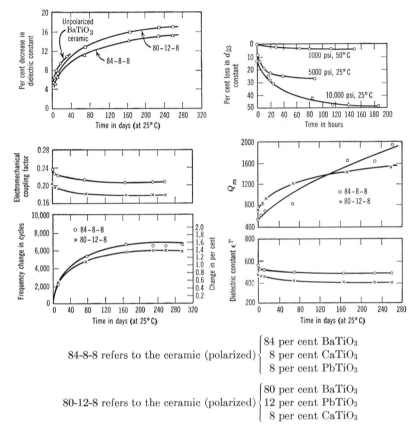

84-8-8 refers to the ceramic (polarized) $\begin{cases} 84 \text{ per cent } BaTiO_3 \\ 8 \text{ per cent } CaTiO_3 \\ 8 \text{ per cent } PbTiO_3 \end{cases}$

80-12-8 refers to the ceramic (polarized) $\begin{cases} 80 \text{ per cent } BaTiO_3 \\ 12 \text{ per cent } PbTiO_3 \\ 8 \text{ per cent } CaTiO_3 \end{cases}$

Figure 11.19. Aging characteristics. (From W. P. Mason, *J. Acoust. Soc. Am.*, **27**, 1, Jan. 1955, pp. 73–85.)

The movement, in turn, is caused by thermal energy and is modified by stresses in the material, which are stored when the crystallite becomes ferroelectric or when it is polarized. Aging begins when the ceramic is made, and it begins again when the specimen is polarized by heating to the Curie temperature and then cooling as a field is applied. In addition to the aging of the above type, if chemical phase changes occur in the material as a function of time, a change in parameters would be expected.

The time variation of dielectric constant, coupling coefficient, $d_{33}$ coefficient, frequency constant, and mechanical $Q$ of certain compositions are shown in Figure 11.19.

From Mason's explanation of aging we would expect that time and temperature stability characteristics would be related. This is indeed the case. In ceramic compositions that are basically $BaTiO_3$ the lowest aging rates are obtained with compositions having better temperature stability than plain $BaTiO_3$. However, compositions having the best temperature stability are inferior to plain $BaTiO_3$ as far as time stability is concerned. In general, the better the temperature stability, the higher the value of mechanical $Q$ and coupling coefficient (78).

The method used for polarizing influences the aging characteristic. Cold polarized specimens usually show more rapid changes initially than the hot polarized specimens. As time passes the hot polarized specimens change more rapidly than the cold polarized. The total change in coupling coefficient is usually greater in the hot polarized specimens but the aged values are higher than those which were cold polarized (58).

On two ceramic compositions Mason has demonstrated that room-temperature aging can be accelerated by heat treatment. After polarization the specimens are placed in an oven at an elevated temperature. The best aging cycle was found to be two weeks at 75° C and two weeks at 45° C. After this cycling the various parameters remain essentially constant at room temperature (75).

## 11.14   References

1. Roberts, R. W., Nice, R. van, "Influence of ID-OD Ratio on Magnetic Properties of Toroidal Cores," *Elec. Eng.*, **74**, No. 10, October 1955.
2. Hass, P., "A Radio-Frequency Permeameter," *J. Research Nat. Bur. Standards*, **51**, 1953, p. 221.
3. Rasmusson, A. L., A. W., Enfield, A. Hass, "Advances in the Design and Application of Radio Frequency Permeameter," *J. Research Nat. Bur. Standards*, **56**, May 1956, pp. 261–267.
4. McKnight, G. P., "Permeameter for Radio Frequencies," *Elec. Mfg.*, **53**, No. 4, October 1953, p. 150.
5. "High Frequency Calibration of Magnetic Materials," *Nat. Bur. Standards*, *Tech. News Bull.*, **36**, October 1952, p. 158.
6. van der Burgt, Gevers, Wijn, "Measuring Methods for Some Properties of Ferroxcube Materials," *Philips Tech. Rev.*, **14**, No. 9, March 1953, p. 245.
7. Conrad, E. E., C. S. Porter, N. J. Doctor, P. J. Franklin, "Expansion of the Thin-Sample Method for the Measurement of Initial Complex Permeability and Permittivity," *J. Appl. Phy.*, **27**, April 1956, p. 346.
8. Owens, C. D., "Analysis of Measurements on Magnetic Ferrites," *Proc. I.R.E.*, **41**, March 1953, p. 359.
9. Bady, I., and Franklin, R. "Measurement of Permeability and $Q$ of Magnetic

Materials over the Frequency Range 50 to 500 Megacycles," Signal Corps, Fort Monmouth, N. J., No. E-1154, September 1955.

10. Artman, J. O., P. E. Tannerwald, "Microwave Susceptibility Measurements in Ferrites," *J. Appl. Phys.*, **26**, September 1955, p. 1124.

11. Spencer, E. G., R. C. LeCraw, F. Reggia, "Measurement of Microwave Dielectric Constants & Tensor Permeabilities of Ferrite Spheres," *Proc. I.R.E.*, **44**, 1956, p. 790; also, *J. Appl. Phy.*, **26**, 1955, p. 250; *J. Appl. Phy.*, **26**, 1955, p. 354; *Proc. I.R.E.*, **44**, 1956, p. 1311.

12. Mullen, E. B., E. R. Carlson, "Permeability Tensor Values from Waveguide Measurements," *Proc. I.R.E.*, **44**, 1956, p. 1318.

13. Field, R. F., "Dielectric Materials and Applications," A. R. von Hippel (editor), John Wiley and Sons, 1954, p. 47.

14. Westphal, W. B., "Dielectric Materials and Applications," A. R. von Hippel (editor), John Wiley and Sons, 1954, p. 63.

15. Mason, W. P., *Piezoelectric Crystals and Applications to Ultrasonics*, D. Van Nostrand Company, Inc. Princeton, N. J., 1954, pp. 489–495.

16. Martin, G. E., "Determination of Equivalent-Circuit Constants of Piezoelectric Resonators of Moderately Low $Q$ by Absolute Admittance Measurements," *J. Acoust. Soc. Am.*, **26**, No. 3, May 1954, pp. 413–420.

17. Lord, H. W., "Dynamic Hysteresis Loop Measuring Equipment," *Elec. Eng.*, **71**, June 1952, p. 518.

18. Mitch, J. E., H. A., Lewis, R. A. Parnell, "Production Testing of Tape Core Materials for Magnetic Amplifiers," *Conference Paper, AIEE*, Pacific Meeting, June 1954.

19. I.R.E. Standards on Piezoelectric Crystals: The Piezoelectric Vibrator, Definitions and Methods of Measurement, *I.R.E.*, 14.S.51.

20. Epstein, D. J., *Dielectric Materials and Applications*, A. R. von Hippel (editor), John Wiley and Sons, 1954, p. 123.

21. Gerber, E. A., "Review of Methods for Measuring the Constants of Piezoelectric Vibrators," *Proc. I.R.E.*, **41**, September 1953, p. 1103.

22. Gerber, E. A., H. P. Wasshausen, "High Frequency Crystals For Frequency Control-Lapping and Polishing Methods," *ATI 136754*, September 25, 1951, Contract No. DA3-99-11-021, Signal Corps Engineering Laboratory, Fort Monmouth, N. J.

23. Van Dyke, K. S., Piezoelectric Investigations, *ATI 94399*, Second Quarterly Progress Report, July 1 to September 30, 1950, Contract No. DA36-039-sc-73, Wesleyan University, Middletown, Conn.

24. Heising, Raymond A., *Quartz Crystals for Electrical Circuits*, D. Van Nostrand, Company, Inc. Princeton, N. J., 1946.

25. Cook, W. R., Jr., "Microscopic and X-Ray Study of Barium Titanate Ceramics," Brush Laboratories Technical Report No. 7, ONR Contract Nonr-1055(00), AD69-486.

26. Kinsler, L. E., A. R. Frey, *"Fundamental of Acoustics,"* John Wiley and Sons, New York, 1950.

27. Andrews, R. D., "Correlation of Dynamic and Static Measurements on Rubberlike Materials," *Industr. Engng. Chem.*, **44**, No. 4, April 1952, pp. 707–715.

28. Javitz, A. E., "The Epoxy-Resin System for Embedded Circuits and Components," *Elec. Mfg.*, **55**, No. 4, April 1955, pp. 74–87.

29. DeBruyne, N. A., R. Houwink, *Adhesion and Adhesives*, Elsevier Press, Houston, 1951.

30. Preiswerk, E., "Aethoxylinharze in der Elektrotechnik," *Elektrotech. Z.*, **5**, No. 1, January 21, 1953, pp. 5–8.
31. Flaschen S. S., L. G. Van Uitert, "New Low Contact Resistance Electrode," *J. Appl. Phy.*, **7**, No. 2, February 1956, p. 190.
32. Pulvari, Charles F., "Determining the Usefulness of Barium Titanate Material for Memory Devices in Large Scale Digital Calculators," Wright Air Development Center Technical Report 55-339, April 1956, Contract AF33(616)-106.
33. Williams, J. C., D. B. Herrman, "Surface Resistivity of Ceramic and Organic Materials at High Relative Humidity," presented at the I.R.E. Electronic Materials and Components Symposium, Philadelphia, June 3, 1955. (Authors from Bell Telephone Laboratories, Inc., Murray Hill, N. J.)
34. Javitz, A. E., "Research Progress in Dielectrics—1954," *Elec. Mfg.*, **54**, No. 6, December 1954, pp. 70–79.
35. Chaikin, S. W., "Surface Contamination of Dielectric Materials," presented at I.R.E. Convention, San Francisco, August 24, 1955. (Author from Stanford Research Institute, Menlo Park, Calif.)
36. Jenkins, J. L., "Ferroelectric Dielectrics Used in Voltage-Sensitive Capacitors," *Elec. Mfg.*, **54**, No. 1, July 1954, pp. 125–129.
37. Weyl, W. A., N. A. Terhune, "Crystal Chemistry Applied to 'Foreign Atoms' in Titanate Ceramics," *Ceramic Age*, August 1953.
38. Sykes, R. A., "Principles of Mounting Quartz Plates," *Bell System Tech. J.*, **23**, No. 2, April 1944, pp. 178–189.
39. Buessem, W. R., P. A. Marshall, Jr., W. A. Weyl, "Study of the Degradation of High K Ceramic Dielectrics," *AD92001*, December 15, 1955, Contract No. DA-36-039-sc-42679, Signal Corps Engineering Laboratory, Fort Monmouth, N. J.
40. Washburn, E. M., "Study of Aging Effects on Military Plated Crystal Units," *ASTIA, AD15549*, February 1 to April 30, 1953, Contract No. DA36-039-sc-42670.
41. Hueter, T. F., E. Dubois, "The Frequency Response of Barium Titanate Transducers," *J. Acoust. Soc. Am.*, **24**, No. 1, January 1952, pp. 85–86.
42. Hueter, T. F., D. P. Neuhaus, J. Kolb, "An Experimental Study of Polarization Effects in Barium Titanate Ceramics," *J. Acoust. Soc. Am.*, **26**, No. 5, September 1954, pp. 696–703.
43. Darner, C. L., R. J. Bobber, "Ultrasonic Shutter," *J. Acoust. Soc. Am.*, **27**, No. 5, September 1955, 908–912.
44. Huntington, H. B., R. D. Southwick, "Ultrasonic Velocities in Polarized Barium Titanate Ceramics," *J. Acoust. Soc. Am.*, **27**, No. 4, July 1955, pp. 677–679.
45. Moseley, D. S., "Anisotropy of Polarized Polycrystalline Barium Titanate," *J. Acoust. Soc. Am.*, **27**, No. 5, September 1955, pp. 947–950.
46a. Mason, W. P., "Use of Temperature- and Time-Stabilized Barium Titanate Ceramics in Transducers, Mechanical Wave Transmission Systems and Force Measurements," *Proceedings of the First ICA-Congress Electro-Acoustics*, W. D. Meinema, Ltd., Delft, *Acustica*, **4**, No. 1, 1954, pp. 200–202.
46b. ———, "Aging of the Properties of Barium Titanate and Related Ferroelectric Ceramics," *J. Acoust. Soc. Am.*, **27**, No. 1, January 1955, pp. 73–85.
47. Smolenskii, G. A., N. P. Tarutin, N. P. Grudstin, "Ferroelectric Characteristics of Solid Solutions of Barium Zirconate in Barium Titanate," *Zhur. Tekh. Fiz.*, **24**, No. 9, 1954, pp. 1584–1593. Abstracted in *Physics Abstr.*, September 1955, Abstract No. 7009.

48. Jaffe, B., R. S. Roth, S. Marzullo, "Improvement of Piezoelectric Ceramics," *AD26747*, Report No. 6, August 17 to January 1, 1954, *Nat. Bur. Standards*, NBS Project No. 0901-10-4448.

49. Baerwald H. G., D. A. Berlincourt, "Electromechanical Response and Dielectric Loss of Prepolarized Barium Titanate Under Maintained Electric Bias, Part I," *J. Acoust. Soc. Am.*, **25**, No. 4, July 1953, pp. 703–710.

50. Roberts, S., "Dielectric and Piezoelectric Properties at Barium Titanate," *Phys. Rev.*, **71**, No. 12, June 15, 1951, pp. 890–895.

51. Sherry, W. L., Jr., R. Adler, "Piezoelectric Effect in Polycrystalline Barium Titanate," *Phys. Rev.*, **73**, No. 10, May 15, 1948, p. 1230.

52. Jaffe, B., "Improvement of Piezoelectric Ceramics," *ASTIA No. AD102412*, Quarterly Progress Report No. 2, July 1 to September 30, 1952, *Nat. Bur. Standards*, NBS Project 0901-10-4448.

53. Chynoweth, A. G., "Surface Space-Charge Layers in Barium Titanate," *Phys. Rev.*, **102**, No. 3, May 1, 1956, pp. 705–714.

54. Sinyak, E. V., I. A. Izhak, "Influence of Mechanical Pressure on the Dielectric Characteristics of Ferroelectric Ceramics," *Doklady Akad. Nauk, S.S.S.R.*, **100**, No. 2, 1955, pp. 243–246 (in Russian); Abstracted in *Physics Abstr.*, September 1955, p. 901, art. No. 7008.

55. Young, D. R., "Temporary Enhancement of Hysteresis in Barium Titanate," *J. Appl. Phy.*, **22**, No. 4, April 1951, pp. 523–524.

56. Hueter, T. F., D. P. Neuhaus, "Ultrasonic Attenuation Studies in Biased BaTiO$_3$ Ceramics," *J. Acoust. Soc. Am.*, **27**, No. 2, March 1955, pp. 292–296.

57. Drougard, M. E., H. L. Funk, D. R. Young, "Dielectric Constant and Loss Measurements on Barium Titanate Single Crystals while Traversing the Hysteresis Loop," *J. Appl. Phy.*, **25**, No. 9, September 1954, pp. 1166–1169.

58. Berlincourt, D. A., "Aging of Barium Titanate Ceramics," *AD60571*, Brush Laboratories Technical Report No. 4, March 30, 1955, ONR Contract No. Nonr-1055(00).

59. Kanzig, W., "Space Charge Layer Near the Surface of a Ferroelectric," *Phys. Rev.*, **98**, No. 2, April 15, 1955, pp. 549–550.

60. Goodman, G., "Ferroelectric Properties of Lead Metaniobate," *J. Am. Ceram. Soc.*, **36**, No. 11, November 1953, pp. 368–372.

61. Goodman, G., "Ferroelectric Solid Solutions Based on Ceramic Lead Metaniobate," 55RL1406, Research Information Services, The Knolls, Schenectady.

62. Jaffe, B., R. S. Roth, S. Marzullo, "Improvement of Piezoelectric Ceramics," *AD17282*, Report No. 4, January 1 to March 31, 1953, *Nat. Bur. Standards*, NBS Project No. 0901-10-4448.

63. ———, "Piezoelectric Properties of Lead Zirconate-Lead Titanate Solid-Solution Ceramics," *J. Appl. Phy.*, **25**, No. 6, June 1954, pp. 809–810.

64. ———, "Improvement of Piezoelectric Ceramics," *AD17281*, Report No. 5, April 1 to June 30, 1953, *Nat. Bur. Standards*, NBS Project No. 0901-10-4448.

65. Roberts, E. O., "Magnetostriction Frequency-Control Units and Oscillator Circuits," *Proc. Nat. Electronics Conf.*, **11**, 1955, pp. 803–819.

66. Graf, R. G., "Effect of Impurities on the Dielectric Properties of Barium Titanate," *Ceramic Age*, **58**, December 1951, pp. 16–19.

67. Boroditsky, N. P., T. N. Verbitskaya, "On the Behavior of Ferroelectrics Near the Curie Point," *Doklady Akad. Nauk S.S.S.R.*, **89**, 1953, p. 447. Translation available from Office of Technical Services, Department of Commerce, Washington 25, D. C.

68. McQuarrie, M., "Time Effects in the Hysteresis Loop of Polycrystalline Barium Titanate," *J. Appl. Phy.*, **24**, No. 10, October 1953, p. 1334.

69. Hueter, T. F., D. P. Neuhaus, "Ultrasonic Attenuation Studies in Biased BaTiO$_3$ Ceramics," *J. Acoust. Soc. Am.*, **27**, No. 2, March 1955, pp. 292–296.

70. Nakamura, T., "Possible Mechanism of Ferroelectric Domain Boundary Movement," *J. Phys. Soc.*, Japan, **9**, 1954, pp. 425–426.

71. Merz, W. J., "Domain Formation and Domain Wall Motions in Ferroelectric BaTiO$_3$ Single Crystals," *Phys. Rev.*, **95**, No. 3, August 1, 1954, pp. 690–698.

72. Little, E. A., "Dynamic Behavior of Domain Walls in Barium Titanate," *Phys. Rev.*, **98**, No. 4, May 15, 1955, pp. 978–984.

73. von Hippel, A., "Ferroelectricity, Domain Structure, and Phase Transitions of Barium Titanate," *Rev. Modern Phys.*, **22**, No. 3, July 1950, pp. 221–236.

74. Merz, W. J., "Domain Properties in BaTiO$_3$," *Phys. Rev.*, **88**, No. 2, October 15, 1952, pp. 421–422.

75. Mason, W. P., R. F. Wick, "Ferroelectrics and the Dielectric Amplifier," *Proc. I.R.E.*, **42**, No. 11, November 1954, pp. 1606–1620.

76. Jaffe, B., R. S. Roth, S. Marzullo, "Properties of Piezoelectric Ceramics in the Solid-Solution Series Lead Titanate-Lead Zirconate-Lead Oxide: Tin Oxide and Lead Titanate-Lead Hafnate," *J. Research Nat. Bur. Standards*, **55**, No. 5, 239-254, November 1955, pp. 239–254.

77. Mattiat, O. E., "Initial Study and Development of Piezoelectric Ceramic I-F Transformers," *ASTIA, AD 82629*, First Quarterly Progress Report, May 15, 1955 through August 14, 1955, Contract DA-36-039-sc-64644.

78. Berlincourt, Don A. "Piezoelectric Titanate Ceramics With Low Temperature Coefficients," *ASTIA, AD 49444*, November 30, 1954, Technical Report No. 2, ONR Contract No. Nonr-1055(00).

79. Van der Burgt, C. M., "Performance of Ceramic Ferrite Resonators as Transducers and Filter Elements," *J. Acoust. Soc. Amer.*, **28**, November 1956, p. 1020.

Appendix one

# Reciprocity
# in Linear Systems

## 1.0   Introduction

The properties of a physical system may be expressed by a set of equations relating the flow of energy or power which takes place between the system and its environment at various terminals. When the system is linear the relationship among a set of variables $f_i$ and $v_i$ can be expressed in matrix form as

$$[f] = [K][v] \tag{1}$$

where $[K]$ is an $n \times n$ matrix of constant coefficients, and $[f]$ and $[v]$ are column matrices. The coefficients $k_{ij}$, are complex constants independent of all the values of $f_i$ and $v_i$. The square matrix $k_{ij}$, which completely describes the interport restrains or external characteristics of the system, is defined as the *consistent matrix* for the system when the $f$'s are generalized forces and the $v$'s are generalized velocities, or vice versa. When coefficients $k_{ij}$ and $k_{ji}$ at mirror image points across the principal diagonal are all equal (i.e., the matrix is symmetrical) then the system is said to be *reciprocal*. When $k_{ij}$ equals the negative of $k_{ji}$ for all off-diagonal terms of the consistent matrix, the system is said to be *antireciprocal*. When neither condition holds the system is *nonreciprocal*.

The objective that is of interest is to determine under what physical conditions one obtains a reciprocal passive system. We can demonstrate with a simple example that the determination must be made by examining the consistent representation. Consider the equation which represents a linear system with only two generalized forces and two generalized velocities:

$$\begin{bmatrix} f_1 \\ f_2 \end{bmatrix} = \begin{bmatrix} a_{11} & a_{12} \\ a_{12} & a_{22} \end{bmatrix} \begin{bmatrix} v_1 \\ v_2 \end{bmatrix} \tag{2}$$

The consistent matrix is symmetrical, and the system is reciprocal. The symmetrical form is preserved if the system is represented by the inverse solution, which is also a consistent representation:

$$\begin{bmatrix} v_1 \\ v_2 \end{bmatrix} = \begin{bmatrix} b_{11} & b_{12} \\ b_{12} & b_{22} \end{bmatrix} \begin{bmatrix} f_1 \\ f_2 \end{bmatrix} \tag{3}$$

However, a mixed grouping of variables is not presented in symmetrical form. For example, the system is equally well represented by the solution

$$\begin{bmatrix} v_1 \\ f_2 \end{bmatrix} = \begin{bmatrix} \dfrac{1}{a_{11}} & -\dfrac{a_{12}}{a_{11}} \\ \dfrac{a_{12}}{a_{11}} & \left( a_{22} - \dfrac{a_{12}^2}{a_{11}} \right) \end{bmatrix} \begin{bmatrix} f_1 \\ v_2 \end{bmatrix} \tag{4}$$

The matrix of coefficients is not symmetrical, although the system is reciprocal.

## 2.0 Energy and Reciprocity

Consider a system which is described completely by a number of independent generalized forces $f_i$ and a corresponding set of generalized coordinates $q_i$; the number may be either finite or infinite. No restrictions are placed on the quantities $f_i$ and $q_i$, dimensionally or otherwise, except that the work done on the system in undergoing a small displacement $\delta q_i$ must be

$$\delta w_i = f_i \, \delta q_i \tag{5}$$

Specific requirements are placed on the system and its vibration:

1. The vibration occurs about a position of equilibrium where the potential energy and the generalized coordinates are assigned the reference value zero.

2. The amplitude of vibration is sufficiently small to allow writing the potential and kinetic energy as homogeneous quadratic functions, with constant coefficients, of the displacements and velocities:

$$U = \tfrac{1}{2} \sum_{i,j} p_{ij} q_i q_j \tag{6}$$

$$T = \tfrac{1}{2} \sum_{i,j} k_{ij} \dot{q}_i \dot{q}_j + k_{ij}' q_i \dot{q}_j \tag{7}$$

where the coefficients $p_{ij}$, $k_{ij}$, and $k_{ij}'$ are constants.

3. All dissipation is of a viscous nature, so that the components of force produced by dissipation are proportional to velocity. Then the rate at which energy is dissipated may be written

$$\mathfrak{F} = \sum_{i,j} d_{ij} \dot{q}_i \dot{q}_j \tag{8}$$

where the coefficients $d_{ij}$ are constants.

Using these specified energy functions, the relations between co-ordinates and forces can be calculated from Lagrange's equations,

$$F_i = \frac{d}{dt}\left(\frac{\partial T}{\partial \dot{q}_i}\right) - \frac{\partial T}{\partial q_i} + \frac{\partial U}{\partial q_i} + \frac{\partial \mathfrak{F}}{\partial \dot{q}_i} \qquad i = 1, 2, 3, \cdots \tag{9}$$

The results of direct calculation are then given by a set of equations of the form

$$f_i = \sum_j E_{ij} q_j \qquad i = 1, 2, 3, \cdots \tag{10}$$

where $E_{ij}$ is the quadratic differential operator

$$E_{ij} = (k_{ij} + k_{ji})\frac{d^2}{dt^2} + (d_{ij} + d_{ji})\frac{d}{dt} + (k_{ij}' - k_{ji}')\frac{d}{dt} + (p_{ij} + p_{ji}) \tag{11}$$

With sinusoidal time variations, represented by $e^{j\omega t}$,

$$E_{ij} = -\omega^2(k_{ij} + k_{ji}) + j\omega(d_{ij} + d_{ji} + k_{ij}' - k_{ji}') + (p_{ij} + p_{ji}) \tag{12}$$

Equation 10 can then be written as the consistent representation

$$[f] = [Z][v] \tag{13}$$

where

$$v_i = \dot{q}_i \tag{14}$$

and

$$
\begin{aligned}
Z_{ij} &= \frac{1}{j\omega} E_{ij} \\
&= j\omega(k_{ij} + k_{ji}) + (d_{ij} + d_{ji}) + (k_{ij}' - k_{ji}') + \frac{1}{j\omega}(p_{ij} + p_{ji})
\end{aligned} \tag{15}
$$

From equation 15 it can be seen that $[Z]$ is symmetrical, hence the system is reciprocal, if and only if all the coefficients $k_{ij}'$ are zero. Conversely, if all coefficients except the $k_{ij}'$ are zero, then the matrix is skew-symmetric and the system is antireciprocal. Antireciprocal coupling impedances appear as pure mutual resistances, provided that the original assumptions are valid; however, since antireciprocal coupling arises from stored energy, it is nondissipative. This lossless nature may also be surmised from equation 15, since the term $(k_{ij}' - k_{ji}')$ is zero for $i = j$.

Since each of the energy functions $T$, $U$, and $\mathfrak{F}$ is reduced in degree by a single differentiation in applying Lagrange's equations, it follows that any linear passive system can be described only by quadratic functions of the generalized coordinates and velocities. Quasilinear systems, which respond in an essentially linear manner to small signals, may be analyzed by expansion of the energy terms into power series; the homogeneous quadratic portions correspond to linear operation.

## 3.0 Examples

It is useful to note that antireciprocal coupling can arise only from stored energy components of the form $q_i\dot{q}_j$. This criterion is often sufficient to determine the reciprocal nature of coupling in a linear system without further analysis.

For example, consider any electrostatic transducer such as a pair of condenser plates, restrained by a spring, whose separation can be varied mechanically and electrically. This will have energy functions of the form

$$U = \tfrac{1}{2}Kx^2 + \tfrac{1}{2}S(x)Q^2 \tag{16}$$

$$T = \tfrac{1}{2}m\dot{x}^2 \tag{17}$$

Quasilinear electromechanical coupling arises through the Coulomb force between the charged capacitor plates, and, since this involves the potential energy term $\tfrac{1}{2}S(x)Q^2$, the coupling is reciprocal.

On the other hand, a magnetic transducer, such as a coil driving a speaker cone, has energy terms

$$U = \tfrac{1}{2}Kx^2 \tag{18}$$

$$T = \tfrac{1}{2}L(x)\dot{Q}^2 + \tfrac{1}{2}m\dot{x}^2 \tag{19}$$

In this case the inductance $L$ is a function of the coil displacement $x$. The current $\dot{Q}$ is written as $i_0 + \dot{q}$, where $i_0$ is a bias current and $\dot{q}$, a small signal variation. The inductance can be written as the first two terms of a Taylor's expansion, $L_0 + L'x$. If these expressions are substituted into equation 19, the only term which contributes to linear coupling is $L'xi_0\dot{q}$. This contains the term $x\dot{q}$, so the system is non-reciprocal.

Other examples of nonreciprocal systems are those involving magnetostriction, Hall effect, Faraday effect, and mechanical systems with moving constraints such as the gyroscope. In general, electromechanical transformers which couple through magnetic fields are antireciprocal and those coupled through electric fields are reciprocal.

## 4.0   The Ideal Gyrator and Applications to Four Pole Theory

The ideal gyrator is a perfect antireciprocal four-terminal network, with mesh equations:

$$\begin{bmatrix} E_1 \\ E_2 \end{bmatrix} = \begin{bmatrix} 0 & -1 \\ 1 & 0 \end{bmatrix} \begin{bmatrix} I_1 \\ I_2 \end{bmatrix} \tag{20}$$

Ideal gyrators in combination with normal reciprocal circuit elements and ideal transformers can be used to synthesize any nonreciprocal network. The circuit analysis of networks containing gyrators can be carried out simply in terms of conventional four-pole matrix analysis. With the ideal gyrator as the basic nonreciprocal building block, the usual matrix methods applicable to series, parallel, and tandem network connections can be used. Since the addition of symmetric and skew-symmetric matrices results in a matrix with off-diagonal terms which are generally unequal in magnitude, nonreciprocal networks of a general nature, such as one-way elements, can be derived from gyrators and conventional reciprocal circuits with series connections, parallel connections, or combinations of the two.

Cascaded combinations also provide particular properties which can be derived with the use of the transmission matrix ($ABCD$):

$$\begin{bmatrix} E_1 \\ I_1 \end{bmatrix} = \begin{bmatrix} A & B \\ C & D \end{bmatrix} \begin{bmatrix} E_2 \\ -I_2 \end{bmatrix}$$

If a network with this ($ABCD$) matrix is also represented by the $z$-matrix,

$$\begin{bmatrix} E_1 \\ E_2 \end{bmatrix} = \begin{bmatrix} z_{11} & z_{12} \\ z_{21} & z_{22} \end{bmatrix} \begin{bmatrix} I_1 \\ I_2 \end{bmatrix}$$

where $z_{12}$ and $z_{21}$ are not necessarily equal, then the matrix elements are related by the equations

$$A = z_{11}/z_{21} \qquad B = (z_{11}z_{22} - z_{12}z_{21})/z_{21}$$

$$C = 1/z_{21} \qquad D = z_{22}/z_{21}$$

$$AD - BC = z_{12}/z_{21}$$

$$z_{11} = A/C \qquad z_{12} = \frac{AD - BC}{C}$$

$$z_{21} = 1/C \qquad z_{22} = D/C$$

$$z_{11}z_{22} - z_{12}z_{21} = B/C$$

The value of the transmission determinant, $AD$–$BC$, is always $-1$ if the network is antireciprocal and $+1$ if the network is reciprocal. When two networks are cascaded the product of their individual transmission matrices is the resultant over-all matrix: *

$$\begin{bmatrix} A & B \\ C & D \end{bmatrix} = \begin{bmatrix} A' & B' \\ C' & D' \end{bmatrix} \begin{bmatrix} A'' & B'' \\ C'' & D'' \end{bmatrix}$$

$$= \begin{bmatrix} A'A'' + B'C'' & A'B'' + B'D'' \\ C'A'' + D'C'' & C'B'' + D'D'' \end{bmatrix}$$

Then, for the resultant network,

$$z_{21} = \frac{1}{C'A'' + D'C''} = \frac{z_{21}'z_{21}''}{z_{11}'' + z_{22}'}$$

Suppose that one of the networks (the first, say) is an ideal gyrator, so that

$$z_{21} = \frac{z_{21}''}{z_{22}''}$$

This value can be any real or complex number. Since the over-all network must be antireciprocal, the value of $z_{12}$ must be the negative of $z_{21}$.

As an example of matrix addition, consider the series connection shown in Figure 1, which has found use as an isolator.

---

* Since the determinant is also the product of the individual determinants, it follows that a cascaded chain of reciprocal and antireciprocal four poles is always antireciprocal if it contains an odd number of antireciprocal four poles and reciprocal, if an even number.

Adding the impedance matrices, the resultant network has the matrix

$$[z] = \begin{bmatrix} 0 & -R \\ R & 0 \end{bmatrix} + \begin{bmatrix} R & R \\ R & R \end{bmatrix} = \begin{bmatrix} R & 0 \\ 2R & R \end{bmatrix} \tag{21}$$

Thus, the resultant network is unilateral, its input voltage being entirely independent of output current. Also, its input impedance is $R$, independent of the load impedance. In particular, if the load impedance is

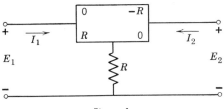

Figure 1.

set equal to $R$, all input power is delivered to the load, none is absorbed by the added loss element, and the efficiency is 100 per cent. If power is applied at the output terminals, it cannot be delivered to the input termination and cannot be dissipated in the ideal gyrator, which is lossless, so it is absorbed by the added loss element. Hence the efficiency of power delivery from the output terminals to the loss element is also 100 per cent.

Comparing the gyrator representation to the microwave concepts further, we may ask for a circuit representation of the directional phase

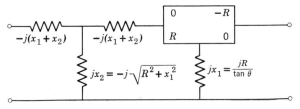

Figure 2.

shifter. This problem has been solved by H. A. Haus (47) with the circuit shown in Figure 2. Direct calculation shows that the transfer matrix for this circuit is

$$\begin{bmatrix} A & B \\ C & D \end{bmatrix} = \begin{bmatrix} e^{j\theta} & 0 \\ 0 & e^{j\theta} \end{bmatrix} = e^{j\theta}[I] \tag{22}$$

This matrix can be used to define the ideal directional phase shifter. A reciprocal phase shifter, in contrast, must have a matrix with determinant equal to $+1$ and would have a matrix with the 2, 2 term replaced with $e^{-j\theta}$.

The final example is a gyrator equivalent circuit for the microwave circulator. From the energy considerations which applied to the isolator it appears that the required circuit should be quite similar. Under matched conditions, and with three sets of driving terminals provided,

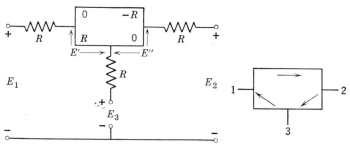

Figure 3.

the circuit takes the form shown in Figure 3. The voltage equations around the left-hand loop and around the outside are

$$E_1 - E_3 + E' + I_1R + (I_1 + I_2)R = 2I_1R \tag{23}$$

$$E_1 - E_2 = E' - E'' + I_1R - I_2R = -2I_2R \tag{24}$$

Subtracting equation 23 from equation 24, a third equation is obtained:

$$E_3 - E_2 = -2(I_1 + I_2)R = 2I_3R \tag{25}$$

Collecting these into a matrix equation for the terminal currents,

$$
\begin{bmatrix} I_1 \\ I_2 \\ I_3 \end{bmatrix} = \frac{1}{2R} \begin{bmatrix} 1 & 0 & -1 \\ -1 & 1 & 0 \\ 0 & -1 & 1 \end{bmatrix} \times \begin{bmatrix} E_1 \\ E_2 \\ E_3 \end{bmatrix} \tag{26}
$$

Therefore, current $I_1$ is independent of the voltage at terminals 2, $I_2$ is independent of $E_3$, and $I_3$ is independent of $E_1$. In other words, transmission occurs only along the discrete paths 1 to 2, 2 to 3, and 3 to 1, as indicated by the single line block diagram in Figure 3. The terminal voltages can arise from generators, additional load impedances, or both. Hence it can be seen that if the terminals are mismatched so that the terminating impedances are not equal to $R$ the mismatch components of impedance give rise to reflections at the terminals. The reflected component, not being absorbed by the load at a mismatched terminal, travels on to the next terminal, where it may be completely absorbed if that terminal is loaded with $R$ or reflection may again occur if that terminal is mismatched. Thus for good circulator performance it is essential that the terminals be carefully matched. This effect can be used advantageously to measure the mutual impedance with considerable precision, not only for the ideal gyrator but for any antireciprocal network.

The construction of passive nonreciprocal networks, as outlined, consists of the combination of passive reciprocal elements with passive antireciprocal elements which result in nonreciprocal systems of the desired characteristics. Since a unilateral device can be synthesized by combining a reciprocal network and a gyrator, considerable interest has been shown in the possibility of synthesizing a gyrator from an active unilateral device. Mathematically, this corresponds to dividing the unilateral matrix into its symmetrical and skew-symmetric parts. The symmetrical or reciprocal parts are then canceled by the addition of shunt elements (allowing the use of negative resistances), leaving an ideal gyrator. In practice, the synthesis of an ideal gyrator from an active unilateral device is limited by the fact that such an ideal gyrator requires total cancelation of the additional shunt elements, leading to an unstable system. Hence a practical active gyrator must always operate at a point close to oscillation. Passive gyrators for microwave frequencies depend on the use of ferrites in waveguides. At lower frequencies Hall-effect gyrators and electromechanical gyrators have been demonstrated.

## 5.0 References

1. Lord Rayleigh, "The Theory of Sound," McMillan and Co., Ltd., London, Vol. I, 1877, Vol. II, 1978; 2nd ed., 1894; reprinted 1926, 1929. American edition, two volumes bound as one, Dover Publications, Inc., New York, 1945.
2. Referenced by Rayleigh: "Helmholtz, *Crelle*, Bd. LVII, 1859."
3. Referenced by Rayleigh: "Betti, II Nuovo Cimento, 1872," See Ref. 1, 109.
4. Lord Rayleigh, "Some General Theorems Relating to Vibrations," *Proc. Math. Soc.*, June 1873.
5. Ehrenfest, P., "Das Prinzip vol Le Chatelier-Braun und die Reziprozitatssatze der Thermodynamik," *Z. Physik. Chem.*, **77**, 1911, pp. 227–244.
6. Carson, J. R., "A Generalization of the Reciprocity Theorem," *Bell System Tech J.*, **3**, July 1924, pp. 393–399.
7. Sommerfeld, A., *Z. Hochfrequentztechnik*, **26**, 1925, p. 93. See also Stuart Ballantine, "The Lorentz Reciprocity Theorem for Electric Waves," *Proc. I.R.E.*, **16**, April 1928, pp. 513–518.
8. Schottky, Walter, "Das Gesetz des Tiefempfangs in der Akustik und Electroakustik," *Z. Physik.*, **36**, April 1926, pp. 689–736.
9. Ballantine, Stuart, "Reciprocity in Electromagnetic, Mechanical, Acoustical, and Interconnected Systems," *Proc. I.R.E.*, **17**, June 1929, pp. 929–951.

10. Carson, J. R., "Reciprocity Theorems in Radio Communication," *Proc. I.R.E.*, **17**, June 1929, pp. 952–956.

11. MacLean, W. R., "Absolute Measurement of Sound Without a Primary Standard," *J. Acoust. Soc. Am.*, **12**, July 1940, pp. 140–147.

12. Foldy L. L., H. Primakoff, "A General Theorem of Passive Linear Electroacoustic Transducers and the Electroacoustic Reciprocity Theorem," *J. Acoust. Soc. Am.*, **17**, 1945, pp. 109–120, and **19**, 1947, pp. 50–58.

13. Poincaré, H., "Etude du recepteur telephonique," *Éclair élect.*, **50**, 1907, pp. 221–234.

14. Norton, Edward L., (B.T.L.), U.S. Patent No. 1,642,506, Issued September 13, 1927, filed September 23, 1926.

15. Firestone, F. A., "New Analogy between Mechanical and Electrical Systems," *J. Acoust., Soc. Am.*, **4**, January 1933, pp. 249–267.

16. Jefferson, H., (letter to the editors), "Gyroscopic Coupling Terms," *Phil. Mag.*, Ser. 7, **36**, 223–224, March 1945, pp. 223–224.

17. Bloch, A., "A New Approach to the Dynamics of Systems with Gryoscopic Coupling Terms," *Phil. Mag.*, Ser. 7, **35**, May 1944, pp. 315–334.

18. ——, "Electromechanical Analogies and Their Use for the Analysis of Mechanical and Electromechanical Systems," *J. Inst. Elec. Engrs. (London)*, **92**, Part I, April 1949, pp. 157–169.

19. Hunt, Frederick V., *Electroacoustics*, John Wiley and Sons, New York, 1954, p. 111.

20. ——, "Symmetry in the Equations for Electromechanical Coupling," *J. Acoust., Soc. Am.*, **22**, 672(A) September 1950, See also reference 19, Chapter 3.

21. Le Corbeiller, P., "Origine des termes gyroscopiques dans les équations des appareils électromécaniques," *Ann. P.T.T.*, **18**, 1929, pp. 1–22.

22. Hahnle, W., "Die Darstellung elektromechanischer Gebilde durch rein electrische Schaltbilder," *Wiss. Veroffentl. Siemens-Konzern*, **11**, Part 1, 1932, pp. 1–11.

23. Olson, H. T., *Dynamical Analogies*, D. Van Nostrand Company, Inc., Princeton, N. J., 1943.

24. Miles, John W., "Coordinates and the Riciprocity Theorem in Electromechanical Systems," *J. Acoust. Soc. Am.*, **19**, 1947, pp. 910–913.

25. Mason, W. P., *Electromechanical Transducers and Wave Filters*, D. Van Nostrand Company, Inc., Princeton, N. J., 1942 (2nd ed. 1948).

26. Le Corbeiller, P., and Ying-Wa Yeung, "Duality in Mechanics," *J. Acoust. Soc. Am.*, **24**, November 1952, pp. 643–648.

27. Smith, P. W., Jr., "Analogies and Schematic Networks," *J. Acoust. Soc. Am.*, **25**, July 1953, p. 828.

28. McMillan, Edwin M., "Equivalent Circuits for Electromechanical Transducers," U.S. Navy Electronics Laboratory, San Diego, January 10, 1942.

29. Black, L. J., H. J. Scott, "Measurements on Non-reciprocity in an Electromechanical System," *J. Acoust. Soc. Am.*, **25**, November 1953, pp. 1137–1140.

30. McMillan, Edwin M., "Violation of the Reciprocity Theorem in Linear Passive Electromechanical Systems," *J. Acoust. Soc. Am.*, **18**, October 1946, pp. 344–347.

31. Tellegen, B. D. H., "The Gyrator-A New Electric Network Element," *Philips Research Repts.*, **3**, April 1948, pp. 81–101.

32. ——, "The Synthesis of Passive, Resistanceless Four-Poles That May Violate the Reciprocity Relation," *Philips Research Repts.*, **3**, October 1948, pp. 321–337.

33. ——, "The Synthesis of Passive Two-Poles by Means of Networks Containing Gyrators," *Philips Research Repts.*, **4**, February 1949, pp. 31–37.

34. Tellegen, B. D. H., E. Klauss, "The Parameters of a Passive Four-Pole That May Violate the Reciprocal Relation," *Philips Research Repts.*, **5,** April 1950, pp. 81–86.
35. ———, "Resonant Circuits Coupled by a Passive Four-Pole That May Violate the Reciprocity Relation," *Philips Research Repts.*, **6,** April 1951, pp. 86–95.
36. Foley, J. S., "Unilateral Four-Terminal Circuits," *Electronics*, February 1954, pp. 186–187.
37. Hogan, C. L., "The Ferromagnetic Effect at Microwave Frequencies and Its Applications—The Microwave Gyrator," *Bell System Tech. J.*, **31,** January 1952, pp. 1–31.
38. Fox, A. G., S. E. Miller, M. T. Weiss, "Behavior and Applications of Ferrites in the Microwave Region," *Bell System Tech. J.*, **34,** January 1955, pp. 5–103.
39. Shekel, J., "The Gyrator as a 3-Terminal Element," *Proc. I.R.E.*, **41,** August 1953, pp. 1014–1016.
40. ———, "Reciprocity Relations in Active 3-Terminal Networks," *Proc. I.R.E.*, **42,** August 1954, pp. 1268–1270.
41. Carlin, Herbert J., "Theory and Application of Gyrator Networks," Final Report R-355-53, PIB-289, Contract No. AF-30(602)-387, Task II-B-5, March 18, 1954.
42. Rodenhaus, K., "The Limiting Frequency of an Oscillating Triode," *Philips Research Repts.*, **5,** February 1950, pp. 46–77.
43. Raisbeck, G., "A Definition of Passive Linear Networks in Terms of Time and Energy," *J. Appl. Phy.*, **25,** December 1954, pp. 1510–1514.
44. Smoll, Allen E., "One-Way Transmission Devices," *Proc. I.R.E.*, **42,** May 1954, p. 860.
45. Guillemin, E. A., "Communication Networks," Vol. 2, John Wiley and Sons, New York, 1935; see also R. F. Shea, "Principles of Transistor Circuits," John Wiley and Sons, New York, 1953.
46. Mason, W. P., W. H. Hewitt, R. F. Wick, "Hall Effect Modulators and Gyrators' Employing Magnetic Field Independent Orientations in Germanium," *J. Appl. Phy.*, **24,** February 1953, pp. 166–175.
47. Hauss, H. A., "Equivalent Circuit for a Passive Non-Reciprocal Network," *J. Appl. Phy.*, **25,** December 1954, pp. 1500–1502.

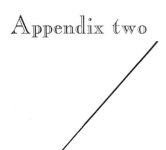

# Appendix two

# Tensor Dielectric Constant of a Plasma

## 1.0 Introduction *

It is perhaps of interest to point out that the gyromagnetic properties possessed by ferrites are shared by the electrons in a low-pressure gaseous plasma which is subjected to a steady magnetic field. Devices utilizing these effects have appeared commercially, but as yet the efficiency of most of these is not so high as the corresponding ferrite components.

If we assume that the heavy ions are not sufficiently disturbed by the fields, then we can compute the electron displacement from its average position in the presence of the r-f fields and a d-c magnetic field. From this calculation we can obtain the frequency dependent polarization, hence the dielectric constant of the gas. This is similar to the ferrite case in which the frequency dependent magnetization was calculated.

## 2.0 Equations of Motion

The force on the electron due to the applied electric and magnetic field is

$$\mathbf{f} = m\mathbf{a} = -q_e(\mathbf{E} + \mathbf{v} \times \mu_0\mathbf{H}) \tag{1}$$

---

* The details of the calculation are carried out primarily to indicate another illustration of the polarization concept.

Let $\mathbf{H} = \mathbf{H}_0 + \mathbf{h}$ where $\mathbf{H}_0$ is the applied d-c magnetic field whose direction is along the $z$-axis, and $\mathbf{h}$ is a small r-f field. To a good first approximation, however, $h \ll H_0$. Hence equation 1 reduces to the following with an assumed time dependence of $e^{j\omega t}$.

$$q_e E_x = \omega^2 m x - j\omega\mu_0 H_0 y q_e \tag{2}$$

$$q_e E_y = j\omega\mu_0 H_0 y q_e + \omega^2 m y \tag{3}$$

$$q_e E_z = -\omega^2 m z \tag{4}$$

The solution for the various displacements are

$$x = \frac{\omega^2 m q_e E_x}{\omega^4 m^2 - \omega^2 H_0^2 q_e^2 \mu_0^2} + \frac{j\omega H_0 \mu_0 q_e^2 E_y}{\omega^4 m^2 - \omega^2 \mu_0^2 H_0^2 q_e^2} \tag{5}$$

$$y = \frac{\omega^2 m q_e E_y}{\omega^4 m^2 - \omega^2 \mu_0^2 H_0^2 q_e^2} - \frac{j\omega\mu_0 H_0 q_e^2 E_x}{\omega^4 m^2 - \omega^2 \mu_0 H_0^2 q_e^2} \tag{6}$$

$$z = \frac{-q_e}{\omega^2 m} E_z \tag{7}$$

The effective polarization $\mathbf{P}$ has components

$$P_x = -q_e x N \tag{8}$$

$$P_y = -q_e y N \tag{9}$$

$$P_z = -q_e z N \tag{10}$$

where $N$ is the number of electrons per unit volume. Hence

$$D_x = \epsilon_0 E_x - q_e x N \tag{11}$$

$$D_y = \epsilon_0 E_y - q_e y N \tag{12}$$

$$D_z = \epsilon_0 E_z - q_e z N \tag{13}$$

Substitution of equations 5–10 yields

$$\mathbf{D} = (\epsilon_T)\epsilon_0 \mathbf{E} \tag{14}$$

where

$$\epsilon_T = \begin{bmatrix} \epsilon_1 & j\delta & 0 \\ -j\delta & \epsilon_1 & 0 \\ 0 & 0 & \epsilon_2 \end{bmatrix}$$

where

$$\epsilon_1 = 1 + \frac{\omega_p{}^2}{\omega_0{}^2 - \omega^2} \tag{15}$$

$$\delta = \frac{\omega_0}{\omega}\left(\frac{\omega_p{}^2}{\omega_0{}^2 - \omega^2}\right) \tag{16}$$

$$\epsilon_2 = 1 + \frac{\omega_p{}^2}{\omega^2} \tag{17}$$

in which

$$\omega_p{}^2 = \frac{N q_e{}^2}{m} \qquad \omega_p = \text{plasma frequency}$$

$$\omega_0{}^2 = \frac{q_e \mu_0 H}{m} \qquad \omega_0 = \text{Larmor frequency}$$

Thus a d-c magnetic field produces a tensor dielectric constant which is antireciprocal. The inclusion of loss terms can be obtained by making each component of the tensor complex. The imaginary portion would be indicative of the losses.

# Appendix three

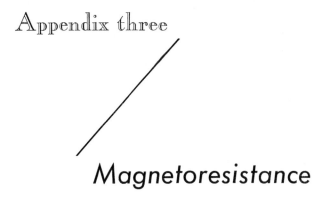

# Magnetoresistance

The recent introduction of new semiconductor materials (e.g., InSb InAs) which have extremely large Hall constants has restimulated interest in the construction of magnetoresistive amplifiers. Essentially, any element whose resistance can be varied electrically can serve as the basis of an amplifier. It is the purpose of this section merely to delineate the nature of the physical effect rather than to provide a detailed description of the properties of these new materials.

Actually, there are two related effects involved in these materials. If a long thin sample is placed in a perpendicular magnetic field (Figure 1), we find that the resistance changes as a function of the applied

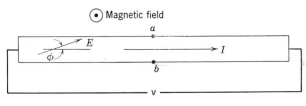

Figure 1.

magnetic field. Since the current path length does not change, we will denote this effect as a change in the basic volume resistivity of the material rather than as an apparent change due to the geometry of the specimen discussed here.

The change in resistance arsises from the statistical redistribution of the carrier velocities in the material due to the presence of the magnetic field. This change is normally small, e.g., a two- or three-to-one change in resistivity for an applied field of about 10,000 gauss.

The second effect noted in the experiment of Figure 1 is the appearance of a Hall voltage across terminals $a$–$b$. In this case the charge carriers are deflected toward the outer surfaces and at equilibrium produce a static electric field equal and opposite to the deflecting force. Thus the current flows in the same direction as it did without the magnetic field. The field intensity $E_{ab}$ is related to the current density ($J$) and the magnetic field by the Hall constant ($R_H$),

$$E_{ab} = R_H JH \tag{1}$$

The general relationship between the volume resistivity and the total electric ($\mathbf{E}$) and magnetic field ($\mathbf{H}$) is given by

$$\rho_H \mathbf{i} = \mathbf{E} + R_H \mathbf{J} \times \mathbf{H} \tag{2}$$

where $\rho_H$ is the resistivity as a function of the magnetic field described. For the case in which the electric and magnetic fields are at right angles to each other we can derive a relationship for the angle $\phi$ between $\mathbf{E}$ and $\mathbf{J}$.

Take the cross product of $\mathbf{E}$ with both sides of equation 2:

$$\rho_H \mathbf{E} \times \mathbf{J} = \mathbf{E} \times \mathbf{E} + R_H \mathbf{E} \times (\mathbf{J} \times \mathbf{H}) \tag{3}$$

$$\rho_H \mathbf{E} \times \mathbf{J} = R_H[\mathbf{J}(\mathbf{E} \cdot \mathbf{H}) - \mathbf{H}(\mathbf{E} \cdot \mathbf{J})] \tag{4}$$

$$\rho_H \mathbf{E} \times \mathbf{J} = -R_H(\mathbf{E} \cdot \mathbf{J})\mathbf{H} \tag{5}$$

since $\mathbf{E} \cdot \mathbf{H} = 0$. Therefore,

$$\rho_H |\mathbf{E}| |\mathbf{J}| \sin \phi = -R_H |\mathbf{H}| |\mathbf{E}| |\mathbf{J}| \cos \phi \tag{6}$$

and

$$\tan \phi = -\frac{HR_H}{\rho_H} \tag{7}$$

Hence the electric field in the center region of the bar of Figure 1 is oriented at an angle $\phi$ to the current path. We can take advantage of the angle $\phi$ by constructing a geometry for which the current path length can change upon the application of a magnetic field. By this means we can change the apparent resistivity by a larger factor than obtained for the bar. One of the most useful forms is the Corbino disk (Figure 2).

In this configuration the semiconductor is in the form of a disk with one metallic contact at the center and another along the outer circumference. The current flow is radial without a magnetic field and is in the form of a logarithmic spiral when a magnetic field is applied perpendicular to the disk. Since all the bounding surfaces are conductors, the electric field $(E)$ is still radial, i.e., there are no surface charges.

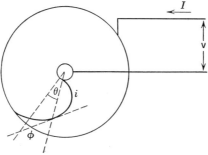

**Figure 2.** Corbino disk.

From equation 2 we can obtain the components of the current density in cylindrical coordinates.

$$j_\theta = -j_r H_z \frac{R_H}{\rho_H} \tag{8}$$

$$j_r = \frac{E}{\rho_H} + \frac{R_H}{\rho_H} j_\theta H_z \tag{9}$$

Therefore,

$$j_r = \frac{E}{\rho_H(1 + \tan^2 \phi)} \tag{10}$$

from equation 7.

If $\rho_0$ is the resistivity in the absence of a field, the change in the measured resistivity of the disk is

$$\Delta\rho = \rho_0 \tan^2 \phi \tag{11}$$

This form of the expression assumes that the actual volume resistivity $\rho_H$ is not a function of $H$.

Since the tangent to the lines of current flow at a point always makes an angle $\phi$ with the radius vector to that point (Figure 2), it can be shown that the equation of the current curve is

$$\theta = \sqrt{\frac{\Delta\rho}{\rho_0}} \ln \frac{r}{a} \tag{12}$$

where $a$ is the inner radius.

Typical data for several materials at room temperature are given in the table below:

|  | $\rho$ (ohm-cm) | $R_H \dfrac{cm^3}{amp\text{-}sec}$ |
|---|---|---|
| In P | 0.67 | $10^3$ |
| In As | $0.2 \times 10^{-3}$ | 0.5 |
| In Sb | $10^{-2}$ | $10^3$ |

For these units and with $H$ in oersteds the Hall angle $\phi$ is given by

$$\tan \phi = \frac{-R_H H}{\rho} 10^{-8} \tag{13}$$

Since $R_H = \alpha/ne$ and $\rho_0 = 1/neu$, where $n$ = density of charge carriers, $e$ = magnitude of the charge, $u$ = mobility of charge, and $\alpha$ = a proportionality factor, equation 7 reduces to

$$\tan \phi = -\alpha\mu H 10^{-8} \tag{14}$$

Large deflection angles are obtained for materials with high mobilities. Typical values are listed:

|  | $u$(cm/sec per v/cm) |
|---|---|
| Ge | 4,000 |
| Si | 1,500 |
| In Sb | 75,000 |
| In As | 40,000 |

A graphical summary of the resistance changes obtainable with rods of different length (1) to width ($W$) ratios and the Corbino disk is given by Willardson (2).

### References

1. Wick, R. F., "Hall Effect Gyrator" *J. Appl. Phy.*, **25**, 1954, p. 742.
2. Willardson, R. K., A. C. Beer, "Magnetoresistance—New Tool for Electrical Control Circuits," *Elec. Mfg.*, January 1956, p. 79.
3. Forman, R., "Measurement and Theoretical Study of Electrical Conductivity and Hall Effect in Oxide Cathodes," *Phys. Rev.*, **96**, November 6, 1954.
4. von Welher, H., "New Materials With a Large Hall-Effect and Large Magneto-resistance Coefficient," *Elektrotech. Z.*, **76**, No. 15, August 1955, p. 517.
5. Justi, E., H. J. Thuy, "Galvanomagnetic Low Frequency Amplifier," *Z. Natur-forsch*, **90**, February 1954, p. 183.

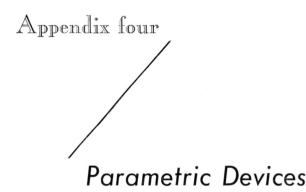

# Appendix four

# Parametric Devices

## 1.0 Introduction

The range of application of the nonlinear properties of magnetic and dielectric materials has been extended in the past few years to computer components of an unconventional variety as well as to amplifiers, oscillators, and frequency converters which exhibit power gain. Various classes of these devices have already been discussed in Chapter 8 under the headings of magnetic amplifier, dielectric amplifier, ferroresonance, etc. However, the modes of operation of the new devices are distinctly different and should be considered separately. Furthermore, this newer material has been included in a separate appendix because of the generality of the principles upon which these devices are based and, in addition, to emphasize more strongly the relationship that exists among them.

The fundamental basis of this subject resides in an analysis of the several possible solutions to a classic differential equation (1, 2). Since the details are quite complex, only the broad results, together with several illustrative examples, are considered.

## 2.0 Periodic Excitation (1, 2, 6)

The basic phenomenon is perhaps best illustrated by the circuit of Figure 1. For the present purpose the capacitor $C$ is to be considered as a linear capacitance in that its magnitude is not a function of the voltage across $C$ but whose magnitude can be controlled mechanically, e.g., by varying the spacing of the capacitor plates. The words "parametric device" then refer to those elements whose parameters can be externally controlled and yet are linear with respect to the currents or voltages in the electrical circuit.

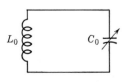

**Figure 1.** Mechanically variable capacitor.

Let us inquire as to the characteristics of the charge which flows in the circuit if an initial charge had been placed on the capacitor and the magnitude of the capacitance is varied sinusoidally at a frequency $\omega$. The differential equation is

$$L_0 \frac{di}{dt} + \frac{q}{c} = 0 \tag{1}$$

Since

$$C = C_0(1 + \beta \cos wt) \tag{2}$$

where $\beta$ is the modulation factor, then

$$\frac{d^2q}{dt^2} + \frac{1}{L_0C_0}(1 - \beta \cos wt)q = 0 \tag{3}$$

if $\beta$ is small compared to 1.

If the inductance instead of the capacitor had been mechanically varied, we would have obtained a different equation with the same form as equation 3, namely,

$$\frac{d^2\phi}{dt^2} + \frac{1}{L_0C_0}(1 - \beta \cos wt)\phi = 0 \tag{4}$$

where $\phi$ = coil flux.

It is the form of equations 3 and 4 that is the particular point of interest. This form may be described as a second-order differential equation in which the coefficient of the first derivative term is zero and the coefficient of the last term is a *periodic* function of time. There are many, apparently unrelated, systems which are described by the same type of equation. Figure 2 is a schematic of several of these systems.

Figure 2a represents the classical one-dimensional crystal lattice in which the positively charged nucleii are spaced *periodically* along the $x$-axis. If Schroedinger's quantum mechanical equation is written for

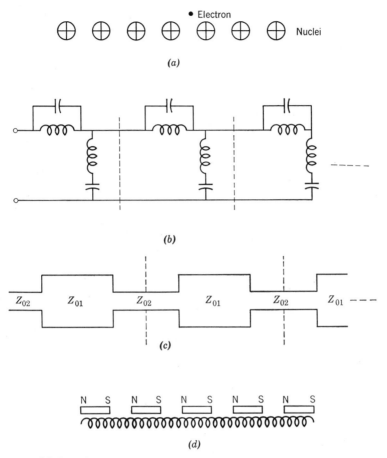

**Figure 2.** (a) One-dimensional crystal; (b) electric filter; (c) transmission-line filter; (d) periodic focusing in TWT.

an electron in the presence of the *periodic* electrostatic potential produced by the nucleii, the result would look exactly like equation 3 or 4, with time replaced by distance.

Figure 2b represents a more familiar case in which a given configuration of inductances and capacitances is repeated *periodically*.

Figure 2c represents a transmission line configuration which is repeated periodically.

Figure 2d represents a traveling wave tube with permanent focusing magnets displaced periodically along the structure.

Since the mathematical description of the systems in Figures 1 and 2 is similar, the solutions must also be similar. It can be shown that the solution will have the following form:

$$q = e^{\mu\tau} \cos (m\tau + \theta) \tag{5}$$

where $\tau = \omega t/2$.

$q$ can represent the charge of Figure 1, the flux density of equation 4, the wave function for the electron, the voltage distribution along the transmission line, etc. In each case the solution represents a periodic term modified by an exponential term. Further analysis yields the fact that $\mu$ can be real or purely imaginary. The former case represents an unstable solution which either decays or increases steadily with time. The latter case represents a stable solution whose peak amplitude remains constant with time.

If we then inquire as to which combination of initial parameters (e.g., $L_0$, $C_0$, $\beta$, $\omega$), yields the stable or unstable condition, we find that each of the systems of Figure 2 yields a "band structure" (Figure 3). In

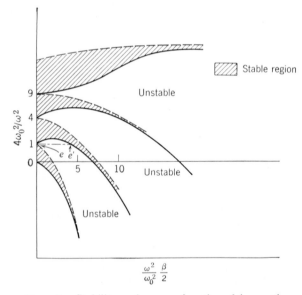

**Figure 3.** Stability regions as a function of ($\omega$, $\omega_0$, $\beta$).

other words, there are stable regions which alternate with unstable regions. For the case of the electron in the crystal lattice this corresponds to the "allowed" and "forbidden" zones for the energy of the electron. For the cases of the lumped constant network and the repeated transmission line, this corresponds to the "pass" and "stop" band regions with respect to frequency (i.e., filter action). The significant feature is that the appearance of "band" structure in many dissimilar physical systems has a common origin in the mathematical representation of the system behavior.

## 3.0 Paramistor (4, 5)

An interesting application of the foregoing principles occurs in a new computer device introduced by the Japanese which has been named the "paramistor." The variable element is a ferrite which has been biased by a d-c current in order to obtain the proper nonlinearity. Unlike the previous systems (Figure 2) which are designed to operate in the stable region, the paramistor is adjusted so that $\mu$ in equation 5 is a positive real number.

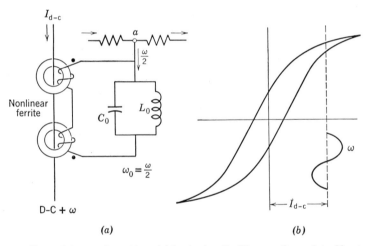

**Figure 4.** Paramistor configuration: (*a*) basic circuit; (*b*) operating point of hysteresis loop.

The circuit arrangement is shown in Figure 4, together with the biasing conditions. The driving frequency $\omega$ and the resonant frequency of the tank circuit $\omega_0$ is adjusted so that the operating range is the line $e$–$e'$ shown in Figure 3. In other words, if a carrier pulse of frequency $\omega$ is applied to the ferrite, a subharmonic of frequency $\omega/2$ is generated in the tank circuit. The subharmonic transient would grow indefinitely with time except for the losses inherent in the circuit which ultimately limit the amplitude.

Figure 5 shows the relationship between the driving frequency and the generated subharmonic. There are two possible subharmonic waveforms which have the same shape but differ in phase by 180° (Figure 5). The growth of a particular phase depends on the initial conditions in the circuit before the carrier frequency is applied. For example, if a small

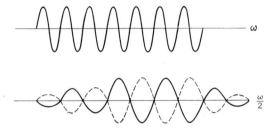

**Figure 5.** Relationship between carrier and subharmonic.

signal of frequency $\omega/2$ (which has been synchronized to the carrier frequency $\omega$ by some external circuit) is initially inserted into the tank circuit at point $a$ Figure 4, then the phase of the transient subharmonic is the same as that of the inserted signal. Basically then, the paramistor is a two-state device in which each state is characterized by a particular phase of the subharmonic with respect to a reference. It should be noted that the amplitude of the carrier is not too critical for the generation of this subharmonic, since the value of $\beta$ can vary along $e$–$e'$ of Figure 3.

## 3.1 Paramistor Shift Register (5)

The simplest illustration of the paramistor as a computer component occurs as a shift register. Figure 6 is a block diagram of the basic shift register circuit. Each block contains the complete circuit of Figure 4

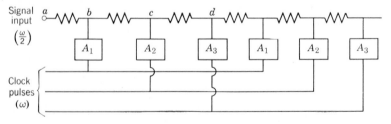

**Figure 6.** Paramistor shift register.

with a carrier frequency of 2 mc and subharmonic of 1 mc. Three paramistors $(A_1, A_2, A_3)$ coupled with a three-phase clock comprise one bit of information in the register. The carrier sequence is shown in Figure

7, together with the generated subharmonic pulses at several points in the register. It should be noted that the carrier pulses overlap somewhat in time.

If a 1-mc pulse enters the register at point $a$, then the first clock pulse produces a 1-mc pulse of increasing amplitude and with the same phase

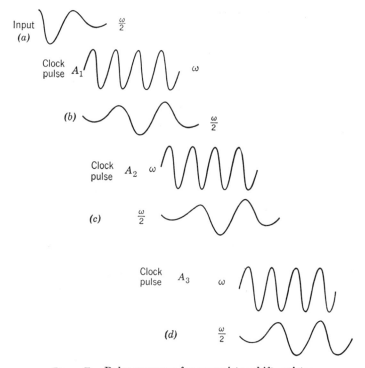

**Figure 7.** Pulse sequence for paramistor shift register.

as the input in the tank circuit of $A_1$. At the completion of the clock pulse the 1-mc signal from $A_1$ (which is also coupled to the tank circuit of $A_2$) begins to decay. The second clock pulse then excites a 1-mc subharmonic in $A_2$ of the same phase as the original input. In a similar manner the succeeding clock pulses propagate a 1-mc signal having the same phase as the input through the register.

A practical computer and a telephone-exchange switching system which utilizes the paramistor as the basic element have been constructed by the Japanese. Although the information rate was only 30 kc, the basic technique has many advantages. The system requires no diodes. The diode function is absorbed by the three-phase clock. In addition, the "zero-to-one" ratio is extremely high (70 db), since the output is read with a phase rather than an amplitude detector. Last, the amount of power required per core is small, since the operation takes place only over a very small portion of the hysteresis loop.

The same parametric generation of a subharmonic can also be used to construct an amplifier. This has been accomplished with the ferrite cores mentioned and also by modulating the electron beam of a klystron whose subharmonic was 4000 mc (12, 13).

## 4.0   Nonlinear Mixing (7, 8, 9)

In the devices discussed the nonlinearity of the reactive element is controlled entirely by the carrier signal. Another very important mode of operation is the case in which two frequencies are mixed by the non-linear reactance to produce either the upper or lower side band with power gain. This mode differs from the magnetic or dielectric amplifier discussed in Chapter 8. In the latter amplifiers a carrier frequency and a signal frequency are inserted into the nonlinear reactance, and the original signal frequency at a higher power level is obtained at the output through the use of another nonlinear detector.

For the former case a very general analysis has been carried out to show the relationship between the power levels of each frequency com-ponent and the frequencies themselves. Figure 8 is a schematic diagram

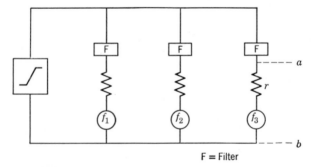

F = Filter

Figure 8.   Basic circuit of nonlinear reactive network.

of the nonlinear single-valued reactance and the connection of three generators. Each generator and its internal impedance is in series with an ideal filter which rejects all frequency components except that of its own generator. The following expression can be shown to hold

$$\frac{P_1}{f_1} = \frac{-P_2}{f_2} = \frac{-P_3}{f_3} \tag{6}$$

in which $P$ represents the flow of positive power into the reactor terminals at the frequency indicated by the subscript. It does not represent the power delivered or absorbed by the respective generators, since this is determined by the particular impedances in series with the generators.

The frequencies have been adjusted so that $f_1 = f_2 + f_3$. Furthermore, the total power delivered into the reactor must be zero; therefore, $P_1 + P_2 + P_3 = 0$. The latter conditions, together with equation 6, indicate the various potentialities that are available with this mode of operation. For example, if $f_1 > f_2 > f_3$ and $f_2$ is a local oscillator ("pumping" source) for which $W_2$ is positive, then an "up" frequency converter can be obtained. In this case $f_3$ is taken as the input signal, and $W_3$ must be positive and $W_1$, negative ($|W_1| > W_3$). Thus under proper matching conditions power is delivered to a load at frequency $f_1$, with a smaller amount of power inserted at the signal frequency $f_3$.

With the same frequency conditions, the nonlinear mixer can be converted to an amplifier. For example, if $f_1$ is considered as the pumping frequency, with $W_1$ positive and no generator at frequency $f_2$, then $W_3$ must be negative. Therefore, power is delivered into the terminals $a$–$b$ (Figure 8). This essentially places a negative resistance across $a$–$b$. If the impedance $r$ (Figure 8) is divided into a generator impedance $R_g$ and a load impedance $R_L$, then under the proper matching conditions a a larger amount of power can be delivered to $R_L$ than is inserted by the generator at the signal frequency $f_3$. Since no generator is inserted at the frequency $f_2$, this frequency is known as the "idling" frequency.

One of the outstanding advantages of this type of amplifier or converter, if the nonlinear reactance can be produced with very little loss, is the possibility of realizing very low noise figures.

## 4.1  Ferromagnetic Microwave Amplifier (10, 11)

A very significant advance in the utilization of the principles discussed in Section 4.0 has been made in the microwave region. Although this amplifier utilizes ferrites similar to those discussed in Chapter 7 on microwave ferrites, the mechanism which introduces the nonlinear coupling is rather complex. In Chapter 7 it was assumed that the entire spin system of the ferrite underwent a uniform precession throughout the volume. However, other spin modes are possible due to thermal fluctuations of the spin system. By the use of the proper configuration it is possible to utilize a pair of these modes, the sum of whose resonant frequencies is equal to the precession frequency, to obtain the necessary conditions for the amplification and frequency conversion discussed.

The ferromagnetic microwave amplifier is at present undergoing intensive development. An experimental amplifier has been constructed with a gain of 8 db at a pumping frequency of 9 kmc and a signal frequency of 4.5 kmc.

## 4.2   Maser (8)

Although this subject does not fall within the scope of the present volume, the MASER (Microwave Amplification by Stimulated Emission of Radiation) bears a close resemblance to the amplifiers discussed and thus should be mentioned.   Rather than utilizing a ferromagnetic medium, this system employs a paramagnetic salt at liquid helium temperatures, which is placed in magnetic field.   Three discrete energy levels are formed whose separation corresponds to frequencies in the microwave region (Figure 9).   The "pumping" frequency $f_1$ saturates

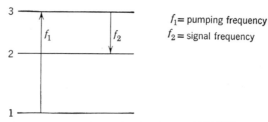

Figure 9.   Energy level scheme of MASER.

energy level 3, whereas a small signal frequency $f_2$ induces transitions from levels 3 to 2 to produce radiation at frequency $f_2$ but at much higher power levels.

Since the saturating power is very small, this type of amplifier is most useful as a low-noise microwave preamplifier.   The ferromagnetic MASER, on the other hand, can operate at much higher power levels and can also be utilized at room temperature.

## 5.0   References

1. Brillouin, L., *Wave Propagation in Periodic Structures*, Dover Publications, Inc., New York, 1953.
2. Ince, E. L., *Ordinary Differential Equations*, Dover Publications, Inc., New York, 1926, p. 381.
3. Bridges, T. J., "Parametric Electron Beam Amplifier," *Proc. I.R.E.*, **46**, No. 2, February 1958, p. 494.
4. Takahashi, H., "*Amplification by Non-Linear Reactance Elements*," University of Tokyo, 1955; *Parametron-Summary and Definitions*, University of Tokyo, 1955.

5. Takahashi, H., E. Goto, *Computing Circuit of Parametron*, University of Tokyo, 1955.
6. McLachlan, N. W., *Ordinary Non-Linear Differential Equations*, Oxford University Press, 1950, p. 114.
7. Manley, J. M., H. E. Rowe, "Some General Properties of Non-Linear Elements," *Proc. I.R.E.*, **44**, July 1956, pp. 904–913.
8. Wittke, J. P., "New Approaches to the Amplification of Microwaves," *R C A Rev.*, **18**, December 1957, pp. 441–457.
9. Bloom, S., K. K. N. Chang, "Theory of Parametric Amplification Using Non-linear Reactances," *R C A Rev.*, **18**, December 1957, pp. 578–593.
10. Suhl, H., "Theory of the Ferromagnetic Microwave Amplifier," *J. Appl. Phy.*, **28**, November 1957, pp. 1225–1236. A treatment of Class IV.
11. Weiss, M. F., "A Solid-State Microwave Amplifier and Oscillator Using Ferrites," *Phys. Rev.*, July 1, 1957, p. 317.
12. Bridges, T. J., "A Parametric Electron Beam Amplifier," *Proc. I.R.E.*, **46**, February 1958, pp. 494–495.
13. Giacoletto, L. G., J. O'Connel, "A Variable-Capacitance Germanium Junction Diode for UHF," *R C A Rev.*, **17**, March 1956, pp. 68–85.

# Appendix five

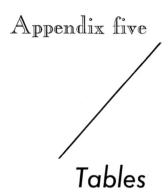

# Tables

## Table 1

### Characteristics of Some Metallic Magnetic Materials

| Type | $\mu_0$(60 cps) | $\mu_{max}$ (d-c) | $B_s$ (gauss) | $B_R$ (gauss) | $H_c$ (oersteds) | Volume Resistivity (ohm-cm) $\times 10^6$ | $(B \times H)_{max}$ $(10)^{-6}$ | $B_R/B_s$ |
|---|---|---|---|---|---|---|---|---|
| Grain oriented 3½ per cent silicon steel | 1,500 | 30,000 | 20,000 | | 0.15 | 40 | | |
| Mu metal | 20,000 | 90,000 | 8,000 | 6,000 | 0.05 | 25–55 | | |
| Molybdenum Permalloy Tape | 10,000– 40,000 | 70,000– 250,000 | 6,500– 8,000 | 4,000– 7,000 | 0.02– 0.07 | 55 | | 0.05–0.90 |
| Supermalloy Tape | 55,000– 120,000 | 300,000– 900,000 | 6,500– 7,800 | 4,000– 5,500 | 0.003– 0.009 | 65 | | 0.05–0.80 |
| Powdered Molybdenum Permalloy | 125 (constant over ±50-oersted drive) (±0.1 per cent change from 30 to 130° F) | | | | | high | | |
| Alnico (Permanent magnet) | | | 16,000 | 12,700 | 600 | | 5.5 | |

Table 2

Characteristics of Some Typical Ferrite Materials

| Type | $\mu_0(10)^6$ cps | $\mu_{max}$ (d-c) | $B_s$ (gauss) | $B_R$ (gauss) | $H_c$ (oersteds) | Curie Temperature (°C) | Volume Resistivity | Loss Factor $1/\mu_0 Q$ | $(B \times H)_{max}$ $(10^6)$ | $B_R/B_s$ |
|---|---|---|---|---|---|---|---|---|---|---|
| General Electric Company MB | 1550 | 4400 | 4200 | 1700 | 0.42 | 230 | | | | |
| General Ceramic Company H | 850 | 4300 | 3400 | 1470 | 0.18 | 150 | medium | 0.00030 [1 mc] | | |
| General Ceramic Company 0-2 | 1100 | 3100 | 4500 | 1600 | 0.30 | 190 | low | 0.000011 [50 kc] | | |
| General Ceramic Company Q | 125 | 400 | 3300 | 1800 | 2.1 | 350 | high | 0.000050 [5 mc] | | |
| Ferroxcube Magnadur (Permanent magnet) | | | 4000 | 2000 | 1600 | | | | 0.8 | |
| General Ceramic Company S-1 | 40 | 515 | 1780 | 1590 | 1.5 | 115 | low | | | 0.90 |
| RCA XF 3627 | | | 1390 | 1110 | 0.06 | | | | | 0.89 |

## Table 3

### Comparison of Published Data on Ferroelectric Ceramics,* 25°C

| | Strain Field $d_{31}$ $10^{-12}$ $\frac{meter}{volt}$ | Dielectric Constant $K_3$ | Field Force $g_{31}$ $10^{-3}$ $\frac{volt \cdot m}{newton}$ | Elastic Modulus $Y$ $10^9$ $\frac{newton}{m^2}$ | Planar Coupling $k_p$ | Specific Gravity $\rho$ $10^3$ $\frac{kg}{m^3}$ | Frequency Constant cps·m | Frequency Drift $\Delta f/f$ per cent (0–50° C) | Mechanical-Q $Q$ | Curie Point °C |
|---|---|---|---|---|---|---|---|---|---|---|
| BaTiO$_3$ (Brush Ceramic A) | 78 | 1700 | 5.2 | 110 | 0.36 | 5.7 | 2200 | 15.3 | 400 | 113 |
| Ba$_{.92}$Ca$_{.08}$TiO$_3$ (Brush Ceramic B) | 58 | 1200 | 5.5 | 116 | 0.33 | 5.5 | 2300 | 5.4 | 500 | 113 |
| Ba$_{.81}$Ca$_{.19}$TiO$_3$ (Brush Labs) | 43 | 810 | 6.0 | 145 | 0.33 | 5.55 | 2550 | 1.0 | 1100 | 110 |
| Na$_{.82}$Cd$_{.18}$NbO$_{3.09}$ (Horizons, Inc.) | 97 | 2500 | 4.1 | 93 | 0.34 | 4.7 | 2300 | 4.0 | ? | 210 |
| PbNb$_2$O$_6$ (General Electric Research) | 30 | 280 | 13.0 | 62 | 0.26 | 6.3 | 1550 | ? | ? | 570 |
| PbZr$_{.55}$Ti$_{.45}$O$_3$ (National Bureau Standards) | 50 | 500 | 11.0 | 75 | 0.37 | 7.1 | 1550 | 1.3 | 100 | 350 |

$g_{33} \sim -2.5 g_{31}$  $\qquad$ $g_{15} \sim g_{33} - g_{31}$

$k_{31} \approx 0.59 k_p$  $\qquad$ $k_{33} \sim 2.5 k_{31}$

$Y_3 \sim Y_1$  $\qquad$ Poisson ratio $\approx 0.30$

* "Recent Developments in Ferroelectric Transducer Materials," Don Berlincourt, *Proceedings of the National Electronics Conference*, 1955, Vol. 11, pp. 777–785.

## Table 4

Piezoelectric, Dielectric, and Elastic Constants for Three Ferroelectric Ceramics,*
25°C

| | Relative Dielectric Constant $K_3$ $K_1$ | | Elastic Moduli $Y_{33}{}^E$ $Y_{55}{}^E$ ($10^{10}$ newton/m$^2$) | | Coupling Coefficients $k_{33}$ $k_{15}$ | | Density $10^3$ kg/m$^3$ |
|---|---|---|---|---|---|---|---|
| BaTiO$_3$ (Brush Ceramic A) | 1872 | 1596 | 11.24 | 4.42 | 0.496 | 0.460 | 5.77 |
| Ba.$_{92}$Ca.$_{09}$TiO$_3$ (Brush Ceramic B) | 1235 | 1333 | 11.33 | 4.52 | 0.450 | 0.446 | 5.65 |
| Lead zirconate titanate | 853 | 1300 | 6.08 | 2.14 | 0.630 | 0.690 | 7.64 |

| | $d_{31}$ $d_{33}$ $d_{15}$ ($10^{-12}$ meter/volt) | | | $g_{31}$ $g_{33}$ $g_{15}$ $\dfrac{10^{-3}\ \text{volt}\cdot\text{meters}}{\text{newton}}$ | | | $\dfrac{g_{15} - (g_{33} - g_{31})}{g_{15}}$ |
|---|---|---|---|---|---|---|---|
| BaTiO$_3$ | $-78.5$ | 191 | 260 | $-4.74$ | 11.5 | 18.4 | 0.117 |
| Ba.$_{92}$Ca.$_{08}$TiO$_3$ | $-52.4$ | 140 | 228 | $-4.79$ | 12.8 | 19.3 | 0.089 |
| Lead zirconate titanate | $-96.0$ | 223 | 505 | $-21.7$ | 29.6 | 43.9 | 0.037 |

* "Recent Developments in Ferroelectric Transducer Materials," Don Berlincourt, *Proceedings of the National Electronics Conference*, 1955, Vol. 11, pp. 777–785.

## Table 5

Properties of Some Single-Crystal Ferroelectrics (Note: All values are approximate)

| Name | Chemical Symbol | Ferroelectric Temperature Range, °C | Curie Temperature, °C | Coercive Field, Volts / cm | Remnant Polarization, Coulombs / cm² | Comments |
|---|---|---|---|---|---|---|
| Rochelle salt | (Typical) $NaKC_4H_4O_6 \cdot 4H_2O$ | $-18° < T < +23°$ | $+23°$ (upper) $-18°$ (lower) | 200 | $0.27 \times 10^{-6}$ | |
| Barium titanate | $BaTiO_3$ | $-180° < T < +120°$ | $+120°$ | 1,500 | $22 \times 10^{-6}$ | |
| Guanadine aluminum sulfate hexahydrate (gash) | $NHC(NH_2)_2AlH$ $(SO_4)_2 \cdot 6H_2O$ | $-180° < T < +200°$ * | $+200°$ * | 1,500 | $0.35 \times 10^{-6}$ | * Reproducible results difficult above 100° C due to loss of water of hydration |
| Lead metaniobate | $Pb(NbO_3)_2$ | $\approx -200° < T < +570°$ | 570° | 17,000 | $0.6 \times 10^{-6}$ | |
| Potassium niobate | $KNbO_3$ | | 350° C (approx.) | 9000 v/cm | $3.8(10)^{-6}$ | |

# Index